INTRODUCTION TO BACTERIAL PHYSIOLOGY

Introduction to Bacterial Physiology

C. E. CLIFTON, Ph.D.

Professor of Medical Microbiology
Stanford University

McGRAW-HILL BOOK COMPANY, INC.

New York   Toronto   London

1957

INTRODUCTION TO BACTERIAL PHYSIOLOGY

Library of Congress Catalog Card Number 56-11046

THE MAPLE PRESS COMPANY, YORK, PA.

Dedicated
to the memory of
Dr. Marjorie Stephenson
and
Professor A. J. Kluyver

PREFACE

During the twenty-some years the author has been teaching a course in bacterial physiology, the study of bacterial function, a cursory examination of students' notes might lead to the conclusion that the bacteria have evolved from rather simple entities of somewhat odd metabolic abilities to complex morphological entities, many of which exhibit dissimilatory and assimilatory abilities far surpassing those of the higher forms of life. Closer examination would show that this evolution has occurred, instead, in the minds of many workers in bacterial physiology and in those disciplines upon which it is based. The tremendous development which has occurred, particularly during the last half of the past quarter of a century, makes it impossible for any individual to canvass completely and digest adequately the available information. At the same time the beginning student encounters many difficulties in attempting to interpret the reviews, monographs, and texts, generally at an advanced level, that are available. In this presentation an attempt is made to survey the field at a relatively elementary level, to indicate the evolution of our concepts from earlier ones, and to develop a broad introduction to the numerous activities of the bacteria. Such a task is not an easy one, and many pathways are open for its development, a primarily biochemical one offering many advantages today.

Bacterial physiology, a comparatively new field, is evolving rapidly and at the same time is making important contributions to other fields of thought. The generally accepted interpretations of observed phenomena do not always keep pace with laboratory observations, and the latter in turn are in part dependent upon the methods employed. Our concepts, with some give and take for human idiosyncrasies, are based upon information available at the time and are subject to change. An attempt is made, therefore, to lay a nondogmatic foundation and to indicate, with a liberal use of the word *may*, that the picture being developed is subject to reinterpretation at any time. Our concepts should be flexible, but we need not be skeptical; all that is needed is an open-minded approach and a willingness to balance, as far as possible, ideas against one another and in relation to the facts upon which they are based.

The presentation is kept at a level which should be comprehensible to a student who has had introductory courses in biology, physics, chemistry, bacteriology, and organic chemistry. Analogies and word pictures are developed wherever it seems desirable as an aid in understanding the behavior of the bacterial cell; they do not always tell the whole story, but they are a help in providing a background for more advanced reading and thinking. To this background can be fitted the details that lead to further understanding of bacterial life, i.e., to a more complete understanding of *what* happens in bacteria, *how* the various changes are induced, and ultimately *why*. Such information regarding the microbe would enrich our understanding of the physiology of higher forms of life, including ourselves, since the various forms of life are interrelated and interdependent.

I wish to thank my colleagues for their assistance, criticism, and advice and at the same time to relieve them of any responsibility for the selection of the material presented and the manner of presentation. My thanks are also extended to my former graduate students who have read parts of the manuscript and have made valuable suggestions. In particular I wish to express my appreciation to Dr. D. F. Rowan for his patient reading of the manuscript and his valuable criticisms and corrections. My thanks are also extended to those numerous workers who have contributed to the development of bacterial physiology and thus made this work possible, and to the various authors, publishing houses, and commercial firms who have so generously made available illustrations pertinent to the study of bacteria and their behavior. Reference is given to the source of borrowed tables or illustrations, or of data upon which they are based, in the accompanying legends. The bibliography is for the most part limited to recent original articles and to reviews, only those which appear to be most relevant to the discussion being cited.

And finally, for many patient months on the part of my family—thanks.

C. E. Clifton

CONTENTS

CHAPTER 1

INTRODUCTION

Physiology in its broadest sense has been defined as the study of the phenomena exhibited by living organisms. The exact definition of what constitutes life still eludes us, but many of the phenomena of life as we recognize it can be described in terms of chemistry and physics. The description of certain essential properties and behaviors of bacteria in chemical and physical terms not only serves to increase our understanding of their nature and functions but also aids in the understanding of more complex cells and organisms. As our ability to describe the bacteria increases we may expect an increased understanding of life as a whole since the fundamental phenomena of life are essentially the same throughout the whole series of living organisms.

The most important universal characteristics of life appear to be (1) the conservation of a distinctive, particulate form, (2) the power to use energy, and (3) the power of adaptation.

The conservation of a distinctive, particulate form, or possibly a hereditary inertia to change, is a characteristic of each species of the bacteria, but we must bear in mind that they can undergo change with age or with the nature of their environment. The influence of the environment, frequently a constantly changing one, is exemplified by growth and reproduction, by changes to resting forms, by modified structural forms, and by the development of somewhat different metabolic patterns. One striking change observed with pathogenic bacteria as a result of adaptation is the loss of virulence, a change which in some species includes a structural change, the loss of a specific capsule.

Early studies of the bacteria dealt primarily with their appearance under the microscope and to a more limited extent with their distribution in nature. The study of bacteria as physiological agents and of their life processes may be said to have its origin in Pasteur's studies on fermentation and its early development at the hands of Winogradsky, Omeliansky, Beijerinck, Harden, and others. Many of the earlier applications of physics and chemistry to the study of bacteria as physiological agents were made in those fields where the changes produced were of economic importance. These studies were frequently carried out by chemists interested in the products of metabolism or by medical bacteriologists primarily interested in methods of identification and control of the pathogenic species. Only in recent years do we find marked interest in the study of bacteria as biological agents rather than as agents of change.

One early attempt to apply chemistry to the study of pathogenic bacteria arose from the observation that some species of bacteria will grow in simple media of known chemical composition, synthetic media. This behavior was of considerable interest since it was difficult to prepare complex broths that would uniformly support growth. The interest of the medical bacteriologist soon waned when most pathogenic species failed to grow in the simpler media. These observations did, however, lead eventually to the question as to why some species would multiply while others would not do so in the same medium.

From the physiological viewpoint the fact that a certain bacterium will multiply only in a complex medium is not of particular importance except in so far as it brings forth the questions as to what substances in the medium are essential for growth, what are their functions, and why does one organism, but not another, require these particular substances. From the same viewpoint the lesions produced in infectious diseases are not of as much interest as are the microbial processes, and their interplay with the host, which lead to the typical disturbances in the host's tissues. Likewise, considerations of the pathway and mechanism of a fermentation and the influence of different factors on the fermentation are of more interest than are observations of the products of the fermentation. Thus the problems become more complex, but their answers lead to a better understanding of the nature and life activities of the bacteria. To form any completely coherent picture of the essential chemical and physical processes involved in the life of a bacterium is still beyond our power, but from the available data an attempt can be made to summarize our knowledge of bacteria as living organisms.

Many bacteria and other fungi occupy more precarious positions in the economy of nature than do the larger and more highly organized forms of life. An autotrophic sulfur bacterium can develop in an inorganic medium, obtaining energy from the oxidation of sulfur, while carbon dioxide ultimately is reduced to cellular organic material. More diverse energy and carbon sources are utilized by the heterotrophic bacteria. Many of these latter have synthetic powers nearly as great as the autotrophs; others require one or more specific chemical structures provided preformed in the medium. The question may arise as to whether all the synthetic powers are at present biologically significant in the natural habitat of an organism or are merely a residue from an evolutionary process in which certain enzymic characteristics of the autotrophic bacteria have not been completely lost. This, of course, rests on the assumption that an autotrophic cell was the original form of bacterial life, but it is also possible that evolution occurred along the opposite pathway.

Regardless of the pathway of evolution of the bacteria, it is possible to recognize different physiological groups of bacteria on the basis of their nutritional requirements. The autotrophic bacterium is able to synthesize its cellular material from water, salts, and carbon dioxide and thereby displays synthetic abilities deficient or lacking in the heterotrophic species. Energy is obtained by some from the oxidation of inorganic matter, by others from light with the aid of photosynthetic pigments. As a result of the growth of these autotrophic forms organic matter would accumulate in a bacterial world, and this would pave the way for the evolution of heterotrophic species of bacteria. Theoretically, at least, it is possible in an environment populated by bacteria alone that one species could become more directly dependent upon another with the resulting development of a parasitic, or at least symbiotic, species.

A more or less continuous spectrum of the bacteria can be established on the basis of their nutritional requirements, a spectrum which suggests nutritional evolutionary stages in the development of bacteria if the original bacterium is assumed to have been autotrophic in character. Knight (1936), on such an assumption, has divided the bacteria into four major groups which, with some modification, can be characterized as follows:

Group 1. Carbon assimilated as carbon dioxide and nitrogen from inorganic sources, generally ammonia. The energy required for the reduction of carbon dioxide is derived (1) from the oxidation of inorganic matter such as sulfur, ammonia, or hydrogen by the *chemosynthetic autotrophs* or (2) from light by the *photosynthetic autotrophs* or *photosynthetic heterotrophs*, the latter utilizing hydrogen from organic matter for the reduction of carbon dioxide.

Group 2. Carbon assimilated primarily from organic matter and nitrogen from inorganic sources, generally ammonia, although amino acids may also be utilized. Energy obtained from the oxidation of organic matter aerobically and/or anaerobically in this and the following groups. These bacteria may be designated as *nonexacting chemosynthetic heterotrophs*.

Group 3. Carbon assimilated from organic matter, but ammonia does not serve as the sole source of nitrogen, one or more specific amino acids being required for growth. *Semiexacting chemosynthetic heterotrophs*.

Group 4. Carbon assimilated from organic matter and generally one or more specific amino acids as well as growth factors are required for growth. Many of these *exacting heterotrophs* are parasitic in nature.

Group 5.   To the groups outlined above might be added the *obligatory heterotrophic parasites,* organisms such as the rickettsiae and filtrable viruses which apparently assimilate carbon and nitrogen in organic matter only from and with the aid of other living and generally highly specific cells.

This type of classification suggests general tendencies regarding the synthetic abilities of bacteria as reflected in their nutritional requirements.   It is presented here as an indication of the wide diversity of nutritional types of bacteria.   There is a progressive increase in the nutritional requirements, or decrease in synthetic abilities, from group 1 to group 5, as regards both the carbon and nitrogen source.   Such a classification is by no means complete or absolute since, for example, growth-factor requirements may be encountered with bacteria ordinarily considered as autotrophic species.   Members of groups 2 to 5 obtain energy from the oxidation of organic matter, aerobically or anaerobically, and the question might arise as to the possible evolution of anaerobic species.   Since anaerobic species are also encountered in group 1 it may well be that these species developed independently of any nutritional evolutionary pathway.   Furthermore, such a classification does not take into account the types of fermentation and other biochemical activities of bacteria and the evolution of the different morphological types.   It illustrates only one type of change evident in the bacteria.

If, for purposes of discussion only, we assume an evolution from autotrophic forms to the heterotrophic ones, growth of the former would provide conditions for development of the latter bacteria by the process of mutation and selection.   With the accumulation of limited amounts of organic matter a semiheterotrophic existence would become possible. Borderline bacteria capable of growth under either autotrophic or heterotrophic conditions do exist.   *Hydrogenomonas facilis,* for example, obtains energy for growth from the oxidation of hydrogen in an autotrophic medium but is also capable of growth on organic nutrients. Ultimately a wide variety of organic compounds could have become available for exploitation by bacteria, thus enabling a differentiation into the now known diverse types employing various energy-yielding reactions and widely different sources of carbon, nitrogen, and energy, a reflection of their natural habitat.

It is possible that with many building materials and oxidizable compounds available to the cell, numerous heterotrophic species could evolve which we differentiate from each other on a morphological or serological basis or on slight differences in their metabolic activities.   On a broad nutritional scale the fundamental requirements remain the same, sources of organic matter to yield energy on oxidation and assimilable forms of carbon compounds together with a simple source of nitrogen.   These bacteria range from the nitrogen-fixing *Azotobacter* through the coliforms and related groups. Symbiotic relationships could have developed with gradual, or even abrupt, decrease in synthetic ability and the consequent need for one or more preformed molecular structures in the culture medium, requirements for tryptophan and vitamin B_1 frequently being encountered. Degrees of dependence are noted ranging from the rhizobia, which can fix molecular nitrogen only when parasitic upon their host legumes, but which are capable of growth apart from their host in the presence of fixed nitrogen, to those species growing poorly or not at all away from their host.

Members of the enteric group of bacteria are commonly found in habitats rich in organic matter, and from such bacteria the evolution of nutritionally exacting species would be a relatively minor step, such cells on prolonged use of certain preformed molecular structures possibly losing the ability to synthesize them. These organisms normally are exposed to waste products of mammalian digestion and quite frequently to dead cells. In time enzymes could have been developed which would attack dead cells and ultimately living cells as well. Natural selection of chance mutants would also influence microbial evolution. Many of the pathogenic species are rather exacting in their nutritional requirements, and their dependency upon the parasitic mode of life is at least in part reflected by their pathogenicity. A nutritionally exacting bacterium need not, however, be a pathogenic one since many environments other than the living organism are rich in organic content of wide variety.

The morphological evolution of bacteria appears for the most part to be independent of nutritional evolution. As the course of evolution is traced backward, that is, from the more complex morphological forms of life to the simpler ones, the main branches appear to come together in the Protozoa. In the smaller forms of microbic life it is more difficult to trace lines of evolution, and in these forms the division between plants and animals tends to disappear. Bacteria are, in appearance, the simplest free-living cells, and it might be argued that such a cell could have been the original form of life on the earth. The possibility also exists that bacteria are the result of a retrograde evolution from some more complex ancestor, or ancestors.

Two possible modes of evolution of morphological types have been proposed in recent years. Kluyver and van Niel (see van Niel, 1946) suggested a coccus as the original form, while Bisset (1952) supports the concept of the most primitive bacteria being spiral, aquatic forms.

Kluyver and van Niel (see Fig. 1-1) postulated that all bacteria might have originated from a common ancestor which in its simplest form would be a coccus since protoplasm, or other fluid material, tends to assume a spherical shape under the influence of surface tension. Furthermore, in the spherical shape the surface exposed to the external medium has a minimum value per unit volume of the material. The development of a more rigid cell wall, which can counteract surface-tension forces, and deformation of the sphere could lead to the evolution of other morphological figures.

In the simplest postulated morphological group, Micrococcaceae, all the cells are spherical and the simplest form would be a single coccus which would be followed in development by cocci tending to remain

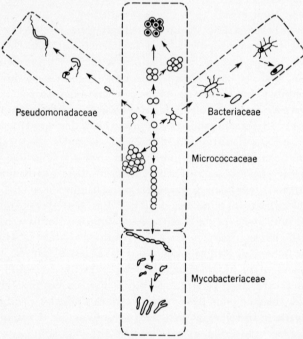

Fig. 1-1. Illustration of a possible evolutionary development of bacteria from a single coccus. (*After Kluyver and van Niel.*)

attached to each other in pairs, chains, or other groupings. A second postulated morphological group, the Mycobacteriaceae, could have originated from the free coccal ancestor by way of the streptococci. The formation of chains could result in internal stresses which tend to cause the cells to elongate, giving rise to short chain-forming rods such as the lactic acid bacilli. Branching forms or cells irregular in appearance might then arise and chain formation become less pronounced, thus leading to the morphologically more complex members of this group, tubercle bacilli for example. The slightly curved and spiral bacteria, the Pseudomonadaceae, could have originated from a monoflagellated coccus, flagellation eliciting deviation from the coccal to the rod-shaped, polarly flagellated form and thence to the curved forms. In a similar manner the peritrichously flagellated rods, the Bacteriaceae, could have evolved from a multiflagellated coccus. Nonflagellated rods could have evolved either from nonmotile cocci or more likely from flagellated rods by loss of flagella. Spore formation and gram positivity apparently developed independently of gross morphological evolution.

Bisset, on the other hand, proposed that the bacteria as we now know them evolved in two ways, from an aquatic to a terrestrial mode of life and from nutritionally less to more exacting species on loss of particular synthetic abilities. Gram positivity appears to be associated with this loss of synthetic ability and adaptation to terrestrial life, although exceptions do occur. According to his concept the polarly flagellated spirilla are best adapted to an aquatic existence. Peritrichous flagellation developed as some cells became adapted to growth on damp surfaces, peritrichous flagella enabling these cells to move by swarming. Other bacteria became adapted to growth and movement on a damp surface by the loss of a rigid cell wall, evolving a muscular wall by means of which they crawl. Nonflagellated rods developed by retrograde evolution, the cocci possibly by diverse pathways. Such a scheme bypasses the question of the original bacterium but does raise interesting questions and ideas for future consideration. No scheme so far proposed satisfactorily accounts for all the known facts, and the need for much more work is apparent. It may prove impossible to determine the course of development in the bacterial world with any degree of completeness. Considerations of this nature may not be very fruitful, but they do at least stimulate thinking and indicate the wide diversity of types of bacteria. This diversity makes study of the physiology of bacteria more complex, but consideration of the differences may in time lead to a better understanding of the bacteria.

The most important role of the bacteria and other fungi in nature is as scavengers, the elements essential for life ultimately being released by microbic action for reuse by other forms. Man has harnessed some of these organisms for his own use; a few have turned the table and exploit man, other animals, or plants for their own purposes. Bacterial physiology is a study of the functions and activities of the bacteria, how they affect their environment and how it in turn influences them. This book represents an attempt to summarize the available information regarding these functions and activities, the nature of the agents involved in these changes, and the mechanisms by which they are induced. Some consideration is given to principles of physical chemistry of particular applicability to problems of bacterial physiology. The major reason for this is that the various functions and activities of the cell are ultimately dependent upon the activities of its constituent enzymes, and these, and other activities, are physicochemical in character.   Whether we consider growth or death, multiplication, movement, genetic changes, anabolic or catabolic reactions, or other activities, physical and chemical changes are involved.   In the living cell these changes must be coordinated in time and in space to give rise to that biological marvel, the unicellular organism.   Numerous equilibria or balances must be established to provide for the orderly multitude of changes involved in the maintenance, growth, and reproduction of bacteria which in their apparently simple structure carry out most or all the activities characteristic of life, many of which occur in higher forms only in specialized cells.   The expression in terms of physics and chemistry of the various phenomena constitutes the goal of bacterial physiology.

REFERENCES

General

Ann. Rev. Biochem., Annual Reviews, Inc., Stanford, Calif.
Ann. Rev. Microbiol., Annual Reviews, Inc., Stanford, Calif.
Baldwin, E.: "Dynamic Aspects of Biochemistry," Cambridge University Press, London, 1949.
Buchanan, R. E., and E. I. Fulmer: "Physiology and Biochemistry of Bacteria," 3 vols., The Williams & Wilkins Company, Baltimore, 1928.
Dubos, R. J.: "The Bacterial Cell," Harvard University Press, Cambridge, Mass., 1945.
Fruton, J. S., and S. Simmonds: "General Biochemistry," John Wiley & Sons, Inc., New York, 1953.
Gale, E. F.: "The Chemical Activities of Bacteria," 3d ed., Academic Press, Inc., New York, 1951.
Gerard, R. W.: "Unresting Cells," Harper & Brothers, New York, 1949.
Harper, H. A.: "Review of Physiological Chemistry," 5th ed., Lange Medical Publications, Los Altos, Calif., 1955.
Kluyver, A. J.: "The Chemical Activities of Micro-organisms," University of London Press, Ltd., London, 1931.
——— and C. B. van Niel: "The Microbe's Contributions to Biology," Harvard University Press, Cambridge, Mass., 1956.
Knaysi, G.: "Elements of Bacterial Cytology," Comstock Publishing Associates, Ithaca, N.Y., 1951.
Lamanna, C., and M. F. Mallette: "Basic Bacteriology," The Williams & Wilkins Company, Baltimore, 1953.
Lilly, V. G., and H. L. Barnett: "Physiology of the Fungi," McGraw-Hill Book Company, Inc., New York, 1951.
Pelczar, M. J., Jr., P. A. Hansen, and W. A. Konetzka: "Quantitative Bacterial Physiology," Burgess Publishing Co., Minneapolis, 1955.
Porter, J. R.: "Bacterial Chemistry and Physiology," John Wiley & Sons, Inc., New York, 1946.
Rahn, O.: "Physiology of Bacteria," The Blakiston Division, McGraw-Hill Book Company, Inc., New York, 1932.
Stephenson, M.: "Bacterial Metabolism," 3d ed., Longmans, Green & Co., Inc., New York, 1949.
Thimann, H. V.: "The Life of Bacteria," The Macmillan Company, New York, 1955.

Werkman, C. H., and P. W. Wilson (eds.): "Bacterial Physiology," Academic Press, Inc., New York, 1951.

Specific

Bisset, K. A.: "Bacteria," The Williams & Wilkins Company, Baltimore, 1952.

Knight, B. C. J. G.: "Bacterial Nutrition," His Majesty's Stationery Office, London, 1936.

van Niel, C. B.: The classification and natural relationships of bacteria, *Cold Spring Harbor Symp. Quant. Biol.*, **11**, 285–301 (1946).

CHAPTER 2

ENERGETICS, KINETICS, AND EQUILIBRIA

Living things are never at rest; they continuously undergo change in one way or another.   An organism may alter its position in its environment, it may alter its structure, it may grow, or it may undergo other changes.   This perpetual change of state of the organism or of its component parts requires the expenditure of energy which ultimately must be obtained from some source outside the organism if life is to be maintained.   The living cell, considered from a physicochemical point of view, is a highly specialized energy transformer through which a continuous flow of energy passes.   No physical-chemical system has yet been devised which is capable of carrying out in a limited space those reactions characteristic of life or possessed of such a degree of internal coordination and ability to adapt itself to changes in the environment. Energy is the underlying cause of all changes in matter, animate or inanimate, and so we must consider the sources of energy for the cell, how it is made available, and how it is utilized in living matter.

All the chemical reactions involved in the life of the cell whereby foodstuff is transformed into cellular material, waste products, and energy for the performance of work are grouped under the general term *metabolism*.   These reactions are spoken of collectively as the metabolic activities of the cell.   Metabolism may thus be defined as the *sum of all chemical changes, both assimilatory and dissimilatory, induced by an organism*.   In former years the assimilatory or anabolic reactions were considered as separate from the dissimilatory or catabolic reactions, a portion of the energy from the latter in some unknown manner being transferred for use in the synthetic and other energy-requiring reactions.   As we shall see, no sharp line of demarcation can be drawn between the assimilatory and the dissimilatory reactions, and there are very close links between the anabolic and catabolic activities of the cell.   Energy must be supplied continuously if the anabolic processes are to exceed those of catabolism, and is derived from the sum total of the respiratory activities of the cell. The struggle for existence of bacterial or other cells is a struggle for energy and building materials.

10

The Concept of Energy. Energy may be defined as the ability of a system to perform work, and the work done affords a measure of the energy expended by a system. The unit of work is the work done when unit force is overcome through unit distance. In the centimeter-gram-second system the unit of work is the erg, an erg being defined as the work done by a force of one dyne acting on a body which moves through a distance of one centimeter. A dyne in turn may be defined as the force which, acting on a gram for a second, would impart to it a velocity of one centimeter per second. Energy stored in a system by virtue of the motion of its particles is known as kinetic energy, while the energy stored in a body by virtue of its position is called potential energy. The sum total of the kinetic and potential energies is the intrinsic energy of a system. When a process occurs in which the energy of a system undergoes change, our measurements merely indicate the gain or loss in the energy of the system as a result of the change, as we have no means for actually determining the absolute energy value of a system. For example, let a mass of one gram fall through a distance of one centimeter under the influence of gravity. The resulting loss in potential energy is

$$1 \text{ g.} \times 980 \text{ cm./sec.}^2 \times 1 \text{ cm.} = 980 \text{ ergs}$$

All we have learned is that the system has lost 980 ergs of potential energy, the absolute energy of the body in its initial and final states not being involved in the calculation. A roller coaster, for example, loses potential energy on each drop, but some of this energy is converted into kinetic energy which will enable the coaster to ascend the next grade. A portion of this kinetic energy is expended in restoring potential energy, but a great deal is lost as heat energy due to frictional forces. The science of thermodynamics deals with the conversion of energy and factors influencing this conversion in physical or chemical systems.

All forms of energy may be considered as the product of two factors, one of *intensity* and the other of *capacity*. A system may have a high intensity factor but a low capacity factor and therefore be capable of doing only a limited amount of work. In the example given above the potential energy involved is the product of a force—the intensity factor—and a distance—the capacity factor. Heat energy is likewise the product of the intensity factor, temperature, and the capacity factor, quantity of heat. We may also postulate that chemical energy is the product of two factors, the intensity factor, or so-called chemical potential of Willard Gibbs, and a capacity factor, the quantity of the substance undergoing change.

The intensity factor determines whether an exchange of energy will occur and in what direction it will flow, while the capacity factor determines to what extent the energy will flow. For example, suppose we have two identical globes connected by a stopcock and that both globes contain an equal volume of the same gas at the same temperature, 50°C., and pressure. If we open the cock there will be no loss or gain in the intensity factor of energy of either system. Systems having the same intensity factor are said to be in equilibrium. The capacity factor has been doubled because two equal systems have been merged into one. However, if one system was at 100°C. and the other at 0°C., there would be no change in the total capacity factor but a flow of energy would occur from the system at the higher temperature to the system at the lower temperature. This exchange of energy would continue until the intensity factor, temperature, was equal throughout the whole system. Work could be accomplished if a suitable rotor was placed between the two globes.

When we consider the transformation of heat into work the following relation holds:

$$W = JQ \qquad (2\text{-}1)$$

where W units of work are produced when Q units of heat disappear in any process, J being a proportionality factor known as the mechanical equivalent of heat. The value of the mechanical equivalent of heat J is 4.183×10^7 ergs per gram-calorie, a gram-calorie (cal.) being defined as the amount of heat required to raise the temperature of one gram of water from 14.5 to 15.5°C. The abbreviation Cal. refers to a kilogram-calorie.

First Law of Thermodynamics. From observation it has been found that one form of energy may be transformed into any other form and that when a quantity of energy in any one form disappears, an exactly equal quantity of another form of energy makes its appearance. *Energy, like matter, is indestructible.* This statement constitutes the first law of thermodynamics. When any change takes place in a substance, there is a corresponding change in its total energy, either an increase due to the reception of energy from the environment or a decrease due to an evolution of energy. This broad principle is not absolute since under certain conditions matter and energy may be interchangeable but the sum total of the two remains constant. Such conversions do not occur in the cell so far as we can ascertain today.

Second Law of Thermodynamics. The total energy of a system in a given state is a definite characteristic of that state, and it is totally independent of how the system reached that state. For example, a gram of glucose has the same energy content under the same conditions of measurement, irrespective of whether the glucose was synthesized from simpler substances or derived from more complex ones. Likewise, when glucose is decomposed into carbon dioxide and water, the alteration in total energy which accompanies the change is altogether independent of the process by which the change is brought about. This latter fact was clearly recognized by Hess in 1840 when he postulated that *the amount of heat generated by a chemical reaction is the same whether it takes place in one or in several steps.* Likewise, *the quantity of heat which is required to decompose a chemical compound is precisely equal to that which was evolved in the formation of the compound from its elements,* a law enunciated by Lavoisier and Laplace in 1780 as a result of their studies in thermochemistry.

Although work can always be transformed into heat, this is not equally true of the reverse process, the transformation of heat into work. The first law of thermodynamics merely states that when heat is converted into work, a definite quantitative relationship exists between the heat absorbed and the work done, but it tells us nothing as to the amount of work which can be obtained from a given quantity of heat. The temperature of the gas in the globes previously mentioned will be increased when heat is absorbed but no useful work can be done since heat by itself simply increases the velocity at which the molecules are moving in all directions in a random manner. It is only when this motion can be directed that unorganized energy can be transformed into organized energy, i.e., work. Experience has shown that *heat of itself will never pass from one body to another at a higher temperature.* This statement is an expression of the second law of thermodynamics, which may also be stated as *every change takes place at the cost of a certain amount of available energy.* This loss of available energy by a system during a transformation from one state to another may be taken as an inverse index of the efficiency of the transformation mechanism.

The cause of all action or change is the tendency of energy to attain the same uniform degree of intensity as that of its environment. Any process which occurs spontaneously always involves a loss of available energy, although the process may be arranged in such a way as to furnish mechanical energy. In 1879 Berthelot showed that the same principle applies to chemical changes and that in general a chemical change occurs without the addition of external energy only if it is accompanied by the liberation of heat. Thus the available energy of a system always tends to become a minimum. Hence we can say that the "mixed-upness" (or "run-downness") of a system tends to increase. As an organized system becomes mixed up its energy is converted into useless heat energy, undirected motion. Organization is continuously being developed or maintained in the cell; yet this can occur only with the expenditure of energy.

Maximum Work. The concepts of thermodynamics are generally clarified by the use of equations representing the changes which occur.

Let us consider a theoretically perfect heat engine supplied with Q units of heat at a temperature T_1 on the Kelvin or absolute scale

$$(273 + °C. = °K.)$$

and dissipated at a lower temperature T_2. It can be shown by thermo-dynamic reasoning that the maximum amount of work W that can be done by such an engine can be expressed by the equation

$$W = Q \frac{T_1 - T_2}{T_1} \tag{2-2}$$

or, by rearrangement,

$$W = Q - \frac{Q}{T_1} T_2 \tag{2-3}$$

The maximum amount of work that can be done is always $(Q/T_1)T_2$ units less than the total amount of energy supplied. One hundred per cent efficiency can only be obtained if the lower temperature is $0°K$. Suppose we have a steam engine with steam supplied at the normal boiling point of water, $373°K.$, and exhausted at $292°K.$ The maximum amount of work that could be accomplished by a perfect engine, i.e., its efficiency, can be calculated per unit of energy supplied by substitution in equation (2-2), or

$$\text{Maximum work} = \text{efficiency} = 1 \left(\frac{373 - 292}{373} \right) = 0.217 = 21.7\%$$

If we assume that a cell operates with an efficiency of 20 per cent at a body temperature of $310°K.$ ($37°C.$), we find on substituting these values in equation (2-2) and solving for T_1 that this would be approximately $388°K.$, or $115°C.$ This would be a highly lethal temperature, and it is apparent that the cell is not operating as a heat engine. Energy must be supplied in a different form. We simply express energy changes in living matter in terms of calories for convenience, particularly since the heat of a reaction can be measured in a calorimeter.

Free Energy. The quantity $(Q/T_1)T_2$ in equation (2-3) can be shown to be a measure of the total energy unavailable for work at the tempera-ture T_2 and, as is apparent, is composed of two components, Q/T_1, which is known as the entropy factor, and T_2, the temperature. The concept of entropy is a complex one, and in simplest terms entropy can be con-sidered *a measure of the total energy of a system (or of a chemical reaction) unavailable for doing useful work.* Entropy is commonly represented by the symbol S, and we can then write equation (2-3) in the form

$$F = H - TS \qquad (2\text{-}4)$$

where F = *free energy*, the amount of energy available for performance
of useful work
H = total heat energy supplied at temperature T
S = entropy factor of the reaction

We cannot measure the absolute values of the variables in equation
(2-4), but the changes that they undergo in passing from one state to
another at constant temperature can be determined. Let us represent
the second state by

$$F' = H' - TS' \qquad (2\text{-}5)$$

and on subtracting equation (2-5) from equation (2-4) we obtain

$$F - F' = (H - H') - T(S - S') \qquad (2\text{-}6)$$

or, in the usual terminology where Δ represents a small change,

$$\Delta F = \Delta H - T\,\Delta S \qquad (2\text{-}7)$$

Expressed in words rather than in mathematical symbols, the free-energy
change, or maximum amount of work, which can be obtained from a
reaction is equal to the heat change in the reaction minus the energy
$T\,\Delta S$ not converted into work. It is common practice to represent a
free-energy decrease and heat evolved in a reaction by $-\Delta F$ and $-\Delta H$,
respectively, the minus sign indicating that energy or heat is lost by the
system.

The amount of energy available to a cell as the result of a chemical
reaction is ordinarily expressed in calories and may be determined by
measuring the heat evolved when the reaction takes place in a calorimeter.
The heat of combustion or the heat of reaction does not necessarily represent the total energy potentially available to the cell for synthetic or
other purposes. For absolute values it is necessary to consider the free
energy of the reaction rather than the total heat evolved. These two
quantities are closely related, and it is possible to determine the value
of the free-energy change in a given reaction by the application of the
laws and equations of thermodynamics.

It is apparent from equation (2-7) that when there is no change in
entropy during a reaction, the decrease in heat content is equal to the
decrease in free energy. Usually, however, there is an entropy change
during a reaction and the decrease in free energy is greater or less than
the decrease in heat content depending on the sign of ΔS. Since entropies
and heats of reaction can be calculated from calorimetric measurements
or other data, it is frequently possible to calculate the free-energy change

in a reaction and also to determine the equilibrium point of a reaction under different conditions of temperature, pressure, and concentration of reactants.   Also, the free energy of a reaction (for unit change in activities, often written $\Delta F°$) can be calculated from the thermodynamic relationship

$$\Delta F = -RT \ln K \qquad\qquad (2\text{-}8)$$

where $K =$ equilibrium constant (to be discussed later) of a reaction at constant temperature and under standard conditions

As illustrations of the energy involved in a reaction the following examples may be considered, the reactions taking place at 298°K. and at a pressure of 1 atm.:

$$C_{(graphite)} + O_{2(gas)} \rightarrow CO_{2(gas)}$$
$$\Delta F = -94{,}260 \text{ cal.}$$
$$\Delta H = -94{,}250 \text{ cal.}$$

The words in parentheses indicate the states in which the reactants and products occur, and when the concentrations are not molar or the pressure not atmospheric this information is also given in a complete equation. In this reaction it will be observed that the values of ΔH and ΔF are nearly the same.   However, in the reactions

$$C_{(graphite)} + \tfrac{1}{2}O_{2(gas)} \rightarrow CO_{(gas)}$$
$$\Delta F = -32{,}510 \text{ cal.}$$
$$\Delta H = -26{,}150 \text{ cal.}$$

or

$$C_6H_{12}O_{6(solid)} + 6O_{2(gas)} \rightarrow 6H_2O_{(liquid)} + 6CO_{2(gas)}$$
$$\Delta F = -686{,}160 \text{ cal.}$$
$$\Delta H = -673{,}000 \text{ cal.}$$

the free-energy changes are greater than the heat changes.

When we consider the reverse process (Baas-Becking and Parks, 1927) as it takes place under the conditions of photosynthesis, we obtain the equation

$$6CO_2(0.0003 \text{ atm.}) + 6H_2O_{(liq.)} \rightarrow 6O_2(0.2 \text{ atm.}) + C_6H_{12}O_{6(s)}$$

and obtain the value of $+708{,}900$ cal. for ΔF, the positive sign indicating that the above quantity of energy must be supplied per mole of glucose synthesized.   However, the value of ΔH under the same conditions changes but little from that reported above, so it is readily seen that the use of values of ΔH so commonly employed in earlier biological literature may introduce considerable error.   The values of ΔF for a particular reaction have to be corrected at times for heat of dilution, heat of ionization, heat of neutralization, or other changes that may occur.

Since a reaction will occur spontaneously only when energy is liberated as a result of the reaction, the value and sign of ΔF provide us with a test for the study of hypothetical reactions. If ΔF is negative, the reaction may occur spontaneously; if positive, it cannot occur spontaneously; and if zero, the system is in equilibrium. A reaction which provides free energy is termed *exergonic*, while the term *endergonic* is applied to a reaction on which energy must be expended to cause it to occur. These terms refer to free-energy changes, while *exothermic* and *endothermic*, respectively, refer to the liberation or the absorption of heat during the course of a reaction. While thermodynamics enables us to predict that a reaction may occur, we must not deduce that the reaction will occur since inherent factors can stabilize the molecule. For example, at normal temperatures glucose is relatively stable and does not readily combine with oxygen, although the ΔF of oxidation has a high negative value. Following the addition of bacteria or other appropriate cells the sugar may be oxidized at a rapid rate. The problem underlying all biological oxidations is to find an explanation for the fact that substances such as the carbohydrates, fats, and amino acids are easily oxidized when in contact with the living cell, while under the same conditions, but in the absence of the cells, they remain quite stable to oxygen.

When we consider the equation for the formation of glucose and oxygen from carbon dioxide and water under the conditions of photosynthesis, we see that a minimum of 708,900 cal. of energy (100 per cent efficiency) must be supplied by light and held in chemical bonds per mole of glucose synthesized. The law of constant heat summation advanced by Hess shows that the energy involved in this reaction is the same irrespective of the intermediate steps involved in the reaction, and the law of Lavoisier and Laplace shows that the same amount of energy must be evolved when the glucose is oxidized to carbon dioxide and water under the same conditions of temperature, pressure, and concentrations as involved in its synthesis.

Theorem of Le Châtelier. A qualitative principle known as the theorem of Le Châtelier is useful in predicting the direction in which a change may be expected to take place. According to this theorem, *if a system is in equilibrium and an external force is applied, the system will shift in such a way as to minimize the effect of the applied force.* If we consider the energy involved in the formation of water from its elements under atmospheric pressure and at a temperature of 298°K., we obtain the equation

$$H_2 + \tfrac{1}{2}O_2 \rightleftarrows H_2O \qquad \Delta F = -56,000 \text{ cal.}$$

At high temperatures the reaction is readily reversible; that is, hydrogen and oxygen are formed from water and at 1000°K. the reaction can be expressed as

$$H_2O \rightleftarrows H_2 + \tfrac{1}{2}O_2 \qquad \Delta F = -67,400 \text{ cal.}$$

Both reactions take place simultaneously, some of the water being decomposed steadily and some being reformed, so that an equilibrium is established between the two reactions. If either hydrogen or oxygen is added to the system at 1000°K., the equilibrium is shifted in the direction of the lower arrow so that a portion of the added constituent undergoes combination. Similarly, if we alter the intensity factor, the temperature, and apply heat to the system, the equilibrium is again shifted and in the direction of the upper arrow. Heat is adsorbed by the system. Similar shifts in the equilibrium of a reaction occurring in biological systems will be considered later.

The principle of Le Châtelier has been broadened in order to apply it to the dynamic equilibrium of living systems, and it may be said that the living organism is such that any disturbing influence elicits in the organism a compensatory reaction which tends to neutralize the disturbance and restore the equilibrium.

Free Energy and Life. A living cell must perform work, and energy must be provided for this purpose. All life processes demand for their continuation and maintenance a continuous supply of matter and of energy. As far as matter is concerned, there is a closed cycle. Plants and certain bacteria feed on terrestrial matter, but energy for synthesis is supplied from outside this world in the form of light. The matter so synthesized serves as food, i.e., a source of organic building material and of oxidizable material to supply energy, for higher forms of life. Ultimately the foodstuff is broken down into simpler molecules which can again serve in the cycle of events. The energy lost in the cycle must be supplied from the outside source if the cycle is to be maintained.

If there is no free energy available, there is no life. The ultimate source of free energy, with the exception of that for the autotrophic bacteria, is radiant energy from the sun. This energy is employed only by those cells containing photosynthetic pigments such as chlorophyll and is stored in the cell as foodstuff which will be utilized later by the same or by other cells. The two basic reactions of life are the storage during photosynthesis of energy derived from the sun and the liberation of this chemically bound energy by dissimilation of the organic products of photosynthesis. These reactions may be represented as

$$\text{Radiant energy} + nCO_2 + nH_2O \rightarrow nO_2 + nCH_2O$$

and

$$nCH_2O + nO_2 \rightarrow nH_2O + nCO_2 + \text{energy}$$

In the left-hand side of the latter equation carbon, hydrogen, and oxygen atoms are linked together, while in the right-hand side hydrogen and carbon atoms are linked separately to oxygen atoms. This rearrangement induced by oxidations in the cell or in a flame is complete, no available free energy for the cells being stored in CO_2 or H_2O. Carbohydrates represent a state of high free-energy level and carbon dioxide and water one of low free-energy level. Where there is such a free-energy-level difference living cells may appear, cause a decrease in free energy, and use a portion of this decrease for their own purposes.

While thermodynamic considerations show that foodstuffs can be oxidized or undergo combustion spontaneously at ordinary temperature, yet the fact remains that they do not do so at an appreciable rate. The breakfast set in the tomb of the Egyptian Emperor Tutenkhamon thousands of years ago was unburned on opening the tomb a few years past. Yet, had the Emperor consumed this food, it would have been oxidized in a short time. The cell utilizes reactions that theoretically can occur at ordinary temperatures; yet, actually, the cell utilizes those reactions only when they are started and directed by the cell itself. The special chemical apparatus, the enzymes, of the cell so guide the reactions that the energy is liberated piecemeal and in such a way that a portion of the available energy can be utilized by the cell while the remainder is finally expended as heat.

Kinetics of Chemical Reactions. We have seen that a reversible chemical reaction will proceed spontaneously in that direction in which there is a decrease in free energy, the reaction occurring until an equilibrium is established with definite concentrations of reactants and products under a given set of conditions. It is possible that the majority of chemical reactions are reversible to some extent, although in many cases the equilibrium point may be immeasurably far to one side.

The importance of the relative amounts of the reacting substances in determining the course of a reaction was first recognized by Wenzel in 1777 and very clearly demonstrated by Berthollet in 1799. Berthollet observed that sodium carbonate and calcium chloride generally react according to the equation

$$Na_2CO_3 + CaCl_2 \rightarrow 2NaCl + CaCO_3$$

In certain saline lakes in Egypt, however, sodium carbonate was deposited along the shore line, and Berthollet pointed out that this was due to a reversal of the above reaction caused by the high concentration of sodium chloride in the water.

It was not until 1865, however, that the law concerning the effect of concentration in controlling chemical reactions was clearly formulated by Guldberg and Waage as follows: *the rate* (speed, or velocity) *of a chemical reaction is proportional to the active masses of the reacting sub-stances present at that time.*   These investigators defined the active mass as the molecular concentration of a reactant per unit volume.

According to the law of mass action the rate of a reaction such as that between an organic acid and an alcohol to give an ester and water, e.g.,

$$CH_3COOH + CH_3CH_2OH \rightleftarrows CH_3COOCH_2CH_3 + H_2O$$

is at the start proportional to the product of the concentrations of acid and alcohol, or

$$Rate_{t_0(\text{forward reaction})} = k_f[a][b] \qquad (2\text{-}9)$$

In this equation k_f is the velocity constant of the forward reaction, t_0 refers to zero time (the time of mixing, or of starting measurements), and a and b to the concentrations (commonly indicated in brackets) of the acid and alcohol, respectively, at that time.   As the reaction pro-ceeds, the concentration of acid and of alcohol will diminish, and the rate of this reaction will, therefore, also decrease with time.   At any time t, x equivalents of acid and of alcohol will have reacted to give x equivalents of ester and of water, the concentration of acid then being $a - x$ and that of alcohol $b - x$.   The rate of the forward reaction at any time t can be expressed by the equation

$$Rate_t = k_f[a - x][b - x] \qquad (2\text{-}10)$$

and the rate of the reverse reaction by

$$Rate_{t(\text{reverse})} = k_r[x]^2 \qquad (2\text{-}11)$$

where k_r = velocity constant of reverse reaction.

After a time, depending on the original concentrations of the reactants and the temperature, the rate of the reverse reaction will equal that of the forward reaction and the system will be in equilibrium.   At equi-librium we may write that

$$k_f[a - x][b - x] = k_r[x]^2 \qquad (2\text{-}12)$$

or, on rearranging the equation,

$$\frac{[x]^2}{[a - x][b - x]} = \frac{k_f}{k_r} = K \qquad (2\text{-}13)$$

where K = equilibrium constant of the reaction.

In this particular reaction at 30°C. and starting with equivalent amounts of acid and of alcohol, equilibrium is established when approxi-mately two-thirds of the original reactants are converted into ester and water or

$$K = \frac{[CH_3COOC_2H_5][H_2O]}{[CH_3COOH][C_2H_5OH]} = \frac{[\tfrac{2}{3}] \times [\tfrac{2}{3}]}{[\tfrac{1}{3}] \times [\tfrac{1}{3}]} = 4.0$$

Having determined the value of the equilibrium constant K, it is possible to calculate equilibrium concentrations for any initial concentrations of the reactants at a given temperature. It should be apparent that the presence of water in the reaction mixture at the start would tend to decrease the speed of the forward reaction and to shift the equilibrium toward the left. Conversely, removal of the water as it is formed would shift the reaction to the right and result in the production of a greater amount of the ester, a type of procedure frequently employed in the laboratory or in industrial practice. Reversible reactions are commonly encountered in biological systems and follow the rules or equations outlined above. Concentrations in these equations are best expressed in terms of activities of the reacting substances, activities being based on thermodynamic considerations and being most simply considered as effective concentrations. The law of mass action is applicable to dissociation as well as to other reactions, ionic equilibria, including that in the dissociation of water, playing an important role in influencing the behavior of bacteria.

The free energy of this reaction can be calculated with the aid of equation (2-8) since we have calculated the value of K to be 4 at 30°C., or 303°K. On substitution of the known values and converting to $\log_{10}$, we obtain

$$\Delta F = -1.987 \times 303 \times 2.303 \log 4 = -834 \text{ cal.}$$

As the value of K increases, a reaction proceeds further to the right and the free-energy change becomes greater, or, in other words, the reaction tends to become less reversible unless energy is supplied from an outside source.

When an organic compound is added to a suspension of bacteria there may be a number of different products which are possible according to thermodynamics. The product which will predominate is the one which is produced by the fastest reaction. The same statements hold true for organic reactions in the absence of living matter or enzymes and for many inorganic reactions as well. It is possible to describe the behavior or rate of the less complex reactions in simple mathematical terms based on the law of mass action. Reactions in which only one substance is undergoing change are known as unimolecular reactions and their rate may be expressed by the following equation:

$$-\frac{dc}{dt} = kc \tag{2-14}$$

where c = concentration of material undergoing change
k = a proportionality factor
$-dc/dt$ = rate at which concentration decreases, i.e., a small decrease in concentration dc in a short period of time dt

It can readily be seen that this equation is a simple mathematical statement of the mass-action law. It is also an expression of the compound-interest law or of the law of exponential growth. This law is frequently met in physical chemistry and in studies on both the growth and death of bacteria.

The unimolecular law is often expressed by the equation

$$-\frac{dx}{dt} = k(a - x) \tag{2-15}$$

where a = initial concentration

x = change in time t

By a process in calculus known as integration the above equation can be converted to the more useful form

$$k = \frac{2.303}{t_2 - t_1} \log \frac{a - x_1{}^*}{a - x_2} \tag{2-16}$$

This equation can be further simplified by taking t as zero time, or as the time at which measurements were started. The concentration at zero time can be denoted by a and at any time t by $a - x$. The equation may then be written:

$$k = \frac{2.303}{t} \log \frac{a}{a - x} \tag{2-17}$$

Applying the equation to a specific case where 1,000 molecules are initially present and during 1 hr. 500 decompose, we obtain

$$k = \frac{2.303}{1} \log \frac{1,000}{500} = 0.6932 \tag{2-18}$$

Having evaluated k, it is now possible to calculate the concentration at any time. For example, knowing the value of k, simple calculation shows that 300 molecules decompose in the first half-hour or that 62.5 molecules remain at the end of 4 hr., the fractional value being a statistical average. It can also be shown by the use of the above equation that the velocity constant of a unimolecular reaction is independent of the initial concentration of the material undergoing change. Time units other than hours can be employed in the determination of k and will give rise to different values.

There are equations for bimolecular and trimolecular reactions based on the law of mass action. The number of reactions, however, to which these equations are applicable is rather limited, the most common complications being due to counter reactions, side reactions, or consecutive

*log refers to logarithms to the base 10, ln to the base e, and the factor 2.303 converts $\log_{10}$ to $\ln_e$; ln of a number = 2.303 × log of that number.

reactions. Certain bimolecular reactions appear to follow the uni-molecular equation when in reality the reaction is not unimolecular. A classical example is the hydrolysis of cane sugar by water in the presence of an acid, the reaction being

$$C_{12}H_{22}O_{11} + H_2O \rightarrow C_6H_{12}O_6 + C_6H_{12}O_6$$
$$\text{Sucrose} \qquad\qquad \text{Glucose} \qquad \text{Fructose}$$

The kinetics of a reaction of this type follow the unimolecular equation because in most experiments the sugar concentration is so low compared to that of water that the decrease in the concentration of water during the reaction is negligible. Reactions which apparently follow the uni-molecular equation are known as pseudo-unimolecular reactions and are frequently encountered in studies on the rate of growth or of death of bacteria, only the concentration of bacteria showing appreciable change during the test periods.

Influence of Temperature on Rate of Reaction. It has long been known as an empirical fact that the rate of many chemical reactions increases with temperature and that in general the velocity of a reaction doubles or trebles with each 10°C. rise in temperature. This generalization is sometimes used in attempting to decide whether an unknown reaction is of a chemical or physical nature, many, but not all, physical reactions, such as those of diffusion or of adsorption, having much lower temperature coefficients. The symbol Q_{10} is employed to designate the temperature coefficient over a range of 10°C. and is the ratio of the velocity constant at the higher temperature to that at the lower, or

$$Q_{10} = \frac{K_t}{K_{t-10}} \qquad\qquad (2\text{-}19)$$

If the constants at any two temperatures, t_1 and a higher temperature t_2, are known, then Q_{10} may be calculated from the equation

$$\log Q_{10} = \frac{10}{t_2 - t_1} \log \frac{K_2}{K_1} \qquad\qquad (2\text{-}20)$$

According to present theories it is necessary for molecules to become activated before they react. If all molecules were equally reactive, it would be difficult to account for the existence of slow reactions since the number of collisions per second is enormous and it might be expected that all reactions would, therefore, be instantaneous.

In 1889 Arrhenius reported that the rate of change of the natural logarithm of the velocity constant K of a reaction is inversely proportional to the square of the absolute temperature T, or, in a modified form,

$$\frac{d \ln K}{dT} = \frac{A}{RT^2} \qquad\qquad (2\text{-}21)$$

where R is the universal gas constant (1.987 cal.) and A a constant, commonly interpreted as the energy of activation, for the reaction under consideration. The term μ is frequently substituted for A in biological studies to indicate that no physical meaning is necessarily involved, and can be considered as the apparent energy of activation. Integration and conversion of equation (2-21) to ordinary logarithms give the equation

$$\log \frac{K_2}{K_1} = \frac{\mu}{2.303R} \frac{T_2 - T_1}{T_1 T_2} \tag{2-22}$$

In many enzymatically catalyzed reactions μ values fall within the range 1,000 to 25,000 cal. If μ has a value around 12,000 cal. and the temperatures are 295 and 305°K., then

$$\log \frac{K_2}{K_1} = \frac{12,000}{4.6} \times \frac{10}{295 \times 305} = 0.29$$

or K_2/K_1 is approximately 2, which means that the rate of reaction has doubled at the higher temperature. This behavior has been interpreted for ordinary reactions on the basis that the kinetic energy of the molecules has not been doubled but instead the fraction of the molecules with energy greater than 12,000 cal. has been doubled. The general nature of activation and catalysis will be considered later along with the nature of enzyme action.

Dissociation of Water. Since water is the most universal solvent and is also the major component of living matter, water and its ions play a highly important role in the activities of bacteria. It is a good conductor of heat and thereby aids in the dissipation of heat liberated by bacterial respiration. Its high specific heat tends to inhibit marked temperature changes. The rate or the course of many biological reactions may be influenced by the concentration of water, high osmotic pressures in particular being inhibitory to most bacteria. The ions of water also influence the rate and the course of biological reactions.

On applying the law of mass action to the dissociation of water we find for the reaction (expressed in its simplest form)

$$H_2O \rightleftarrows H^+ + OH^-$$

that equilibrium conditions and the equilibrium or dissociation constant are expressed by the equation

$$\frac{[H^+][OH^-]}{[H_2O]} = K \tag{2-23}$$

In pure water and dilute solutions the concentration of water is practically constant and so large in comparison with the concentration of ions that it can be neglected in the numerator of equation (2-23). This gives rise to the equation for the apparent dissociation constant K_w of water which can be expressed as

$$K_w = [\text{H}^+][\text{OH}^-] \qquad (2\text{-}24)$$

The concentration of hydrogen and of hydroxyl ions, as determined by appropriate methods, is 1×10^{-7} at approximately 22°C., and the apparent dissociation constant or product of these two concentrations is 1×10^{-14}. Any shift in the concentration of either ion will, according to the law of mass action, result in such a change in concentration of the other ion that the product of the two concentrations will remain constant at 1×10^{-14}. The apparent dissociation constant will alter with temperature, increasing with increase in temperature, although the change is not highly significant over the range commonly employed in studies with bacteria.

The symbol pH is commonly employed to indicate the relative degree of acidity or alkalinity of a solution since the use of actual hydrogen-ion (or hydronium, H_3O^+, hydrated-hydrogen-ion) concentrations would involve a cumbersome numerical range from 10^1 to 10^{-14}. This range is indicated on the pH scale by numbers from 0 to 14, a pH of 7.0 representing neutrality at room temperature, lower values acidic solutions, and higher values alkaline ones. The term pH may be defined as *the logarithm of the reciprocal of the hydrogen-ion concentration*, or

$$\text{pH} = \log \frac{1}{[\text{H}^+]} \qquad (2\text{-}25)$$

It is essential to remember that the pH scale is a logarithmic one, and accordingly a pH of 6 represents a hydrogen-ion concentration ten times that at pH 7 or a hydroxyl-ion concentration one-tenth that in the neutral solution. Fractional values are also misleading if the logarithmic nature of the scale is neglected, the difference in hydrogen-ion concentration being much greater, for example, between 5.0 and 5.1 than between 4.9 and 5.0.

Accurate knowledge of the pH of culture media is important from two different points of view. The initial reaction of a culture medium should be carefully adjusted if good growth and consistent results are to be obtained, and the final reaction after growth has occurred is often of diagnostic value, qualitatively in tests for acid or alkali production and more quantitatively in such reactions as the methyl red test. Accurate pH control is also of importance in studies on bacterial metabolism, growth, or death. Marked changes in the hydrogen-ion concentration of a medium or of a suspending fluid can frequently be prevented, or greatly reduced, by the addition of buffer agents to the medium, a buffer being defined as *a substance which by its presence in solution increases the amount of acid or alkali that must be added to cause unit shift in pH*. Buffers are generally mixtures of weak acids and their salts or of weak bases and their salts.

A weak acid or base is characterized by a large proportion of the substance in solution in water being present in the form of undissociated molecules, and accordingly the dissociation constant has a low value. In the case of acetic acid, for example, only a small fraction is dissociated and the dissociation constant at room temperature is 1.8×10^{-5}. Addition of sodium acetate, which ionizes to a much greater extent, increases the concentration of the acetate ions, and to restore the equilibrium, acetate ions must combine with hydrogen ions to form undissociated acetic acid molecules. Sodium acetate not only causes a decrease in the concentration of hydrogen ions but also tends to stabilize it, or, in other words, buffers the solution against change in pH when small amounts of acid or base are added to the solution. All reactions in living cells occur in a buffered medium, carbonate, bicarbonate, and phosphate being the principal buffers although proteins and amino acids may act as secondary or less efficient ones.

Buffers not only are of importance in the maintenance of a suitable pH in cells or in media but also serve as standards for the adjustment of the hydrogen-ion concentration of media or of suspending fluids to a definite pH. Full discussion of the action of buffers and detailed theoretical and practical consideration of buffer solutions can be found in various publications, Clark's "The Determination of Hydrogen Ions" being a classical reference book.

The actual determination of pH or hydrogen-ion concentration is based on measurements made with the hydrogen electrode, which, because of technical difficulties, is generally replaced by other electrometric systems or by colorimetric tests. The theory of hydrogen-ion-concentration determinations can be developed briefly as follows: when a stick of metal dips into water, some of the metal dissolves and passes into solution as metallic ions bearing a positive charge. This leaves the metal negatively charged, and the metal attracts positively charged ions, thus establishing a potential difference between the metal and the solution. The magnitude of the potential difference depends upon two factors, the tendency of the metal to pass into solution (its solution pressure) and the osmotic pressure exerted by its ions in solution. When the two pressures are equal there is no difference in potential. The larger the difference which exists between the solution pressure of the metal and the osmotic pressure of its ions, the greater is the difference in electrical potential. It can be shown by thermodynamic considerations that the potential difference between the metal and the solution is represented by the equation

$$E = \frac{2.303RT}{nF} \log \frac{p}{P} \qquad (2\text{-}26)$$

where E = potential difference or electromotive force, volts
  R = universal gas constant expressed in electrical units, 8.315 volt-coulombs
  T = absolute temperature
  n = valence of the ion
  F = faraday, 96,496 coulombs
  p = osmotic pressure of the metallic ions
  P = solution pressure of the metal

When a platinum electrode is coated with platinum black it is capable of absorbing large quantities of hydrogen and this electrode will act as if it were a stick of metallic hydrogen when hydrogen gas is bubbled over it. The above equation, therefore, applies to this hydrogen electrode. When two hydrogen electrodes dipping into two solutions of different pH are connected together and contact between the two solutions is made with a salt bridge, a current will flow and the potential difference between the two electrodes can be measured. This observed potential will be the difference between the separate potentials as calculated from equation (2-26), and since all terms are equal except the osmotic pressures of the hydrogen ions p_1 and p_2, we obtain on subtraction

$$E_{observed} = \frac{2.303RT}{nF} \log \frac{p_1}{p_2} \quad \text{or} \quad \frac{2.303RT}{nF} \log \frac{a_1}{a_2} \qquad (2\text{-}27)$$

where a, the activity of the hydrogen ion, is substituted for its osmotic pressure. If the activity of the hydrogen ion in one of the solutions is 1 (approximately 1 gram-equivalent of hydrogen ions per liter) and the temperature is 25°C., then

$$E_{observed} = 0.059 \log \frac{1}{a_2} = 0.059 \text{ pH} \qquad (2\text{-}28)$$

and

$$\text{pH} = \frac{E_{observed}}{0.059} \qquad (2\text{-}29)$$

In practical work it is much easier to substitute a calomel electrode for the hydrogen electrode dipping into the normal acid of unit activity, and this electrode (saturated potassium chloride–calomel) is 0.246 volt more positive than the normal or standard hydrogen electrode at 25°C.

Then

$$pH = \frac{E_{observed} - 0.246}{0.059}$$
(2-30)

Other electrodes, in particular the glass electrode, have replaced the hydrogen electrode for general use since they are more convenient to employ, but the hydrogen electrode remains as the basic standard.

The electrometric method for the determination of hydrogen-ion concentration is very accurate but does involve the use of expensive and intricate apparatus. Indicators that change color over a definite pH range are frequently employed for routine studies and are sufficiently accurate for many purposes. In order to understand the use of pH indicator dyes it is necessary to remember that they are generally weak organic acids which are capable of existing in two or more tautomeric forms in equilibrium with each other. In the simplest case one of these forms, which we can designate by the formula HIn, is a nonelectrolyte, while the other form HIn' is an electrolyte which ionizes in water. The equilibrium may be represented by the general equation

$$HIn \rightleftarrows HIn' \rightleftarrows H^+ + In'^-$$
(2-31)

The form HIn shows one color in solution and the ion In'^- a different one, preferably of marked contrast to the first. The addition of an acid displaces the equilibrium to the left with the development of more of the so-called acid color, while alkali would displace it to the right with the production of the alkaline color form In'^-. The neutral color of the indicator is observed when the concentration of hydrogen ions in the solution is such that one-half of the indicator is in the HIn form, the other half in the forms In' and MIn', where M represents the metal of the added base. According to the law of mass action

$$K = \frac{[H^+][In'^-]}{[HIn]} \quad \text{or} \quad [H^+] = K \frac{[HIn]}{[In'^-]}$$
(2-32)

If we denote the fraction of the indicator which exists in the alkaline color by x, then $1 - x$ represents the portion exhibiting the acid color and equation (2-30) then becomes

$$[H^+] = K \frac{[1 - x]}{[x]}$$
(2-33)

Since the indicator exhibits its neutral color when one-half is in each color form, the dissociation constant of the indicator is numerically equal to the hydrogen-ion concentration of the solution in which the neutral color is evident. Different indicators have different dissociation constants, and therefore they change color over different pH ranges.

In the determination of the pH of a medium or of a culture one selects an indicator that changes color over a range in which it is suspected that the pH of the solution falls. A few drops of the indicator are added to the solution, and the color developed is compared with those produced by the same volume of indicator in equivalent amounts of buffer solutions covering the pH range. If the tint produced in the solution of unknown pH corresponds with that in a buffer of known pH, then the hydrogen-ion concentrations in the two solutions are the same. The pH of a culture medium can be adjusted to a desired value with the aid of a suitable indicator, acid or alkali being added until the color matches that of a standard of the desired pH. Various factors influence the accurate determination of pH values in different solutions either with indicators or with electrometric methods, and standard references should be consulted for the proper procedures and details to be observed.

REFERENCES

Standard texts on physical chemistry.
Baas-Becking, L. G. M., and G. S. Parks: Energy relations in the metabolism of autotrophic bacteria, *Physiol. Rev.*, **7**, 85–106 (1927).

CHAPTER 3

SURFACE CHEMISTRY

The preceding considerations have dealt primarily with reactions occurring in homogeneous systems, but with the bacteria and their environment one has to deal not only with substances in true solution but also with heterogeneous systems. In a heterogeneous system there are at least two distinct phases in contact with each other, e.g., the bacterial cell and its environment. The colloidal state represents a heterogeneous system, and no complete understanding of the properties of bacteria is possible without some knowledge and consideration of the properties of matter in this state.

Colloidal Systems. Thomas Graham in 1861 differentiated all solutes into two classes, crystalloids and colloids (glue-like substances). Crystalloids were characterized by their ability to diffuse through semipermeable membranes which retained colloids. In the latter class he placed gums, proteins, glue, and similar agents which not only diffuse slowly in aqueous solution but also exert little effect on osmotic pressure and other characteristics of solutions which are markedly influenced by ordinary acids, bases, and salts or by simple organic molecules. A substance cannot strictly be spoken of as a colloid because the term now implies a state rather than a form of matter. A colloidal system can be defined as *a system in which one material is stably dispersed in a second with a degree of subdivision ordinarily coarser than molecular.* This implies that colloidal systems are composed of at least two phases in intimate contact with each other. Since a colloid, in the loose sense of the term, is a heterogeneous system, it is necessary to distinguish between the substance which is dispersed and the dispersion medium. The terms disperse phase and dispersion medium are commonly employed although there is a tendency to speak of the dispersed material as micelles and the medium as the intermicellar phase.

When the size of the particles of one component in a two-component system is gradually reduced until the particles become microscopic in size, a coarse suspension is produced. Dust in air, silt in water, and bacteria suspended in a culture medium are familiar examples of this type of suspension. The particles are relatively large and tend to settle out fairly readily from these coarse suspensions unless stabilizing forces exist. When the size of the dispersed particles is reduced to submicroscopic dimensions relatively stable colloidal systems result. Further decrease in size ultimately results in particles of molecular size which tend to give true solutions, i.e., homogeneous systems. The colloidal state lies in the rather indistinct zone between particles exhibiting the behavior of matter in mass and those of molecules in true solution. In general it is arbitrarily considered that the dispersed phase in a colloidal system is composed of particles ordinarily with diameters between 1 and 100 millimicrons (mμ). Actually, there is a continuous gradation in properties from homogeneous systems through colloidal ones to coarsely divided suspensions of different degrees of stability.

Colloidal chemistry is frequently spoken of as surface chemistry since surface forces play an important role in colloidal systems. The surface energy of a cube 1 cm. on a side is relatively small and is exerted over a total surface area of 6 sq. cm. On dividing this cube into ones 100 mμ on a side we obtain 10^{15} cubes with a total surface area of 60 sq. m. Continuing this subdivision until the approximate lower limit of the colloidal state, 1 mμ, is reached results in 10^{21} cubes with a surface area of 6,000 sq. m., or approximately 1.5 acres. The surface energy per unit area may remain constant, but with the immense surface areas involved in colloidal systems the total surface energy per unit volume of dispersed material can become a very significant quantity.

Bacteria have a large surface in comparison to their volume, and they do exhibit many properties characteristic of colloidal systems. A typical cell, 1 μ in diameter and 2 μ in length, has a surface area of 0.000,01 sq. mm., and in a culture containing 1 billion cells per milliliter (ml.) the total surface area is 10,000 sq. mm., through which the cells carry out numerous activities. A high percentage of the cellular contents may be colloidally dispersed with additional surface forces involved, probably the most important single characteristic of colloidal systems.

The influence of surface forces is well illustrated by a simple experiment. When a platinum wire is dipped into a solution of hydrogen peroxide little decomposition of the peroxide is noticeable. If the platinum wire, however, is finely divided, marked evolution of oxygen can be observed. When the platinum is colloidally dispersed and added to the peroxide the latter will decompose with explosive violence. No change in the platinum has occurred except for the great increase in surface and the accompanying enormous increase in catalytic surface forces involved in the decomposition of the peroxide.

The properties of a colloidal system are controlled by the degree of subdivision of the dispersed phase, its nature and surface characteristics, and the nature of the dispersion medium. The dispersed phase can be either a liquid, a solid, or a gas, and the same holds true for the dispersion medium.   In bacteriology we generally encounter dispersions of solid or of semisolid matter and of liquids in a liquid.   The former type of colloid is commonly spoken of as a *suspensoid*, the latter as an *emulsoid*.   A colloidal system, such as agar in water, which is semisolid or jelly-like in consistency is termed a *gel*.   An indication of the degree of dispersion can frequently be obtained by observation under the ultramicroscope which employs the same principles as the dark-field microscope for the observation of bacteria, and in some instances the microscope systems are identical.

When a beam of light passes through a darkened room, dust and other particles suspended in the air become apparent since they reflect light striking their surfaces.   This is known as the *Tyndall phenomenon*.   Air free of suspended particles would be a homogeneous system, and no light would be reflected.   Tyndall demonstrated in the early days of bacteriology that such optically void air was free of bacteria, an observation that aided in disproving the theory of spontaneous generation.   A similar reflection of light is observed in the ultramicroscope, bacteria or other particles in suspension reflecting light into the optical axis of the instrument.   The suspended particles are observed to be in more or less continuous motion in a haphazard manner in all directions, a phenomenon termed *Brownian movement*.   Brownian movement of a particle is the resultant of more molecules, or of molecules with greater velocity, striking one surface than hit other surfaces at a particular instant with consequent displacement of the particle.   This molecular bombardment also tends to hold the particles in suspension, acting against sedimentation under the influence of gravitational force.   Brownian movement does tend to bring the particles into contact with each other, resulting in the formation of larger aggregates which, if stable, would separate out more readily from the suspension.   Other forces, particularly electrostatic ones, tend to prevent actual contact of the particles.

When an electrical field is established in a colloidal suspension under the ultramicroscope it will be noted that the particles generally migrate toward one of the electrodes.   This movement, *electrophoresis*, indicates that the particles carry an electrical charge.   As they approach each other in Brownian movement, the like electrical charges cause a mutual repulsion and contact is not established.

The electrical charge carried by a particle in suspension is of considerable importance in stabilizing the suspension and can arise in several ways, particularly (1) by ionization of molecular groups at the surface of the particle, (2) by adsorption of ions, and (3) by orientation of polar molecules at the interface between the particle and the medium.   Ionization of chemical groups at the surface is particularly evident with colloidal suspensions of proteins in water. On the alkaline side of the pH at which a protein is electrically neutral, its *isoelectric point*, the protein can be pictured reacting like an acid dissociating to give positively charged hydrogen ions and becoming negatively charged in the process. On the acidic side the protein reacts like a base and acquires a positive charge. At the isoelectric point the molecules are electrically neutral; they tend to agglomerate and then settle out of suspension. Here the forces acting to bring the particles into contact with each other exceed those of repulsion. A protein, therefore, can be crystallized most readily at its isoelectric point.

Whether the electrical charges are the result of ionization or of other forces inherent in the molecular structure of the particle, ions of opposite charge are attracted and tend to form an immobile film, a Helmholtz-Gouy double layer, around the particle, thus establishing electrical neutrality of the suspension as a whole. A colloidal suspension, for example, will not charge an electroscope, but the particles will move in an electrical field. The electrical charge, or potential difference between the particle and the medium, can be calculated from the rate of migration of the particle in the electrical field. In general the greater the potential difference, the greater the stability of the suspension.

One ion may replace another in the double layer, and this selective adsorption of ions is frequently encountered in studies with the bacteria. Ions of the heavier metals tend to replace those of the lighter ones, at the same time reducing the charge on the bacterial surface and thereby the stability of the suspension. Ions of heavy metals such as silver or mercury, even in low concentrations, have a marked tendency to replace lighter ones, and this may in part explain their germicidal activity in dilute solutions. Ionic-exchange reactions also appear to be involved in the staining reactions and will be considered further when the mechanism of staining is discussed.

Many particles suspended in water are hydrated, i.e., carry adsorbed layers of water molecules, and these molecules may be definitely oriented. Hydration frequently confers additional stability upon the colloidal suspension. The adsorption and orientation of molecules at a surface can best be considered after a brief discussion of surface or interfacial tensions.

Surface Tension. Molecules in the interior of a liquid are equally attracted in all directions by the molecules surrounding them. The molecules at the surface of the liquid, however, are attracted only sideways and downward by their fellow molecules, and hence an unbalanced force is established at the interface between the liquid and air or other unlike phases. One result is that the molecules in the surface do not have the freedom of motion possessed by those in the body of the liquid. This results in their being held together and acting as though they constituted a definite film or membrane at the surface.   This cohesive or unbalanced attractive force is termed *surface tension* or *interfacial tension*, the former term usually being applied to the force exhibited at an interface between a liquid and air.   This is the force that produces a meniscus in a pipette or supports mosquito larvae or pellicles of bacteria on water.   The larvae or pellicles sink when oil is applied to the surface, since it lowers the surface tension and the force of gravity then exceeds the supporting force of surface tension.   Tubercle bacilli normally produce a pellicle on liquid media, but grow diffusely when a suitable surface-tension depressant is added to the medium.

The interfacial tension existing at the boundary between two liquids or between a solid and a liquid is of most interest in bacteriology.   The interface between the cell and its environment is an important one since all solutes and waste products of metabolism must pass through this area. It is also of importance in considerations of disinfection and of the immune reactions.   Likewise, surface forces at the surfaces of enzymes no doubt exert marked influence on the activity or characteristics of the enzyme, either within or when freed from the cell.   Surface tension may also influence growth of bacteria and in particular does influence pellicle formation as mentioned above.   These interfacial forces are difficult to evaluate, but some insight concerning them can be gained from a consideration of the interface between two immiscible liquids and the orientation of molecules in this boundary.

When an oil is shaken vigorously with water, the oil forms fine droplets, and a coarse suspension, or unstable emulsion, of oil in water is formed. The droplets soon coalesce, and the oil separates from the water.   The addition of a little vinegar to the water results, on shaking the mixture, in a more stable emulsion, a behavior employed in the preparation of certain salad dressings.   This is due to an adsorption and orientation of acetic acid molecules at the oil-water interfaces.   A more stable emulsion results when a soap, a salt of a higher fatty acid, is employed as the emulsifying agent.

A simple analogy well illustrates the orientation of molecules at an interface.   Observation indicates that small sticks will float on water with their longitudinal axis parallel to the surface.   If a heavy weight is attached at one end of each stick, a different orientation will be observed, the longitudinal axis now being vertical.   The force of gravity pulls the heavy end of the stick well under the surface of the water.   When the weight is too great the stick will be entirely submerged.   Acetic acid can be considered as analogous to the weighted stick, but the "weight" is so great that it is completely submerged in the water, in other words, is soluble in the water.   Acetic acid is composed of two distinct parts, the CH_3— or methyl group and the —COOH or carboxyl group.   The methyl group can be considered as analogous to the stick, the carboxyl group to the weight added at one end of the stick. Water exerts a much greater pull on the carboxyl group than on the methyl group because of certain chemical affinities. Chemical groups attracted by water are spoken of as *polar groups*, while those not attracted are termed *nonpolar groups*. This definite attraction can be considered analogous to the pull of gravity upon the weighted end of the stick, nonattraction as analogous to the buoyancy of the stick. As the length of the hydrocarbon chain, $CH_3CH_2 \cdots$ —, in fatty acids is increased, the attraction of water for the polar group becomes much less than the repulsive force between the hydrocarbon portion of the molecule and water, and the molecule is no longer readily submerged. Solubility of fatty acids in water, therefore, decreases with increasing length of the hydrocarbon chain. Conversely, if an oil, primarily a hydrocarbon, is the solvent, the behavior is reversed.

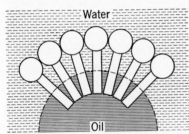 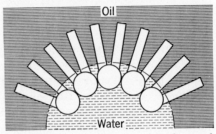

FIG. 3-1. Schematic representation of the orientation of molecules at an interface and the influence thereof on the type of emulsion formed. Closest packing is obtained with univalent soaps when oil is the dispersed phase, with bivalent soaps when oil is the dispersion medium.

Emulsions of oil and water stabilized by the addition of higher fatty acids, or preferably their salts such as the sodium and calcium soaps, exhibit a similar orientation of the acid molecules at the surface of the droplet. In an oil-in-water emulsion the nonpolar hydrocarbon chain is oriented toward the oil, the polar carboxyl group toward the water. The type of emulsion formed, oil-in-water or water-in-oil, depends to a great extent upon the nature and spatial characteristics of the emulsifying agent. A sodium soap tends to produce an emulsion of oil-in-water since it is more soluble in water than in oil and also closest packing of the soap molecules can be obtained.

The methods of studying the orientation of molecules at a surface or interface, and factors influencing these films, are discussed in various texts and monographs. Study of oriented films has enabled calculations to be made of the size and shape of various molecules comprising them and also affords an approach to the solution of various problems concerning the nature and behavior of proteins, fats, and enzymes. Substrates probably are definitely oriented on their enzymes; other substances may affect this orientation. Still other orientations of molecules occur on the numerous interfaces in the cell, and these adsorbed molecules may make up part of the structure of membranes or influence their permeability and other characteristics. Consideration of molecular orientation also offers one approach to a better understanding of adsorption.

Adsorption. Surfaces have unneutralized fields of force, free valences, interfacial tensions, or other forces which have the power of more or less strongly attracting and holding other molecules. This increase in concentration of a substance at an interface is termed *adsorption*. Numerous types of adsorption reactions are possible, but we will deal primarily with the one most frequently encountered in bacterial physiology, adsorption from a liquid medium. Willard Gibbs and J. J. Thomson formulated a principle governing adsorption which may be stated as *substances which decrease interfacial energy tend to concentrate in the surface layer, while those which increase interfacial energy become more concentrated in the body of the fluid.*

Adsorption involves a change in concentration of a substance, a distribution of the substance between two phases. The term adsorption commonly refers to the taking up of a substance at a surface, while absorption signifies accumulation within the body of a substance or material. Since it is difficult at times to differentiate between the two, the more general term sorption is frequently employed. The general behavior can be illustrated most readily by a consideration of a somewhat analogous behavior, the simple distribution of a solute between two immiscible solvents. When a solution of iodine in aqueous potassium iodide solution is shaken with an immiscible organic solvent such as carbon tetrachloride, part of the iodine will pass into solution in the organic liquid. When this distribution is followed quantitatively it is found that at equilibrium

$$\frac{C_1}{C_2} = K \qquad \text{or} \qquad C_1 = KC_2 \qquad (3\text{-}1)$$

where C_1 represents the concentration of iodine in the aqueous phase and C_2 in the carbon tetrachloride, K being the distribution constant. Fatty acids, for example, show definite and different distributions, or distribution constants, between water and ether. Determination of the distribution between water and ether of fatty acids from a fermentation mixture gives a clue to the identity of the acids. Distribution is reversible, and any change in the amount of solute, water, or organic solvent will result in a redistribution of the solute until equilibrium is reestablished.

Distribution of a solute between two immiscible solvents also serves as the basis for the separation of different solutes by the various procedures of chromatography (Strain, 1945; Block, Le Strange, and Zweig, 1952).

The lower fatty acids, for example, can be separated in a silica-gel column saturated with water containing a suitable indicator. A chloroform solution of the fatty acids is added to the column, which is then developed (acids separated from each other) by passing chloroform containing suitable amounts of n-butanol through the column. The higher fatty acids, being more soluble in the organic solvent, will flow through the column more rapidly than the lower ones, i.e., will not be retained as readily. The position of each acid will be indicated by color changes of the indicator in the column. The different bands can be washed through the column, collected separately, and their amounts determined by titration. Amino acids, pigments, and various other substances showing different solubilities in water and an organic solvent can be separated in a similar manner. Substances such as silica gel have been replaced to a great extent by filter paper as the inert support. A drop of the material is placed near the end of a strip of filter paper which dips into the developing solvent, usually a water-containing organic solvent. The fluid flows past the spot of material and down (or moves up, depending on the technique employed) the filter paper, carrying with it, at different rates, the materials to be separated. Bands or areas of the different solutes form, and these substances can be recognized by suitable tests. Paper chromatography may function in some instances by selective distribution (partition) but more commonly acts by a combination of partition, adsorption, and ion exchange. It is a valuable tool in bacterial physiology and widely used for the separation from each other of amino acids, of fatty acids, of intermediates of metabolism, and so on.

When the distribution of benzoic acid between benzene and water is studied it is found that the value for the distribution constant is not constant. Molecular-weight determinations indicate that the benzoic acid molecules are associated in the benzene to form complexes consisting of two molecules of the acid. A ratio of $C_1/C_2^{1/2}$ is constant for this distribution, or we can state that the amount of benzoic acid dissolved in the water is proportional to the square root of the concentration of benzoic acid in the benzene, or $C_1 = KC_2^{1/2}$. A quite analogous distribution is noted in adsorption reactions, although we cannot conclude that association of the molecules occurs.

Freundlich has pointed out that the lowering of surface tension at constant temperature by a dissolved substance in moderate concentration can be represented by the equation

$$d\gamma = sc^{1/n} \tag{3-2}$$

where $d\gamma$ = lowering of surface tension
   c = concentration of solute
   s, n = constants for a given system

This equation indicates that the observed decrease in surface tension is proportional to a fractional power of the concentration of the solute. A similar relationship for the adsorption of a substance at a surface is observed, or

$$\frac{x}{a} = kc^{1/n} \tag{3-3}$$

where x = amount adsorbed on a surface of area a

$k, 1/n$ = constants characteristic of the system

This equation is called the *Freundlich adsorption isotherm* and may also be expressed as

$$\log \frac{x}{a} = \log k + \frac{1}{n} \log c \tag{3-4}$$

The same general equation holds for the adsorption of a gas, and since the pressure of the gas is proportional to its molar concentration, pressure can be substituted for concentration in equation (3-4). The surface area of an adsorbent is difficult to determine, but since the area is proportional to the mass m of the adsorbent, the latter quantity can be substituted for the former in the Freundlich adsorption isotherm. Other equations have been proposed and do in some cases fit the experimental data more closely than does the Freundlich adsorption isotherm. Since they introduce more complexities to the discussion they will not be considered here.

Typical plots of adsorption data are presented in Fig. 3-2. In A, amounts adsorbed per unit area of surface, as indicated by surface-tension measurements [equation (3-2)], are plotted against concentrations of the material being adsorbed. It is readily apparent that adsorption is relatively greatest from dilute solutions. This suggests that the adsorption process can give rise to considerable displacements in concentration, particularly in dilute solutions, and thereby explains in part the efficacy of cellular poisons active in low concentrations or of enzymes which have such a marked effect on rates of reaction. As a result of adsorption the concentration of the reactant at an interface is markedly increased, a factor which by itself would increase the rate of reaction. When media are lightly inoculated, growth frequently is initiated most rapidly around foreign particles in suspension. This may be due to an increased local concentration of foodstuff, or of bacteria, as a result of adsorption on the foreign matter. Adsorption is generally a rapid reaction and would, therefore, tend to maintain an effective concentration of the reactant at the interface, cellular or enzymatic. In B of Fig. 3-2 the data for A are plotted on a logarithmic scale [see equation (3-4)]. It will be noted that the lines are nearly parallel, which means that their slope, $1/n$ in equations (3-3) and (3-4), is a quantity of little specific character. It has a value between 0.3 and 0.7 for many systems. The value of $\log k$ in the same equation can be obtained from the intercept of the curve on the log x/m axis.

When an adsorbent such as charcoal is added to an aqueous solution of a dyestuff, the intensity of the color will decrease or the color may

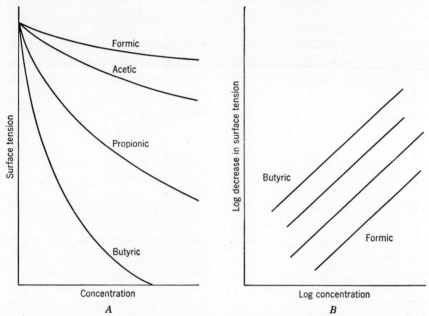

FIG. 3-2. The influence (A) of the nature and concentration of fatty acids on surface tension (and hence of adsorption) and (B) plots of the same data on a logarithmic scale, the equivalent of log x/a being plotted against log concentration of the adsorbed material.

almost entirely disappear, depending on the concentrations of the adsorbent and adsorbed materials. This process is an equilibrium reaction and is quantitatively expressed by the adsorption isotherm, i.e.,

$$\frac{x}{m} = kc^{1/n} \qquad (3\text{-}5)$$

where m = mass of adsorbent.

Dyes are readily adsorbed from aqueous solution but much less readily so from alcoholic ones. Alcohol is readily adsorbed by charcoal, and in general any substance which is well adsorbed is a poor adsorption medium. This behavior is depicted in Fig. 3-3, which illustrates the influence of the dye on the surface tension (γ) of water and of alcohol and also of alcohol on the surface tension of water. This behavior illustrates at least in part the reason for employing aqueous rather than alcoholic solutions of the dyes in the staining of bacteria.

Since the amount of material adsorbed changes with the nature of the medium, it is possible to adsorb a substance in one medium and to liberate the adsorbed substance by placing the complex in a second medium, sometimes one differing only in pH from the first. This principle is involved in the purification of enzymes, toxins, and filtrable viruses by adsorption from an aqueous solution or suspension at a given pH and releasing it by elution in a second medium at a different pH. The adsorption of electrolytes is, however, more complex than the adsorption of organic compounds, and other less well understood principles are involved in this method of purification. This influence of the medium on adsorption may also explain in part the fact that phenol dissolved in water is a strong disinfectant, while its action as such is much less when dissolved in oil or in alcohol.

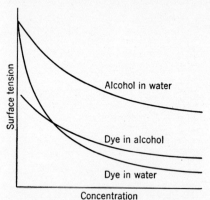

FIG. 3-3. The influence of concentration and nature of a solute and of nature of the solvent on the amount of solute adsorbed as indicated by surface-tension measurements.

While we have discussed adsorption primarily from the theory of surface or interfacial tension, it must be borne in mind that electrical and other forces are also involved in many instances and that adsorption may at times be more in the nature of a chemical union in which the forces of primary valence are operating. Secondary reactions occurring after adsorption can further complicate the picture.

The phenomena of adsorption have been discussed in a very broad and general manner, primarily to present a concept rather than a working knowledge of the subject. This concept is summarized in the following principles governing adsorption:

1. The Gibbs-Thomson principle; any substance which decreases interfacial energy tends to concentrate at that interface.
2. The adsorbed molecules tend to be oriented in a definite manner relative to the adsorbent and to each other.
3. The Freundlich adsorption isotherm indicates that the amount adsorbed per unit of adsorbent is proportional to a fractional power of the concentration of the material adsorbed. The process of adsorption, therefore, differs from a true chemical reaction in that stoichiometric relationships do not maintain.
4. Adsorption is a reversible process, equilibrium being established as indicated by the adsorption isotherm.
5. Adsorption is generally a rapid reaction, equilibrium being established in a short period of time.

6. Adsorption frequently proceeds most rapidly at low temperatures, the reverse behavior being noted with most chemical reactions.
7. Adsorption is more nearly complete when the ratio of adsorbent to material adsorbed is high, i.e., it proceeds to a greater extent in dilute solutions.
8. The amount adsorbed is proportional to the surface area of the adsorbent and varies with the nature of this surface, of the adsorbed material, and of the medium from which adsorption occurs.

The general concepts of physical chemistry developed in this and the preceding chapter are encountered in widely different considerations of the physiology of bacteria. The brief presentation of these concepts is sketchy but should suffice to define them sufficiently to enable the student to develop a better understanding of various phenomena of bacterial behavior.

REFERENCES

Block, R. J., R. Le Strange, and G. Zweig: "Paper Chromatography: A Laboratory Manual," Academic Press, Inc., New York, 1952.
Strain, H. H.: "Chromatographic Adsorption Analysis," Interscience Publishers, Inc., New York, 1945.

CHAPTER 4

THE BACTERIAL CELL

Proper understanding of the bacteria entails knowledge not only of their activities but also of their component parts and of the organization of these parts to constitute the cell. It is generally recognized that the bacterial cell consists of five main entities, the *cytoplasm*, which contains the *chromosomal structures* and which is bounded by the *cytoplasmic membrane* pressing against the *cell wall*, which in turn is surrounded by the *slime layer*. Vacuoles, globules, granules, pigment-bearing bodies, and other structures may be observed in the cytoplasm, and, in many species, flagella are attached to, or spores formed within, the cells. These various bodies are for the most part characteristic of a species or group rather than of all species.

In the majority of microscopic observations of bacteria the cells are examined in heat-fixed, stained smears in which they have a characteristic appearance but not one necessarily truly indicative of their structure in the living state. These ordinary preparations are of value in routine bacteriology and are employed primarily for convenience. Special techniques and more specific staining reactions, together with correct usage of illumination and the microscope, are essential for the demonstration of the finer details of the structure of a bacterial cell. Limits of resolution of the light microscope soon exert their retarding influence on the observation of minute structures, and the use of the electron microscope then becomes essential. Phase microscopy is also of value, particularly for the observation of resolvable structures in the living cell. One of the most illuminating demonstrations of the structure of bacteria is in an electron micrograph (Fig. 4-1) by Chapman and Hillier (1953) of a thin longitudinal section of *Bacillus cereus*. A hypothetical representation of the structure of a bacterial cell is presented in Fig. 4-2.

Mechanism of Staining. A dye may be considered as a colored organic compound which is capable of combining with a variety of substances and imparting color to them. Color is imparted to dyestuffs by particular structures, chromophore groups, within their molecules. Combining or auxochrome groups, possessing the property of electrolytic dissociation, enable the colored substance to combine with the material being stained.

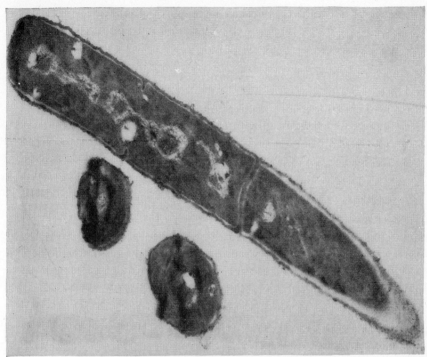

Fig. 4-1. Electron micrograph of a thin longitudinal section of *Bacillus cereus.* (*Courtesy of Chapman and Hillier, 1953, and The Williams & Wilkins Company.*)

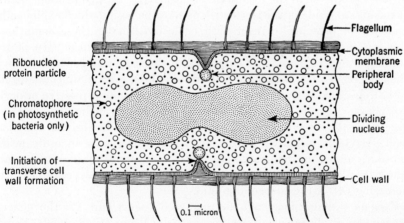

Fig. 4-2. Schematic cross section of a flagellated, rod-shaped bacterium, showing relative sizes of various cell structures. Only the basal portions of flagella are shown. (*Courtesy of E. Jawetz and Lange Medical Publications, from E. Jawetz, J. L. Melnick, and E. A. Aldeberg, "Review of Medical Microbiology."*)

Other groups may impart more specific properties to the molecules.   Dyes are classified as acidic or basic dyes, depending respectively upon their ability to act as acids or bases and form salts with basic or with acidic substances.   Basic dyes in aqueous solution carry a positive charge and react most readily with bacteria in neutral or slightly alkaline solutions in which bacteria are predominantly negatively charged.   Their charge is reversed in rather acidic solutions, and under these conditions the positively charged bacteria react with the negatively charged acidic dyes.   A few dyes are particularly soluble in fats and are employed for the staining of fatty structures or globules.   Certain agents, when added to the dye solution, enhance its staining properties and act, therefore, as intensifiers. Detergents (wetting agents), phenol, and aniline appear to increase permeability of the cell, while dilute alkali tends to increase the amount of dye bound.   Such agents, therefore, act as intensifiers.   On the other hand, substances which do not necessarily enhance the staining activity of a dye but instead increase the firmness of the union between the dye and the substance stained are known as mordants.   Typical examples are tannic acid in the cell-wall stain and iodine in the gram stain.

As a general rule the dyes react with the proteins of the bacterial cell, the union probably being with amino or carboxyl groups of the constituent amino acids and being dependent upon the acidic or basic character of the dye and upon pH.   On the acidic side of its isoelectric point a protein dissociates as a base to yield positively charged amino groups which react most readily with the negatively charged acidic dyes.   Dissociation of carboxyl groups with the formation of negatively charged proteins occurs on the alkaline side of the isoelectric point, a behavior which explains the tendency of proteins to react with basic dyes under these conditions. This simplified explanation suggests the relative nonspecificity of the staining reactions commonly employed in the bacteriological laboratory. The cells react with ordinary dyes at different pH's in a manner analogous to that observed with pure proteins.   The possession of positive or negative charges, or the excess of one over the other, can be demonstrated directly by the direction of migration of proteins or of cells in an electrical field.   Bacteria migrate toward the negative electrode in quite acidic solutions, and from their rate and direction of migration it can be established that the charge decreases and changes to negative values with increasing pH of the suspending fluid.

Various explanations have been offered to account for the general mechanism of staining and are discussed by Conn (1948, 1953), Dubos (1945), Knaysi (1951), Lamanna and Mallette (1953), Bartholomew, Roberts, and Evans (1950), and others.   The great variation in the reactivity of the components of bacteria and the relatively unknown behavior of dyes at the complex surfaces existing in the cell render it dangerous to attempt to advance a simplified explanation of the complex reactions which occur in the staining process. It is rather generally accepted, however, that staining can be considered as an ionic-exchange reaction analogous to the exchange reactions where one ion replaces another in combination with agents such as the exchange resins. McCalla (1940, 1941) has shown that bacteria will absorb different ions when the ionic composition of their environment is changed, e.g., magnesium ions replacing sodium ions when the cells are suspended in a solution of a magnesium salt. This replacement reaction can be represented as

$$0.5n\text{Mg}^{++} + (B)n\text{Na} \rightleftarrows 0.5n\text{Mg}\ (B) + n\text{Na}^+$$

where B = bacterial cell

n = number of negative, reactive charges carried in B

When positively charged dye ions (or other ions) are added to a suspension of magnesium-treated cells, the dye ion will compete with magnesium for places around or within the cell and may replace it entirely. A similar competition can occur between different dyes. Bartholomew, Roberts, and Evans (1950) have shown that any one of 22 different basic dyes tested could replace another already present in the bacterial cell. The dyes were known to react with carboxyl groups, the extent of the replacement was shown to be influenced by concentration of dye and time of application, and replacement of one dye by another appeared to follow the law of mass action for reversible reactions. Bartholomew, like McCalla, concluded that the staining of bacteria under ordinary circumstances is an adsorption-exchange reaction.

The ability of one dye to replace another is utilized in the Shaeffer-Fulton spore stain, safranin replacing the malachite green in the vegetative areas of the cell. This differential decolorization and staining is explained on the basis of the more rapid rate of replacement of malachite green in the vegetative portion, the malachite green eventually being replaced in the spore when counterstaining is prolonged. Replacement phenomena may be encountered to some extent in the gram and other stains.

The Gram Stain.   Gram's stain is the most commonly employed stain in the bacteriology laboratory and serves to divide bacteria into two major groups, the members of each group having more in common with each other than their reaction to the staining procedure alone. There is a considerable degree of correspondence between the gram reaction of bacteria and other properties that they exhibit, gram-positive cells tending to react with many agents in a manner at least quantitatively different from that of gram-negative cells. As a general rule the gram-positive bacteria are more susceptible than the gram-negative ones to inhibition or lysis by acids, to inhibition by the basic dyes, antibiotics, and sulfa drugs, and are less able to synthesize a number of their molecular components from simple substrates. The gram-negative bacteria, on the other hand, are more susceptible to alkalies, to digestive enzymes, and to mechanical agents. Any complete explanation of the gram-staining behavior of bacteria would no doubt offer an explanation at the same time for many of the observed differences between the two broad groups of bacteria.

After staining with gentian or crystal violet and subsequent treatment with a solution of iodine in aqueous potassium iodide many species are rather resistant to decolorization with alcohol, others are somewhat variable in their response, while still others are decolorized rapidly and readily. When a standardized technique is employed it is possible to control the decolorization process, some of which may also take place during counterstaining, and thereby divide the bacteria into the two groups, gram positive and gram negative. Three main groups of theories have been advanced (Bartholomew and Mittwer, 1952) concerning the mechanism of gram differentiation. These are (1) permeability differences between the two groups; (2) differences in degree of retention of the original dye due to the more acidic nature of gram-positive cytoplasm; and (3) gram positivity due to a particular structure or chemical complex in the cell.

Benians, around 1920, strongly supported the concept that differences in permeability account for the gram-staining behavior of bacteria, stressing that gram positivity is lost when the cells are disrupted and that no cellular substance obtained from bacteria exhibits the phenomenon of gram positivity. Benians divided bacteria into three groups on the basis of permeability characteristics: (1) gram-positive species in which an iodine-dye complex is formed that is not extracted readily from the cell; (2) gram-negative ones into which the dye does not penetrate; and (3) the intermediate species such as the gonococcus within which an iodine-dye complex is formed but from which the complex can be extracted fairly readily with alcohol. The techniques employed by Benians are subject to a number of criticisms, and his conclusions are therefore open to question. Permeability, however, is not ruled out as a contributing factor in the gram stain. Bartholomew and his coworkers concluded that the primary dye must not only stain the cells deeply but must also form a precipitate with the iodine that is not too soluble in alcohol and that is relatively insoluble in the safranin or other counterstain. Any dye and mordant can be employed in the gram stain if they meet these requirements.

Stearns and Stearns, around 1926, associated gram positivity with a more acidic type of protoplasmic material in gram-positive cells. They concluded that stainable substances in gram-positive species have lower isoelectric points than do the materials binding the stain in gram-negative species. Their fundamental concept was that the strength of union between bacteria and dye increased with increasing difference between the isoelectric point of the cell and the pH of the dye solution. This difference is greatest between gram-positive species and the dye and leads to a firmer union, one less readily altered by alcohol, between dye and gram-positive cells than between dye and gram-negative ones. The action of the mordant, according to the Stearns' concept, was to lower the isoelectric point of gram-positive cells to a greater extent than that of gram-negative species, thus enhancing gram differentiation. It should be emphasized that their concept of the isoelectric point was based on the staining behavior of bacteria at different pH's and not on the surface isoelectric point as determined by electrophoretic measurements. An isoelectric point based on staining characteristics cannot be determined with a high degree of accuracy and represents tendencies rather than absolute values. Some evidence does suggest that gram-positive bacteria may contain more acidic substances than do gram-negative ones, but this factor alone does not suffice to explain gram positivity in its entirety. One might conclude that some cellular materials should be gram positive by themselves if they possessed low isoelectric points. It is of interest to note that Fischer and Seidenberg (1951) and Fischer and Larose (1952) have reported that wool is gram negative in its staining reaction but that after heating in dilute alkali its isoelectric point is decreased. This degraded wool exhibits gram-positive staining characteristics. They further demonstrated that the combining power of degraded wool for various substances paralleled the bactericidal activity of these substances against gram-positive species.

Churchman, around 1926, advanced the concept that gram-positive bacteria possess a gram-positive cortex which surrounds a gram-negative medulla. No gram-positive layer was evident around gram-negative cells. Some observations, on the other hand, indicate that the gram-positive area is within the cell and that it can be ascribed to no one cellular structure. Many workers have attempted to correlate gram positivity with chemical rather than physical structures of the cell. One early idea was that a dye–iodine–fatty acid complex was quite resistant to decolorization with alcohol. Subsequent workers incriminated lecithin or lipids rather than fatty acids as the determining factor, but there is little evidence that such substances play a major role unless they might be concerned with a permeability factor. Deussen, in the early 1920's, presented evidence that nucleic acids are involved in gram staining, and this concept was elaborated by Henry and Stacey in 1943. They found (Bartholomew and Mittwer, 1952) that gram-positive bacteria can be converted to a gram-negative state on treatment with bile salts, this treatment liberating magnesium ribonucleate, some polysaccharide, and traces of protein. Gram positivity could be restored under certain conditions by "replating" the cells with magnesium ribonucleate, while gram-negative cells could not be converted to positive ones under the same, relatively mild conditions of treatment. Various observations suggest that a nucleic acid forms a complex with a protein or other substance within the cell and that the complex, not the nucleic acid alone, is involved in gram positivity. Lamanna and Mallette (1954) have presented evidence suggesting that crystal violet stains the cell wall of gram-positive but not of gram-negative species and that iodine-mordanted organisms with stained walls resist both decolorizer and counterstain. It is entirely possible that chemical composition and behavior of one or more substances and the location of the material in the cell together with permeability factors are involved in the determination of the gram-staining property and allied characteristics of bacteria. Reference should be made to the original papers and various reviews for details concerning the mechanism of the gram stain.

The Slime Layer. The surface of a bacterial cell might be considered as being analogous to a series of shells merging into one another, possibly without very definite borders. The outermost layer is actually not an integral part of the cell; it is an ionic atmosphere or cloud loosely held or attracted by electrical charges on the cell. Any change in pH or ionic composition of the medium is reflected by a change in composition of this ionic layer. Inside this cloud there is a slime layer (termed a capsule if well organized), and this again may be a dynamic structure although one more stable than the ionic cloud. The material comprising it may be undergoing solution or dispersal along the outer boundary, while more is being synthesized and deposited during periods of marked metabolic activity of the cell. It is possible that the layer adjacent to the cell wall is of a different nature than the bulk of the slime layer, lipids or nucleoproteins predominating here rather than the polysaccharides so commonly found in the slime layer. This outer layer probably is rather highly hydrated and more complex than generally envisaged. It is rather difficult, for example, to picture a negatively charged pneumococcus if the cells are surrounded only by a heavy capsule of nonionizable polysaccharide unless one resorts to the concept of long-range forces. Some of these factors were considered at a symposium on the nature of the bacterial surface (Miles and Pirie, 1949).

In flagellated bacteria the flagella influence the nature of the bacterial surface as indicated by agglutination reactions, loose floccules of flagellated cells being formed in contrast to the more dense clumps noted with nonflagellated forms of the same species. The agglutination of bacteria by antibodies, or by ions, is an indication of surface phenomena. Actually, our knowledge of the nature of the bacterial surface or surface layers is very sketchy and to a great extent highly speculative.

The slime layer can be demonstrated with the aid of staining methods employed for observation of the cell wall. In cells mordanted with tannic acid–alum and suspended in carbol fuchsin, the slime layer stains a somewhat different shade than the cell wall. The slight amount of dye held in the slime layer is readily rinsed out on washing with water. The slime layer can be demonstrated in electron micrographs of some species but generally has very slight electron-absorbing capacity. Capsules as a rule can be demonstrated more readily than the slime layer, either in negatively stained preparations, in smears heavily stained and rinsed momentarily with concentrated copper sulfate solutions, or in the electron microscope. On treatment with homologous antiserum the capsular material appears to swell and becomes more readily apparent. This effect is due to the binding of antibodies.

Chemically the slime layer or capsule is composed either of polypeptide or of polysaccharide material, the latter sometimes having proteinaceous or lipoidal material associated with it. The classical examples of capsular material are the polysaccharides, frequently containing nitrogenous complexes such as glucosamine, responsible for the type specificity of the pneumococci and the unnatural or D(−)glutamic acid polypeptide of *B. anthracis* capsular material. The slime layer can be extracted from the cell by mechanical means or with dilute alkalies or other aqueous solutions. Removal of the capsule or slime layer need have no appreciable effect on the viability of the cell, thus indicating the relatively nonessential character of this structure in vitro.

Antigenic analyses of bacteria have contributed to our understanding of the chemical structure of these organisms, revealing not only the presence of distinct antigens but also their relative amounts and possible anatomic locations. If a virulent, flagellated strain of *Salmonella typhosa* is used as an antigen, the antiserum obtained after successful immunization will contain antibodies against the flagella, against surface antigens, and against antigenic components located deeper in the cell. The use of appropriate antibody-adsorption techniques can provide purified preparations of antibodies against the individual antigens. Serological tests between these reagents and cells treated in different ways, or with variants of the same species, give important clues to the antigenic structure of a bacterium (Raffel, 1953). An antigenic map of group *A* hemolytic streptococci, for example, would indicate the location of the *M* and the *T* groups of protein antigens in a superficial position, possibly the slime layer or the cell wall since the cells can be agglutinated readily by anti-*M* or -*T* antibodies. The *M* and the *T* antigens are type-specific, chemical agents, each varying enough in its antigenic specificity to give the type characteristics of a strain. The M antigen appears to be the one most important as regards virulence and against which protective antibodies must be directed. In cells possessing both these antigens, the M protein appears to be the outer one since enzymic digestion removes it first. The group-specific C antigen, a polysaccharide, appears to be a subsurface antigen since it can be detected most readily by precipitin tests with cellular extracts. Finally, the nucleoprotein (P-substance) antigens common to all groups of streptococci are found deeper in the cell. Mapping of antigens is provisional; physical arrangement of the antigen molecules in the cell may lead to steric hindrances that create an appearance of different locations rather than this actually being the case.

The surface layer of smooth bacteria is different from that of rough variants of the same species and probably overlays the rough surface. The stability of suspensions of R variants is controlled to a great extent by the charge carried by the cells, this behavior suggesting that the surface of R forms is more hydrophobic in its nature than that of smooth forms. The charge, or potential difference between the cell and medium, is highest in the most stable suspensions of the R forms, and their stability is due primarily to the charged cells mutually repelling one another. Suspension stability of S forms, whose surface charge may be quite low, is due to the hydrophilic character of the surface to a much greater extent than to the actual charge. This has been explained on the basis that although the cells may come into contact with each other there is so little mutual attraction that molecular impacts responsible for Brownian movement are sufficient to separate the cells.

Antigenic analysis (Morgan in Miles and Pirie, 1949) of smooth and rough forms of *Shigella dysenteriae* (Shiga) well illustrates the surface characteristics of these forms. *S. dysenteriae* possesses in the S form a surface antigen designated as the O antigen. It is a relatively stable complex of polysaccharide, phospholipin, and protein. This O antigen, as indicated by the amount of material extracted with cold diethylene-glycol, constitutes about 10 per cent of the total cellular material. The extracted bacilli are largely unchanged in their staining characteristics and general morphology. Antigenic specificity is controlled by the poly-saccharide component which comprises 50 to 60 per cent of the O antigen and contains N-acetylglucosamine, D-galactose, and L-rhamnose. The phospholipin contains palmitic, oleic, and α-glycerophosphoric acids and constitutes around 10 per cent of the complex. The protein component is antigenic by itself, but antibodies formed against it do not agglutinate smooth cells. This suggests that the protein is covered by its phospho-lipin and polysaccharide partners in the surface layer. Furthermore, smooth bacteria from which the polysaccharide has been extracted behave in the agglutination reaction like rough bacteria. Microchemical tests indicate that the surface layer of S cells of $S.$ *dysenteriae* is polysaccharide in character, that of R forms proteinaceous.   Lipoid, however, is also present in the surface of R cells and, because of its hydrophobic character, is primarily responsible for the instability of suspensions of these forms. Extraction of R cultures of $S.$ *dysenteriae* with alcohol removes much of this lipoidal material and results in suspensions of much greater stability.

Morphological differentiation has been demonstrated in capsules of some species of *Bacillus* by Tomcsik (1953; see also Mudd, 1954).   These

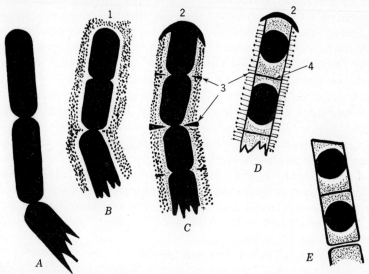

FIG. 4-3. Representations of *Bacillus* M as observed by phase contrast. A, appearance of the cells before treatment with immune serum. B, the same bacilli after addition of antipolypeptide serum. C, appearance after addition of polysaccharide antibodies to B. D and E, *Bacillus* M after successive stages of lysozyme treatment followed by antipolysaccharide serum, cytoplasm assuming a spherical shape. 1 = polar depression; 2 = polar cap; 3 = transverse septa; 4 = cross wall.   (*Redrawn after Tomcsik and Guex-Holzer, 1954.*)

capsules are comprised of a structural framework of polysaccharide con. tinuous with the cell wall, the interstices being filled with a polypeptide- The structure of the capsule can be demonstrated under the phase microscope following treatment of the cells with specific antisera.   Following the addition of antipolysaccharide serum the capsules show dense transverse septa continuous with the cross walls, and these extend outward to the surface of the capsule (Fig. 4-3).   Subsequent treatment of the same cells with antipolypeptide serum demonstrates the polypeptide within the polysaccharide structure.   The bacillary cell wall, after removal of the capsular material by treatment with lysozyme, reacts only with the antipolysaccharide antibodies.   Prolonged treatment with lysozyme dissolves the mucopolysaccharides in the cell wall, and rounded protoplasts are liberated from the cells, thus demonstrating the role of the cell wall in determining the shape of the cell.

The slime layer, particularly when pronounced or existing as a capsule, may afford the cell some protection against drying and also against blockage of the cell wall by large molecules present in the environment. It might possibly serve as a source of foodstuff when the cell faces starvation conditions, the enzymes involved in its synthesis acting in reverse under these conditions. The dextran- and levan-synthesizing enzymes (Chap. 12) involved in the production of these capsular materials are active apart from the cell and are reversible in their activity. Some studies suggest that these enzymes are extracellular, at least in *Leuconostoc mesenteroides*, or may be located in or on the cell wall. If intracellular synthesis of slime-layer materials does occur, it is difficult to explain how such polymers, often of very high molecular weight, are able to pass through the cell membrane while simpler substances of the same general type are retained.

Bacteria, such as *Leuconostoc*, which synthesize considerable amounts of polysaccharides, are particularly troublesome in some industries as they tend to accumulate in and block pipes employed for transfer of sugar solutions. Capsules appear to be highly important virulence factors for some pathogenic bacteria and are, as mentioned above, important antigens both for protective-immunization procedures and for serological determinations of type specificity.

The Cell Wall. The cell wall is a very thin structure, probably of the order of 0.02 to 0.1 μ, but even so it does possess considerable rigidity and a degree of elasticity. It may at times be observed directly in plasmolyzed cells and in normal cells stained by suitable techniques. It is not stained by ordinary procedures and is rendered visible by mordanting the cells in a 10 per cent solution of tannic acid, after which treatment the wall takes up a dye such as crystal violet more readily than does the cytoplasm. The cell wall is evident at times in cells suspended in dilute fuchsin or crystal violet. When stained by the tannic acid–crystal violet method the cell wall appears to be a rather complex structure and transverse cell walls can be observed in various stages of formation in those cells comprising the multicellular forms. The so-called ghost cells observed in electron micrographs consist of the cell wall with or without remnants of the cytoplasmic membrane and of the cytoplasm clinging to it.

The cell wall appears to be a ductile structure and could be stretched during growth by increase in turgor of the cytoplasm. Bisset (1952) advanced the concept that growth of the cell wall occurs at one end of typical, unicellular bacteria, the cell membrane secreting cell-wall substance at the growing tip of the cell. The formation and deposition of cell-wall material become more complex in those species exhibiting multi-cellular characteristics.

Little is known concerning the structure or chemical nature of the cell wall. Chemical tests indicate that in some species it is primarily poly-saccharide in character, often resembling cellulose or hemicellulose. In other species it is composed of complex nitrogenous compounds, often conjugated with carbohydrates, lipids, or nucleic acids. Some evidence of rather indirect nature suggests the presence of certain enzymes in the cell wall, but these may be adsorbed during the preparation of cell-wall material.

Observations of bacteria under the polarizing microscope indicate that regularly oriented molecules must be present in the cell wall since the color effects observed when the cells are rotated are similar to those noted with regularly oriented solids. Electron micrographs (Knaysi, 1951) indicate the presence of rod-shaped macromolecules in the cell walls of some species. Houwink and Kreger (1953) noted that the cell walls of certain yeasts appear quite smooth on the outer side, while the inner surface consists of a network of very fine fibrils in an amorphous base. For a species of *Spirillum*, Houwink (1953) reported the cell wall is composed of at least two membranes (Fig. 4-4), the outer one consisting of a single layer of spherical macromolecules with a diameter of 120 to 140 angstrom units arranged in a hexagonal pattern. These studies suggest consider-able complexity in the structure of cell walls and that the wall may be composed of a mosaic of materials in a rather homogeneous matrix.

The cell walls of bacteria are quite resistant to the digestive action of trypsin, while slime-layer proteins, such as the M protein of *Streptococcus pyogenes*, are attacked readily and can be removed without apparent harm to the cell. The cell wall of this species has been reported (McCarty, 1952) to be composed of approximately two-thirds carbohydrate and the remainder protein. The carbohydrate, which is the group-specific C antigen, consists primarily of N-acetylglucosamine and rhamnose.

The surface components, whether slime layer, capsule, or cell wall, of pathogenic bacteria appear to be of considerable importance as virulence factors. The so-called Vi, or virulence antigen, of *Salmonella typhosa*, which is not essential for in vitro growth, is an acidic complex composed of phosphate, protein, and carbohydrate and appears to be located on the external surface of the cell wall. It may function as a protective coating, hindering interaction between somatic antigens and antibodies directed against them. Other Salmonellae may also possess this antigen. Inva-sive strains of *Escherichia coli* have peripheral components classified as K (capsule or envelope) antigens which are absent from ordinary laboratory strains.

Specific components or configurations in the surface of the cell act as specific receptor sites not only for antibodies but also for bacteriophages. In some species the two may be identical, in others, different. The

Fig. 4-4. Electron micrograph of the cell wall from a disrupted cell of *Spirillum serpens*. (*Courtesy of A. L. Houwink.*)

receptors are lipomucoproteins in some species, the lipocarbohydrate component possessing the property of causing the corresponding phage particles to discharge their deoxyribonucleic acid contents (Chap. 18).

Streptococcus pyogenes, in addition to the *M* surface antigen, generally has an extracellular mucoid coat of hyaluronic acid. This is a normal component of mammalian connective tissue and so is not a substance strictly foreign to the animal body. It may serve as a protective device against phagocytosis (Mudd, 1953), inhibiting this defensive force of the

host in a manner analogous to that of capsular material of the pneumococcus. Tubercle bacilli in the virulent form also have a protective layer,
lipoidal in character and possessed of marked toxicity for phagocytes.
This material, called the cording factor, causes tubercle bacilli to cohere
and form serpentine cords during growth. Strains lacking this factor
tend to be avirulent.

A major defensive factor of a host is the production of antibodies
(globulins) which, upon reaction with the bacteria eliciting their production, make the diverse alien surfaces of pathogenic species more alike and
hence more readily engulfed by phagocytes. This property is also possessed to a minor extent by normal serum globulins. Studies on the
nature of the bacterial surface should lead to a better understanding of
certain of the factors of virulence and also of protective mechanisms
possessed by the parasite's host.

The Cell Membrane. Little is known of the structure or chemical
composition of the cell membrane. It can be demonstrated by the fact
that it displays a different color than other parts of the cell suspended in
carbol fuchsin and is readily evident in electron micrographs of plasmolyzed cells after pulling away from the cell wall. It probably does not
exceed 0.1 μ in width. The membrane appears to be relatively rich in
lipoids or lipoproteins and may contain some nucleoprotein. Its function
appears to be the same as that of membranes of other cells, the control
of the passage of dissolved substances into and out of the living cell. It
therefore is a structure extremely vital to the life of the cell. Numerous
theories have been advanced in explanation of the mode of action of
cellular membranes but none is entirely satisfactory (Knaysi, 1951;
Chap. 12). In addition to its regulatory function it may act as a secretory
organ involved in the formation of the cell wall and slime layer and the
formation of transverse septa preceding the division of the cell.

Plasmolysis and plasmoptysis of bacteria can be observed under suitable conditions but are generally less pronounced than with animal cells.
The cell membrane functions in such a manner that the turgor pressure,
i.e., osmotic pressure of the cell minus osmotic pressure of the medium,
tends to remain fairly constant. It does vary with age of the culture, the
osmotic pressure of *E. coli* (Knaysi, 1951) in a glucose broth culture
(medium = 4.8 atm.) being approximately 8 atm. at the time of inoculation, reaching a maximum near 25 between the first and second hours,
falling to about 9 atm. at the end of the fifth hour, and then remaining
quite constant near this value. Fivefold dilution of the medium induced
a relatively minor decrease in turgor of the cellular contents. This turgor
of the cell indicates active functioning of the cell membrane as an osmotic
barrier. The influence of age of the culture on turgor of the cells suggests
a concentrating effect whereby optimum intracellular amounts of food-

stuff are made available to the cell during the period of most rapid growth. The dependence of the cell on diffusion from a gradually dwindling external food supply in the medium could, in part at least, account for the decreasing rate of cellular multiplication observed with increasing age of the culture.   This could apply either to the bulk supplies of building material or to an essential substance required only in minute amounts.

Roberts et al. (1955), with the aid of radioactive isotopes, found that *E. coli* is readily permeable in both directions to Na^+, K^+, SO_4^{--}, PO_4^{3-}, and other ions and to organic compounds such as glucose-1-phosphate, fructose-1,6-diphosphate, glutamic acid, and glutathione.   Ions or compounds will also diffuse out of the cells if they are not utilized rapidly or if not bound to cellular components.   An equilibrium is rapidly established between the medium and the cells, generally of such a nature that the radioactivity per gram of wet cells is equal to that of 0.75 ml. of the suspension medium.   Roberts and his coworkers concluded that the cells have a "water space" of about 0.75 ml. per gram of wet cells and that this space attains the same concentration of ions and small molecules as the medium.   They liken the protoplasm of *E. coli* to a sponge, the cell membrane to a fine net unable to prevent the entrance or exit of small molecules.   Intermediates of metabolism are presumed to be held within the cell in union with coenzymes or other carriers of large molecular size. The concept of *E. coli* acting much like a sponge is not in agreement with the studies by Knaysi and others discussed above.

Rothstein (1954) has developed a much more complex concept concerning the structure of yeast.   He pictures a double membrane surrounding the yeast cell, an outer zone of the cell being separated from the environment by a membrane relatively impermeable to anions and from the interior by a membrane relatively impermeable to both anions and cations.   This outer zone may contain enzymes (such as invertase) which catalyze the dissimilation of larger molecules.   Since cations can penetrate the outer membrane, rates of reaction in the outer zone are influenced markedly by the concentrations of ions such as K^+ or H^+ in the external environment. K^+ ions tend to inhibit competitively the metabolically inhibitory action of high extracellular concentrations of H^+ ions.   Reactions in the interior of the cell, according to Rothstein's hypothesis, are relatively unaffected by extracellular K^+ and H^+ ions, being protected from them by the impermeable inner membrane.   Uptake of K^+ ions by the cell appears to require an expenditure of energy by the cell, transport across the inner membrane apparently being accomplished by a metabolism-linked carrier system in this structure.

Certain concepts of the nature of the gram stain involve differences in permeability to iodine or iodine-dye complexes and to alcohol between gram-positive and gram-negative cells.   The permeability of gram-negative bacteria appears to be greater to many agents than that of gram-positive cells. This was particularly well illustrated by Gale and his coworkers (Gale, 1948) in studies on amino acid assimilation (uptake) by different species of bacteria. Gram-positive bacteria were shown to concentrate amino acids such as lysine and glutamic acid within the cells, while gram-negative ones were unable to do so. When *Streptococcus faecalis*, for example, was suspended in a solution of lysine the internal concentration of amino acid was from 2 to 20 times the external concentration, while there were ratios of 50 to 60 times with glutamic acid. Lysine was able to diffuse into the cell directly, glutamic acid only when a source of energy was available at the same time. The intracellular concentration of the latter amino acid in *Micrococcus pyogenes* var. *aureus* was in some instances 400 times as high as that in the suspension medium. In the case of the streptococci no leakage of glutamic acid occurred from the cell in the absence of an energy source such as glucose, leakage occurring in the presence of glucose. Glucose, however, prevented leakage of glutamic acid from staphylococci, a slow outward diffusion being observed in its absence. It is readily apparent that the phenomena of membrane permeability are complex and no adequate explanation of the observed behaviors is available, even for larger cells that have been studied in more detail. Electrical forces, differential solubilities, and formation of various complexes in the cell no doubt are important factors involved in the passage of substance through the cell membrane and their retention within the cell.

Green and Larson (1922), as a result of conductivity studies with bacterial suspensions, concluded that bacteria accumulate various salts within the cell to a higher concentration than that in the medium. A portion of these salts diffused from the cells following death by heat or on treatment with formaldehyde. Guillemin and Larson (1922) concluded that there are two distinct groups of salts in the cell, the fixed, or structural, ones and the unbound, or physically functioning, ones. The former constitute an integral part of the protoplasm and approximate constant composition; the latter vary in composition and serve to maintain equilibrium with the salts in the culture medium. Chloride and sodium ions, generally present in relatively high concentrations in culture media, were of low concentration in the fixed salts and appeared to be involved primarily in the maintenance of ionic or osmotic equilibria. In a typical analysis of *E. coli* approximately 43 per cent of the total inorganic content of the cells was fixed in the protoplasm while the remainder was free to diffuse out of the cell into distilled water.

The major function of the cell membrane must be the maintenance of a relatively isolated internal environment in the cell. It does this, not by acting as an inert barrier, but instead is the site of processes of active transfer between the cytoplasm and the cell's environment and must be of such a nature as to adapt readily to various changes. Some, but not necessarily all, of the activity of the membrane is lost upon death of the cell. It no longer is a dynamic structure but probably can function as an inert, semipermeable membrane. Vital staining takes cognizance of this differential permeability, the living cell remaining unstained. Vital staining, however, is very difficult to accomplish with the bacteria.

In an actively growing cell several hundred thousand molecules of glucose may be utilized per second, and this involves the passage of even more molecules of oxygen into the cell and of carbon dioxide out of it. Such figures suggest the enormous extent of the activities involved in the functioning of these membranes.

Weibull (1953a,b) has used the depolymerizing action of lysozyme on the mucopolysaccharide in the cell wall of *Bacillus megaterium* to lyse the cells, lysis giving rise to spherical, empty "ghosts" and lipid granules. No nuclear elements could be observed in the lysates, the nucleic acids forming gels upon breakdown of the cells. When the depolymerization was conducted in sucrose solutions the cell wall was attacked but the remainder of the cell was maintained as an intact structural unit, the protoplast. Flagella remained attached to the protoplasts, an observation lending further support to their intracellular origin. These protoplasts were quite fragile but under carefully controlled conditions were shown to retain marked respiratory activity. Dilution of the sucrose solution containing the protoplasts led to their dissolution with the liberation of ghosts and lipid granules. The ghost fraction was shown to consist of cytoplasmic membranes and not cell-wall material, electron micrographs suggesting some degree of structure. Cell-wall material was white, cytoplasmic membranes yellow, and this color was traced to the presence of cytochrome in or attached to the cytoplasmic membrane.

Cytoplasm. The bulk of the bacterial cell, the cytoplasm and its contents, is enclosed by the cell membrane and must be a highly complex but extremely well integrated site of marked activity during the active life of the cell. The chemical composition of the bacterial cell (Buchanan and Fulmer, 1928) varies to some extent with age of the cell, the nature of the medium, and the particular organism, the major variable apparently being in the chemical composition of the cytoplasm proper. The percentage composition of cytoplasmic inclusions and of slime-layer material, however, also may show considerable variation, their chemical compositions showing less change. In general 75 to 85 per cent of the cell is free and bound water, and the remainder is composed of approximately 50 per cent carbon, 8 to 15 per cent nitrogen, 2 to 15 per cent salts, with hydrogen and oxygen making up the balance. Phosphorus, sulfur, and iron are important inorganic constituents together with potassium, sodium, calcium, magnesium, manganese, and trace elements such as molybdenum, silicon, boron, copper, zinc, and cobalt. Proteins, primarily in combination with nucleic acids but also with lipids or polysaccharides, make up to 50 to 90 per cent of the dried organic cellular matter; carbohydrates 10 to 30 per cent; lipoids generally not more than 10 per cent but up to 40 per cent in the mycobacteria; and various vitamins, pigments in some species, and miscellaneous substances constitute the remainder. Some of these substances, as indicated earlier, are concentrated in or are found entirely in the surface layers and not in the cytoplasm.

The amino acid content of the proteins present in *E. coli* (Polson, 1948) is typical of proteins in general. The bacterial cell appears to be richer in nucleoproteins than are many other cells, the high ribonucleoprotein content of the cytoplasm tending to mask the deoxyribonucleoproteins of the nucleus in most stained preparations. Otherwise, as judged by macrochemical analysis and specific microchemical tests, the bacterial cell does not differ appreciably from other cells in chemical composition. The staining characteristics of bacteria depend to a considerable extent upon their ribonucleic acid content. During the period of active growth the cytoplasm is particularly rich in nucleic acids, free and bound, and tends to stain deeply and uniformly with basic dyes. Ribonucleic acids decrease in concentration as the cell ages and the cytoplasm stains less deeply and often less uniformly. In media deficient in nitrogen and phosphorus, intracellular ribonucleic acids are used as a source of these elements and the bacteria that do develop are feebly stainable and are more transparent in the electron microscope. The apparent isoelectric staining point may increase as much as two pH units (Knaysi, 1951) because of loss of acidic groups which bind basic dyes.

The cytoplasm proper is considered to be a heterogeneous or colloidal system of various substances dispersed in water and probably at the same time of water dispersed in other materials. In addition to this ultramicroheterogeneity there are microparticles or droplets dispersed in the ground material. When bacteria are observed in the dark-field microscope the cytoplasm appears dark, unless light is reflected by particles within it, and is surrounded by a bright line, the cytoplasmic membrane. In an avian strain of *M. tuberculosis* (Knaysi, Hillier, and Fabricant, 1950) electron micrographs indicate that the ground substance contains micelles 50 by 300 angstrom units, generally oriented lengthwise of the cell. No other definite orientation of cytoplasmic constituents could be detected, vacuoles and nuclei, however, being apparent in the cytoplasm.

The cytoplasm may contain, in addition to the nuclei and macromolecules or micelles mentioned above, vacuoles and inclusions of various sorts that can be seen in the light microscope. Many species of bacteria contain, at least at times, demonstrable cell-sap vacuoles which appear to be involved primarily in the maintenance of turgor of the cytoplasm but possibly also are recipients of excess or waste products of metabolism. Inorganic inclusions of sulfur or calcium carbonate may be observed in certain of the sulfur bacteria, organic inclusions in the heterotrophs. Vacuoles generally are most evident in young, actively growing cells, inclusions in cells after the period of most active growth but not necessarily in actually old cells. The inclusions are relatively insoluble products of metabolism and can be of carbohydrate, lipid, or nitrogenous nature. The latter is generally ribonucleic acid and is termed volutin. Volutin granules have a strong affinity for basic dyes and frequently have been confused with nuclear material. One differential criterion is the solubility of volutin in water at 80°C. In old solutions of methylene blue, volutin granules take a purple color due to methylene violet, a polymer of methylene blue, combining more readily with these bodies than with the cytoplasm. The difference in coloration between granules and cytoplasm is termed metachromatism, and the granules, therefore, are spoken of as metachromatic granules. There is some evidence that metaphosphates play a role in this differential staining. These granules may, in part at least, be the result of the fixing and staining procedures and often are not as evident in cells that have not been fixed and dried before staining. Bisset (1950) in particular regards the metachromatic granules as artifacts, considering them to be produced by aggregation of nuclear and, probably, reserve food materials during the shrinkage of the cell that occurs on drying. Various data (see review by Mudd, 1954) support the hypothesis that the metachromatic granules of *Corynebacterium* and *Mycobacterium* species are accumulations of metaphosphate and ribonucleic acid serving as an energy accumulator and formed with the aid of energy-yielding reactions within the mitochondria.

Certain granular structures recently have been interpreted as mitochondria. The existence of these bodies in bacteria could be postulated by analogy with higher cells in which they are regarded as sites of intense and well-organized enzymatic activity (Green, 1951). Winterscheid and Mudd (1953) have presented evidence for the existence in mycobacteria of cellular areas or structures showing marked reducing ability with triphenyltetrazolium chloride or neotetrazolium chloride redox indicators. These areas generally are located near the poles of the cell and were shown to be different from the nuclei in both arrangement and staining ability, both types of structure being evident in cells stained by a combination of the redox-indicator and nuclear-stain techniques. The relation of these strongly reducing bodies to the macromolecules observed by Knaysi is uncertain. Bisset (1952, 1953) reported the existence of more deeply staining areas at the growing tip of a bacterial cell and concluded that this is due to a higher concentration of active nucleic acids at this point. He, however, would not interpret this as evidence for the existence of mitochondria and, unfortunately, did not report on the use of the more specific redox dyes used by Winterscheid and Mudd. Polar granules are also evident in electron micrographs, and, reasoning by analogy which is not without error, these areas or bodies could be considered as mitochondria.

Burns and Militzer (1953; see also Georgi, Militzer, and Decker, 1955) have demonstrated the presence in a thermophilic bacterium of granules possessing marked ability to reduce triphenyltetrazolium chloride. These granules are enzymatically active when separated from the cells and are capable of catalyzing the oxidation of members of the citric acid cycle. This strongly implicates that these granules are metabolically similar to the mitochondria of higher organisms.

It is difficult to observe and to interpret slight differences in structures as indicated in stained preparations or electron micrographs, particularly when these bodies have the small size of intracellular bodies in bacteria. The tetrazolium dyes do have greater specificity than ordinary ones, and their reduction to the colored, insoluble, reduced form in specific areas of the cell is highly suggestive of reaction with the "cyclophorase" system of enzymes found in mitochondria of larger cells.

We have considered that Weibull was unable to observe any structures other than cytoplasmic membranes and lipid granules in lysates of *B. megaterium*. This suggests that there are no mitochondria in this organism, although the same worker (1953c) observed colored granules in *B. megaterium* cells incubated with triphenyltetrazolium. He followed the formation of these granules under the microscope and observed that the reduction of the dye led to the deposition of its red, insoluble, reduced form at primary sites in the cells. This suggests a localization of centers of intense reducing activity within the bacterium. Continued reducing activity led to the formation of large secondary granules considered to be cytological artifacts. Rupture of the tetrazolium-treated cells and removal by centrifugation of these large granules, interpreted as mitochondria by other workers, gave rise to a colorless supernatant fluid still able to reduce the indicator at a relatively rapid rate. These observations indicate the presence of reducing enzymes in solution or in suspension as submicroscopic units. Weibull stressed that from aqueous solutions the deposition of formazans (the insoluble, reduced form of the tetrazolium indicators) resulted in the formation of granules much like those observed in the cells. He therefore concluded that tetrazolium staining is not specific for the demonstration of mitochondria in bacteria.

Stanier, Gunsalus, and Gunsalus (1953) reported that the intracellular enzymes liberated upon sonic disintegration of *Pseudomonas fluorescens* can be divided into three groups: (1) a coarse-particle fraction sedimentable by high-speed centrifugation; (2) a fine-particle fraction precipitated from the supernatant fluid by ammonium sulfate in 0.3 saturated solution; and (3) a more soluble fraction precipitable by 0.7 saturated ammonium sulfate solution.   The coarse particles (1) were largely submicroscopic cellular components from 10 to 100 mμ in diameter and contained enzymes which catalyzed the oxidation of mandelic acid to benzylformic acid, succinic and malic dehydrogenases, and those enzymes required to link the dehydrogenases to oxygen through the cytochrome system.   This would suggest that the cytochromes need not be associated entirely with the cytoplasmic membrane (Weibull, 1953b) and points to the possibility that mitochondria-like bodies, considered as being centers of intense oxidation-reduction activity, may exist as submicroscopic units in the bacterial cell.   The small size of bacterial cells and of their components, as well as the limited work that has been done in this field, leaves the existence of true mitochondria in bacteria open to question.   Mudd (1954) has reviewed the recent studies on microsomes and macromolecules observed in disintegrated bacteria.

Nucleic Acids.   During the past few years the existence of nuclei in bacteria has been generally accepted.   This, in part, is due to an increased understanding of the nature and distribution of nucleic acids in bacteria. Early general cytologists recognized from staining characteristics that the nucleus of higher cells contained a highly acidic material which they called nucleic acid.   A somewhat similar substance was found in the cytoplasm, and today we recognize two types of nucleic acid: ribose nucleic acid (RNA), which commonly is found in the cytoplasm, and deoxyribose nucleic acid (DNA), primarily or entirely in the nucleus.   The nucleic acids are conjugated with proteins to yield nucleoproteins, and they may be regarded as prosthetic groups of these conjugated proteins.

Nucleic acids (Chap. 9) are composed of purine and pyrimidine bases attached to D-2-deoxyribose molecules in DNA, to D-ribose in RNA. The structural formulas of these components are as follows:

Pyrimidines

Uracil   Thymine   Cytosine   5-Methyl cytosine

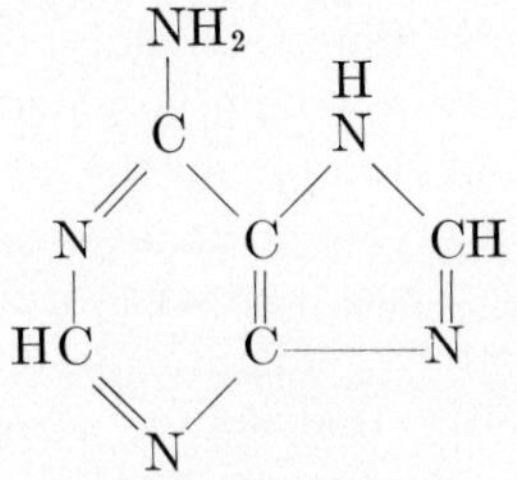

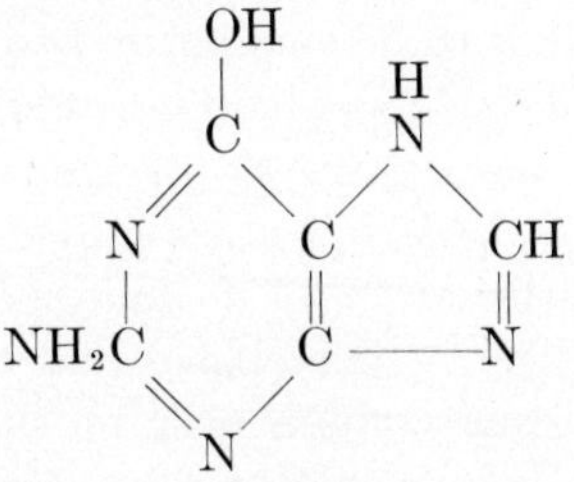

$$
\begin{array}{cc}
\text{Adenine} & \text{Guanine}
\end{array}
$$

Purines

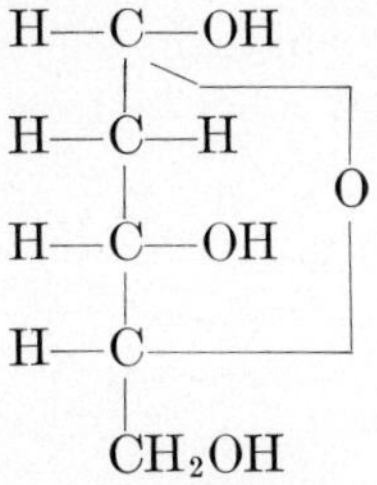

Adenine Guanine

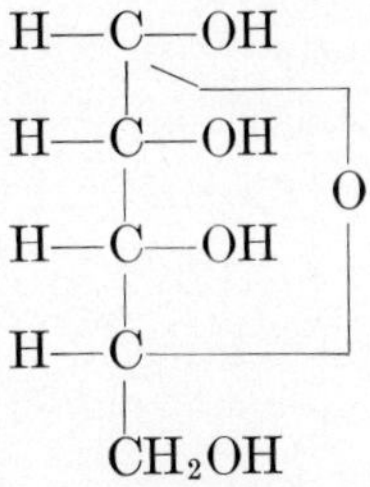

$$
\begin{array}{cc}
\text{D-Ribose} & \text{D-2-Deoxyribose}
\end{array}
$$

Two purine and two pyrimidine molecules are found in a molecule of nucleic acid, cytosine occurring in both RNA and DNA, while uracil is found in the former, thymine in the latter. Methyl cytosine has not been reported in bacterial DNA. The nitrogenous bases tend to occur in approximately equal molar amounts, Wyatt (1952) reporting molar ratios in *E. coli* of 0.92 for adenine, 1.10 for thymine, 0.96 for guanine, and 1.03 for cytosine. Other reports indicate that yeast DNA contains 1.67 molecules of adenine per molecule of guanine, while this ratio is 1.05 for *E. coli*, 0.7 for *Serratia marcescens*, and 0.4 for the avian strain of the tubercle bacillus. The ratio of thymine to adenine and of cytosine to guanine is approximately unity in most cases.

A purine or pyrimidine base combined with a pentose sugar is known as a *nucleoside*. When the nucleoside is phosphorylated, it is called a *nucleotide*. Combinations of nucleotides are spoken of as polynucleotides, or *nucleic acids*. Nucleic acids combined with proteins are called nucleoproteins. Nucleotides in other combinations are also found in the cell, adenosine di- and triphosphates being important compounds in energy transfer, while adenine in nucleotide linkages with flavins or niacin is found in hydrogen-transfer systems (Chap. 5) and in other coenzymes. Nucleic acids are composed of nitrogenous bases linked to pentose molecules which are attached to each other through phosphate linkages as indicated in Fig. 4-5.

DNA molecules are quite fibrous or elongated and give rise to highly viscous solutions, RNA solutions being less viscous and the molecules of

RNA tending to be smaller and to branch more than those of DNA. A molecule of DNA is a complicated structure, a high polymer which may contain as many as 3,000 molecules of deoxyribose plus the accompanying nitrogenous bases and phosphate groups, giving it an apparent molecular weight of the order of 1 million. The order and arrangement of the purine and pyrimidine bases and the native configuration of the deoxyribose phosphate chain may be the factors that control specificity. In many animal cells the DNA is in union with a simple protein, a protamine of a molecular weight around 3,000. The nature of the protein partner in bacterial DNA is not known. The amount of DNA per cell is quite constant, while the concentration of RNA varies with the age of the culture and other factors.

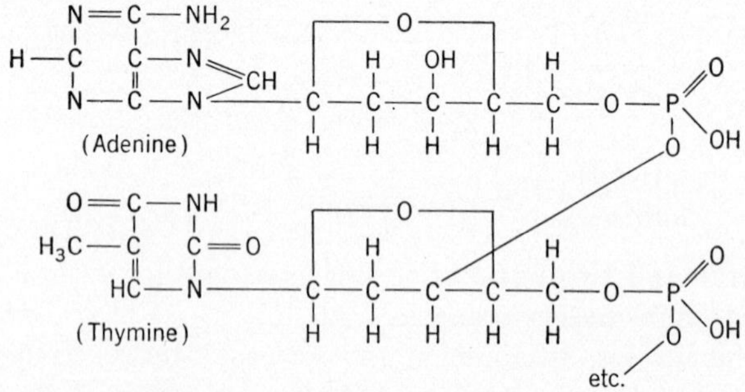

FIG. 4-5. Portion of a deoxyribonucleic acid molecule.

The Nucleus. While the existence of nuclei in bacteria is generally accepted, there is considerable doubt concerning the nature of the nucleus and the changes that occur in it during division and maturation of the cell. Current concepts have been reviewed by Knaysi (1951), Bisset (1950, 1952), in symposia edited by Bowen (1952) and Penso (1953), by Mudd (1953, 1954), and by DeLamater (1954). The studies of Robinow (1945), in which a modification of the Feulgen reaction for the demonstration of nuclear material was employed, did much to awaken, in this country, interest in the nuclear apparatus of bacteria. In the Feulgen reaction hydrolysis of DNA with acid leads to the liberation in deoxyribose of free aldehyde groups which react with sulfite-decolorized fuchsin to give a fuchsin color to the material. Hydrolysis of RNA does not give rise to a free aldehyde group in the sugar molecule, and at the same time much of the RNA is removed from the cells.

The cytoplasm of most bacterial cells has a marked affinity for basic dyes because of its high RNA content, and this tends to mask any staining characteristics of the more acidic DNA of the nucleus. The uniform staining of bacteria that results suggests a homogeneous structure, but it is actually an indication that cytoplasm and nuclear material are staining to about the same extent with the basic dyes commonly employed. It is therefore necessary to remove most or all of the RNA from the bacterial cell before the nucleus can be stained in such a manner that it can be differentiated from the cytoplasm. Piekarski and Robinow substituted Giemsa's stain for the decolorized fuchsin used in the Feulgen reaction and obtained more distinct staining of nuclear bodies in bacteria. Hydrolysis of RNA and DNA is carried out, after fixation of the bacteria to the slide by osmic acid fumes or by other suitable fixatives, for 5 to 10 min. in $N/1$ HCl around 60°C. Nuclear material can then be stained with decolorized fuchsin, or the cells can be stained differentially with Giemsa's solution or with other dyes or dye mixtures. Correspondence in size, shape, and position of the differentially stained bodies with those stained by the Feulgen technique lead to the conclusion that nuclear bodies are being observed. The Feulgen reaction is quite specific but not an absolute one for chromatin (DNA), actually being specific for free aldehyde groups in products of hydrolysis. DNA is the only substance generally present in sufficient amounts in an organized body within the cell to give a positive reaction, and the test is quite reliable, but not absolute, for chromatinic material. Other observations lend support to the belief that nuclear bodies are actually being observed in the treated cells.

Hydrolysis of RNA can be accomplished in a more specific manner with the aid of the RNA-splitting enzyme, ribonuclease. Nuclear bodies are evident after proper treatment of the cells with ribonuclease and subsequent staining. Treatment of the cells with deoxyribonuclease destroys the DNA, and the characteristic staining properties of the nucleus are no longer evident. Spores of *Bacillus mycoides* can germinate in a medium free of nitrogen and phosphorus, obtaining these elements from RNA in the spore. The cells that develop are deficient in RNA, and their nuclei can be stained directly. Certain bacteria, e.g., *Micrococcus flavo-cyaneus*, have a low content of RNA, and nuclei can be demonstrated in many of these organisms without preliminary acid hydrolysis. Nuclei have also been demonstrated in electron micrographs of a number of bacteria and in actively growing cells under the phase microscope. The use of the latter technique eliminates the possibility of any of the structures being artifacts produced during fixing and staining or by the drying involved in the preparation of specimens for observation in the electron microscope. The pictures (Fig. 4-6) obtained in phase microscopy are not always as sharp as might be desired, but they do (Clifton and Ehrhard, 1952) indicate in the living cell the existence and development of structures analogous in size and location to those bodies interpreted as nuclei in preparations of dead cells. There appears to be no reason to doubt the existence of nuclei in bacteria. Three major problems exist, however, and these are (1) the actual structure of the nucleus, (2) the changes

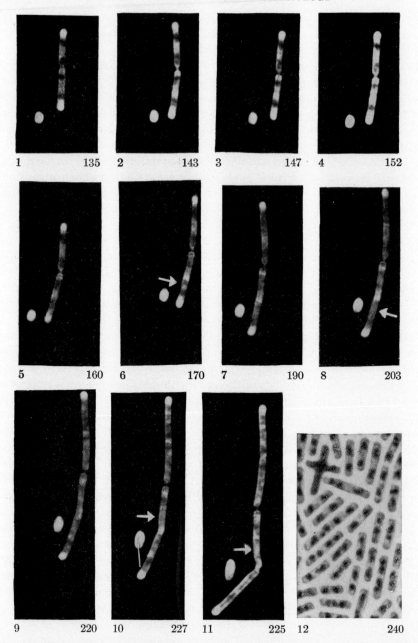

FIG. 4-6. Phase microscope pictures of growth and nuclear division in a microculture of a *Bacillus anthracis* variant. Age of the culture in minutes is given at right of figure numbers. 12 is a nuclear stained impression from a 240-min. culture for comparison. (*Clifton and Ehrhard, 1952, courtesy of The Williams & Wilkins Company.*)

that occur in the nucleus during or preceding cell division, and (3) changes in the structure of the nucleus accompanying aging of the cell.

Considerable doubt prevails regarding the structure of bacterial nuclei, and the possibility exists that variation may be observed between different species. Bisset has described vesicular nuclei in *Azotobacter, Corynebacterium*, and certain gram-negative cocci and reports short rods lying transversely of the cell in other species, these rods being considered as paired chromosomes or chromosome complexes. Bisset and others consider that complex nuclear cycles occur during the formation of resting cells (microcysts) or of spores. According to this concept the nuclear material fuses to form a chromatinic rod which divides into two halves and fuses again into a central nucleus. In many species of asporogenous bacteria the resting nucleus in the microcyst appears to possess a nuclear membrane surrounding the nucleoplasm which contains one or several peripheral, chromatinic granules. In the sporogenous bacteria the chromatinic, rod-shaped fusion nucleus was reported to divide into four short rods in rough bacilli, two in smooth ones. In either case one rod is enclosed in the spore that is formed, the other rod or rods being rejected. Eventually a typical, eccentrically staining, resting nucleus is formed in the maturing spore.

Knaysi (1951) questions the formation of fusion nuclei and concludes, on correlation of the form, size, number, and arrangement of the nuclei with the form, size, and state of growth of the cells, that it is more likely that they are the result of slow growth and slow division or of slow growth and delayed division. He suggests that in the period of rapid growth the rate of growth may be several times greater than the rate of cell division. These large cells are multinuclear, and cell walls may be seen in different stages of formation. A tendency to the uninuclear state is observed frequently as the growth rate decreases. A definite change in appearance of the nucleus is generally evident with aging and the formation of resting cells. The resting cell is uninucleate, and the nucleus appears to possess a more definite structure than in the vegetative phase. A rather general concept of the vegetative nucleus is that of two paired bodies or of what appears as a dumbbell-shaped body. This may be the result of chance, and such appearances are not so evident in the living cell observed under the phase-contrast microscope. Knaysi, however, calculated that the pairing and dumbbell-form appearances were about 10 times more frequent in *Micrococcus flavo-cyaneus* than would have been expected from chance alone.

DeLamater, Hunter, and Mudd (1952) concluded that bacteria, like higher organisms, form nuclei which possess definite nuclear membranes and filamentous chromosomes and which divide by true mitosis. They also conclude that bacteria can undergo a conjugation process which includes nuclear fusion and chromosomal pairing, with the formation of diploid nuclei and generations of cells differing from the haploid ones generally observed.   Marshak (1951) describes large particles in *E. coli* that can be liberated by sonic vibration of the cells.   These particles are of approximately the same size as the nuclei observed in stained preparations.   Electron micrographs indicate that they contain helical structures analogous in number and morphology to the chromonemata of higher plants.   Bisset (1953) strongly challenges the existence of mitotic spindles in bacteria.   Fitz-James (1954) advanced alternate schemes of chromatin duplication and separation and concluded that a true mitosis does not occur during spore germination.   It appears that the nuclei of bacteria may not differ appreciably from those of higher forms, varying primarily only in size.   Their small size leads to complications of observation and interpretation.

From a physiological viewpoint the cytology of the nucleus is of less interest than the manner in which the nucleus acts as a carrier of the characters of the cell and, consequently, as the structure which ultimately controls the physiological activities of the cell.   Breeding experiments with higher forms of life showed, along with microscopic observations, that chromosomes carry hereditary factors; more recent experiments with *Neurospora* and other microorganisms have shown that hereditary characters in chromosomes have a precise controlling influence on nutritional requirements and metabolic activities of the cell.   The controlling body in bacteria is quite small; in the resting cell of *Micrococcus flavo-cyaneus* it is a spherical body of approximately 0.4 μ diameter and 0.034 μ^3 volume and constitutes 5 to 6 per cent of the volume of the cell.

−A−T−V−S−L−G−A−P−   Replica film

−A−T−V−S−L−G−A−P− } Nucleoprotein template
Nucleic acid

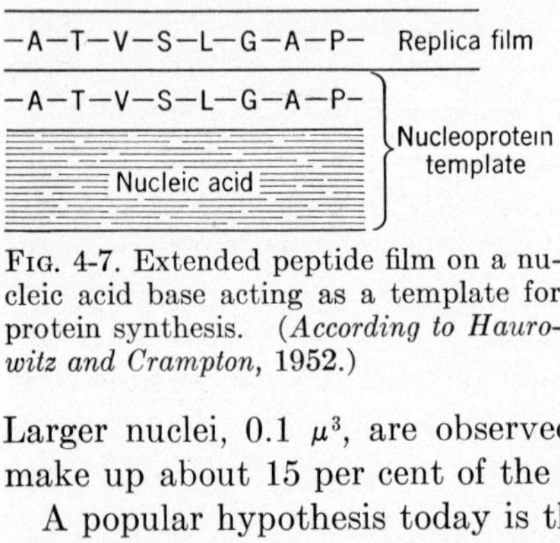

Fig. 4-7. Extended peptide film on a nucleic acid base acting as a template for protein synthesis. (*According to Haurowitz and Crampton,* 1952.)

Larger nuclei, 0.1 μ^3, are observed in the vegetative phase, and these make up about 15 per cent of the protoplasmic volume.

A popular hypothesis today is that the genes are DNA-protein molecules that act as templates or models for their own duplication and either directly or indirectly for enzyme-protein production.   Haurowitz and Crampton (1952) support the hypothesis that RNA molecules act as templates for the synthesis of protein molecules in the cytoplasm.   They visualize (Fig. 4-7) a RNA protein, consisting of an expanded peptide film on a nucleic acid base, acting as the template.   According to this concept amino acids are specifically adsorbed on identical amino acids in the template, peptide-bond formation occurs between the adsorbed amino acids, and an identical film is formed.   The replica may pull away from the parent surface and fold in the second phase of protein synthesis to give the free protein molecule. The high specificity of the replica is due to the specific amino acid pattern in the template rather than to a multiplicity of enzymes acting in a highly coordinated manner. While such concepts are highly speculative in character, they do serve in the development of mental pictures of possible cellular processes.

The arrangement of the hereditary factors in a chromosome implies that DNA must be attached in a definite and precise manner to a protein-forming part of the chromosome. Mirsky (1953) points out that a strongly basic protein can be extracted from chromosomes with a slightly acidified, concentrated saline solution and that these treated chromosomes appear unchanged under the microscope. The structural proteins can be digested away with trypsin, resulting in the liberation of DNA as a thick gel. When the DNA was removed by hydrolysis by its specific enzyme, the structural protein was left as a mass of minute coiled threads. It is quite possible that chromosomes of bacteria are constituted in a similar manner. Any combination of two proteins and a nucleic acid gives rise to an extremely complicated system that is difficult to interpret in terms of its action in chromosomes and genes. We know that effects of chromosome activity are seen in the cytoplasm and that cytoplasm in its turn influences the behavior of the nucleus. Much more information concerning the bacterial nucleus and its behavior is needed; likewise the establishment of a more complete understanding of the nature and mode of action of the gene and of the interrelationships between it and the cell as a whole are basic to an understanding of the bacterial cell.

The Flagella. A considerable number of bacteria are motile by means of organs of locomotion, flagella, while a few species move about through the agency of waves of contraction causing alterations in the shape of the cells. Pijper (1947), among others, has questioned the existence of flagella, suggesting that the appendages seen in stained preparations and in the dark-field microscope are merely "mucous twirls" of slime-layer material trailing from the surface of a cell. Kingma-Boltjes (1948) and Houwink and van Iterson (1950) have presented extensive studies and discussions which support the concept of the existence of flagella and of their activity as organs of locomotion. The latter authors, using auto-lyzed swarm cells of *Proteus vulgaris*, were able to obtain electron micrographs showing definite basal granules 100 mμ in diameter at the base of flagella within the cell. These workers also reported observations of filaments smaller than the flagella on many cells, the nature and function of these filaments being unknown.

Weibull (1948) has established by chemical methods the identity of flagella as proteins, an observation in agreement with their behavior as antigens. Astbury and Weibull (1949), in X-ray diffraction studies, found that flagellar proteins closely conform to the keratin-myosin-fibrinogen group of elastic fibrous proteins.　They suggested that flagella of *Proteus* may be monomolecular hairs or muscles.　Starr and Williams (1952) reported that a helical fine structure constituted the flagella of a motile diphtheroid, the structure being that of a left-handed, triple-threaded helix with a diameter of 19 mμ and an axial periodicity of 50 mμ.

Flagellar antigens are of particular importance in the salmonellae, the classification of these bacteria on the basis of their antigenic structures being dependent on both their flagellar and somatic antigens.　In some species the flagellar antigens undergo marked variation, at times being present in what is termed phase 1 which is characteristic of the species, at other times in the phase 2 state which is shared by many species.　No valid explanation as to the cause of the difference between the two phases is at hand.

Endospores.　Endospore formation constitutes the only generally recognized cyclostage in bacteria, and although limited primarily to species of the genera *Bacillus* and *Clostridium*, is of considerable biological interest.　The endospores are also the controlling factor in sterilization procedures, their heat resistance determining the time and temperature required for the sterilization of food, media, surgical equipment, and so on. The endospore consists of a dense cytoplasm containing a nucleus and is surrounded by a cytoplasmic membrane and one or two spore coats depending upon the species (Knaysi, 1948, 1951; Williams et al., 1952). From studies by Robinow (1953) on thin sections of spores and by Fitz-James (1953) on mechanically disrupted ones it appears that the spore coat of *B. cereus* is a single membrane and that two major layers can be distinguished around the spore of *B. megaterium*.　The chromatinic matter is arranged in a ring-shaped, sometimes beaded structure situated superficially in the cytoplasm.　The core of the spores of these species is basophilic and in the electron microscope appears quite dense and homogeneous.

The chemical composition of the spore differs little from that of the sporangium, possibly being a little richer in lipid and having more of its water content in a bound form.　Friedman and Henry (1938), from studies on the effect of spores and of vegetative cells on the freezing point of water, concluded that the percentage of free water in cells of *B. subtilis* is 68.9, in spores 3.4; similar figures for *B. megaterium* are 60.2 and 4.5, and for *B. mycoides* 50.0 and 11.9.　They advanced the theory that the heat resistance of bacterial endospores is due, in part at least, to the relatively high percentage of bound rather than free water in the spore. Considerable doubt exists, however, as to the validity of the methods employed for the determination of bound water.　Powell and Strange (1953) have suggested that the spore contains little water and that during germination there is an exchange of water from the medium for solids from the spore. They noted a loss of about 30 per cent in dry weight, the material excreted being mainly amino acids, hexosamine, peptides, and dipicolinic acid. Another concept is that the enzymes present in the spore are in an inactive state. Waldham and Halvorson (1954), as a result of studies on the vapor pressure of spores and of vegetative cells of a *Bacillus* sp., concluded that the spore is heat-resistant because its proteins are immobilized through linkages involving polar groups bound to some solid material, free polar groups being necessary to attract water. In other words the resistance is due to "bound protein" rather than to "bound water," bound protein being less susceptible to thermal agitation and denaturation.

The existence of antigens in the spore different in their serological reactivity from those present in the vegetative cell has been reported. Doak and Lamanna (1948) presented evidence that the endospore contains a mosaic of antigens, some of which are characteristic of the spore whereas others are held in common with the parent cell.

Knaysi (1951) pictured endospore formation as a process in which the first observable step is a migration (or pushing away) of any inclusions in the cytoplasm from the area in the cell where spore formation is to occur. When several nuclei are present in the cell they formed two groups in the cleared portion of the cytoplasm. A denser area could then be observed moving from each group toward the other, and these finally merged to form the spore primordium, or forespore. This body is surrounded with a nuclear membrane and subsequently by one or two spore coats. Some shrinkage is noted during the process of maturation of the forespore to form the endospore. In some species the sporangium disintegrates rapidly; in others it may persist for some days. More recently Knaysi (in Williams et al., 1952) described endospore formation in *B. cereus* as being initiated around one terminal nucleus, dense material of characteristic staining property being deposited around it, forming an envelope enclosing the forespore. As long as the forespore nucleus remains visible it occupies a central position within the forespore and may consist of a pair of chromosome-like bodies that divide in some instances to form two pairs. A highly refringent coat develops within the boundary of the forespore, the peripheral layer becoming the outer layer of the spore.

Bisset (1952), on the other hand, concludes that nuclear changes during spore formation are more complex and are sexual in character. He reports the fusion of two nuclei in unicellular forms, of four units in multicellular bacteria, resulting in the formation of a longitudinal rod, a diploid nucleus. Nuclear reduction precedes the maturation of the spore and results in the formation of a haploid spore, the nuclei not entering into spore formation being discarded or undergoing disintegration.

The endospore does not exhibit any marked metabolic activity. Crook (1952) has demonstrated a very slight oxygen uptake by washed spores of *B. anthracis* or *B. subtilis*, while Spencer and Powell (1952) were unable to detect any metabolic activity. These determinations are complicated by possible adherence of enzyme systems or other substances to the spore and by incipient germination induced by an energy source added to the spore suspension. Some observations indicate that the enzyme content of spores is much less than that of the vegetative cells and that the enzymes exist in an inactive state within the spore. Hardwick and Foster (1953) were unable to demonstrate in spore extracts any activity on the part of 17 enzyme systems studied, these systems being active in extracts of the vegetative cells. Enzymatic activity became apparent under conditions favorable for germination and growth.

The conditions required for the formation of endospores are not well established other than that the optimum conditions for spore formation appear to be similar to, but fall within narrower limits than, those optimum for growth of the species. Sporulation is generally initiated after the period of most rapid growth. Unfavorable conditions in the environment are frequently stated to be the causative factor of sporulation; yet conditions inhibitory to growth that are arbitrarily induced will not by themselves necessarily favor sporulation. As a culture grows conditions develop that are inhibitory to multiplication, and this results in a decrease in the rate of multiplication with time. Such inhibitory conditions, if they do not exceed limits of pH and other factors inhibitory to sporulation, appear to be conducive for the initiation of spore formation.

Hardwick and Foster (1952) reported that sporulation of *B. mycoides* did not occur until virtual completion of growth in a nutrient medium, then started in a very short period of time and went to 90 per cent completion within 2 hr. Under the same conditions *B. lacticola* likewise did not begin to sporulate until marked decrease in the growth rate was evident, but sporulation did not approach completion until about 12 hr. later. It should be noted that the decrease in growth rate of *B. lacticola* was less abrupt than in cultures of *B. mycoides*. They also noted that washed vegetative cells of various species of *Bacillus* sporulate readily and abundantly in distilled-water suspension under aerobic conditions. No spores were evident in cells of *B. mycoides* harvested near the end of the logarithmic period of growth, and these cells were large and stained deeply with crystal violet. After shaking for 8 hr. in distilled water the cells were smaller, their affinity for crystal violet was markedly reduced, and a few spores could be observed. Sporulation was virtually completed by the end of an 11-hr. shaking period in water. Glucose in low concentrations suppressed sporogenesis in the water suspensions, and this inhibition was relieved by the addition of ammonia to the suspension. Sporulation did not occur when the cell suspensions during incubation were exposed to nitrogen or to air containing 5 per cent carbon dioxide. Nitrogen, per se, had no noticeable effect on the spores, sporulation occurring after replacement of the nitrogen with air. They presented evidence that sporogenesis is an aerobic endogenous process that is initiated under otherwise favorable conditions when the supply of endogenous energy and carbon becomes a limiting factor for growth.

According to Hardwick and Foster (1953) the development of nutritionally poor conditions leads to a breakdown of oxidative enzymes and then of other types, their degradation products being employed in the *de novo* synthesis of spore proteins. Sporogenesis is, therefore, considered to be a process involving the adaptive synthesis of protein in a manner analogous to the formation of adaptive enzymes. This concept might be broadened to include a reversal of this behavior when the spores are transferred to a suitable growth medium, conditions then favoring the synthesis of cellular enzymes and completion of the growth cycle. On the other hand, Powell and Hunter (1953) report that sporulation does not occur in distilled water unless considerable lysis of the cells takes place, some of the survivors then sporulating. They concluded that this metamorphosis can never occur without an extracellular supply of the necessary nutrients. Perry and Foster (1954), however, presented further evidence that *B. mycoides* can sporulate in distilled water without lysis of the cells.

Germination of the endospore generally occurs under conditions that favor vegetative growth of the species. Spores of some species may germinate when a suitable energy source is supplied, growth occurring at the expense of nitrogenous and other constituents of the spore and being limited by the amount of such material available in the spore. Heating the spores at sublethal temperatures may accelerate germination, possibly as a result of increased permeability induced in the spore. An increased rate of metabolism is noted after spores are heat-shocked. Wynne (in Williams et al., 1952) concludes that spore germination is a process that differs from vegetative growth on the basis that various agents or factors may exert different influences on the two processes.

The first evidence of germination is generally a slight swelling of the spore, a reduction in its birefringence, and the development of an increased affinity for basic stains. Under the phase-contrast microscope resting spores of *B. anthracis* (Clifton and Ehrhard, 1952; Fig. 4-6) appeared as darkly outlined ovals, their interior being light with very little or no observable differentiation. The germinating spore developed a purplish appearance, increased in size to some extent, and nuclear structures became evident shortly thereafter. The developing bacillus emerged through one end of the spore, the spore case ultimately being discarded.

In other species the spore case may be absorbed.   A considerable number
of papers on the biology of bacterial endospores have appeared in recent
years, and continued interest in this field should lead to a more complete
understanding of the nature and function of the spore.

Cell Division. Vegetative reproduction of bacteria usually takes
place by transverse division of the cell, a process which appears to be of
two general types, depending upon whether the strain is of smooth or
rough morphology.   The smooth types of bacteria divide by constriction
of the cell wall after the deposition of a transverse septum, derived from
the cell membrane, across the middle of the cell.   The lateral wall grows
inward, forming a cross wall which splits the membranous septum into
two parts.   Differentiation of the cross wall into two layers, each belong-
ing to one of the daughter cells, occurs during this process, and upon its
completion the two daughter cells part.   In cells of typical rough morphology the parent cell is divided into two parts by a membranous septum,
but the cross wall is deposited within this septum rather than developing
inward from the cell wall.   Before division occurs, particularly during
the phase of rapid multiplication, a septum is deposited across each half
of the two incipient daughter cells and deposition of cell walls in these
septa is initiated.   Actual separation does not necessarily occur immediately after cell division appears to be complete, and instead long filaments
may develop, these chains being responsible for the filamentous or
Medusa-head type of colonies characteristic of rough bacteria.   In some
species the formation of the membranous septum does not go to completion before the deposition of the cell wall occurs, a central portion
remaining open, with the daughter cells being connected through a protoplasmic bridge called a plasmodesm.   More recent studies by Chapman
and Hillier (1953; Fig. 4-1) indicate in *B. cereus* that a ring of cell-wall
material is deposited centripetally from the inside surface of the cell wall
without evidence of a preliminary partitioning of the cell by a cytoplasmic
membrane.   This annular disk completely partitions the cell, thickens,
and splits, forming a transverse cell wall for each daughter cell.   Chance
(1953) has reported that a cell plate is formed in the nucleus of *Gaffkya
tetragena* and is extended so as to intercept the walls and divide the cell
into two portions.   Observations such as these may alter to some extent
the generally accepted ideas regarding cell division.

The existence of sexual reproduction is suggested in reports of apparent
fusion and segregation of nuclear material during some stages of cellular
growth and division, by morphological changes interpreted as the formation of fusion tubes, and more definitely by recombination between biochemical and other marked mutants (Chap. 15).   Progress has been rapid
in the field of bacterial cytology in recent years, but different interpretations have been advanced and considerable work must be done, or ideas

verified, before any generally accepted, complete picture can be established.   Greater complexity of structure and behavior is noted with many species of the higher bacteria which have not been included in this discussion.   Most of the available evidence suggests that the bacterial cell does not differ as markedly from other cells as was suggested by many earlier workers, but the differences that do exist create additional interest in the study of bacteria.

Mudd (1954) has summarized his concept of bacterial cytology as follows:

Bacteria share with other cells the essential features of biological organization: cell walls and septa affording protection and contributing to defining shape and size; a protoplast, with the potentiality of reversible sol-gel transformation, enclosed in a cytoplasmic membrane which regulates exchange with the external medium; within the protoplast a true nucleus and centers of coordinated, enzymatic oxidative-reductive processes, the functional equivalents of mitochondria; within the protoplast also stored inclusions of fat, carbohydrate, and high-energy phosphate, and a highly refined organization of function whose structural basis still can be imagined only vaguely; organs of locomotion, the cilia, and often extracellular capsules or amorphous slime.   Various bacteria are known to possess highly-specialized metabolic capabilities, such as the ability to oxidize iron or sulfur, to fix atmospheric nitrogen, to grow at high temperatures, or, in the case of pathogens, the possession of a whole armory of defensive and offensive characters adapting them to parasitism.   Genetic continuity, we believe, has been demonstrated in certain well-studied bacteria to be maintained by mitotic nuclear division, probably complemented by accessory features such as reversible polyploidization. . . . Mechanisms of genetic change are in a very early stage of discovery but may be seen already to include meiosis and such special mechanisms as transformation and transduction. . . . The methods by which such metabolic and genetic attributes may be discovered and explored have attained a refinement not yet available for investigation of the structural substrata which must underlie the manifold functions.   Further refinements of preparative procedures and of applications of light and electron optical equipment will doubtless serve both to consolidate recognition of the basic community of micro- and macrobiologic forms and to disclose specific differentiations of structure implementing differentiated functions.

While there are details in the above quotation that are not acceptable to all, the concept as a whole has much in its favor.

REFERENCES

Astbury, W. T., and C. Weibull: X-ray diffraction study of bacterial flagella, *Nature*, **163**, 280–282 (1949).
Bartholomew, J. W., and T. Mittwer: The gram stain, *Bacteriol. Rev.*, **16**, 1–29 (1952).
———, M. A. Roberts, and E. E. Evans: Dye exchange in bacterial cells, and the theory of staining, *Stain Tech.*, **25**, 181–186 (1950).

Bisset, K. A.: "The Cytology and Life-History of Bacteria," E. and S. Livingstone, Ltd., Edinburgh, 1950.

———: "Bacteria," The Williams & Wilkins Company, Baltimore, 1952.

———: Do bacteria have mitotic spindles, fusion tubes, and mitochondria? *J. Gen. Microbiol.*, **8**, 50–57 (1953).

Bowen, V. T. (ed.): The chemistry and physiology of the nucleus, *Exptl. Cell Research, Suppl.* 2 (1952).

Buchanan, R. E., and E. I. Fulmer: "Physiology and Biochemistry of Bacteria," vol. 1, The Williams & Wilkins Company, Baltimore, 1928.

Burns, L., and W. Militzer: Organella nature of a cell granule from a thermophilic bacterium, *Proc. Soc. Exptl. Biol. Med.*, **82**, 411–413 (1953).

Chance, H. L.: Cytokinesis in *Gaffkya tetragena*, *J. Bacteriol.*, 593–595 (1953).

Chapman, G. B., and J. Hillier: Electron microscopy of ultra-thin sections of bacteria, *J. Bacteriol.*, **66**, 362–373 (1953).

Clifton, C. E., and H.-B. Ehrhard: Nuclear changes in living cells of a variant of *B. anthracis*, *J. Bacteriol.*, **63**, 537–543 (1952).

Conn, H. J.: "The History of Staining," Biotech Publications, Geneva, N.Y., 1948.

———: "Biological Stains," 6th ed., Biotech Publications, Geneva, N.Y., 1953.

Crook, P. G.: The effect of heat and glucose on endogenous endospore respiration utilizing a modified Scholander microrespirometer, *J. Bacteriol.*, **63**, 193–198 (1952).

DeLamater, E. D.: Cytology of bacteria, II, *Ann. Rev. Microbiol.*, **8**, 23–46 (1954).

———, M. E. Hunter, and S. Mudd: Current status of the bacterial nucleus, *Exptl. Cell Research, Suppl.* 2, 323–343 (1952).

Doak, B. W., and C. Lamanna: On the antigenic structure of the bacterial spore, *J. Bacteriol.*, **55**, 373–380 (1948).

Dubos, R. J.: "The Bacterial Cell," Harvard University Press, Cambridge, Mass., 1945.

Fischer, R., and P. Larose: Contribution on the behavior and structure of the cytoplasmic membrane of bacteria, *Can. J. Med. Sci.*, **30**, 86–105 (1952).

——— and S. Seidenberg: Homologous mechanism of bactericidal action and gram-staining, *Science*, **114**, 265–266 (1951).

Fitz-James, P. C.: The structure of spores as revealed by mechanical disintegration, *J. Bacteriol.*, **66**, 312–319 (1953).

———: The duplication of bacterial chromatin, *J. Bacteriol.*, **68**, 464–473 (1954).

Friedman, C. A., and B. S. Henry: Bound water content of vegetative and spore forms of bacteria, *J. Bacteriol.*, **36**, 99–105 (1938).

Gale, E. F.: The nitrogen metabolism of gram positive bacteria, *Bull. Johns Hopkins Hosp.*, **83**, 119–175 (1948).

Georgi, C. E., W. E. Militzer, and T. S. Decker: The organelle nature of a particle isolated from *Bacillus stearothermophilus*, *J. Bacteriol.*, **70**, 716–725 (1955).

Green, D. E.: The cyclophorase complex of enzymes, *Biol. Rev. Camb. Phil. Soc.*, **26**, 410–455 (1951).

Green, R. G., and W. P. Larson: Conductivity of bacterial cells, *J. Infectious Diseases*, **30**, 550–558 (1922).

Guillemin, M., and W. P. Larson: The relation between the fixed and free salts of bacteria, *J. Infectious Diseases*, **31**, 349–355 (1922).

Hardwick, W. A., and J. W. Foster: On the nature of sporogenesis in some aerobic bacteria, *J. Gen. Physiol.*, **35**, 907–927 (1952).

——— and ———: Enzymatic changes during sporogenesis in some aerobic bacteria, *J. Bacteriol.*, **65**, 355–360 (1953).

Haurowitz, F., and C. F. Crampton: The role of the nucleus in protein synthesis, *Exptl. Cell Research*, *Suppl.* 2, 45–54 (1952).

Houwink, A. L.: A macromolecular mono-layer in the cell wall of *Spirillum* spec., *Biochim. et Biophys. Acta*, **10**, 360–366 (1953).

—— and D. R. Kreger: Observations on the cell wall of yeasts: an electron microscope and X-ray diffraction study, *Antonie van Leeuwenhoek*, **19**, 1–24 (1953).

—— and W. van Iterson: Electron microscopical observations on bacterial cytology, *Biochim. et Biophys. Acta*, **5**, 10–44 (1950).

Kingma-Boltjes, T. Y.: Function and arrangement of bacterial flagella, *J. Pathol. Bacteriol.*, **60**, 275–287 (1948).

Knaysi, G.: The endospore of bacteria, *Bacteriol. Rev.*, **12**, 19–77 (1948).

——: "Elements of Bacterial Cytology," 2d ed., Comstock Publishing Associates, Ithaca, N.Y., 1951.

——, J. Hillier, and C. Fabricant: The cytology of an avian strain of *Mycobacterium tuberculosis* studied with the electron and light microscopes, *J. Bacteriol.*, **60**, 423–447 (1950).

Lamanna, C., and M. F. Mallette: "Basic Bacteriology," The Williams & Wilkins Company, Baltimore, 1953.

—— and ——: The cytological basis for the role of the primary dye in the gram stain, *J. Bacteriol.*, **68**, 509–513 (1954).

Marshak, A.: Chromosome structure in *Escherichia coli*, *Exptl. Cell Research*, **2**, 243–251 (1951).

McCalla, T. M.: Cation adsorption by bacteria, *J. Bacteriol.*, **40**, 23–32 (1940).

—— and F. E. Clark: Dye adsorption by bacteria at varying H-ion concentrations, *Stain Tech.*, **16**, 95–100 (1941).

McCarty, M.: The lysis of group A hemolytic streptococci by extracellular enzymes of *Streptomyces albus*. II. Nature of the cellular substrate attacked by the lytic enzymes, *J. Exptl. Med.*, **96**, 569–580 (1952).

Miles, A. A., and N. W. Pirie (eds.): "The Nature of the Bacterial Surface: A Symposium," Charles C Thomas, Publisher, Springfield, Ill., 1949.

Mirsky, A. E.: The chemistry of heredity, *Sci. American*, **188**, 47–57 (1953).

Mudd, S.: Aspects of bacteria as cells and as organisms, *International Rev. Cytology*, **2**, 133–177 (1953).

——: Cytology of Bacteria, I, *Ann. Rev. Microbiol.*, **8**, 1–22 (1954).

Penso, G. (ed.): "Symposium: Bacterial Cytology," Charles C Thomas, Publisher, Springfield, Ill., 1953.

Perry, J. J., and J. W. Foster: Non-involvement of lysis during sporulation of *Bacillus mycoides* in distilled water, *J. Gen. Physiol.*, **37**, 401–409 (1954).

Pijper, A.: Methyl cellulose and bacterial motility, *J. Bacteriol.*, **53**, 257–269 (1947).

Polson, A.: Quantitative partition chromatography and the composition of *Escherichia coli*, *Biochim. et Biophys. Acta*, **2**, 575–581 (1948).

Powell, J. F., and J. R. Hunter: Sporulation in distilled water, *J. Gen. Physiol.*, **36**, 601–606 (1953).

—— and R. E. Strange: Biochemical changes during the germination of bacterial spores, *Biochem. J.*, **54**, 205–209 (1953).

Raffel, S.: "Immunity—Hypersensitivity—Serology," Appleton-Century-Crofts, Inc., New York, 1953.

Roberts, R. B., P. H. Abelson, D. B. Cowie, E. T. Bolton, and R. J. Britten: Studies of biosynthesis in *Escherichia coli*, *Carnegie Inst. Wash. Publ.* 607, Washington, 1955.

Robinow, C. F.: Nuclear apparatus and cell structure of rod-shaped bacteria. An addendum to R. J. Dubos, "The Bacterial Cell," Harvard University Press, Cambridge, Mass., 1945.

————: Observations on the nucleus of resting and germinating spores of *Bacillus megaterium*, *J. Bacteriol.*, **65**, 378–382 (1953a).

————: Spore structure as revealed by thin sections, *J. Bacteriol.*, **66**, 300–311 (1953b).

Rothstein, A.: The relationship of cell surface enzymes to ion transport in yeast cells, *J. Cell. Comp. Physiol.*, **44**, 329 (1954).

Spencer, R. E. J., and J. F. Powell: Flavinadenine dinucleotide and diaphorase in resting and germinated spores and vegetative cells of *Bacillus subtilis* and *Bacillus megaterium*, *Biochem. J.*, **51**, 239–245 (1952).

Stanier, R. Y., I. C. Gunsalus, and C. F. Gunsalus: The enzymatic conversion of mandelic acid to benzoic acid. II. Properties of the particulate fractions, *J. Bacteriol.*, **66**, 543–547 (1953).

Starr, M. P., and R. C. Williams: Helical fine structure of flagella of a motile diphtheroid, *J. Bacteriol.*, **63**, 701–706 (1952).

Tomcsik, J.: Immunopolysaccharides, *Ann. Rev. Biochem.*, **22**, 351–370 (1953).

———— and S. Guex-Holzer: A specific cell-wall reaction in *Bacillus* sp., *J. Gen. Microbiol.*, **10**, 317–324 (1954).

Waldham, D. G., and H. O. Halvorson: Studies on the relationship between equilibrium vapor pressure and moisture content of bacterial endospores, *Appl. Microbiol.*, **2**, 333–338 (1954).

Weibull, C.: Some chemical and physico-chemical properties of the flagella of *Proteus vulgaris*, *Biochim. et Biophys. Acta*, **2**, 351–361 (1948).

————: The isolation of protoplasts from *Bacillus megaterium* by controlled lysis with lysozyme, *J. Bacteriol.*, **66**, 688–695 (1953a).

————: Characterization of the protoplasmic constituents of *Bacillus megaterium*, *J. Bacteriol.*, **66**, 696–702 (1953b).

————: Observations on the staining of *Bacillus megaterium* with triphenyltetrazolium, *J. Bacteriol.*, **66**, 137–139 (1953c).

Williams, O. B. (ed.): Symposium on the biology of bacterial spores, *Bacteriol. Rev.*, **16**, 89–143 (1952).

Winterscheid, L. C., and S. Mudd: The cytology of the tubercle bacillus with reference to mitochondria and nuclei, *Am. Rev. Tuberc.*, **67**, 59–73 (1953).

Wyatt, G. R.: Specificity in the composition of nucleic acids, *Exptl. Cell Research*, *Suppl.* 2, 201–215 (1952).

CHAPTER 5

ENZYMES

The method by which particulate food is broken down in the body long remained a mystery, one concept being that it underwent mechanical disintegration during a sort of grinding action occurring in the stomachs of mammals. In the latter part of the eighteenth century Spallanzani fed animals with bits of meat contained in tiny wire cages to which threads were attached. He retrieved the cages at different time intervals from the stomach of an animal and noted that the meat was slowly digested in them. He also observed that gastric juice by itself was able to bring about the liquefaction of meat in vitro and concluded on the basis of these observations that digestion is a chemical rather than a mechanical process. At about the same time Lavoisier demonstrated that life is accompanied by a continuous uptake of oxygen and liberation of carbon dioxide. This suggested the occurrence of oxidations similar to those which occur in a flame, the lungs at first being assumed to be the site of combustion. A little later he reported that fermentation consists chemically of a decomposition of sugar into ethyl alcohol and carbon dioxide, the quantitative aspects of this reaction being established as

$$C_6H_{12}O_6 \rightarrow 2C_2H_5OH + 2CO_2$$

by Gay-Lussac in 1815. Fermentation, however, was not yet ascribed to the activity of living cells.

It was noted around this time that certain cellular secretions or extracts possessed the ability to decompose starch, others brought about the degradation of proteinaceous matter, while others accomplished hydrolysis of fatty material. The reason for these chemical changes became more apparent around 1835 with the development of the concept of catalysis by Berzelius. He noted that the rate of a number of chemical reactions increased in the presence of certain foreign matter which could be recovered unchanged at the end of the reaction. Hydrogen peroxide, for example, decomposed rapidly following the addition of finely divided platinum or of fibrin. The agents which increased the rate at which a reaction occurred were called *catalysts* by Berzelius, and the process by which the rate of reaction was increased, *catalysis*, or *catalytic action*.

This action he ascribed to contact forces which decreased the stability, or increased the reactivity, of a molecule, hence the term catalysis, which literally signifies "a loosening down." He also considered fermentation to be a catalytic process, the change of sugar into alcohol and carbon dioxide taking place under the influence of an insoluble catalytic agent termed a *ferment*. Berzelius postulated that numerous catalytic reactions occur in the body and that the cause of these reactions ultimately would be discovered in the organs.

Schwann, Cagniard-Latour, and Kützing around 1837 independently suggested that certain decompositions in nature were induced by microorganisms, the fermentation of sugar being ascribed to yeast. Shortly thereafter Liebig attempted to explain fermentation in a manner similar to the concept of Berzelius, suggesting that it is induced by the instability of certain molecules which in turn confer an instability upon the sugar molecules. The latter then break down to give alcohol and carbon dioxide, yeast being a residue incidental to the fermentation rather than the inducing agent.

Pasteur, during the period 1857 to 1861, quite conclusively proved that the alcoholic, lactic acid, and butyric acid fermentations were elicited by specific microorganisms, and he reached the conclusion that fermentations are physiological processes, life without air. During the same period Traube, primarily on speculative rather than on experimental grounds and also by analogy with certain chemical reactions, advanced the theory that fermentations are brought about by means of ferments which the cells contain. These ferments were considered as proteinaceous in character. A distinction between the catalytic activities of intact cells and of cell-free extracts developed, the latter's catalytic activity being ascribed to unorganized ferments while those of the former were ascribed to the intact cell, an organized ferment. The Buchners in 1897 ground yeast cells with sand, pressed out a cell-free juice, and demonstrated that the extract was able to catalyze the fermentation of sugar. This paved the way for the theory that all reactions in living cells are carried out under the influence of ferments formed by the living cell but capable of acting independently of the cell. The term enzyme, which literally means "in yeast," was introduced by Kühne in 1878 and has practically replaced the older term, ferment.

Catalysis. A catalyst can be defined as *a substance which alters the velocity of a chemical reaction without being used up in the reaction.* Most catalysts bring about an increase in the rate of reaction, i.e., exert a positive effect, but examples of negative catalysis are known. We have considered that a chemical reaction may occur spontaneously if there is a decrease in free energy, but although the reaction is possible theoretically, it need not occur at an appreciable rate. Foodstuffs can be oxidized spontaneously to carbon dioxide and water in the presence of oxygen. ΔF has a negative value for the oxidations, but the reaction does not occur at an appreciable rate with most foods at low temperatures and in the absence of catalysts. Oxidation of these foods can occur with rapidity in the living cell under the influence of the biological catalysts, the enzymes.

We have considered (Chap. 3) that metallic platinum, a catalyst for many chemical reactions, is catalytically most active when present in a finely divided state in the reaction mixture. A large total surface area is, therefore, available for the adsorption and activation of the reactant. The forces operative at these surfaces tend to bring about localized increases in concentration, and this alone could result in an increased rate of reaction. As a result, however, of the union between the catalyst

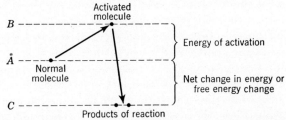

Fig. 5-1. Hypothetical illustration of energetics of activation and reaction.

and the adsorbed material it is probable that stresses or strains are established in the adsorbed molecules. These molecules, therefore, become more reactive, or are said to be activated, and undergo change at a greater rate than when present in the free state. This concept of adsorption and activation, while not necessarily complete, does enable one to form a mental picture of the process of catalysis and to consider in simple terms the cause of the increased rate of reaction so frequently observed.

The concept of activation by a catalyst does not contradict the laws of thermodynamics. Let us assume that a reactant molecule has an energy content represented by the level A in Fig. 5-1 and that the product of the reaction is at an energy level C. In the presence of the catalyst, adsorption and activation of the molecule occur, and thereby the energy level of the adsorbed molecule is increased from level A to B. When the reaction occurs, there is a decrease in energy from level B of the activated reactant to level C which represents the energy content of the product of the reaction. The energy of activation is represented by the difference between levels A and B, and this same amount of energy is released to the catalyst when the reaction occurs; hence it balances and cancels the energy of activation. The net energy change, therefore, is from level A to level C, and this free-energy change is the same whether the reaction occurs in the presence or absence of a catalyst.

It should be pointed out that the above discussion deals with heterogeneous catalysis in the sense that two distinct phases are involved, generally a catalyst in the solid state and the reactant either in solution or in the gaseous state. Homogeneous catalysis also occurs, the catalytic agent being in the same physical state as the reactant and only one phase being evident. Hydrogen ions, for example, catalyze the hydrolysis of cane sugar, and this can be considered as being due to the formation of an intermediate or addition compound which is more unstable than the sucrose molecule itself. Enzymatic catalysis possibly can be considered as being somewhat intermediate in character, the enzyme being reactive when in solution with the substrate or when present in a heterogeneous cellular complex. In either case the substrate molecule is adsorbed by, or forms an addition compound with, the enzyme, is activated, and the way is paved for the reaction to occur. The over-all picture of catalysis remains the same, the difference being one of detail.

In many instances catalysts are not very specific as regards reactions which they catalyze, particularly when compared with the specificity generally exhibited by enzymes. It might be sufficient to point out that the hydrogen ion can catalyze a wide variety of reactions, particularly hydrolytic ones, while the hydrolytic enzymes are much more specific as regards the substrates they activate. When a reaction occurs at an increased rate under the influence of a catalytic agent, the reaction still follows the ordinary laws of chemistry. A catalyst, for example, cannot alter the equilibrium point of a reaction but only increases the rate at which the equilibrium is established. It therefore must be able to increase the rate of reaction in either direction in a reversible reaction. The same equilibrium constant is noted for the hydrolysis of an ester (Chap. 2) at constant temperature with either hydrogen ions or the specific enzyme acting as the catalyst.

Some reactions are catalyzed by the activity of one or more of the products of the reaction. Such reactions are said to be autocatalyzed. The rate of solution of copper in nitric acid increases with time owing to the catalytic action of the oxide evolved in the reaction. Likewise, the rate of hydrolysis of an ester by water is increased in weakly acidic solutions by hydrogen ions formed from the acid produced during the course of the hydrolysis. In other cases products of a reaction may exert an inhibitory effect apart from that predicted from the law of mass action. Autocatalysis may also at times be noted in biological systems.

The activity of a catalyst may be altered in the presence of even extremely small amounts of a foreign substance. Some substances tend to enhance the activity of a catalyst, and these are termed *promoters;* others which tend to inhibit catalytic activity are known as *inhibitors* or *poisons.* The presence of finely divided oxides of metallic catalysts often augments the catalytic activity of the metal, i.e., the oxides act as promoters. Sulfides, on the other hand, may act as poisons, particularly when they are able to form a stable compound with the metal. Catalytic iron, either in ordinary catalysts or in the prosthetic group of an enzyme, can be poisoned with hydrogen sulfide. Enzymes behave in many respects like the catalysts of nonbiological origin.

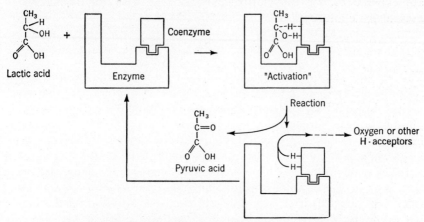

FIG. 5-2. Hypothetical illustration of mode of enzyme action.

Enzymes. Enzymes may be defined as *complex organic catalysts of biological origin,* or in more functional terms, as *simple or conjugated proteins which catalyze reactions generally essential to the activities of the cell, at the same time imparting order and direction to those reactions occurring within the cell.* The latter definition is not without its faults, but it does serve as a starting point for discussion of enzymes and their activities.

As far as is known, all enzymes are proteins or are composed of proteins in association with another component or components. The active complex is termed a *holoenzyme,* while the specific protein by itself is called an *apoenzyme.* An apoenzyme active by itself must contain particular arrangements of amino acids or of groups on its surface which confer activity and specificity upon the protein. In many instances the activity of an enzyme (Fig. 5-2) is associated with the presence of a metal and/or an organic prosthetic group chemically different from protein. In those enzymes requiring a metal ion for their activity, the ion is known as an *activator.* The ionic requirements is not always specific in an absolute sense, although the activity is usually greatest with a specific metal. In some cases the prosthetic group is readily separated from the apoenzyme, such a dissociable group being known as a *coenzyme.* The distinction between a prosthetic group firmly bound to the apoenzyme and a coenzyme is one of degree.

Urease can serve as an example of an apparently pure protein enzymatically active by itself; catalase as an enzyme containing a firmly bound prosthetic group, an iron porphyrin; and the holoenzymes of dehydrogenation are composed of specific proteins plus readily dissociable groups (coenzymes), a metal-ion requirement being noted in many or all instances.

Metal Cofactors or Activators. Various yeasts and a few bacteria are capable of decarboxylating pyruvic acid with the formation of acetaldehyde and CO_2, or

$$CH_3COCOOH \xrightarrow{\text{carboxylase}} CH_3CHO + CO_2$$

This enzyme can be extracted from dried cells, but if the enzyme preparation is dialyzed, all activity is lost. It has been determined that magnesium ions and a phosphorylated form of vitamin B_1, thiamine pyrophosphate, pass through the dialysis membrane, leaving the apoenzyme in an inactive state. Upon addition of the concentrated dialysate, or of magnesium salts and pure thiamine pyrophosphate, activity is restored to the enzyme protein. Thiamine pyrophosphate is the coenzyme (cocarboxylase) in this example, magnesium ions the cofactor or activator. Other ions, e.g., Mn^{++}, Co^{++}, and Ca^{++} can be substituted for the Mg^{++}, but generally with reduction in activity of the enzyme. The coenzyme requirement is specific, the activator one not in this instance.

It is generally assumed that enzymes form definite compounds with their substrates, and it is believed that these compounds may, in many instances, be of the chelate type. Metal ions can form complex compounds with a variety of ligands, a ligand being defined as an atom or group of atoms which donates electrons to a separate metal atom to form a more or less homopolar bond. When two or more of these ligands (L) are themselves united in some manner, the compound is said to be a chelate compound and can be represented as

Smith (1949; McElroy and Glass, 1954) discussed the factors involved in the specificity of enzyme action with particular reference to the metal peptidases, enzymes catalyzing the hydrolysis of proteins or peptides at peptide bonds, the basic reaction being

$$-CO-NH- + H_2O \xrightarrow{\text{peptidase}} -COOH + H_2N-$$

ENZYMES

First of all, the role of the metal appears to involve formation of a complex between it and both the apoenzyme and the substrate molecules. Secondly, the substrate may also be bound to its protein partner through terminal, or other, groups on the substrate molecule. A third factor is that the deformation or electronic stress produced as a result of chelate formation lowers the free energy of activation for hydrolysis of the peptide bond. Metal ions by themselves may catalyze the hydrolysis of acids such as oxalosuccinic with which they form chelate compounds. Chelate formation with the metal does not suffice for activation of the hydrolysis of a more stable acid such as acetoacetic, the enzyme protein being required in addition to the metal for activation. Another factor accounting for specific effects may be steric in character. Leucine aminopeptidase, for example, catalyzes the hydrolysis of a number of peptides

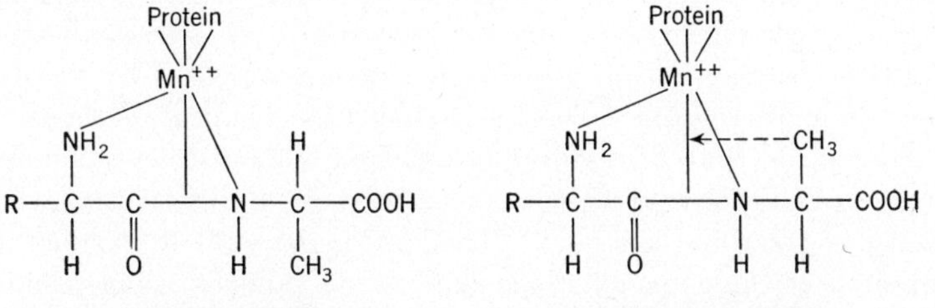

L·Leucyl—L·alanine L·Leucyl—D·alanine

FIG. 5-3. Postulated chelate formation or coordination between leucyl-alanine and leucine aminopeptidase, activation of the D-alanine-containing compound not occurring because of steric effect indicated by arrow. (*After Smith*, 1949.)

including L-leucyl-L-alanine, but not that of the closely related L-leucyl-D-alanine, the only difference between these compounds being in the relative positions of the CH_3— and the H— groups in alanine. This, together with chelate formation, is illustrated in Fig. 5-3.

Chelate compounds possessing catalytic activity are hemoglobin, chlorophyll, the cytochromes, and enzymes such as the peptidases, catalase, peroxidase, cytochrome oxidase, enolase, arginase, phosphatase, phosphorylase, and others. There appears to be widespread agreement that the chelate complexes are of importance in enzyme activity. The ideas concerning the nature of the complexes, including the bonds between the enzyme and the substrate, are, however, subject to question, and the complexes may differ in different substrate-enzyme systems. McElroy and Nason (1954) have concluded that Mg^{++}, and to a certain extent Mn^{++}, ions play a predominant role in promoting the formation of the enzyme-substrate complex by chelation, particularly in those enzymes involved in group transfer. In general iron, copper, and molybdenum appear to function as electron couplers from one system to another rather than to be involved in enzyme-substrate complex formation. Mn^{++},

Mg^{++}, and Zn^{++} ions are involved in decarboxylation reactions, manganese being the predominant metal here and less agreement being noted as to the mechanism by which these ions exert their effect.

Specificity. Enzymes make up a special group of catalysts in that they are composed of proteins of biological origin which so far have not been duplicated by man in the laboratory and which exert their maximum activities under mild conditions as compared with the majority of catalyzed reactions employed in the chemical laboratory and in industry. Furthermore, they have an extremely specific action, limited in some to attack on one type of chemical linkage (reaction specificity), in others to a few specific substrates possessing a particular chemical group or groups (group specificity), and frequently to one substrate (substrate specificity) where stereochemical specificity is often exhibited if different optical isomers of the substrate exist. This marked specificity of biological reactions greatly influenced the course of Pasteur's studies from the time he observed the production of optically active amyl alcohol by yeast, only an optically inactive mixture being produced by chemical methods. The later observation that a green mold attacked one optical isomer but not the other optical form of tartaric acid further impressed him with the specificity of microbic activity. This no doubt guided Pasteur in the development of the concept of specific microorganisms being responsible for specific diseases of wine and beer and eventually for the same concept regarding the causative agents of infectious diseases of man and other animals. We depart from Pasteur in ascribing specific activity to the enzymes of the cell rather than to the cell as an entity.

Pasteur considered fermentations and other reactions as being essential to the life of the cell, and this concept still holds, with modifications made necessary as a result of our better understanding of the processes. Enzymes can catalyze reactions apart from the living cell; alcohol and carbon dioxide, for example, can be formed by the enzymes in yeast juice or by these same enzymes in the intact cell. In the test tube the energy made available by cell-free fermentation is dissipated as heat; in the living cell a portion of it can be utilized in the processes essential for life of the cell. There are instances, for example the ability of certain bacteria to reduce chlorates to chlorites, where the enzymatic activity does not appear to be essential to the life of a cell, but exceptions of this sort may be due to a carry-over from an unusual ancestor. Enzymatically controlled reactions provide the energy, much of the building matter, and the synthetic mechanisms for the formation and maintenance of cellular material. These reactions must proceed in an orderly manner in the normal cell. We could conclude that enzymes participate in the cell in reactions such that the original substrate molecule is converted into a product which in turn serves as the substrate for a second enzyme, and so on until the chain is complete. The integrated complex of such dissimilatory and assimilatory changes in space and in time provide the energetic, synthetic, and configurational relationships that result in maintenance, growth, and multiplication of living cells. The bacterial cell cannot be regarded as just a bag of enzymes; many of the constituent enzymes must be arranged in definite order or position as, for example, in the mitochondria of cells in higher organisms and possibly also in bacteria.

Coenzymes. The Buchners' discovery of the fermentative ability of yeast juice led to the concept that alcoholic fermentation is induced by zymase, an enzyme complex formed in the yeast cell but not dependent upon the cell for its activity. Harden and Young in 1906 reported that zymase is composed of at least two components which can be separated from each other by dialysis. The agent that passed through the dialysis membrane was called cozymase. They observed that cozymase is resistant to boiling while the nondiffusible portion of zymase is heat-labile. Since their report it has been found that zymase is actually a mixture of enzymes and that cozymase is also a mixture. Yeast dialysate would contain adenosine triphosphate, cocarboxylase, coenzyme I, magnesium, and phosphate, all of which are involved in the fermentation process. The term cozymase is frequently employed as synonymous with coenzyme I, a prosthetic group involved in the transport of hydrogen and electrons from a number of substrates under the influence of their specific dehydrogenases. Coenzyme I (CoI), also termed codehydrogenase I, is composed of adenine, nicotinamide (niacinamide), ribose, and two phosphate molecules. It is therefore a diphosphopyridine nucleotide, and the abbreviation DPN is used more generally today than is CoI. The structural formula of CoI, or DPN, is given in Fig. 5-4. Coenzyme II (CoII, or triphosphopyridine nucleotide, TPN), which serves as a coenzyme for certain dehydrogenases, differs from CoI in that the former possesses three rather than two phosphate groups, the third phosphate group being attached to a ribose molecule in place of the H indicated with an asterisk in Fig. 5-4. These, and other coenzymes, generally take part in reactions catalyzed by various enzymes and are primarily specific for the transfer of an atom or group rather than being specific for a substrate or enzyme.

Harden and his coworkers can also be credited with an observation that ultimately led to the recognition of adenosine triphosphate as the coenzyme of phosphorylation. They were attempting to prepare antibodies (antiferments) against zymase and noted that the addition of either "immune" serum or normal serum to yeast juice resulted in an increased rate and extent of fermentation. They finally traced the cause to phosphates in the serum and observed that phosphates alone had the same effect, the phosphate being coupled to glucose with the formation of phosphate esters. Hexose diphosphate accumulated, along with alcohol and carbon dioxide, in the degradation products of glucose by yeast juice. Phosphates, however, had no stimulating action on fermentation induced by the intact cells.   The reason for this behavior will be discussed under alcoholic fermentation.   About twenty years later Embden and Zimmerman discovered an adenosine phosphate in their studies on muscle metabolism, and ultimately it was shown that these compounds act as phosphate carriers in a manner analogous to the transport of hydrogen and electrons

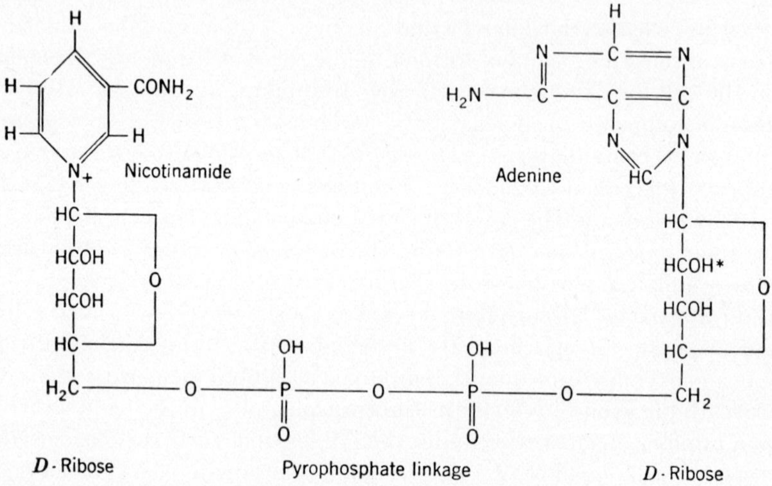

FIG. 5-4. Coenzyme I, or DPN, a diphosphopyridine nucleotide.   One hydrogen and two electrons are taken up on reduction at the $\overset{\displaystyle CH}{\underset{\displaystyle \underset{CH_2}{|}}{N_+}}$ linkage in the nicotinamide moiety to yield $\underset{\displaystyle |}{\overset{\displaystyle |}{N}}$ (DPNH), while a second hydrogen from the substrate is liberated as a hydrogen ion.   Coenzyme II, or TPN, differs from DPN by the possession of an additional phosphate group in place of the hydrogen atom indicated by the asterisk.

by DPN.   The phosphorylating-dephosphorylating activity of this coenzyme system is associated with a number of enzymes and is involved in the transfer and storage of energy.   The activity of the adenylic acid–adenosine diphosphate–adenosine triphosphate system is associated with rather unique phosphate bonds (Kaplan, 1951), high-energy bonds, the hydrolysis of which liberates around 12,000 cal. per mole as compared with 2,000 to 3,000 cal. associated with ordinary phosphate bonds involving ester linkages.   These high-energy bonds are commonly indicated by a wavy line, $\sim$, rather than by a straight bond, —, and phosphate groups in general by the symbol Ⓟ.   The significance of these bonds will be discussed in Chap. 7. Adenosine triphosphate (ATP), and probably adenosine diphosphate (ADP) to a much lesser extent, act in combination with different phosphorylating apoenzymes as coenzymes in shifting phosphate groups from phosphate donors to acceptor compounds. These reactions of the coenzyme system are reversible, and adenylic acid or adenosine diphosphate act as phosphate acceptors under appropriate conditions. Adenosine triphosphate and its component parts have the structural formulas illustrated in Fig. 5-5.

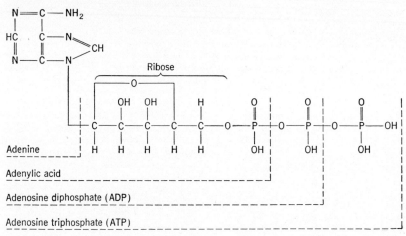

FIG. 5-5. The adenylic acid system, adenosine triphosphate being the coenzyme of phosphorylation.

Adenine and/or D-ribose (actually D-ribitol, the alcohol form) are also found in the structures of riboflavins serving as hydrogen and electron carriers or coenzymes in the pathway of oxidation of some compounds. Riboflavin phosphate serves as the prosthetic group or coenzyme for the apoenzymes involved in the oxidation of several natural or L-amino acids (L-amino acid oxidase) and of TPN (cytochrome c reductase), while the riboflavin adenine dinucleotide is a coenzyme for other hydrogen transfers, e.g., the oxidation of certain D-amino acids, the unnatural amino acids. The first riboflavin complex (the "old yellow enzyme") was isolated by Warburg and Christian in 1933, and since that time a number of flavoproteins have been isolated. The structural formula of riboflavin phosphate (alloxazine mononucleotide) is given in Fig. 5-6 and of riboflavin adenine dinucleotide (alloxazine adenine dinucleotide) in Fig. 5-7.

Thiamine pyrophosphate, also known as cocarboxylase or aneurin diphosphate, is the coenzyme or prosthetic group involved in the decarboxylation of α-keto acids. Auhagen in 1933 reported that pyruvic acid carboxylase (decarboxylase) consists of an apoenzyme and a prosthetic group that could be dissociated from the holoenzyme. Its identity as the diphosphate of thiamine, thiamine pyrophosphate (Fig. 5-8), was established by Lohmann and Schuster in 1937. The yeast system brings about the decarboxylation of pyruvic acid with the formation of acetaldehyde and carbon dioxide. Thiamine pyrophosphate is also found in many

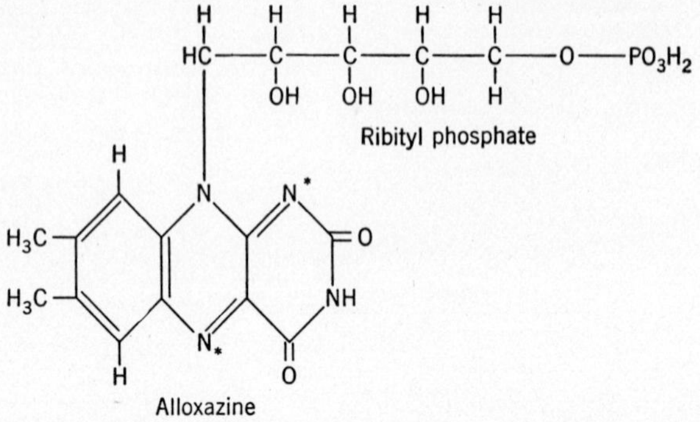

Fig. 5-6. Riboflavin phosphate, an alloxazine mononucleotide coenzyme of oxidation. The asterisks indicate the atoms within the molecule that accept hydrogen and electrons.

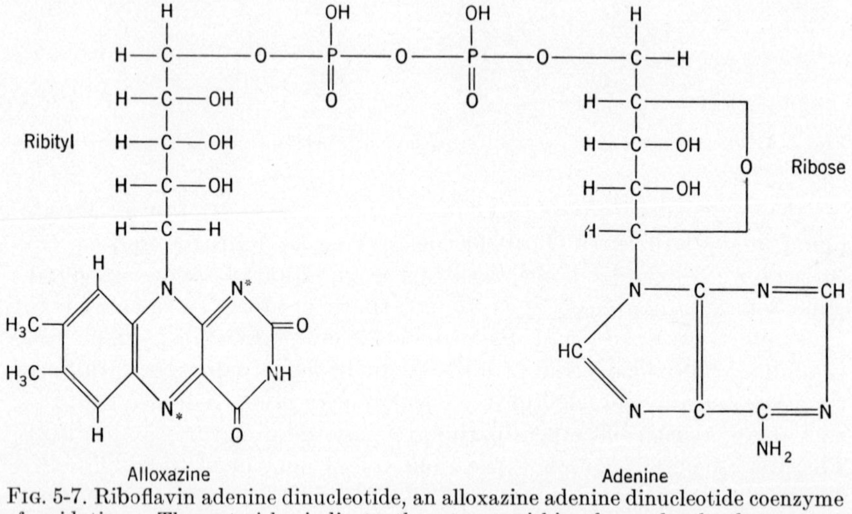

Fig. 5-7. Riboflavin adenine dinucleotide, an alloxazine adenine dinucleotide coenzyme of oxidation. The asterisks indicate the atoms within the molecule that accept hydrogen and electrons.

bacteria where it apparently serves as a coenzyme in the metabolism of α-keto acids in reactions other than the decarboxylation induced by yeast. α-Lipoic acid (Fig. 5-9), also known as thioctic acid, the acetate replacement factor, or the pyruvate oxidation factor, is associated with it to give lipothiamide pyrophosphate, which appears to act as a cocarboxylase in many organisms. It has also been reported to undergo reduction

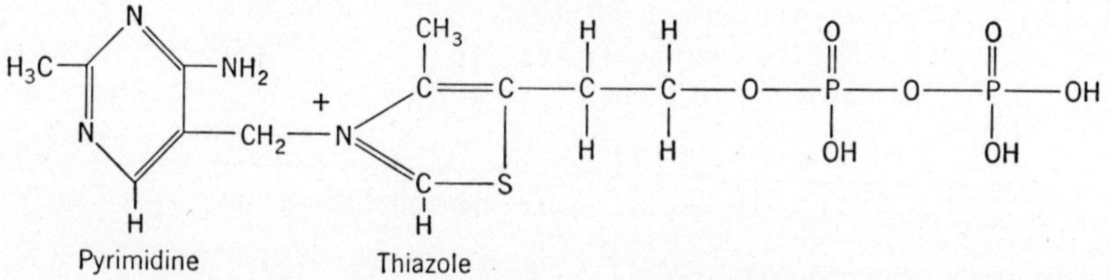

FIG. 5-8. Thiamine pyrophosphate, a pyridine-phosphorylated thiazole coenzyme, the cocarboxylase of pyruvic acid decarboxylation by yeast.

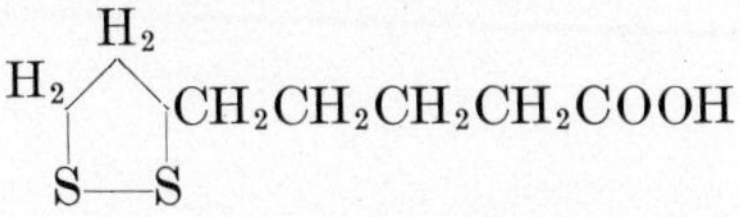

FIG. 5-9. α-Lipoic acid, a compound associated with thiamine pyrophosphate to yield lipothiamide pyrophosphate, which is active in the oxidative decarboxylation of α-keto acids. Hydrogen and electrons are taken up by the sulfur atoms, and the bridge between them is broken on reduction.

during the oxidation of pyruvate, lipoic acid dehydrogenase then transferring hydrogen to DPN.

Other coenzymes have been recognized in recent years, and many appear to be involved in group transfer. Pyridoxal phosphate (Fig. 5-10) and its amine, pyridoxamine phosphate, were recognized as natural forms of vitamin B_6 by Snell in 1942. It soon became apparent that pyridoxal phosphate acts as a coenzyme involved in transamination, the transfer of amino groups to a keto acid. It is also a prosthetic group for amino acid decarboxylases and appears to be involved in other reactions of amino acids.

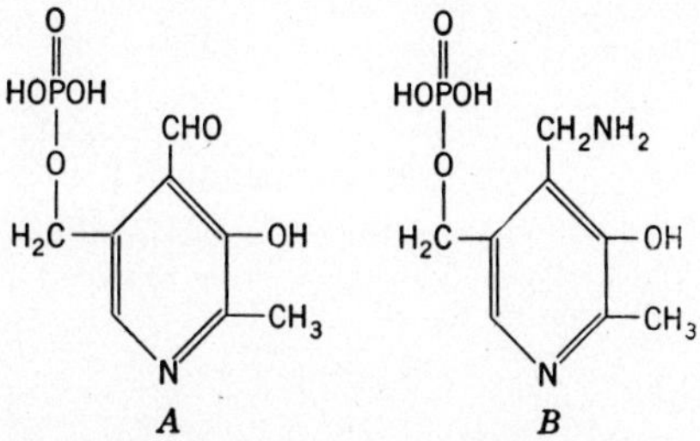

FIG. 5-10. Pyridoxal-5-phosphate (A), an amino acid cocarboxylase, and (B) pyridoxamine-5-phosphate, which may serve as a transaminase.

Coenzyme A (Fig. 5-11), which contains pantothenic acid (Lipman, 1953), is the prosthetic group in enzymes of acetic acid metabolism involving "active acetate" and the transfer of such groups. It also serves as coenzyme for the transfer of acyl groups in general. Folic acid (Fig. 5-12) appears to be involved in purine and pyrimidine synthesis, vitamin B_{12} in the linkage of purine and pyrimidine bases with deoxyribose, and inositol possibly with amylases. Uridine diphosphate glucose (Fig. 5-13) has been found to be a coenzyme for the reaction

Galactose-1-phosphate $\rightleftarrows$ glucose-1-phosphate

in which the uridine diphosphate is transferred to galactose phosphate, a change in configuration occurs around carbon atom 4 of galactose, and

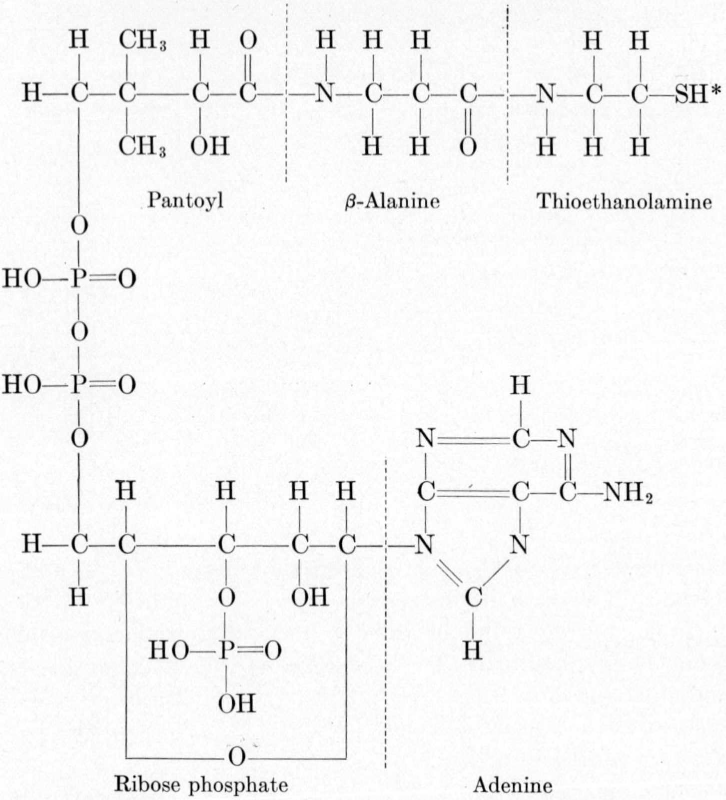

FIG. 5-11. Coenzyme A, a carrier for acetyl and other acyl groups. The asterisk indicates the hydrogen atom replaced by acetyl (or other groups) to give acetyl coenzyme A, R—S—COCH₃.

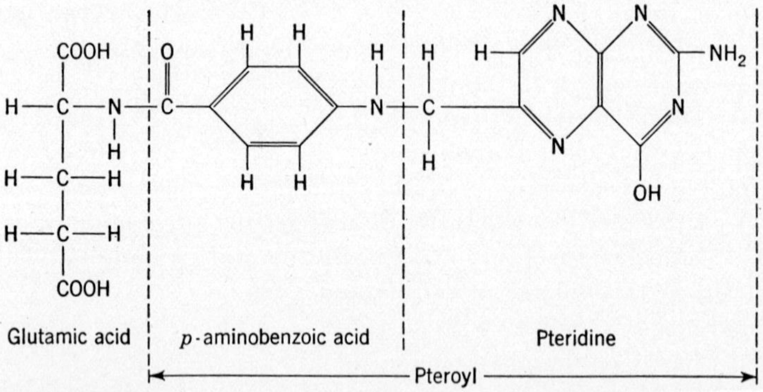

FIG. 5-12. Folic acid, one of the pteroyl glutamates serving as a growth factor for various bacteria and apparently involved in the synthesis of amino acids and of thymine and purine bases.

uridine diphosphate glucose is formed as a result of the conversion.   This coenzyme also may react with fructose to yield sucrose and the uridine diphosphate.   Other coenzyme systems probably will be discovered as bacterial and other enzymes are studied more fully.   Hematin (Fig. 5-14)

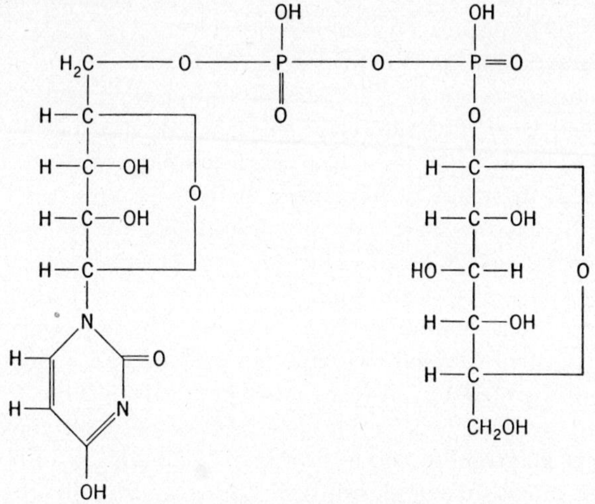

FIG. 5-13. Uridine diphosphate glucose, a uracil nucleotide coenzyme involved in the conversion of galactose-1-phosphate to glucose-1-phosphate and in transglycosidation reactions.

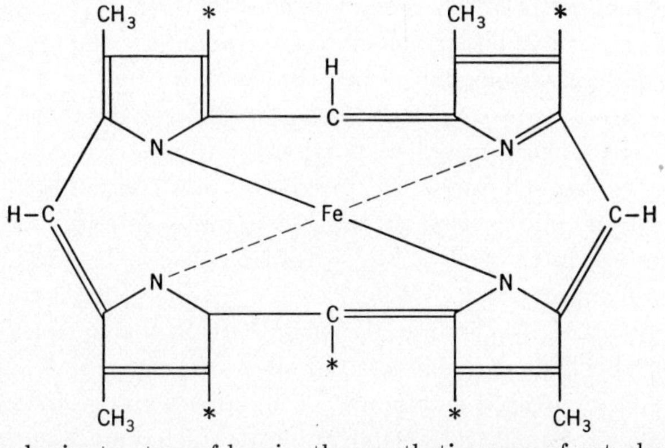

FIG. 5-14. The basic structure of hemin, the prosthetic group of cytochrome oxidase, catalase, and peroxidase.   Side chains, indicated by asterisks, may differ in different enzymes.   The same basic structure is present in chlorophyll, Mg replacing Fe as the metallic constituent.

and bacterial chlorophyll may also be regarded as coenzymes, but these prosthetic groups are bound more firmly to their enzymes than the other coenzymes considered above.   Hematin is particularly important, being found in catalase, cytochrome, and apparently in certain dehydrogenases and in nitrate reductase.

Many of the coenzymes are composed of, or contain as constituent parts, substances commonly known as vitamins or growth factors. This is undoubtedly the important role of the growth factors, the provision of chemical structures needed in the coenzymes and other chemically functioning constituents of the cell and which the cell is unable to synthesize for itself. This hypothesis will be considered further in the discussion of growth factors. The apoenzyme carries substrate specificity, is also a protein specific (serologically) for the species producing it, and therefore must be formed as such by the cell; coenzymes are not species-specific and can, therefore, be utilized as such if they gain entrance into the cell.

The Study of Enzymes in Bacteria. A few enzymes, the extracellular or exoenzymes, characteristically are found outside the cell and bring about the hydrolysis of large molecules into smaller ones that can be taken up by the cell. Centrifugation or filtration through bacteria-retaining filters (e.g., Chamberland, Berkefeld, or fine sintered-glass filters) serves to furnish a cell-free enzyme preparation which can be concentrated and purified by physical and chemical methods. Gelatinase, cellulase, and amylase can serve as examples of exoenzymes, and the liquefaction of gelatin and the hydrolysis of cellulose or of starch can be demonstrated in cultures of appropriate bacteria, or in filtrates from these cultures.

The ability of a species to utilize a particular substrate can be demonstrated by chemical methods using cultures or washed suspensions of the test bacterium. Washed suspensions are frequently spoken of as resting cells or resting-cell suspensions since the cells, washed in saline or buffer solution to remove adsorbed foodstuff and then separated from the suspension by centrifugation, are suspended for test purposes in buffer solutions free of combined nitrogen to prevent multiplication of the cells. The term resting cells as used by the physiologist should not be confused with the same term as used by the cytologist, the latter's usage referring to cells in a dormant state. When a substrate is utilized by intact cells and not by filtrates, it is commonly assumed that utilization is due to the presence of specific intracellular enzymes or endoenzymes. Enzyme activity can be expressed as amount of chemical change in unit time per unit of enzyme. Since the actual amount of enzyme cannot be determined, it is necessary to express units in arbitrary terms.

Permeability is at times a factor in the study of bacterial metabolism. Citric acid, for example, is not oxidized at an appreciable rate by *E. coli* in cultures or washed suspensions, but it can be oxidized by dehydrated cells. A cell paste can be treated in the cold with acetone to dehydrate the cells, and such a dried preparation is capable of carrying out a number of reactions, including the oxidation of citric acid. The enzymes often can be extracted from such preparations on incubation in appropriate buffer solution, and some of them can be separated from each other by precipitation or adsorption and elution methods. Typical procedures are outlined by Umbreit, Burris, and Stauffer (1949).

Some enzymes can be extracted from the cell debris obtained on treatment with enzymes such as pepsin, trypsin, papain, or lysozyme or after disintegration of the cells (Hugo, 1954) by various grinding methods or by ultrasonic vibration. In some instances reactions occurring within the bacterial cell cannot be duplicated with cellular extracts, either the enzyme being inactivated in the procedure or organized structures such as mitochondria (Green, 1951) being required for the series of reactions in which the enzyme is a constituent part. Further consideration of bacterial enzymes will be included under discussions of individual enzymes or the reactions they catalyze. Considerable information regarding the influence of various factors on the activity of enzymes in the cell or in cellular extracts has been obtained and is discussed below.

pH. The hydrogen-ion concentration of the medium has a marked influence on the activity of enzymes either in the cell or in a purified state. There is an optimum pH or pH range for every enzyme, and at values greater or less than the optimum, enzyme activity decreases. In a very few instances, two optima may be recognized. When the concentration of hydrogen or of hydroxyl ions is too high, the enzyme can be inactivated. A complicating factor with intact bacteria is their varying degree of permeability with pH for the substrate, particularly substrates that dissociate and may be taken up most readily in the nonionized state. The union between ionized substrates and their enzymes is influenced by different degrees of ionization of the partners, making it necessary to determine whether the effect of pH is on the enzyme or the substrate. The optimum pH for the activity of a proteolytic enzyme, for example, does vary with the nature of its substrate. Ions, other than the hydrogen or hydroxyl ones, also influence the activity of an enzyme, and therefore the salts and their concentration in a buffer should be specified along with the pH value. Typical pH- and temperature-enzyme activity relationships are presented in Fig. 5-15.

Temperature. Just as there is an optimum pH for the activity of a particular enzyme, likewise there is an optimum temperature or temperature range. Enzyme activity ordinarily increases with temperature in a manner analogous to that discussed for other chemical reactions in Chap. 2, doubling or trebling with each 10°C. increase in temperature. In other words the Q_{10} value is in the neighborhood of 2 to 3 as determined by the ratio of the velocity constants of the reaction, K_1 and K_2, at temperatures T_1 and T_2 that are 10°C. apart. It is frequently observed that the apparent energy of activation μ [equation (2-22)] has a smaller value in enzymatically catalyzed reactions. In the decomposition of hydrogen peroxide by catalase the value of μ is about 2,000 cal., near 12,000 when catalyzed by colloidal palladium, and about 18,000 in the absence of a catalyst.   Some enzymes may exhibit slight activity at temperatures below the freezing point of water if free water is present.   The rate of enzyme activity rapidly decreases at temperatures above the optimum, and at still higher temperatures the enzyme is inactivated.   Heat inactivation follows a course similar to that for the heat inactivation or denaturation of proteins in general, and similar Q_{10} values for inactivation are observed.   These values may be as high as 100 or more at 60 to 70°C. In general, union of substrate and enzyme tends to confer increased heat stability upon the latter.   One unexplained phenomenon is the greater heat resistance of certain enzymes from thermophilic bacteria, the same enzymes from ordinary bacteria generally being much less heat-stable.

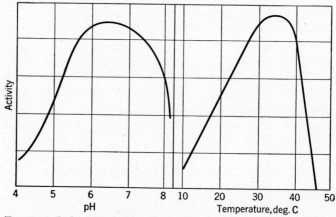

Fig. 5-15. Influence of pH and of temperature on enzyme activity.

Enzyme and Substrate Concentration.   In general the rate of enzyme activity is proportional to the concentration of the enzyme as long as substrate is present in amounts sufficient to keep the enzyme saturated. This, of course, holds true only if all other factors are maintained constant and if products of the reaction are not inhibitory.   The production of ethyl alcohol, for example, is inhibited by the accumulation of alcohol in the fermentation mixture.

Likewise the rate of enzyme activity is in most instances proportional to the substrate concentration when the latter is present in low amounts. When the concentration of the substrate is increased beyond a relatively definite value for a given system, the reaction velocity increases less rapidly with substrate concentration and slowly approaches a maximum value.   Still higher concentrations may be inhibitory, often as a result of osmotic-pressure effects, or depletion of available water.   Some enzymes are saturated at low substrate concentrations, others at only relatively high ones. This behavior is employed in the characterization of an enzyme and can be expressed numerically in terms of the Michaelis constant K_m.

When the activity (velocity of reaction) of an arbitrarily selected concentration $[E]$ of an enzyme is plotted against substrate concentration, as in Fig. 5-16, the concentration at which the rate of reaction is equal to one-half the maximum rate has a numerical value equal to K_m. This relationship can be illustrated by the following considerations suggested by Michaelis and Menten in 1913 on the basis of the law of mass action and chemical kinetics. It is apparent in Fig. 5-16 that the velocity v of the enzymatically catalyzed reaction increases rapidly at first with increase in substrate concentration, less rapidly with further increases in concentration, and slowly approaches a limiting and maximum velocity that can be represented by V. Michaelis and Menten assumed that an unstable and highly reactive complex was formed between enzyme and substrate and that the observed velocity was a resultant of the velocities of three separate reactions, the reversible union of enzyme E and of substrate S and the breakdown of ES to yield E and the reaction product P. These equations, together with the velocity constants of the reactions and the concentrations of the reactants (represented in brackets), can be expressed as

$$\text{Enzyme} + \text{substrate} \underset{k_2}{\overset{k_1}{\rightleftarrows}} \text{complex} \overset{k_3}{\rightarrow} \text{reaction product}$$

$$[E - ES] + [S] \rightleftarrows [ES] \rightarrow [P] \tag{5-1}$$

When the system is in equilibrium, we can write on the basis of the law of mass action applied to reactions 1 and 2 that

$$[S][E - ES]k_1 = [ES]k_2 \tag{5-2}$$

and therefore

$$\frac{[S][E - ES]}{[ES]} = \frac{k_2}{k_1} = K_m \tag{5-3}$$

The reaction velocity v at any substrate concentration will be proportional to the concentration $[ES]$ of the complex, or

$$v = k_3[ES] \tag{5-4}$$

When the enzyme is fully saturated and the substrate is present in marked excess, most of the enzyme will be present in the complex ES, practically no enzyme remaining in the free state. The concentration of free enzyme $[E - ES]$ will therefore be negligible, and the rate of reaction will have its maximum value V. On the basis of this assumption, and since we cannot determine experimentally the value of $[ES]$, we can conclude that the maximum velocity under these conditions is proportional to the total concentration $[E]$ of the enzyme, assuming that it is all present in the combined form, or

$$V = k_3[E] \tag{5-5}$$

The constant k_3 represents the maximum number of substrate molecules one enzyme molecule can cause to react in unit time. Its numerical value was termed the turnover number by Warburg. On dividing equation (5-4) by equation (5-5) we obtain

$$\frac{v}{V} = \frac{[ES]}{[E]} \tag{5-6}$$

which indicates that the ratio of the velocity v of the reaction at any substrate concentration to the maximum velocity V is equal to the ratio obtained on dividing the respective enzyme-substrate concentrations, i.e., $[ES]$ by $[E]$.

Numerical values of $[E]$ and of $[ES]$ cannot be determined experimentally, but the velocity at any substrate concentration and the maximum velocity can be determined. The ratio v/V can then be calculated and its value substituted for the ratio $[ES]/[E]$ in our equations. Equation (5-3) can be rearranged to give

$$[S] = \frac{[ES]}{[E]} ([S] + K_m) \tag{5-7}$$

and on substituting v/V for $[ES]/[E]$ we obtain

$$[S] = \frac{v}{V} ([S] + K_m) \tag{5-8}$$

Substrate concentrations and velocities of reaction can be determined and their values substituted in equation (5-8), leaving K_m as the only unknown. Its value can be calculated most readily if equation (5-8) is rearranged to the form

$$K_m = [S] \left(\frac{V}{v} - 1 \right) \tag{5-9}$$

It is apparent from equation (5-9) that K_m is equal to $[S]$ when the substrate concentration is such that the velocity of the reaction is equal to one-half the maximum velocity, or

$$K_m = [S] \quad \text{if } \frac{V}{v} = 2 \tag{5-10}$$

Knowing the value of K_m, it is possible to calculate the velocity of the reaction at any substrate concentration. This can be done most readily if equation (5-8) is rearranged to solve for v, or

$$v = \frac{V[S]}{[S] + K_m} \tag{5-11}$$

When v has a value one-half that of V, substitution in equation (5-11) would again show that $K_m = [S]$, or, in other words, the Michaelis constant K_m is numerically equal to the substrate concentration when the reaction velocity is one-half the maximum. Equation (5-11) enables one to calculate the effect of substrate concentration on the velocity of the reaction, all other factors being maintained constant. Referring to Fig. 5-16, the plot of reaction velocity against time is seen to be that of a rectangular hyperbola which is expressed by equation (5-11), and K_m can be determined directly from the graph.

Deviations from the behavior expressed by equation (5-11) are encountered in experimental work, but in general the behavior predicted on the basis of the equation agrees quite closely with the observed one. It is necessary to determine the velocities as soon as possible after mixing enzyme and substrate in order to prevent both marked change in substrate concentration and any inhibitory effect of products of the reaction. The agreement between observed

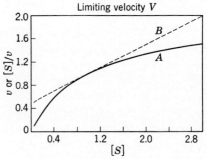

Fig. 5-16. Hypothetical plots (A) of velocity v of enzymatic activity, and (B) of $[S]/v$ against concentration $[S]$ of substrate. The point at which the two lines touch is equal to K_m [equation (5-10)] on the $[S]$ axis and is 1.0 in this example.

and predicted influences of substrate concentration on enzymatic activity lends further support to the concept advanced by Michaelis that enzyme and substrate form an unstable, highly reactive complex.

The value of K_m also gives a clue to the affinity of an enzyme for a substrate, the lower the value the greater the affinity. At 35°C. maltase has a K_m value of approximately 0.2 mole per liter, that for invertase acting on raffinose is 0.4 and on sucrose 0.02, while certain dehydrogenases have K_m values less than 1×10^{-6}. Also, the lower the value of K_m, the more readily the reaction occurs in dilute solutions of the substrate. When an enzyme is active against more than one substrate (see invertase above), one can determine the relative affinities of the enzyme for the different substrates. In those instances where a substrate is still utilized after substitution of different chemical groups in the molecule, it is possible to determine the influence of the substituent groups on enzymatic activity.

Such applications, at times, are of value in the study of inhibitory or possible chemotherapeutical agents.

Just as enzyme and substrate concentrations influence reaction velocity, so likewise the concentration of cells and of foodstuffs influences the growth and activity of bacteria. The K_m values for different substrates may indicate the important role specific enzymes play in determining the shape or slope of growth curves for cultures of bacteria in different media.

Inhibition. Enzymes in general can be poisoned by agents that induce irreversible denaturation of proteins. Those agents which, in appropriate concentrations, bring about a reversible inactivation or inhibition of enzyme activity are of more interest in enzymology. There are two classes of agents which reversibly inhibit enzymatic activity, *competitive inhibitors* and *noncompetitive inhibitors*, and these agents play an important role in the study of growth-factor analogues, bacteriostasis, and chemotherapy.

The classical example of competitive inhibition is the inhibition of succinic acid dehydrogenase activity by malonic acid. It is relatively easy to obtain a preparation of succinic acid dehydrogenase and to measure its activity in terms of rate of reduction of methylene blue. When malonic acid is added to the system the rate of oxidation of succinate to fumarate is reduced, but it increases if the concentration of succinate is increased. Malonic acid, $COOHCH_2COOH$, is structurally related to succinic acid, $COOHCH_2CH_2COOH$, and combines with the active site of the succinic acid dehydrogenase. It is not activated, and therefore the enzyme-malonate complex effectively removes some of the enzyme from participation in the oxidation of succinate. The reactions can be pictured as follows:

$$E \Big\langle \begin{array}{l} + \ S \rightleftarrows ES + MB \rightleftarrows E + F + MB{\cdot}2H \\ + \ M \rightleftarrows EM \end{array}$$

where E is the enzyme, S, F, and M succinic, fumaric, and malonic acids, and MB is methylene blue. According to the law of mass action and the preceding considerations of the influence of substrate concentration on enzymatic activity, the rate of succinate oxidation is dependent upon the concentration of the enzyme-substrate complex ES. The rate of oxidation, in the presence of a constant amount of enzyme, can be increased within limits by increasing the concentration of succinate and, therefore, of enzyme-succinate complex. The concentration of ES is reduced by an amount EM in the presence of malonate, and the rate of succinate oxidation, therefore, decreases. Increasing the concentration of S would diminish the effect of M and lead to an increased rate of reaction. Malonate and succinate compete with each other for the enzyme, the relative amounts of each in combination with the enzyme control the rate of oxidation and therefore the inhibition is a competitive one. Another example of competitive inhibition is that of the sulfanilamides for an enzyme involved in the utilization of *p*-aminobenzoic acid. This, and similar competitions, will be considered in Chap. 18 under the mode of action of chemotherapeutical agents.

Noncompetitive inhibitors reversibly inactivate enzymes by combination with, or by reaction upon, groups essential for the activity of the enzyme, but not necessarily ones involved in the actual combination of enzyme and substrate. Cyanide, sulfide, sodium azide, and carbon monoxide are inhibitors for the activity of iron-containing enzymes and mercury or silver for enzymes in which sulfhydryl (—SH) groups are active. Cytochrome oxidase is inhibited by carbon monoxide in the dark, but this inhibition is reversed in the light, light apparently breaking down an iron-monoxide complex. Likewise the inhibitory action of mercury may be reversed by hydrogen sulfide which precipitates the mercury as the sulfide or by compounds such as BAL which bind mercury. The activity of succinate dehydrogenase is reduced by oxygen or other oxidizing agents which bring about the oxidation of —SH groups to the —S—S— state. Succinic and a number of other dehydrogenases are active only when the sulfur is present in the reduced state, —SH, and the oxidation of these groups in enzyme preparations can be prevented by the addition of reducing agents such as reduced glutathione or thioglycolic acid to the medium. The sulfhydryl groups do not appear to be involved in the union of these enzymes with their substrates, the relative amounts of poison and of substrate do not influence the inhibition, and therefore the inhibition is a noncompetitive one.

Classification of Enzymes. The names first applied to enzymes give no clue as to the activity of the enzymes or to the substrates upon which they are active. Pepsin, trypsin, emulsin, and zymase are terms which have no connection with the reactions or substrates involved and are employed for historical reasons only. Since our knowledge of the exact nature of enzymes is very limited, the chemical changes which they elicit are used as a basis for nomenclature and classification. At least three systems of nomenclature have been employed, and these in brief are as follows: (1) combining the termination -*ase* with a name indicating the substrate upon which the enzyme acts, e.g., amylase, urease, and protease; (2) combining -*ase* with the name of one of the end products of the reactions, e.g., alcoholase and glucase; and (3) combining -*ase* with a base indicating the nature of the reaction, e.g., oxidase, dehydrogenase, reductase, and invertase. Whenever possible it is desirable to use a name indicating the substrate and type of reaction involved, examples being lactic acid dehydrogenase, saccharophosphorylase, and cytochrome oxidase. It must be remembered that many enzymatically catalyzed reactions are reversible ones and that the same enzyme is involved in either the forward or the reverse reaction. The lactic acid dehydrogenase system catalyzing the oxidation of lactate to pyruvate can bring about the reduction of pyruvic acid to lactic acid under suitable conditions. The presence of hundreds of enzymes within a cell makes it necessary to consider their general types of action rather than each enzyme separately. Furthermore, the particular enzymic content of a cell may vary with its age, with the nature of the medium, and with variation in genetic composition of the species (Chap. 15). The types of reaction catalyzed remain more or less the same.

No attempt will be made to classify enzymes in any complete manner. The broadest classification, based upon five major types of enzymatic activity, gives *splitting*, *oxidizing*, *adding*, *isomerizing*, and *transferring* enzymes which catalyze the corresponding types of reaction. The cell is frequently confronted with the necessity of cleaving large molecules into smaller ones, of altering the molecular structure of a metabolite, of adding groups to a molecule, and of transferring groups between pairs of molecules. The oxidizing enzymes will be considered in the following chapter, the other types will be illustrated here, and all will be encountered in considerations of the various and multitudinous activities of the living cell.

The splitting enzymes, i.e., the hydrolases and phosphorylases, catalyze the hydrolytic or the phosphorolytic splitting of polysaccharides, fats, or proteins into simpler molecules and, under appropriate conditions, the reverse reactions. The phosphorylases are much more active in the reverse, or synthetic, reactions than are the hydrolases. The hydrolases act in conjunction with water, the phosphorylases with phosphoric acid, or

$$R—R' + HOH \rightleftarrows R—OH + R'H$$

and

$$R—R' + ⑭OH \rightleftarrows R—O⑭ + HR'$$

where ⑭ represents $—PO_3H_2$ (or its ionized form).

A third type of splitting reaction may occur in which no substance is added to the substrate molecule. This reaction can be represented as

$$R—R' \rightleftarrows R + R'$$

This reaction, considered in reverse, is actually an adding reaction, the adding enzyme catalyzing the addition of a molecule R' to R. The R' molecule can be water, ammonia, carbon dioxide, or other substances.

Typical reactions catalyzed by the adding enzymes are:

$$
\begin{array}{c}
\text{COOH} \\
| \\
\text{CH} \\
\| \quad + H_2O \\
\text{CH} \\
| \\
\text{COOH}
\end{array}
\xrightleftharpoons{\text{fumarase}}
\begin{array}{c}
\text{COOH} \\
| \\
\text{CH}_2 \\
| \\
\text{CHOH} \\
| \\
\text{COOH}
\end{array}
$$

Fumaric acid   Malic acid

$$
\begin{array}{c}
\text{CH}_2 \\
\| \\
\text{CO} \sim \text{\textcircled{P}} + H_2O \\
| \\
\text{COOH}
\end{array}
\xrightleftharpoons{\text{enolase}}
\begin{array}{c}
\text{CH}_2\text{OH} \\
| \\
\text{CHO\textcircled{P}} \\
| \\
\text{COOH}
\end{array}
$$

Enol-phosphopyruvic   2-Phosphoglyceric
acid   acid

$$
\begin{array}{c}
\text{COOH} \\
| \\
\text{CH} \\
\| \quad + NH_3 \\
\text{CH} \\
| \\
\text{COOH}
\end{array}
\xrightleftharpoons{\text{aspartase}}
\begin{array}{c}
\text{COOH} \\
| \\
\text{CH}_2 \\
| \\
\text{CHNH}_2 \\
| \\
\text{COOH}
\end{array}
$$

Fumaric acid   Aspartic acid

$$
\begin{array}{c}
\text{COOH} \\
| \\
\text{CH}_2 \\
| \\
\text{CH}_2 \quad + CO_2 \\
| \\
\text{C}=\text{O} \\
| \\
\text{COOH}
\end{array}
\xrightleftharpoons[\text{decarboxylase}]{\text{oxalosuccinic}}
\begin{array}{c}
\text{COOH} \\
| \\
\text{CH}_2 \\
| \\
\text{CH}-\text{COOH} \\
| \\
\text{C}=\text{O} \\
| \\
\text{COOH}
\end{array}
$$

α-Ketoglutaric acid   Oxalosuccinic acid

Some of the decarboxylase enzymes, e.g., the pyruvic and probably the oxalacetic acid decarboxylases, do not appear to react reversibly in the absence of a source of energy.

Isomerizing enzymes, the isomerases and mutases, bring about an intramolecular rearrangement or isomerization such as that of dihydroxyacetone phosphate to 3-phosphoglyceraldehyde, or

$$
\begin{array}{c}
\text{CH}_2\text{O\textcircled{P}} \\
| \\
\text{C}=\text{O} \\
| \\
\text{CH}_2\text{OH}
\end{array}
\xrightleftharpoons[\text{isomerase}]{\text{phosphotriose}}
\begin{array}{c}
\text{CH}_2\text{O\textcircled{P}} \\
| \\
\text{CHOH} \\
| \\
\text{CHO}
\end{array}
$$

and of 3-phosphoglyceric to 2-phosphoglyceric acid, or

$$
\begin{array}{ccc}
CH_2O\textcircled{P} & & CH_2OH \\
| & & | \\
CHOH & \xrightarrow{\text{phosphoglyceromutase}} & CHO\textcircled{P} \\
| & \longleftarrow & | \\
COOH & & COOH
\end{array}
$$

The function of the isomerizing enzymes appears to be alteration of molecular structure to better fit the compound for a particular reaction carried out by the cell.

A number of catalytic systems have been discovered in recent years in which the function of the enzymes is the transfer of a group or radical from one molecular species to another.   Actually, the dehydrogenase systems could be considered as transferring enzymes, but we will limit the discussion to those enzymes involved in the transfer of groups such as amino-, methyl-, acetyl-, or phosphate or such units as glucose.

Transaminases in bacteria were first described by Lichstein and Cohen (1944), who demonstrated that an amino group could be transferred from glutamic acid to oxalacetic acid with the formation of α-ketoglutaric and aspartic acids.   This reaction is reversible and appears to be mediated by pyridoxal phosphate as the coenzyme or carrier of the amino group. The reaction can be represented as

Glutamic acid + pyridoxal $\textcircled{P}$ $\rightleftarrows$ α-ketoglutaric acid + pyridoxamine $\textcircled{P}$

Pyridoxamine $\textcircled{P}$ + oxalacetic acid $\rightleftarrows$ pyridoxal $\textcircled{P}$ + aspartic acid

It is probable that two enzymes are involved, one with glutamic acid, the other with oxalacetic acid.   Many amino acids will act as amino donors to α-ketoglutaric acid with the formation of glutamic acid.   This amino acid acts as a rather general amino group donor to α-keto acids with the formation of other amino acids.   A well-known reaction is the transfer of an amino group from glutamate to pyruvate with the formation of alanine.

Transmethylation has not been studied to any extent with bacteria, but there is evidence that it can occur.   The best-known example of biological methylation is the transfer of a methyl group from methionine to glycocyamine (guanidoacetic acid, $HN{-}CNH_2NHCH_2COOH$) with the formation of creatine and homocysteine.   The transfer of acetyl, formyl, succinyl, and other acyl groups also appears to be involved in many biological reactions.

A number of bacteria possess an enzyme, sucrose phosphorylase, which catalyzes the phosphorolytic splitting of sucrose to glucose-1-phosphate and fructose (Hassid, Doudoroff, and Barker, 1951).   This enzyme when catalyzing the reverse reaction brings about the synthesis of sucrose.   The reaction can be represented as

$$\text{Glucose-1-}\textcircled{P} + \text{sucrose phosphorylase} \rightleftarrows \text{glucose-enzyme} + \textcircled{P}$$

and

$$\text{Glucose-enzyme} + \text{fructose} \rightleftarrows \text{sucrose} + \text{enzyme}$$

In these reactions it can be seen that the sucrose phosphorylase acts as either a glucose acceptor or donor and the reaction can be considered as a transfer of glucose. This enzyme can catalyze the transfer of glucose from many different disaccharides to monosaccharides with the formation of another disaccharide, e.g.,

$$\text{Sucrose} + \text{sorbose} \rightleftarrows \text{D-glucose-1-sorboside} + \text{fructose}$$

Sucrose phosphorylase, acting in this manner, is related to a group of bacterial enzymes which catalyze the synthesis of polysaccharides without the participation of glucose-1-$\textcircled{P}$. These enzymes catalyze the exchange of glycosidic linkages of disaccharides for those of polysaccharides and are known as transglycosidases. Bacterial dextrans and levans can be formed from sucrose under the direction of these enzymes as follows:

$$n\text{C}_{12}\text{H}_{22}\text{O}_{11} \rightleftarrows (\text{C}_6\text{H}_{10}\text{O}_5)_n + n\text{C}_6\text{H}_{12}\text{O}_6$$
$$\qquad\text{Sucrose}\qquad\qquad\text{Dextran}\qquad\quad\text{Fructose}$$

and

$$n\text{C}_{12}\text{H}_{22}\text{O}_{11} \rightleftarrows (\text{C}_6\text{H}_{10}\text{O}_5)_n + n\text{C}_6\text{H}_{12}\text{O}_6$$
$$\qquad\text{Sucrose}\qquad\qquad\text{Levan}\qquad\quad\text{Glucose}$$

These, and similar reactions, are of considerable interest since they are involved in the synthesis of complex carbohydrates found in the bacteria and their capsules or slime layers.

Other groups, such as the amidine $\left(-\text{C}\!\!\begin{array}{c}\nearrow \text{NH} \\ \searrow \text{NH}_2 \end{array} \right)$, thiol (—SH), and phosphate groups, can be transferred with the aid of the appropriate enzyme systems. The transfer of phosphate groups, and the high-energy phosphate bonds associated with them, is of particular importance in the provision and transmission of energy in living organisms, as we have noted, and will also be considered in the following chapter.

Enzymes are recognized by what they do, and their activities can be expressed and understood more readily as we consider the reactions they catalyze. It is the function of the enzymes to activate the foodstuff molecules and their dissimilation products and to so direct the reactions they undergo that energy and building materials are made available in an orderly manner for the cells.

REFERENCES

General

Laidler, K. J.: "Introduction to the Chemistry of Enzymes," McGraw-Hill Book Company, Inc., New York, 1954.

Lardy, H. A. (ed.): "Respiratory Enzymes," Burgess Publishing Co., Minneapolis, 1949.

Neilands, J. B., P. K. Stumpf, and R. Y. Stanier: "Outlines of Enzyme Chemistry," John Wiley & Sons, Inc., New York, 1955.

Sumner, J. B., and K. Myrbäck (eds.): "The Enzymes," 2 vols., 2 pts., Academic Press Inc., New York, 1950–1951.

Specific

Green, D. E.: The cyclophorase complex of enzymes, *Biol. Rev. Camb. Phil. Soc.*, **26**, 410–455 (1951).

Hassid, W. Z., M. Doudoroff, and H. A. Barker: Phosphorylases, phosphorolysis and synthesis of saccharides, in "The Enzymes," vol. 1, pt. 2, chap. 31, Academic Press, Inc., New York, 1951.

Hugo, W. B.: The preparation of cell-free enzymes from microorganisms, *Bacteriol. Rev.*, **18**, 87–105 (1954).

Kaplan, N. O.: Thermodynamics and mechanism of the phosphate bond, in "The Enzymes," vol. 2, pt. 1, chap. 45, Academic Press, Inc., New York, 1951.

Lichstein, H. C., and P. P. Cohen: Transamination in bacteria, *J. Biol. Chem.*, **157**, 85–91 (1944).

Lipman, F.: On chemistry and function of coenzyme A, *Bacteriol. Rev.*, **17**, 1–16 (1953).

McElroy, W. D., and B. Glass (eds.): "The Mechanism of Enzyme Action," Johns Hopkins Press, Baltimore, 1954.

——— and A. Nason: Mechanism of action of micronutrient elements in enzyme systems, *Ann. Rev. Plant Physiol.*, **5**, 1–30 (1954).

Smith, E. L.: Catalytic action of the metal peptidases, *Federation Proc.*, **8**, 581–588 (1949).

Umbreit, W. W., R. H. Burris, and J. F. Stauffer: "Manometric Techniques and Tissue Metabolism," Burgess Publishing Co., Minneapolis, 1949.

CHAPTER 6

BIOLOGICAL OXIDATION

The formation and maintenance of the bacterial cell require the provision of a considerable amount of energy. The chemical reactions through which energy is made available to the cell are included collectively under the general term *biological oxidation* as employed in its broadest sense. The living cell, considered from a physiochemical point of view, is a complicated transformer of energy and matter through which a continual flux of energy passes, and the entire life of a cell can be considered as an expression of alterations or variations in the rate of energy flow. No artificial system has yet been devised of so complicated a nature as a cell or possessed of such a degree of internal coordination and ability to adapt itself to change. During the course of the dissimilatory or catabolic reactions, some compounds are formed of higher free-energy content than their precursors. This increase in free energy of an oxidant is inherent in an oxidation-reduction reaction of the type

$$DH_2 + A = D + AH_2$$

in which DH_2 undergoes an energy loss while the free energy of A is increased to the level of AH_2. Some compounds formed during the course of dissimilation of a substrate may serve as building blocks for the synthesis of more complex molecules and structures. The energy-providing reactions, therefore, are not always separate from the assimilatory or anabolic ones. The term *metabolism* applies not only to the actual energy-providing reactions but also to all those reactions, assimilatory and dissimilatory, involved in the aerobic or anaerobic utilization of foodstuff. No sharp line of demarcation can be established between the anabolic and the catabolic activities of a cell.

Bacterial life is accompanied by a continuous series of oxidations, aerobic or anaerobic, and an understanding of the processes involved necessitates a consideration of oxidation-reduction reactions and of the enzymatic mechanisms involved. Concepts of both factors have undergone marked change over the years. The original concept of oxidation was an uptake of oxygen by the substance being oxidized. This was broadened to include either the gain of oxygen or the loss of hydrogen and ultimately to a loss of electrons as well. The loss of an electron, or electrons, is the feature common to all oxidations, although, for convenience, we ordinarily picture biological oxidations in terms of hydrogen loss and the concomitant reductions as hydrogen gains.

Energy from light is converted in the green plant to chemical-bond energy, and the energy inherent in these bonds can be released when they are broken. This, however, is not the whole story since the free energy of an oxidation reaction is also dependent upon the nature of the oxidant (the substance reduced) and is the resultant of two over-all processes. These are the removal of electrons from the sphere of attraction of the atom being oxidized and their passage into that of the oxidant. Energy is actually expended in the first step, released in the second, and the difference is the free energy of the reaction. When acetaldehyde is oxidized to acetic acid, approximately 61,000 cal. are liberated when oxygen is the oxidant and only 5,000 when another molecule of acetaldehyde is the oxidizing agent, this second molecule being reduced to ethyl alcohol. The difference between the two values represents energy stored in chemical bonds in the ethyl alcohol. Oxidations by molecules other than oxygen, and particularly by carbon compounds, yield much less energy than those utilizing oxygen. This is the reason anaerobic life is such a wasteful one.

Oxidation is not a simple reaction; even the oxidation of a simple substance such as carbon monoxide occurs in stages. It has been shown that the following steps are involved:

$$CO + HOH \rightarrow HCOOH$$
$$HCOOH \rightarrow CO_2 + H_2$$
$$H_2 + O_2 \rightarrow HOOH$$

and

$$HOOH \rightarrow HOH + 0.5O_2$$

These reactions proceed most readily at higher temperatures, since heat is required to activate the molecules, while similar reactions in the cell are catalyzed by enzymes and occur at ordinary temperatures. It should be apparent in the above equations that oxygen is not added directly to the monoxide and that the additional oxygen atom in carbon dioxide comes from water, as also do the hydrogen atoms that ultimately are found in the reduced product, water. Oxidations were considered as simpler reactions in the earlier theories of biological oxidation, and stress was placed upon the activation of one of the reactants, either the substrate or oxygen.

Activation of Hydrogen—the Wieland Concept. Wieland, around 1913, began to develop the theory that biological oxidations are dependent upon the activation of hydrogen atoms in the substrate molecule. The fundamental observation upon which Wieland based his theory is that a number of organic molecules are oxidized in the presence of colloidal palladium (palladium black), a substance which has the property of absorbing considerable quantities of hydrogen. Oxidation involved the loss of hydrogen from the organic molecule, and the hydrogen was absorbed by the palladium. The occurrence of this latter reaction could be demonstrated on removing the palladium from the system, either by the liberation of hydrogen on heating the palladium or by transfer of hydrogen to a suitable dye serving as an indicator of reduction. These reactions can be represented as

$$DH_2 + (Pd) \rightarrow D + (Pd)2H \left[\begin{array}{l} + \text{ heat} \rightarrow H_2 \\ + A \rightarrow AH_2 \end{array} \right.$$

where DH_2 is a hydrogen donor and A an acceptor of hydrogen. Reduction of the dye A also occurred when it was added to the mixture of the organic donor and palladium black but not when added to the solution of organic matter alone. These observations indicated that palladium black serves both as a catalyst and as an intermediate carrier of hydrogen. Reactions in which oxygen enters the molecule were explained by Wieland as due to the preliminary formation of a hydrated form of the molecule and subsequent dehydrogenation of the latter. Acetaldehyde, for example, could form a hydrate with water, and this complex then could be oxidized by dehydrogenation, under anaerobic conditions through palladium to a suitable hydrogen acceptor, under aerobic conditions through the palladium to oxygen, or

$$CH_3C \overset{H}{\underset{O}{\diagdown}} + HOH \rightarrow CH_3C \overset{H}{\underset{OH}{\diagup}} OH + (Pd) \rightarrow CH_3C \overset{O}{\underset{OH}{\diagup}} + (Pd)2H$$

and

$$(Pd)2H \left[\begin{array}{l} + A \rightarrow AH_2 + (Pd) \\ + O_2 \rightarrow H_2O_2 + (Pd) \end{array} \right.$$

On the analogy between such reactions and processes which appeared to take place in the cell, Wieland developed his theory of biological oxidations as enzymatic activations and transfers of hydrogen to suitable acceptors.

Dehydrogenase Activity. Wieland's theory was based primarily upon oxidations well known to the organic chemist but ones which are seldom encountered in the living cell. He did carry out a few biological studies such as that of the oxidation of ethanol to acetic acid by dried preparation of acetic acid bacteria, but it was really the studies of Thunberg around

1920 that demonstrated the important role of dehydrogenation in biological oxidations. Thunberg observed that washed, chopped muscle reduced methylene blue very slowly under anaerobic conditions and that the rate of reduction was increased manyfold upon the addition of a substrate such

as succinic acid or glucose. The slow rate of reduction of the dye by the washed tissue alone is due to the oxidation of cellular material. The term *endogenous respiration*[1] (or endogenous oxidation) is applied to the oxidation of intracellular matter, while *exogenous respiration* refers to the utilization of a substrate supplied to the cells. The substrate by itself ordinarily does not reduce methylene blue under the conditions of the experiments.

The Thunberg tube (Fig. 6-1) provides a convenient vessel for the study of dehydrogenase activity, using methylene blue or other suitable oxidation-reduction indicators as the indicator system. It consists of a glass tube provided with an inverted U-shaped hollow stopper with a ground-glass joint and side arm. Cells, buffer, and substrate (none in the endogenous control) are placed in the tube, and the

Fig. 6-1. A Thunberg tube for the study of the reducing activity of tissues and cells. (*Courtesy of the Scientific Glass Apparatus Co.*)

dye in the stopper. The tube is evacuated, filled with an inert gas if desired, and then placed in a constant-temperature bath. The contents are mixed after thermal equilibration, and the time required for reduction of the dye noted. The ability of many tissues and of bacterial and other cells to oxidize various substrates under different conditions, and the influence of different poisons on dehydrogenase activity, have been investigated in this manner. Methylene blue reduction is also used in a rapid, approximate test for the numbers of bacteria in milk (the time required being roughly proportional to the numbers of bacteria), as a test for leucocyte activity, and as

[1] The term respiration frequently is employed in place of oxidation. Strictly speaking, respiration applies to the interchange of the two gases, oxygen and carbon dioxide, between the body and the air. At the cellular level the term respiration has been broadened by many workers to include any chemical reaction that yields energy to the cell, regardless of whether the reaction involves the gaseous exchange mentioned above. Terms such as exogenous respiration, aerobic respiration, anaerobic respiration, and similar ones are encountered in the literature, and the term respiration as employed in this text refers to the broader concept as implied by these terms, i.e., the energy-yielding reactions along with the preparatory reactions involved in the dissimilation of a substrate and its products. In this sense the term respiration has been broadened in meaning much like the change that has occurred in the definition of the term oxidation.

an indicator for reducing or anaerobic conditions in media or in cultures of bacteria. Litmus is both a pH and an oxidation-reduction indicator and has been used in bacteriology for many years in the familiar litmus milk-culture tests for acid and gas production, curd formation, peptonization, and reducing ability of bacteria. The dehydrogenases (those enzymes activating specific hydrogen atoms and electrons in the substrate) present in various species of bacteria have been determined, and also the influence of numbers of bacteria, of age of the cells, of pH, and of cellular poisons on reducing ability has been studied. The technique developed by Thunberg was extensively applied to the study of bacterial respiration by Quastel and others at Cambridge University in the 1920's. Their results will be considered a little later.

Activation of Oxygen—the Warburg Concept. Warburg, on the other hand, developed in the 1920's the theory that activation of oxygen is the important step in biological oxidations; that activated oxygen reacts directly with the substrate; and that it does not act as a simple hydrogen acceptor in the Wieland sense. In a way Warburg's theory was a relatively logical development from earlier theories of biological oxidation in which hypothetical "active oxygen atoms" or highly active organic peroxides were considered to be the important reactant in oxidations by living organisms. In 1921 Warburg noted that alcohols, urethanes, and other narcotics inhibited oxygen uptake, particularly when present in high enough concentrations to form a film of adsorbed molecules over the active centers of respiration. Hydrogen cyanide, and to a lesser extent hydrogen sulfide, were also found to be inhibitory, but in concentrations markedly less than those required to block the enzymes by adsorption. Warburg also found the same relationship to hold with suspensions of blood charcoal capable of oxidizing oxalic acid or certain amino acids. He postulated that the specific effect of cyanide, or sulfide, was on the iron present in blood charcoal and demonstrated that iron-free charcoal had no catalytic effect on these oxidations.

Warburg also noted that carbon monoxide was inhibitory to cellular respiration in the dark and that this inhibition could be reversed either by light or by increased oxygen tensions. It was known at the time that carbon monoxide formed addition compounds with hematin; that this combination was photoreversible; that carbon monoxide and oxygen competed for hemoglobin; and that hematin compounds are widely distributed in nature. On the basis of these facts, and also of his studies showing that the wavelengths of light most effective in restoring the respiratory activity of monoxide-poisoned cells corresponded to the absorption bands of hematin, Warburg concluded that the oxidation enzyme is a derivative of hematin. This iron porphyrin was named the respiratory enzyme (*Atmungsferment*) by Warburg. He concluded "the primary reaction of respiration is the reaction between molecular oxygen and iron, and molecular oxygen can only react in the cell by this reaction, and not with the organic molecules." This reaction was represented as

$$XFe + O_2 \rightarrow XFe\cdot 2O$$

and

$$XFe\cdot 2O + 2A \rightarrow XFe + 2AO$$

This theory, at the time, appeared to give a fairly satisfactory explanation of the method of utilization of oxygen but failed to account for the mecha-

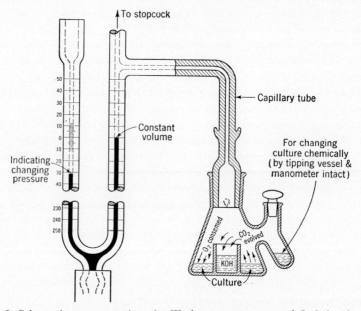

FIG. 6-2. Schematic representation of a Warburg manometer and flask for the study of the gaseous exchange of tissues and cells. (*Courtesy of the American Instrument Co.*)

nism of anaerobic oxidations which could be explained quite simply in terms of Wieland's theory.

Manometry. Warburg quantitatively studied oxygen uptake with the aid of a respirometer system he developed from an earlier type used by Barcroft. The basic feature of the Warburg respirometer, pictured in Fig. 6-2, is that it provides an easy method for the determination of small changes in gas pressure during respiration, these changes being measured at constant temperature and constant volume. Cells, tissues, or extracts are suspended in buffer solution and placed in the main part of a Warburg flask. Substrate is placed in the side arm and potassium hydroxide solution, to absorb carbon dioxide, in the center well. The flask is attached to the manometer, and the latter is fastened to a shaking mechanism in such a manner that the flask is immersed and continuously shaken in a constant-temperature water bath. The system is shaken to promote diffusion of gases and to maintain a uniform suspension. After thermal equilibrium, the fluid in the arm of the manometer to which the flask is attached is adjusted to a fixed level and a reading is made of the position of the manometer fluid in the other arm. The experiment is started by tipping the substrate from the side arm into the cell suspension, and manometer readings are made at appropriate time intervals, the manometer fluid being adjusted to the fixed level before each reading is made. In this manner, pressure changes due to oxygen consumption (the carbon dioxide produced is absorbed by the potassium hydroxide) are measured at constant volume and these readings can be converted, with the aid of an equation based on the gas laws, into volumes of oxygen consumed. Carbon dioxide production or gas exchanges under anaerobic conditions can also be determined by appropriate techniques. The reader is referred to books by Dixon (1934) and by Umbreit, Burris, and Stauffer (1949) for technical information on the use of Warburg respirometers.

The Warburg apparatus is employed in many studies on bacterial respiration, where the consumption and/or production of gas is involved. The results are expressed in terms of total amounts of the different gases consumed or produced, or as rates of gaseous exchange. A common method, particularly valuable for comparative purposes, for expressing rates is in terms of the number of cubic millimeters (microliters, μl.) of a gas consumed or produced per milligram dry weight of cells per hour. Other units can be employed in expressing the value of this quotient Q, and one specifies the conditions of measurement in the Q term in the form $Q_{(\text{gas measured})}^{(\text{gas atmosphere})}$ (cell unit). The term Q_{O_2} indicates the amount (cubic millimeters) of oxygen consumed per milligram dry weight of cells per hour in an atmosphere of air. Q_{O_2} (cell) would indicate the same thing except that the result is expressed as oxygen consumption per cell. The term $Q_{CO_2}^{N_2}$ (C) refers to the cubic millimeters of carbon dioxide produced per milligram of cellular carbon of cells respiring in an atmosphere of nitrogen, and so on. Omission of the gas-atmosphere and the cell-unit terms in the general expression given above signifies that the measurements were made in air and expressed on the dry-weight basis. Mammalian cells generally exhibit Q_{O_2} values of the order of 2 to 10, yeasts and bacteria from 2 to 100 or more, and values as high as 1,000 for *Acetobacter* and 3,000 for *Azotobacter* species have been reported.

Cytochromes. Different workers soon demonstrated that cellular respiration is not inhibited completely by cyanide, and they suggested the existence of iron-free oxidative enzymes. The problem became more complex when Keilin, in 1925, reported the existence of three iron-porphyrin, respiratory pigments that could be demonstrated with the aid of a spectroscope. These pigments were named cytochromes *a*, *b*, and *c* by Keilin. They give characteristic absorption bands when present in the reduced state. Keilin demonstrated that the cytochromes are alternately oxidized and reduced in the cell; that they are reduced and remain in this state in the absence of oxygen or in the presence of cyanide; and that they are not reduced in the presence of cell narcotics. The *a* and *b* cytochromes in particular appear to differ in different species, i.e., somewhat different absorption bands are noted, and these are designated as a_1, a_2, a_3, b_1, and b_2.

The observations outlined above suggested that cytochromes are reduced by the substrate and that the reduced forms are oxidized under aerobic conditions, oxygen being the final hydrogen acceptor. The inhibition of cytochrome reduction in the presence of narcotics such as urethane suggested participation of dehydrogenases in the reduction of cytochromes; various observations indicated that the cytochromes might act in series; and inhibition of oxygen uptake in the presence of cyanide, sulfide, or carbon monoxide pointed to the probable activity of Warburg's respiratory enzyme in the oxidation chain. The following general scheme illustrates the main course of oxidation, and the influence of poisons thereon, as pictured by the early workers in this field.

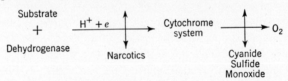

Combinations of Warburg's and Wieland's theories were proposed as early as 1924 by Fleisch and by Szent-Györgi and in 1925 by Kluyver and Donker. Kluyver (1931) summarized his views of aerobic respiration in the statement " . . . the chemistry of respiration processes can be reduced to a chain of reactions, each of which consists in a catalytic transference of hydrogen from the substrate to oxygen, according to the scheme:

$$AH_2 + O_2 = A + H_2O_2$$

(as a rule followed by a catalytic decomposition of H_2O_2 into water and free oxygen)." The studies of the Delft school on bacterial fermentations suggested similar hydrogen-transfer reactions under anaerobic conditions, substances other than oxygen acting as the final hydrogen acceptor.

Keilin came to the conclusion that the reduction systems in the cell are the dehydrogenases and that the catalyst involved in the oxidation of reduced cytochrome is identical with indophenol oxidase, an enzyme widely distributed in nature. This enzyme is recognized by coloration of the "Nadi" reagent, a reaction which consists of an oxidation of p-phenylenediamine by "activated" oxygen to yield a product which couples with β-naphthol to form indophenol blue. Keilin gave a new name, cytochrome oxidase, to this enzyme to indicate its function. It was found to be identical with Warburg's respiratory enzyme and with cytochrome a_3, a component of the cytochrome system recognized by its characteristic absorption band in the violet region of the spectrum. The basic contributions of Wieland, Warburg, and Keilin were fundamental to the development of the present concept of biological oxidations. Their divergent views were gradually fitted into the picture as a whole; the role of phosphates, of various enzymes and coenzymes, and of other factors was discovered in studies with cells or cellular extracts; and definite reaction chains were established. These systems and reactions will be considered in more detail after a summary of the concept of oxidation-reduction potentials, which has led to a better understanding of biological oxidations.

Oxidation-Reduction Potentials. Ehrlich, in 1893, reported that cells are able to reduce a number of dyes to a colorless form. He arranged the dyes he employed in a series according to the ease with which they were reduced by the cell, thus noting an intensity factor in oxidation. He found methylene blue to be a convenient dye to use in studying biological oxidations, and it is widely used today, a major reason being its location, on the oxidation-reduction scale, at a position intermediate between the reducing and the oxidizing systems of the cell. Ehrlich was handicapped by being unable to measure accurately the different degrees of reducibility of the dyes he employed and to establish a rational basis for interpretation of his results. The fundamental basis for an understanding of the reversible oxidation of dyes and of biological systems was developed by Clark and by Michaelis. The applications of their concepts to bacteriology are reviewed by Hewitt (1948).

Oxidation, as defined earlier in this chapter, consists basically of the loss of an electron or electrons, reduction being the gain of electrons by an atom or ion. Some substances are stronger oxidizing agents than are others; this can be interpreted on the basis of the powerful oxidizing agents having chemical bonds exhibiting a stronger electron-accepting tendency than those in the weaker oxidants. A strong reducing agent is a compound that is readily oxidized, or, in other words, it can give up electrons more readily than do the weaker reductants. Reversible oxidation-reduction systems can be placed on a scale indicating the relative tendency for electrons to escape from them or to be taken up by them. This scale can be established from measurements of the oxidation-reduction (redox) potentials of the different systems at constant temperature and pH.

When solutions of an oxidant and a reductant are placed in separate containers joined by a salt bridge and platinum or gold (inert) electrodes dipping into the solutions are connected together through a galvanometer, it is usually found that an electrical current flows through the system. This system, in many respects, is similar to a galvanic battery, and a flow of electrons occurs from the reducing agent to the electrode and through the circuit to the other electrode where they are taken up by the oxidant. The fact that a current flows in such a system is an indication that potential differences exist between the electrodes and the solutions and that these potential differences are not the same.

It is possible to make a definite determination of the potential difference between an electrode and a solution containing both oxidized and reduced forms of the same substance when the potential difference between the second electrode and the solution bathing it is known.   A hydrogen electrode (Chap. 2) dipping into a solution normal with respect to the activity of hydrogen ions (pH = 0) is taken as an arbitrary standard and is assigned a potential difference, or electromotive force (E), of zero.   The observed electromotive force is reported in number of volts more positive or negative than the zero value assigned the normal hydrogen electrode. A calomel electrode, for convenience in laboratory use, is generally employed in place of the normal hydrogen electrode, and observed potentials are corrected for this and reported in reference to the latter.

When a substance is oxidized by a second one, there must be a decrease in free energy of the system.   In a reversible voltaic cell, e.g., a zinc electrode dipping into a solution of zinc sulfate separated by a salt bridge from a copper sulfate solution bathing a copper electrode, electrical energy is developed and flows through an external circuit.   Zinc enters solution in one cell, copper is deposited on the copper electrode in the other cell, and electrons flow from the zinc through the external circuit to the copper electrode.   The reaction can be represented as

$$Zn + Cu^{++} \rightleftarrows Zn^{++} + Cu$$

The maximum amount of work that can be done by a reversible cell at constant temperature is expressed by the equation

$$\Delta F = -nFE \qquad (6\text{-}1)$$

where ΔF = change in free energy

n = number of electron-equivalents involved in the reaction

F = Faraday's constant (96,500 volt-coulombs or 23,068 cal.)

E = potential difference between electrodes

If an electrical cell is prepared with platinum electrodes in the two compartments, one of which contains stannous ions and the other stannic ions, it is observed that electrons are given up by the stannous ions to the platinum electrode, they flow along the wire to the other electrode, and are taken up there by the stannic ions, which are reduced to stannous ions. The oxidation of stannous to stannic ions in one compartment and the reduction of stannic ions in the other continue until equilibrium is established, i.e., the ratio of stannic to stannous ions is the same in both compartments. The oxidation of one ion by another at a distance may appear strange, but it is brought about by electron transfer.

Another theoretically reversible galvanic cell is the hydrogen-oxygen cell, in which one platinum electrode is saturated with hydrogen, the other with oxygen, both gases being at atmospheric pressure. When a current is developed by the cell, hydrogen ionizes at its electrode while oxygen ionizes and unites with water to form hydroxyl ions at the other, or

$$H_2 \rightleftharpoons 2H^+ + 2e$$

and

$$O + 2e \rightleftharpoons O^{--} + H_2O \rightleftharpoons 2OH^-$$

Hydrogen is oxidized by loss of electrons at its electrode, oxygen at its electrode accepts these electrons and is reduced, and the potential difference between these electrodes is 1.23 volts. The hydrogen-oxygen cell can be regarded as an oxidation-reduction cell and the potential difference of 1.23 volts as an oxidation-reduction potential. The oxygen electrode is 1.23 volts more positive than the hydrogen electrode, and this value can be used in the calculation of the free energy of the oxidation. Substituting the potential difference for the hydrogen-oxygen cell in equation (6-1), we obtain

$$\Delta F = -(2 \times 23,068 \times 1.23) = -56,750 \text{ cal.} \tag{6-2}$$

When the normal hydrogen electrode is used as the standard and a platinum electrode dips into a mixture of the oxidized and reduced forms of a reversible redox system, the potential that is developed at this electrode can be measured directly in terms of volts positive or negative with respect to this standard electrode. The potential E_h at the redox electrode can also be calculated by use of a classical equation of electrochemistry developed by Peters in 1898. The reversible oxidation-reduction reaction can be expressed as

$$[\text{Red}] \rightleftharpoons [\text{Oxid}] + n[e] \tag{6-3}$$

where [Red] represents the concentration of the compound in the reduced state, [Oxid] in the oxidized form, and $n[e]$ the number of electrons transferred per molecule. At equilibrium

$$\frac{[\text{Oxid}][e]^n}{[\text{Red}]} = K \tag{6-4}$$

The potential difference E_h at the electrode in a reversible system is controlled by the electron-escaping tendency (fugacity) and by the relative amounts of the oxidized and reduced forms. It can be expressed by the equation

$$E_h = E_0 + \frac{2.303RT}{nF} \log \frac{[\text{Oxid}]}{[\text{Red}]} \tag{6-5}$$

where R is the universal gas constant expressed in volt-coulombs, T is the absolute temperature, 2.303 is the factor for converting $\log_{10}$ to $\log_e$ values, and the other symbols are as defined above. E_0 is a constant, the value of which depends upon the nature of the redox system and the pH. E_h is equal to E_0 when $[\text{Oxid}] = [\text{Red}]$, i.e., when the compound is 50 per cent oxidized, 50 per cent reduced, and the ratio of $[\text{Oxid}]$ to $[\text{Red}]$ is 1.0, thus giving a value of zero to the last term in equation (6-5).

Equation (6-5) can be expressed as

$$E_h = E_0' + \frac{0.06}{n} \log \frac{[\text{Oxid}]}{[\text{Red}]} \tag{6-6}$$

where E_0' is the electrode potential at 50 per cent oxidation and at constant pH, and 0.06 is the numerical value of $2.303RT/F$ at 30°C. (303°K.). A plot of E_h values for the methylene blue system is presented in Fig. 6-3. The percentages of the substance present in the oxidized and the reduced forms can be calculated from E_h values with the aid of equation (6-6) when the value of E_0' is known. E_0' values are measures of the oxidizing or reducing intensities of different systems at a constant pH; they enable one to give a numerical value to each redox system and to place each system on a quantitative intensity scale rather than the qualitative scale introduced by Ehrlich.

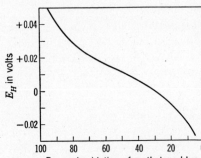

FIG. 6-3. Oxidation-reduction potentials of the methylene blue–methylene white system at pH 7.0 and 30°C.

It should be pointed out that the E_0' values of many systems alter with pH owing to differences in dissociation of the compounds and to other factors. Also we have considered oxidation-reduction reactions as occurring in one step; actually two or more steps may be involved. A transfer of two electrons is generally involved in biological oxidations, but such transfer reactions generally occur in steps of one electron transfer each, a free radical being formed in the first step of the reaction. The reader is referred to the monograph by Hewitt (1948) and earlier publications by Clark and by Michaelis for the details.

E_0' is a measure of intensity and not of capacity since it is dependent on a ratio of oxidized to reduced substance of 1.0 rather than to the absolute amounts of each. The amount of an oxidant or reductant determines the extent to which a reaction occurs, the E_h values whether or not the reaction may occur. It should be unnecessary to point out at this time that a catalyst or appropriate enzyme systems may be required to enable the reaction to proceed at a measurable rate. E_0' values are employed for comparing the oxidation-reduction intensities of different systems at a given pH, a system being theoretically able to oxidize any other system

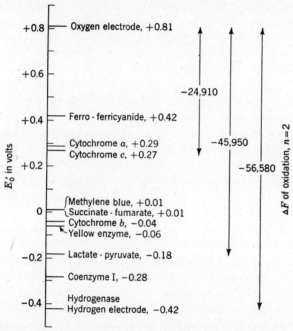

FIG. 6-4. Oxidation-reduction potentials of typical redox systems encountered in bacteriology.

below it on the E_0' scale or to reduce any system above it, the extent of the reaction being dependent upon the amounts of the two systems. The greater the separation that exists between two systems on the scale, the greater the free energy of the reaction. The intensity scale is the important thing to consider in bacterial physiology since it is possible to predict from it what may happen when two redox systems are mixed and to calculate the free energy of the reaction. E_0' values of typical redox systems employed or encountered in studies with bacteria are plotted in Fig. 6-4.

It can be noted in Fig. 6-4 that the methylene blue system has a potential of +0.011 volt, and on the basis of this intensity scale we can predict that it is able to oxidize any system below it or to reduce any system above it on the scale. The lactate-pyruvate system lies below the methylene blue one, and in the presence of a suitable enzyme preparation, e.g., a lactic acid dehydrogenase from *E. coli*, lactate can be oxidized to pyruvate and methylene blue be reduced to the colorless leuco base. The E_0' potential of the lactate-pyruvate system (50 per cent of each, pH 7.0) is -0.186 volt, and the difference between the two systems is 0.197 volt. The free energy of oxidation of one mole of lactate to pyruvate by methylene blue can be calculated with the aid of equation (6-1), and since a transfer of two electrons is involved, ΔF would be equal to $-2 \times 23,068 \times 0.197$, or $-9,089$ cal. If oxygen acted as the hydrogen acceptor for the oxidation of lactate to pyruvate, ΔF would equal $-2 \times 23,068 \times 0.996$, or $-45,950$ cal., and for the oxidation of reduced methylene blue, $-2 \times 23,068 \times 0.799$, or $-36,860$ cal. Biological oxidations generally occur in such a manner that the hydrogen and electrons involved are transferred to oxygen in a series of steps and the free energy of each step is relatively small. There would, therefore, be no sudden release of a large amount of energy as involved in the direct oxidation of lactate. Hess's law (Chap. 2) tells us that the energy change would be the same in either case, the stepwise procedure making it possible for hydrogen and electrons to be brought into union with oxygen (or other acceptors under anaerobic conditions) in controlled steps of such a nature that a portion of the energy can be bound and made available for doing work.

The concept of oxidation-reduction potentials has been developed here in a relatively simple manner; actually many complexities are encountered in such studies even with the simpler systems. Some systems react readily; others are sluggish in establishing equilibrium with an electrode. The redox potential of a coenzyme-reduced coenzyme system alone may be markedly different from that of the same system in combination with its protein partner. Flavin, for example, has an E_0' approximately 0.15 volt more negative than that of its combination with a protein in the yellow enzyme of Warburg. The redox intensity of coenzyme I may be different when in combination with different proteins. This may account, in part at least, for the fact that lactate can be oxidized by its dehydrogenase and coenzyme I, although the latter lies below lactate on the E_0' scale in Fig. 6-4. Another fact must also be taken into account here; the cell is not dealing with equal amounts of oxidized and reduced forms as depicted on the scale and employed in our calculations. When the ratios of lactate to pyruvate and of coenzyme I to its reduced form are both high, it is possible that the potential of the coenzyme system is above that of the lactate one, and therefore it could oxidize lactate to pyruvate. The equilibrium point of this reaction is such, however, that the reaction would soon come to equilibrium unless the pyruvate is utilized further. Since the potential difference between any two redox systems may vary some depending upon the relative amounts of oxidized and reduced forms of both systems, more or less energy may be released than indicated in our calculations. The calculated values should be regarded as approximations and the redox scale as indicative rather than absolute in complex biological systems.

Why is more energy released in the oxidation of lactate to pyruvate than in that of methylene white to methylene blue, or why do other systems differ in this respect when the same number of hydrogens and electrons are involved? This question was answered in preliminary remarks about oxidations in the first part of this chapter, but the answer can be restated here in a different manner. Substances low on the redox scale part with the electrons involved in their oxidation with less expenditure of energy on change in their molecular structure than do substances higher on the scale. Since less energy is expended on molecular rearrangement, more energy is set free as heat energy or may be available for doing work. Stepwise transfer of electrons enables bacteria and other cells to handle in a more efficient manner the available energy arising from the oxidation of substrates of widely different free energies of oxidation.

It might be mentioned at this time that methylene blue acts so well as a redox indicator in studies of the Thunberg type because of its position above many of the common dehydrogenase-substrate systems on the redox scale. It is autoxidizable, and these factors make it a good indicator for the detection of oxygen in media employed for the cultivation of anaerobes. It is reduced to its colorless form by reducing compounds in various media and will remain in this state in the absence of oxygen. Other indicators also can be employed in studies on biological oxidations. The tetrazolium dyes are of particular value for the study of intracellular oxidations, these dyes being reduced to insoluble, colored formazans which are deposited at the site of the oxidation. Ferricyanide is also employed to some extent since changes in potential of this system can be followed quite readily and the potential is independent of pH over a rather wide pH range on either side of neutrality.

The electrode potentials of reversible biological oxidation-reduction systems are of considerable value in the study of biological oxidations as outlined above. Many measurements have been made of electrode potentials developed in cultures of bacteria, and they do indicate that marked differences exist between different bacteria in this respect. High oxidation intensities are observed in cultures of hydrogen peroxide–producing bacteria that are devoid of catalase, high reducing potentials in cultures of bacteria liberating hydrogen gas, and intermediate values with other bacteria. The actual value depends to a considerable extent on the nature of the medium and the degree of aeration of the culture. The values themselves are not true redox potentials and are resultants of many factors. They primarily reflect reducing intensities of substances liberated by the cells rather than any absolute characteristic of the bacterial cells under study.

Some enzymes are not active when the E_h is above a certain level, e.g., urease has a limiting potential of $+0.150$ volt at pH 6.8. The growth of obligate anaerobes (Hanke and Bailey, 1943) also appears to depend upon enzymes which have reversibly oxidizable and reducible groups; these enzymes are active only in the reduced form, and there is a limiting potential above which these enzymes are not active. Knight and Fildes (1930) reported that *Clostridium tetani* spores will not germinate in media with an E_h above $+0.110$ volt at pH 7.2, while Hanke and Bailey found limiting values of $+0.150$ and $+0.090$ volt for *C. welchii* and *C. histolyticum*, respectively, at pH 6.6. They concluded that oxygen per se has little to do directly with the prevention of growth of anaerobic bacteria if the E_h of the medium is below the limiting value. It is believed that anaerobic bacteria such as those of the tetanus and gas-gangrene groups are unable to develop in the tissues unless strong reducing conditions prevail. These conditions develop only in the absence of oxygen and in the presence of reducing substances, a combination encountered in deep wounds.

Types of Biological-oxidation Chains. We have considered that biological oxidations involve the transfer of hydrogen and electrons through a series of redox systems in association with the appropriate enzymes. The oxidative process is initiated by action of a dehydrogenase specific for the substrate undergoing oxidation, the substrate molecule in some instances having to be made ready for the oxidation by action of other enzyme systems to be considered later. The transfer of hydrogen and electrons to oxygen can occur over a number of pathways, the route being dependent upon the nature of the dehydrogenase system. Five general types of reaction chains (Fig. 6-5) will be considered in the following discussion.

Type 1. The simplest type of oxidation is that in which hydrogen and electrons are transferred directly from the substrate to molecular oxygen under the influence of the appropriate dehydrogenase system. The term dehydrogenase is somewhat misleading in that the dehydrogenase protein (apoenzyme) combines with the substrate molecule and activates it in such a manner that hydrogen and electrons can be withdrawn (or added) more readily, the actual dehydrogenation being accomplished by the coenzyme (prosthetic group). The term dehydrogenase, as employed in these discussions, refers to the complete enzyme system, the protein plus its prosthetic group. Those aerobic dehydrogenase systems which react directly with molecular oxygen are commonly termed oxidases, hydrogen peroxide generally being formed as a result of the transfer. The reaction may be expressed as

$$DH_2 + O_2 \xrightarrow{\text{oxidase}} D + H_2O_2$$

This type of oxidation is observed in the oxidation of D-amino acids by animal tissues, of certain α-amino acids by bacteria, of polyphenols, and other substances. The prosthetic groups of these oxidases are either metal ions, generally copper, or a flavin. The glucose oxidase of molds

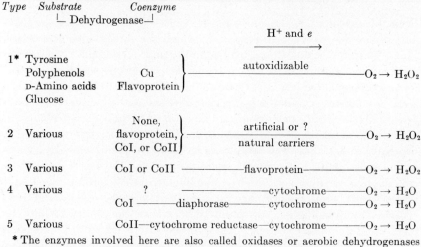

* The enzymes involved here are also called oxidases or aerobic dehydrogenases since the reduced enzyme system can react directly with oxygen.

FIG. 6-5. General types of biological-oxidation chains involved in the transfer of hydrogen and electrons to oxygen.

and bacteria is a flavin-adenine-dinucleotide protein complex and catalyzes the oxidation of glucose to gluconic acid with the formation of hydrogen peroxide. This enzyme is also known as notatin. At one time *Penicillium notatum* was suspected of producing two antibiotic agents, penicillin and an unknown compound. It was soon observed that the unknown bactericidal effect was due to hydrogen peroxide formed during the oxidation of glucose, and the bactericidal activity was traced to the action of this enzyme. These oxidases may be of greatest importance in facultative anaerobes, such as the lactic acid bacteria, which do not possess the cytochrome system. One difficulty encountered in a consideration of these aerobic dehydrogenases is that of energy utilization from the reactions they catalyze, the direct transfer of hydrogen and electrons to oxygen involving the liberation of considerable energy.

Type 2. Other dehydrogenase systems cannot react directly with molecular oxygen but can reduce a number of redox systems, methylene blue, as previously noted, frequently being employed as the oxidant in in vitro studies. The reduced form of many of these carriers can react directly with oxygen; they act as hydrogen and electron carriers and give rise to a second type of oxidation system, such as

$$DH_2 \quad \diagdown \quad MB \quad \diagup \quad H_2O_2$$
$$D \quad \diagup \quad MB \cdot 2H \quad \diagdown \quad O_2$$

Dehydrogenase autoxidation

Using this method, developed by Baldwin (1949), of illustrating the reaction emphasizes the cyclical manner in which the carrier acts, a molecule being alternately reduced and oxidized over and over again. The methylene blue technique for studying biological oxidations was first applied to bacteriological oxidations by Harden and Zilva in 1915 and was extensively developed by Thunberg for animal tissue and by Quastel for bacterial-oxidation studies as previously mentioned. Quastel and Whetman (1925) observed that *E. coli* is able to oxidize over fifty different organic substrates under anaerobic conditions with methylene blue as the hydrogen acceptor at pH 7.4. Sugars were observed to be the most reactive reducing agents when activated by the bacteria, then formic, lactic, and succinic acids, while the ordinary fatty and amino acids were least active.

Various poisons influenced, to different extents, the ability of the cells to oxidize different substrates. Those observations led to the conclusion that a cell contains different centers of activation specific for different molecular groupings or structures. These postulated active centers are now considered to be actual dehydrogenase enzymes, specific for a particular substrate in most instances. The concept of adsorption at specific centers was also based in part on observations such as the inhibition of succinic acid oxidation by the structurally related malonic acid, the latter compound being adsorbed, but not activated at the center, and hence inhibiting oxidation of succinate.

The methylene blue technique of Thunberg and Quastel provides a rapid method for screening the dehydrogenase activities of different species, for studying the influence of various conditions and substances on such oxidations, and also serves in the study of isolated dehydrogenase systems. The lactic acid dehydrogenase, obtained by purification of the material liberated on rupture of cells such as *E. coli* or the gonococcus, oxidizes lactate to pyruvate with methylene blue as the oxidant. This enzyme by itself will not oxidize lactate, even under aerobic conditions, in the absence of a carrier such as methylene blue, thus indicating the need for an additional factor(s) in the cell serving as a hydrogen and electron acceptor or carrier.

Gaseous hydrogen, as well as organic substrates, can be oxidized by many organisms, using methylene blue as the hydrogen acceptor. This oxidation of hydrogen occurs under the influence of an enzyme, hydrogenase, which catalyzes the reaction

$$H_2 \xrightarrow{\text{hydrogenase}} 2H^+ + 2e$$

Various studies with cell extracts of *E. coli* indicate that a carrier system is involved between the hydrogenase and methylene blue. Hydrogen acceptors other than methylene blue can also be reduced by hydrogenase-containing bacteria, e.g., nitrate being reduced to nitrite by bacteria possessing the enzyme nitratase. This reduction normally proceeds as far as ammonia, hydroxylamine (NH_2OH) being a probable intermediate in the reaction. The hydrogenase system does not belong to the type 2 oxidation chain but was included here to illustrate another use of methylene blue as an oxidation indicator. Methylene white can be used as a reduction indicator since it can be oxidized to methylene blue with, e.g., fumarate acting as a hydrogen acceptor, the fumarate being reduced to succinate with the participation of the succinic acid dehydrogenase system acting in "reverse." The methylene blue carrier system is an artificial one, but other autoxidizable redox carriers such as pyocyanin (a pigment of *Pseudomonas aeruginosa*) possibly may act in the cell in a manner similar to that observed with methylene blue in vitro.

Type 3. This type of biological oxidation is very similar to type 2, with the exception that an autoxidizable flavoprotein acts as the carrier between the dehydrogenase system and oxygen. The reaction, therefore, is of a more complex type than the type 2 one, and the flavoprotein might be regarded as a dehydrogenase system for the oxidation of reduced coenzyme. It is doubtful if this type of reaction is of much importance, except possibly in cytochrome-free cells, since the rate of autoxidation of a flavoprotein is generally low.

Type 4. This type differs from the previous ones in that a cytochrome (or cytochromes) acts as the intermediate carrier of electrons. Cytochrome *b* can act as an intermediate, autoxidizable electron carrier in a reaction chain of type 4. In most oxidations of this type cytochrome *b* is not oxidized directly, the oxidation proceeding more readily through other cytochromes. A few dehydrogenases, the succinic one having been studied the most thoroughly, oxidize the substrate directly without participation of a recognized coenzyme and reduce cytochrome *b*. Cytochrome *b* is oxidized, possibly with participation of the "Slater factor" (see type 5), by cytochrome *c*, which in turn is oxidized by cytochrome *a*. Electrons from cytochrome *a* are transferred to oxygen under the influence of cytochrome oxidase, and this "activated" oxygen unites with hydrogen ions to form water, thus completing the oxidation chain. This reaction chain can be represented as

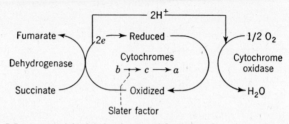

Slater factor

Type 5.   Most aerobic biological oxidations do not utilize direct cyto-chrome-linked dehydrogenases and instead use the nicotinamide and flavin coenzymes as hydrogen and electron transport systems between the substrate and the cytochrome molecules.   Not all details of this transfer have been established, and the schemes presented in Figs. 6-5 and 6-6 are to be considered as tentative ones for types 4 and 5 reaction chains. In the indirect pathway the substrate, activated by its specific dehydro-genase, is oxidized by loss of hydrogen and electrons to DPN or TPN. The coenzyme involved in this oxidation is determined by the nature and source of the dehydrogenase.   Oxidation of the reduced coenzyme is mediated by a second system, a flavoprotein with a flavin adenine dinucleotide (FAD) as the prosthetic group when DPN is the coenzyme for the substrate dehydrogenase, a flavin mononucleotide (FMN) when TPN is involved in the reaction chain.   The FAD-proteins are termed diaphorases by some workers; the FMN-proteins, cytochrome reductases. An additional system, called the Slater factor and indicated in Fig. 6-6, may participate in reactions between reduced cytochrome b or reduced FAD and cytochrome c.   This system (Slater, 1950) is recognized by observations that substances such as BAL (British anti-Lewisite, 2,3-dimer-captopropanol) or antimycin A (an antibiotic) prevent interaction between reduced cytochrome b or diaphorase and cytochrome c.   Neither the reduction of cytochrome b by succinate nor the reduction of cyto-chrome c by p-phenylenediamine is inhibited by these agents, thus sug-gesting that their point of attack is between cytochromes b and c.   These reaction chains must not be considered as definitely established in their entirety, the major doubt being centered around the connecting link between the reduced flavins and the cytochrome system.   We can, how-ever, summarize with considerable certainty the nature of many of the reactions in the chain.

The substrate activated by its dehydrogenase is oxidized by loss of two hydrogens, one hydrogen atom and two electrons being taken up by DPN^+ (or TPN^+) at the N=C group where N bears a + charge as indicated in Fig. 5-3.   The other hydrogen as hydrogen ion probably is held by a phosphoric acid group in the coenzyme molecule, and some authors use the abbreviation $DPNH_2$ to represent the reduced form of this coenzyme. (This second hydrogen is released as hydrogen ion when the oxidation is

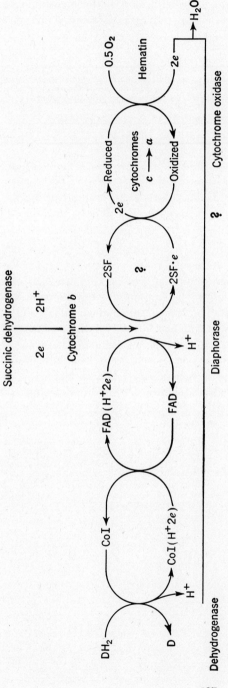
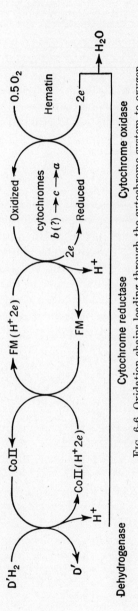

Fig. 6-6. Oxidation chains leading through the cytochrome system to oxygen.

127

studied in an enzyme preparation.)   The reduction of the nicotinamide coenzymes, in which the valence of the participating N atom is changed from 5 to 3, can be represented as

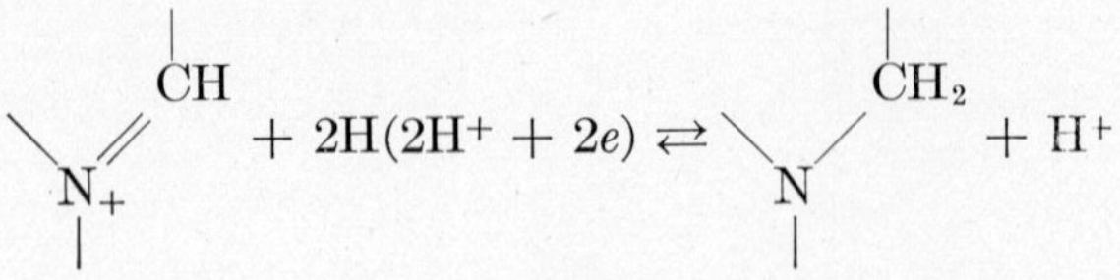

$$\text{(structure with CH, } N_+) + 2H(2H^+ + 2e) \rightleftharpoons \text{(structure with } CH_2, N) + H^+$$

or as

$$DPN^+ + 2H^+ + 2e \rightleftharpoons DPNH + H^+$$

The reduced coenzyme can be oxidized by the appropriate flavoprotein, DPN^+ being regenerated with the formation of reduced FAD (TPN^+ with the formation of reduced FMN).   This oxidation can be represented as

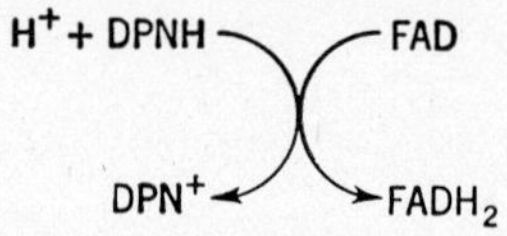

$$H^+ + DPNH \underset{DPN^+}{\overset{FAD}{\rightleftarrows}} FADH_2$$

Reduction of FAD or FMN occurs in the isoalloxazine ring, the N atoms indicated with asterisks in Figs. 5-5 and 5-6 being involved in the reaction. These N atoms in the reduced state can fluctuate between valences of 3 and 5, and it is possible for one N at valence 5 to be oxidized while the other is still in the reduced condition.   In this manner one electron can be passed at a time to the cytochrome system while a H^+ ion is released, an equivalent being involved in the reduction of oxygen to water in the final stage of cellular oxidation.   These reactions can be represented as

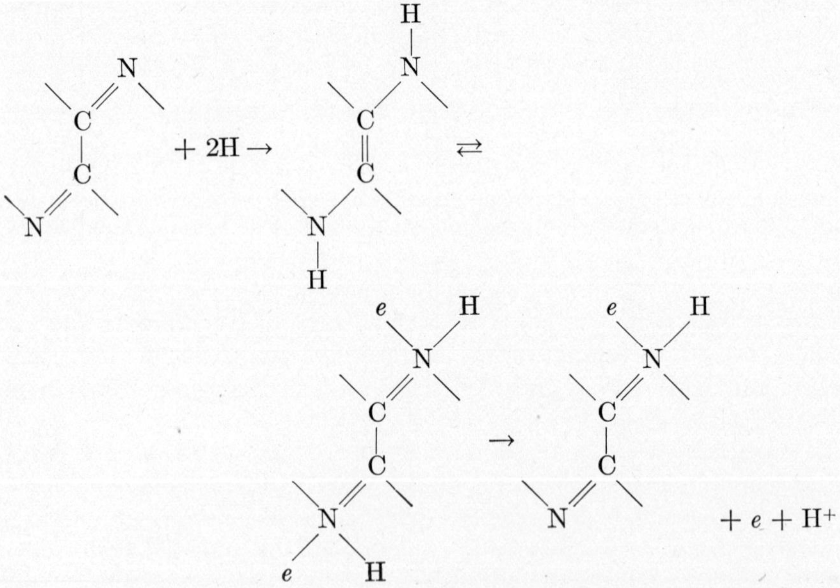

$$\text{(structure)} + 2H \rightarrow \text{(structure)} \rightleftharpoons$$

$$\text{(structure)} \rightarrow \text{(structure)} + e + H^+$$

While certain details of these reactions are debatable, they do serve to develop a mental picture of what may occur with particular reference to the mode of transfer of one electron at a time to the cytochrome system, ferric iron being reduced to ferrous iron as a result of the electron transfer. As indicated earlier, this electron transfer may occur from $FADH_2$ through the not as yet definitely established Slater factor. The electrons then pass through the cytochrome system to cytochrome, oxidase where they unite with oxygen, this "activated" oxygen reacting with H^+ ions to form water. As far as is known, $FMNH_2$ reacts directly with cytochrome c. High-energy phosphate bonds can be generated during these oxidations or transfer of electrons through the cytochrome system. This method of trapping energy will be considered later.

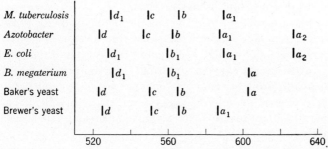

Fig. 6-7. Location of characteristic adsorption bands of cytochrome in different organisms.

Some uncertainty exists as to which cytochromes are involved and in what order they react. Available redox data suggest the order $b \rightarrow c \rightarrow a$ when all cytochromes are involved in electron transport. Cytochrome c is the one which has been studied in greatest detail since it can be obtained in a highly purified, water-soluble form. Cytochromes a and b are more closely bound to cellular material than is cytochrome c. There are different forms of these cytochromes, some are absent from various species of bacteria, and the cytochrome content of a species may vary with cultural conditions (see review on bacterial cytochromes by Smith, 1954). Since bacteria differ to some extent in the cytochromes they possess, somewhat different reaction chains would be utilized by different species. Characteristic absorption bands of the cytochrome system in different species are depicted in Fig. 6-7. The cytochrome system is absent from most strict anaerobes.

Cytochrome oxidase (cytochrome a_3) of bacteria also may differ from that found in other cells and may differ between different species as well. In some species the inhibition of cytochrome oxidase activity by carbon monoxide is not reversed by light, and in others the oxidase does not combine readily with this gas. Many details of cytochrome activity remain to be determined, and the reaction chains considered here must be considered as tentative ones.

Most of the enzymes involved in reactions of the type 5 or similar oxidation chains are intimately associated with each other, and with other enzymes, in mitochondria or other organized components of the cell. Biological oxidations, therefore, occur in the intact cell more readily than in reconstructed systems because of this organization. Mitochondria have been isolated from many tissues (see review by Green, 1951) and have been shown to possess high respiratory activity. The existence of such systems in bacteria has been demonstrated primarily either by the presence of areas of high reducing ability in the cell, these areas being made evident by the selective deposition of formazans in bacteria respiring in the presence of the tetrazolium redox indicators, or by marked metabolic activities of particles from disrupted cells.

It is readily apparent in reaction chains such as those of types 4 and 5 that hydrogen and electrons are transported in a series of steps, each one of which involves only a small free-energy decrease, and that each step is controlled by a specific enzyme. Actually, the important reaction is the flow of electrons, probably from one enzyme protein to another next to it, and so on. The cell, employing these steps, is more able to control the flow of energy than in reactions involving simple chains such as the type 1 or 2 oxidation.

Catalase. In oxidations of types 1, 2, or 3, hydrogen peroxide is formed on transfer of hydrogen and electrons to oxygen; possibly also in reactions 4 and 5, but if so, it is decomposed as it forms. Accumulation of hydrogen peroxide in the cells or medium would be inhibitory or toxic to most organisms, and means must be provided for its removal. Hematin compounds, such as the cytochromes, in general exert some ability to decompose peroxides, but the most active and specific action is associated with catalase, an enzyme containing heme as the prosthetic group. A second enzyme, peroxidase, may be involved in the disposal of hydrogen peroxide, activating it to donate an oxygen atom for the oxidation of substrate molecules. Peroxidases are present in plants, but there is doubt as to their presence or activity in bacteria. In recent years Chance (1951) and others have presented evidence that catalase itself exerts peroxidatic activity, and its reactions can be pictured as

$$FeOH + H_2O_2 \text{ (acting as a hydrogen acceptor)} \rightarrow FeO \cdot OH + H_2O$$

and

$$FeO \cdot OH + H_2O_2 \text{ (acting as a hydrogen donor)} \rightarrow FeOH + H_2O + O_2$$

where Fe represents the active iron in catalase.

In the first reaction given above, hydrogen peroxide reacts with one of the FeOH groups in the catalase molecule, as indicated, to form the complex FeO·OH, one —OH group of the peroxide accepting an atom of hydrogen to form water. The catalase-peroxide complex can then react as a peroxidase with another molecule of hydrogen peroxide as a hydrogen donor as shown above, or with an organic substrate such as ethanol in a peroxidatic reaction of the type

$$-\text{FeO·OH} + \text{CH}_3\text{CH}_2\text{OH} \rightarrow -\text{FeOH} + \text{CH}_3\text{CHO} + \text{HOH}$$

Ethanol is oxidized to acetaldehyde in this reaction with the catalase-peroxide complex acting as a hydrogen acceptor and being reduced with the formation of water. In this manner hydrogen peroxide is broken down. When relatively high concentrations of hydrogen peroxide develop, the peroxide itself acts as a hydrogen donor and is reduced, the —FeO·OH complex being oxidized with reformation of —FeOH and the liberation of oxygen. The peroxidatic decomposition of hydrogen peroxide, if such a reaction occurs in bacteria, could be considered as a safety valve to prevent the accumulation of toxic concentrations of peroxide. The oxidation of nitrites to nitrates also can be induced by some species of bacteria, employing the peroxidatic action of catalase. In the catalase-negative bacteria (e.g., pneumococci or lactic acid bacteria), hydrogen peroxide does accumulate under highly aerobic conditions and is toxic.

Oxygen consumption in some species appears to be involved in preparatory rather than energy-providing reactions. *Streptococcus faecalis* will grow in a glucose medium without oxygen being consumed under aerobic conditions, the glucose being fermented with the production of lactic acid. With glycerol as the substrate there is an uptake of oxygen corresponding to the amount required to oxidize the glycerol to triose phosphate, which is fermented to yield lactic acid. Approximately the same amount of growth is obtained from two moles of glycerol as from one mole of glucose utilized, two moles of lactic acid being formed in each case. These cells do not possess mechanisms capable of using the energy potentially available from the oxidation of glycerol to triose phosphates, and when oxygen is consumed by these catalase-negative bacteria hydrogen peroxide may accumulate in toxic amounts. The anaerobic bacteria are also catalase-negative, and for many years hydrogen peroxide formation under aerobic conditions was the explanation for the toxic effect of air. It is probable that oxygen, or hydrogen peroxide, oxidizes —SH or other reducing groups essential for the activity of many enzymes, and metabolism is inhibited until reducing conditions are reestablished.

Miscellaneous Oxidations. A highly interesting terminal respiration is observed in the luminescent bacteria. These organisms, particularly when oxidizing glucose or glycerol, emit a portion of the waste energy of oxidation in the form of bluish or greenish light rather than as heat. A substance known as luciferin appears to be the final compound in the oxidation chain and is oxidized by oxygen under the influence of an enzyme, luciferase. Some of the oxygen utilized by luminous bacteria (van Schouwenburg, 1938) in the oxidation of substrates passes through the cytochrome system (cyanide-sensitive), some through a cyanide-insensitive one, and the remainder through luciferin as the hydrogen carrier. In the luminescent reaction it appears that the luciferin molecule acquires excess energy, becomes excited, and emits this energy as a quantum of light or else the excess energy is transferred to luciferase which may be the actual emitter of light. McElroy and Ballentine (1944) have suggested the following scheme:

$$LH_2 \text{ (luciferin)} + A \text{ (luciferase)} \rightarrow ALH_2$$

$$ALH_2 + 0.5O_2 \rightarrow ALH_2O$$

$$ALH_2O \rightarrow A' \text{ (excited luciferase)} + L + H_2O$$
$$\qquad\qquad \rightarrow A + h\nu$$

The emission of light by luminous bacteria can occur under very low oxygen tensions, and this reaction provides a very sensitive test for the detection of oxygen. It has, for example, been employed in attempts to detect oxygen production during photosynthesis by photosynthetic bacteria. The luminous bacteria also have been employed in numerous tests on the influence of temperature, pressure, acidity, and various poisons on bacteria (Johnson et al., 1945).

Species of the genus *Acetobacter* are characterized by their tendency to oxidize various substrates to organic acids or other incomplete oxidation products which accumulate in the medium. These waste products may be oxidized to carbon dioxide and water in subsequent oxidations which are dependent to a considerable extent upon the species and environmental conditions. Three main types of incomplete oxidation are recognized:

1. The oxidation of primary alcohols to the corresponding acids, e.g., the oxidation to acetic acid of ethyl alcohol, or

$$CH_3CH_2OH + O_2 \rightarrow CH_3COOH + H_2O$$

   The commercial production of vinegar involves the use of these acetic acid bacteria growing as a film either on the surface of wine or cider (slow process) or on wood chips or other supports, wine or cider trickling over these supports placed in a large container through which a stream of air passes (quick process).
2. The oxidation of aldehyde-type sugars to their corresponding acids, e.g., species of *Acetobacter* oxidize glucose to gluconic acid, $CH_2OH(CHOH)_4COOH$.
3. Oxidation of a hydroxyl to a keto group at a β-carbon atom in a polyhydric alcohol. The —OH group must be adjacent to a second —OH group as in D-sorbitol or glycerol. Glycerol is oxidized by *Acetobacter* to dihydroxyacetone, and the over-all

reaction may be represented as

$$H-\underset{\underset{OH}{|}}{\overset{\overset{H}{|}}{C}}-\underset{\underset{OH}{|}}{\overset{\overset{H}{|}}{C}}-\underset{\underset{OH}{|}}{\overset{\overset{H}{|}}{C}}-H + 0.5O_2 \rightarrow H-\underset{\underset{OH}{|}}{\overset{\overset{H}{|}}{C}}-\underset{\underset{O}{\|}}{C}-\underset{\underset{OH}{|}}{\overset{\overset{H}{|}}{C}}-H + H_2O$$

The polyhydric alcohol, D-sorbitol, can be produced by chemical means from glucose, the β-carbon in it is oxidized by *Acetobacter* with the formation of L-sorbose, $CH_2OH(CHOH)_3C = OCH_2OH$, and this compound is converted on chemical treatment to L-ascorbic acid (vitamin C) in the industrial production of this agent. Persulose can be prepared from persetol (a 7-carbon polyhydric alcohol); erythrulose from erythritol (a 4-carbon polyhydric alcohol); acetylmethylcarbinol from 2,3-butanediol; and tartaric, gluconic, and 5-ketogluconic acids from glucose, using the proper species and favorable environmental conditions, on an industrial scale (Prescott and Dunn, 1949).

The production by species of *Acetobacter* of these incomplete products of oxidation is usually spoken of as a fermentation, this term being employed in its broadest sense, i.e., the production of organic end products more reduced than carbon dioxide. It is an aerobic rather than an anaerobic fermentation. Acetic acid is produced from ethyl alcohol with acetaldehyde probably being formed as an intermediate compound in the fermentation. The actual enzymes involved have not been isolated and studied in detail. One explanation for the accumulation of the characteristic end products of fermentations induced by the acetic acid bacteria is that they possess two oxidation systems, a rapid one leading to the production of the characteristic products of incomplete oxidation of the substrate and a slow one involved in the oxidation of these intermediate compounds.

The incomplete oxidation of organic substrates is observed very frequently with different species of the higher fungi. Molds, in their natural environment, are limited in their rate of metabolism by the amount and types of foodstuff available. In such an environment, or in laboratory media containing low concentrations of sugar, they tend to oxidize their foodstuffs to completion. High concentrations of sugar are commonly used in media employed for cultivation of these organisms, their normal metabolism becomes deranged, and intermediate products of metabolism accumulate. Various workers (see Foster, 1949) have suggested that when the sugar supply is low the enzymes in the oxidation chains can handle in the normal manner all foodstuff available to the cell. The rate of conversion of the hexose molecules into simpler units increases with increase in available sugar, the enzymes involved apparently being saturated only at relatively high substrate concentrations [high values for the Michaelis constant, equation (5-9)]. The terminal, respiratory enzymes, however, appear to be working at or near their maximum rate under normal conditions and cannot oxidize the additional amounts of intermediates. The result is that these intermediates accumulate within the cells. These split products of hexose utilization are secreted as such, or they are shunted to secondary or subsidiary enzymes which are able to effect only minor changes in these compounds before they are liberated from the cells. Foster speaks of this as shunt metabolism and points out that it can be observed in various types of organisms, particularly when relatively abnormal conditions prevail. There is a possibility that the partial oxidations observed with the *Acetobacter* represent a shunt metabolism that has become a permanent characteristic of members of this genus. This tendency for molds to utilize metabolic shunts when a utilizable sugar is present in high concentration in the medium is employed in the commercial production of a number of substances such as citric, fumaric, and gluconic acids.

The Pasteur Effect. In the facultative anaerobic bacteria, and in many other types of cells, pyruvic acid is oxidized to carbon dioxide and water under fully aerobic conditions. Under anaerobic conditions pyruvate is reduced to lactate or converted into other characteristic products of fermentation, depending upon the nature of the organism and of its environment. Fermentation is suppressed by oxygen, and this suppression is known as the Pasteur effect. To obtain the same amount of energy from the fermentation of glucose to lactic acid as from the complete oxidation of glucose, it is necessary for the cell to ferment about twelve times as much sugar as would be required in aerobic respiration. Usually the cell is unable to ferment sugar at a rate sufficient to supply the energy demand observed under aerobic conditions, and the rates of growth and of other activities decrease. That life without air is a wasteful process was pointed out by Pasteur in 1861, who at the same time discovered the sparing effect of oxygen on substrate consumption.

In a typical experiment (Dickens, 1951) the $Q_{CO_2}^{N_2}$ of yeast was 250, and in air the Q_{CO_2} value for fermentation was 10, the Q_{O_2} value being 90. These values, expressed in relative terms, indicate that for every 125 molecules of glucose fermented anaerobically, only 5 were fermented aerobically and 15 oxidized to completion. In other words, the cells had the ability to activate many more glucose molecules than were actually used aerobically. Hence there appears to be a regulatory mechanism that limits the amount of sugar utilized aerobically, or spares sugar, the Pasteur effect.

Numerous explanations (Dickens, 1951) have been advanced concerning the Pasteur effect, the suppression of fermentation by air. It is generally assumed that pyruvate is formed from sugar in the same manner under either aerobic or anaerobic conditions and is oxidized to completion aerobically, dissimilated otherwise anaerobically. Warburg in 1926 suggested that the aerobic pathway of carbohydrate dissimilation might be different from the glycolytic one in animal tissues. Ethyl isocyanide caused an increase in aerobic glycolysis (lactic acid formation) to about the anaerobic level, while having little influence on the rate of aerobic respiration or of anaerobic glycolysis. Iodoacetate selectively poisons glycolysis, and other poisons may influence respiration differently. Pickett and Clifton (1943), for example, have shown that the aerobic oxidation of glucose by yeast is inhibited by $M/10,000$ sodium azide, while aerobic fermentation is increased and a portion of the alcohol formed is oxidized. Higher concentrations of this poison inhibited the oxidation of alcohol to a greater extent, and alcohol accumulated in the medium. Synthesis of cellular material was blocked by azide under both aerobic and anaerobic conditions.

Various observations suggest that pyruvate may be formed from carbohydrate by more than one mechanism, the familiar glycolytic one operating under anaerobic conditions and being inhibited by oxygen (Pasteur effect), while in the aerobic pathway a sugar such as glucose is oxidized to phosphogluconic acid. This compound in turn is oxidized to a ketogluconic acid which may be converted to ribose, which is metabolized further. This hexose monophosphate shunt metabolism will be considered under the general pathways of oxidation. Uncertainties exist regarding the possible multiplicity of pathways of dissimilation of a sugar in the same cell. We will, for convenience of discussion, consider that the aerobic and anaerobic pathways of dissimilation generally follow the same pattern to the pyruvate state. The shunt pathway may exist in many cells but be operative to an appreciable extent only under abnormal conditions. Much work may be required before the picture is completed in all its details. It is important that the student realize that deficiencies do exist in our knowledge and that many of our schemes of action will be modified to some extent with increase in available information. The Pasteur effect is a true one; the explanations for it are numerous and range from the postulated existence of a specific Pasteur enzyme through oxygen causing a shift in type of dissimilation to an influence of phosphate deficiency under anaerobic conditions.

Anaerobic Oxidations. Biological oxidations occur under either aerobic or anaerobic conditions, the factor limiting the extent to which they can occur being the ability or lack of ability of many organisms to use terminal hydrogen and electron acceptors other than molecular oxygen. The majority of bacteria are facultative anaerobes and utilize oxygen as the final hydrogen acceptor under aerobic conditions, other hydrogen acceptors being substituted for it under anaerobic conditions. These terminal hydrogen acceptors in the absence of oxygen can be portions of the substrate molecule or entirely different molecules, including inorganic ones such as nitrate or carbon dioxide, if the species possesses the requisite enzymes. Since oxidation of the substrate does not proceed to completion, the energy per unit of foodstuff utilized is much less than under aerobic conditions. Anaerobic respiration is, therefore, a wasteful process, although it may be of survival value. Much less is known about the enzymes involved in many of the anaerobic oxidations than is known concerning the aerobic ones, but the essential mechanisms appear to be the same or very similar. The oxidations appear to be mediated by DPN and TPN without participation of flavoproteins or the cytochromes, and the reaction chains are simple ones (see chapters on fermentation).

The Transfer of Energy. We have seen that biological oxidations involve hydrogen and electron transfer through a series of enzyme systems, a specific dehydrogenase catalyzing the original oxidation. The hydrogen and electrons are transferred through the appropriate, reversible redox systems to molecular oxygen under aerobic conditions, to other terminal hydrogen acceptors under anaerobic ones. For many years the mechanism of energy transfer between the energy-yielding oxidations and the energy-requiring reactions was unknown. Since the cell is not a heat machine a portion of the free-energy decrease in an oxidation must be trapped as chemical-bond energy rather than being utilized as heat. In recent years it has been established that the transfer of energy in biological systems occurs primarily through the agency of high-energy (energy-rich) bonds and that energy is trapped and stored for the most part in the form of high-energy phosphate bonds. These can be represented by the symbol $\sim$ⓅⓅ, where $\sim$ represents a high-energy bond and Ⓟ a phosphate group ($-PO_3H_2$, or the ionic form as determined by the pH). The high-energy phosphate compounds, by storing energy and later delivering it in suitable reactions, can be considered to act in a manner analogous to a storage battery.

The classical studies of Harden and Young early in this century demonstrated the need for phosphate and the formation of phosphorylated sugars during alcoholic fermentation by yeast juice. During the 1920's it was demonstrated that phosphate is split off of creatine phosphate and adenylpyrophosphate during muscular activity and that these compounds were resynthesized under either aerobic or anaerobic conditions. In the next decade many of the intermediate compounds of carbohydrate fermentation by muscle or by yeast were isolated, and their formation and utilization have been studied in considerable detail with the aid of purified enzyme systems. The importance and role of phosphates became evident from the studies of Lipmann and of Kalckar around 1941 (see reviews by Ball, Kalckar, and Meyerhof, 1944; Kaplan, 1951; and Colowick, 1951).

It was observed that when certain phosphate esters were hydrolyzed the heat of hydrolysis was around 2,000 to 3,000 cal., while a yield of 10,000 to 15,000 cal. was obtained from the hydrolysis of other phosphate esters.   If cleavage of a phosphate bond releases a low amount of heat, the bond is considered as a low-energy or energy-poor bond; if a large amount of heat is generated the bond is designated as a high-energy or energy-rich bond.   In the sense implied by biologists, the release of energy by splitting of a bond means a redistribution of electron pairs rather than the splitting of molecular bonds, forming atoms.   The energy of the phosphate bond depends upon the configuration of the entire molecule and the particular linkage between the phosphate group and the remainder of the molecule.   In high-energy phosphate compounds the energy-rich bond is of the anhydride type because it joins one acid group to another with the elimination of water, the anhydride linkage being characteristically energy-rich.

Lipmann (1955) points out that it would be less ambiguous to refer to the energy-rich and energy-poor bonds as groupings with *high* or *low* group potentials.   The caloric value for a particular bond determines the amount of energy required to raise a group into the bonding from the free state, the zero level such as that of free acetate or inorganic phosphate.   Thus, 12,000 or more calories are required to lift acetate from zero level to the potential level of the acetyl-to-phosphate link in acetyl phosphate.   The energy-rich phosphate group, or phosphate-group potential, serves as a medium for trapping and for exchange of energy obtained from cellular oxidations.   The cell possesses many mechanisms for the utilization of phosphate-bond energy through "transformer reactions" which lead to the activation of other groups.   Other high-energy bonds, or high group potentials, are found in bonds such as the acetyl-thioester link in acetyl CoA and will be considered later.   These group potentials play an important role in biosynthesis and have been considered as energy packages, "biochemical energy quanta," roughly analogous to physical-energy quanta.

Trapping of Energy.   A general picture of the nature of energy trapping in phosphate bonds can be developed from a consideration of a typical oxidation such as that of an aldehyde to an acid which can be represented as

$$R-\underset{\underset{H}{|}}{C}{=}O + H_2O \rightarrow R-\underset{\underset{H}{|}\ \ OH}{\overset{OH}{C}} \quad -2H \rightarrow R-\underset{\underset{OH}{|}}{C}{=}O$$

$$\Delta H = \text{about } -13{,}000 \text{ cal.}$$

When this oxidation, a dehydrogenation of the hydrated aldehyde molecule, occurs in the cell, an enzyme catalyzes the addition of a phosphate group instead of a molecule of water yielding a phosphorylated aldehyde containing an energy-poor bond.   This phosphorylated aldehyde is oxidized by loss of hydrogen to the appropriate coenzyme, the aldehyde group is thereby converted into an acidic group, and most of the free-energy decrease of the oxidation is retained in the newly formed anhydride linkage between the carboxyl group and the phosphate, only approximately 1,000 cal. being liberated as heat energy. The difference between the two heats of reaction, approximately 12,000 cal., is retained in the energy-rich bond. These reactions may be represented as

$$
R-\underset{\underset{H}{|}}{C}=O + H_3PO_4 \rightarrow R-\underset{\underset{H}{|}}{\overset{\overset{OH}{|}}{C}}-O-\underset{\underset{OH}{|}}{\overset{\overset{O}{\parallel}}{P}}-OH - 2H \rightarrow R-\overset{\overset{O}{\parallel}}{C}-O\sim\underset{\underset{OH}{|}}{\overset{\overset{O}{\parallel}}{P}}-OH
$$

$$\Delta H = \text{about} - 1,000 \text{ cal.}$$

This high-energy linkage can be transferred to another molecule such as the coenzyme of phosphorylation reactions, adenosine diphosphate accepting it with the formation of adenosine triphosphate, which is the major storehouse of trapped energy in the bacterial cell. Creatine $\sim$ⓅⒹ and arginine $\sim$Ⓟ contain an energy-rich bond, and these compounds may also serve as storehouses of energy, particularly in mammalian and possibly in bacterial cells. One outstanding feature of $\sim$Ⓟ transfer is that nearly all the energy associated with the bond is retained on transfer to the adenylic acid system or from it to other energy-rich compounds such as acetyl $\sim$Ⓟ. Loss of bond energy occurs when phosphate is transferred from ATP to glucose, an energy-poor bond linking the phosphate to the glucose molecule, but this serves to activate the glucose molecule. The transfer reactions will be considered in following chapters. The transfer of phosphate can be inhibited by an agent such as 2,4-dinitrophenol, which at the same time may stimulate oxygen uptake. This inhibition appears to be due to a dinitrophenol activation or stimulation of the enzyme (ATPase) which splits inorganic phosphate from ATP.

We have considered the oxidative formation of a high-energy phosphate bond as illustrated by the dehydrogenation of an ordinary phosphate ester of an aldehyde. A high-energy bond can also be formed by dehydration of a molecule, a reaction that can be illustrated by the conversion of 2-phosphoglyceric acid to the enol form of phosphopyruvic acid, or

$$
\begin{array}{c}
O{=}C-OH \\
| \\
{}^*H-C-O-Ⓟ \\
| \\
H-C-OH^* \\
| \\
H
\end{array}
\underset{\text{enolase}}{\overset{\longrightarrow}{\longleftarrow}}
\begin{array}{c}
O{=}C-OH \\
| \\
C-O\sim Ⓟ + H_2O \\
\parallel \\
H-C \\
| \\
H
\end{array}
$$

the hydroxyl group and the hydrogen atom removed in the dehydration being indicated by asterisks. This conversion of the primary alcoholic phosphate group into the energy-rich bond involves a marked change in molecular structure.

Three types of energy-rich phosphate bonds are known: (1) as in the two terminal bonds in ATP, $-\text{(P)}\sim\text{(P)}\sim\text{(P)}$, or

$$
\begin{array}{ccc}
\text{O} & \text{O} & \text{O} \\
\parallel & \parallel & \parallel \\
-\text{P}-\text{O}\sim\text{P}-\text{O}\sim\text{P}-\text{OH} \\
| & | & | \\
\text{OH} & \text{OH} & \text{OH}
\end{array}
$$

(2) the $\text{C}-\text{O}\sim\text{(P)}$ bond as in the enol form of phosphopyruvic acid (a) and acetyl phosphate (b),

$$
(a)\quad
\begin{array}{cc}
\text{CH}_2 & \text{O} \\
\parallel & \parallel \\
\text{C}-\text{O}\sim\text{P}-\text{OH} \\
| & | \\
\text{COOH} & \text{OH}
\end{array}
\qquad
(b)\quad
\begin{array}{cc}
\text{CH}_3 & \text{O} \\
| & \parallel \\
\text{C}-\text{O}\sim\text{P}-\text{OH} \\
\parallel & | \\
\text{O} & \text{OH}
\end{array}
$$

and (3) the $-\text{N}-\text{C}-\text{N}\sim\text{(P)}$ bond as in creatine phosphate, or

$$
\begin{array}{c}
\text{CH}_2\text{COOH} \\
| \\
\text{N}-\text{CH}_3 \\
| \\
\text{C}=\text{NH} \\
| \quad\quad \text{O} \\
| \quad\quad \parallel \\
\text{H}-\text{N}\sim\text{P}-\text{OH} \\
| \\
\text{OH}
\end{array}
$$

Ochoa (1943) has calculated that as many as six high-energy phosphate bonds can be formed per molecule of oxygen consumed during the oxidation of glucose to carbon dioxide and water. Using 12,000 cal. as the average value for hydrolysis of the energy-rich phosphate bond, the combustion of one mole of glucose could give rise to the formation of 36 high-energy bonds or the trapping of 432,000 cal. in $\sim\text{(P)}$ energy. Other calculations indicate that there is enough potential energy theoretically available in glucose to form 56 of these bonds. An energy-rich bond theoretically can be formed in the oxidative chain when a difference of approximately 0.25 volt exists on the redox scale, ΔF being equal to $-nFE$, or $2 \times 23,068 \times 0.25 = -11,500$ cal.

Krebs (1954) has concluded that seven reactions are involved in the utilization of carbohydrate by animals, and probably by many bacteria, that lead to the formation of ATP. These can be depicted as follows:

1. Oxidation of glyceraldehyde phosphate to phosphoglyceric acid, or

Glyceraldehyde—(P) + DPN^+ + ADP + (P) →

phosphoglyceric acid + DPNH + H^+ + ATP

2. Formation of pyruvic acid, or

Phosphopyruvate + ADP → pyruvate + ATP

3, 4, 5. Three steps in the electron carrier chain between DPNH and oxygen.

6. Oxidative decarboxylation of α-keto acids, or

RCOCOOH + DPN^+ + ADP + (P) → RCOOH + CO_2 + DPNH + H^+ + ATP

7. Succinic acid oxidation to fumaric acid, or

Succinate + ferricytochrome + ADP + (P) → fumarate + ferrocytochrome + ATP

Energy can also be trapped in ATP in other reactions elicited by bacteria, e.g., in the conversion of citrulline to ornithine or from acetyl phosphate formed in the splitting of pyruvate in reactions involving coenzyme A, phosphate replacing coenzyme A in acetyl-CoA under the influence of phosphotransacetylase.

REFERENCES

General

Clark, W. M., N. O. Kaplan, and M. D. Kamen: Symposium on electron transport in the metabolism of microorganisms, *Bacteriol. Rev.*, **19**, 234–262 (1955).
Sumner, J. B., and K. Myrbäck (eds.): "The Enzymes," 2 vols., 2 pts., Academic Press, Inc., New York, 1950–1951.

Specific

Baldwin, E.: "Dynamic Aspects of Biochemistry," Cambridge University Press, London, 1949.
Ball, E. G.: Energy relationships of the oxidative enzymes, *Ann. N.Y. Acad. Sci.*, **45**, 363–375 (1944).
Chance, B.: The iron-containing enzymes. C. The enzyme-substrate compounds and mechanism of action of the hydroperoxidases, in "The Enzymes," vol. 2, pt. 1, chap. 56, Academic Press, Inc., New York, 1951.
Colowick, S. P.: Transphosphorylating enzymes of fermentation, in "The Enzymes," vol. 2, pt. 1, chap. 46, Academic Press, Inc., New York, 1951.
Dickens, F.: Anaerobic glycolysis, respiration, and the Pasteur effect, in "The Enzymes," vol. 2, pt. 1, chap. 63, Academic Press, Inc., New York, 1951.
Dixon, M.: "Manometric Methods," Cambridge University Press, London, 1934.
Foster, J. W.: "Chemical Activities of Fungi," Academic Press, Inc., New York, 1949.
Green, D. E.: The cyclophorase complex of enzymes, *Biol. Rev. Camb. Phil. Soc.*, **26**, 410–455 (1951).
Hanke, M. E., and J. H. Bailey: Oxidation-reduction potential of *Cl. welchii* and other clostridia, *Proc. Soc. Exptl. Biol. Med.*, **59**, 163–166 (1943).
Hewitt, L. F.: "Oxidation-Reduction Potentials in Bacteriology and Biochemistry," 5th ed., London County Council, 1948.

Johnson, F. H., H. Eyring, R. Stebly, H. Chaplin, C. Huber, and G. Gherardi: The nature and control of reactions in bioluminescence, *J. Gen. Physiol.*, **28**, 463–537 (1945).

Kalckar, H. M.: The function of phosphate in enzymatic syntheses, *Ann. N.Y. Acad. Sci.*, **45**, 395–408 (1944).

Kaplan, N. O.: Thermodynamics and mechanisms of the phosphate bond, in "The Enzymes," vol. 2, pt. 1, chap. 45, Academic Press, Inc., New York, 1951.

Kluyver, A. J.: "The Chemical Activities of Microorganisms," University of London Press, Ltd., London, 1931.

Knight, B. C. J. G., and P. Fildes: The positive limit of oxidation-reduction potential required for the germination of *B. tetani* spores in vitro, *Biochem. J.*, **24**, 1496–1505 (1930).

Krebs, A.: Energy production in animal tissues and in microorganisms, in E. Racker (ed.), "Cellular Metabolism and Infections," Academic Press, Inc., New York, 1954.

Lipmann, F., Coenzyme A and biosynthesis, *Am. Scientist*, **43**, 37–47 (1955).

McElroy, W. D., and R. Ballentine: The mechanism of bioluminescence, *Proc. Natl. Acad. Sci., U.S.*, **30**, 377–382 (1944).

Meyerhof, O.: Energy relationships in glycolysis and phosphorylation, *Ann. N.Y. Acad. Sci.*, **45**, 377–393 (1944).

Ochoa, S.: Efficiency of aerobic phosphorylation in cell-free heart extracts, *J. Biol. Chem.*, **151**, 493–505 (1943).

Pickett, M. J., and C. E. Clifton: The effect of selective poisons on the utilization of glucose and intermediate compounds by microorganisms, *J. Cell. Comp. Physiol.*, **22**, 147–165 (1943).

Prescott, S. C., and C. G. Dunn: "Industrial Microbiology," McGraw-Hill Book Company, Inc., New York, 1949.

Quastel, J. H., and M. D. Whetman: Dehydrogenations produced by resting bacteria, I, II, *Biochem. J.*, **19**, 520–531, 645–651 (1925).

van Schouwenburg, K. L.: On the respiration and light emission in luminous bacteria, Dissertation, Delft, 1938.

Slater, E. C.: The dihydrocozymase-cytochrome-c reductase activity of heart muscle preparations, *Biochem. J.*, **46**, 499–502 (1950).

Smith, L.: Bacterial cytochromes, *Bacteriol. Rev.*, **18**, 106–130 (1954).

Umbreit, W. W., R. H. Burris, and J. F. Stauffer: "Manometric Techniques and Tissue Metabolism," Burgess Publishing Co., Minneapolis, 1949.

CHAPTER 7

ALCOHOLIC FERMENTATION

Glucose can be regarded as the most universal source of carbon and of energy for bacteria and other heterotrophic organisms. Either directly or as a component of higher sugars, it is able to supply these bulk requirements of the diet to a greater extent than any other single substance commonly employed in culture media. A major problem confronting the physiologist is the nature of the reactions, both assimilatory and dissimilatory, by means of which energy and building materials are made available and utilized by the cell. Since more is known about the utilization of glucose and other sugars than about other foodstuffs, much of the discussion in this and following chapters will deal with mechanisms of carbohydrate metabolism. A considerable portion of our knowledge of this has been gained from studies on alcoholic fermentation, and this process will be considered in detail. Before discussing the mechanism of fermentation it might be well briefly to review the structure and nature of carbohydrates.

Carbohydrates. In general the true carbohydrates can be defined as aldehyde or ketone derivatives (or potentially so) of polyhydric alcohols. They are classified as monosaccharides if they cannot be hydrolyzed into simpler carbohydrates, as disaccharides if they yield two monosaccharides on hydrolysis, and as polysaccharides if more than two units are formed. The term oligosaccharides is frequently employed for polysaccharides of known monosaccharide content. The structural formula for glucose indicates that it is an aldehyde sugar (aldose), a hexose since it contains 6 carbon atoms, and a pyranose because its cyclic form contains a 5-carbon–1-oxygen–membered ring as is present in pyran. Sugars containing a 4-carbon–1-oxygen ring structure are known as furanoses for a similar reason, fructose being an example of this type of sugar.

Glucose in solution exists in two forms, a small amount of a straight-chain molecule in equilibrium with the remainder in the form of a pyranose ring compound. The straight chain and the cyclic structures are represented as

(Fischer structure)   (Haworth structure)

The complete designative term for glucose existing in the cyclic form is α-D(+)-glucopyranose. The meaning of these prefixes will be discussed below. The use of the Fischer or the Haworth structural representation is partly a matter of choice, the latter structure more graphically illustrating the spatial arrangement of the atoms in the molecule. In the Haworth formulation the plane of the ring must be considered as being perpendicular to the printed page with the heavy lines located closest to the reader. The other atoms or groups are located above or below this plane as indicated in the formula. The Fischer representation will be used in much of the discussion on fermentation but for the sake of convenience only.

The figures in brackets alongside the straight-chain form of the glucose molecule indicate the system employed in numbering the carbon atoms. Numbering commences with the terminal aldehyde carbon atom or with the terminal carbon nearest the keto group in the ketoses. Inspection of the straight-chain formula shows that four asymmetric carbon atoms (ones with four different atoms or groups attached to them) are present in the glucose molecule. A fifth asymmetric carbon appears in the glucose molecule upon formation of the pyranose ring. The arrangement of the hydrogen and hydroxyl groups around these asymmetric carbons makes possible the formation of different stereoisomers and, depending upon the arrangement around atoms 2, 3, 4, and 5, eight different hexoses are possible (Fig. 7-1). Furthermore, each of these hexoses can exist in two forms, one of which is the optical (mirror) image of the other. This mirror-image type of isomerism is indicated by the use of small Roman capitals, D or L, in the complete name of the sugar.

By convention the designation of a sugar as a D isomer indicates that the orientation of the H and OH groups around the highest numbered asymmetric carbon atom is the same as that around the simplest, or parent, standard carbohydrate, D-glyceraldehyde. The L isomer is the optical image of the D form, and this type of isomerism can be represented as

$$\begin{array}{cc}
\text{CHO} & \text{CHO} \\
| & | \\
\text{H—C—OH} & \text{HO—C—H} \\
| & | \\
\text{CH}_2\text{OH} & \text{CH}_2\text{OH} \\
\text{D(+)-Glyceraldehyde} & \text{L(−)-Glyceraldehyde}
\end{array}$$

The + or − signs in parentheses indicate whether the compound is dextrorotary (+) or levorotary (−), i.e., in aqueous solution causes the plane of polarized light to rotate toward the right or left, respectively. This optical-rotation type of isomerism is independent of spatial isomerism, some D isomers exhibiting rotary power opposite to that of the arbitrary standard, D(+)-glyceraldehyde, and being designated as D(−). Likewise, members of the L series may exhibit dextrorotary power and would be designated as L(+). In former years optical rotation was indicated by the use of small italic letters, *d* or *l*, and this causes some confusion in the literature.

The H and OH groups on carbon atom 1 of the cyclic form of the aldose hexoses are somewhat unstable as regards their point of attachment to this atom. An equilibrium is slowly established in solution between two forms, the *alpha* in which the OH group is located on the right-hand side of the molecule as represented by the Fischer structure (HCOH) and the *beta* in which the position of the H and OH groups is reversed (HOCH). This change from one form to the other is termed mutarotation. The rate of this change is greater in slightly acidic or alkaline solutions than it is in pure water and is also increased by a specific enzyme present in some organisms.

The sugars glucose, fructose, and mannose are interconvertible in solutions of weak alkalies and possibly to some extent in the cell. This interconvertibility can be visualized as occurring through an intermediate, enediol form common to these sugars in the open-chain form as follows:

$$\begin{array}{c}
\text{Mannose} \\
\text{H—C=O} \\
| \\
\text{HO—C—H} \\
|
\end{array}$$

$$\text{H—C=O} \qquad \text{H—C—OH} \qquad \text{H} $$
$$| \qquad\quad || \qquad\quad | $$
$$\text{H—C—OH} \rightleftharpoons \text{C—OH} \rightleftharpoons \text{H—C—OH} $$
$$| \qquad\qquad | \qquad\qquad | $$
$$\text{Glucose} \qquad\qquad\qquad \text{C=O} $$
$$\qquad\qquad\qquad\qquad\quad | $$
$$\qquad\qquad\qquad\qquad \text{Fructose}$$

Sugars can undergo a variety of reactions, among them being oxidation, reduction, changes in form, and substitution reactions. Oxidation of sugars under mild conditions leads to the formation of sugar acids, reduc-

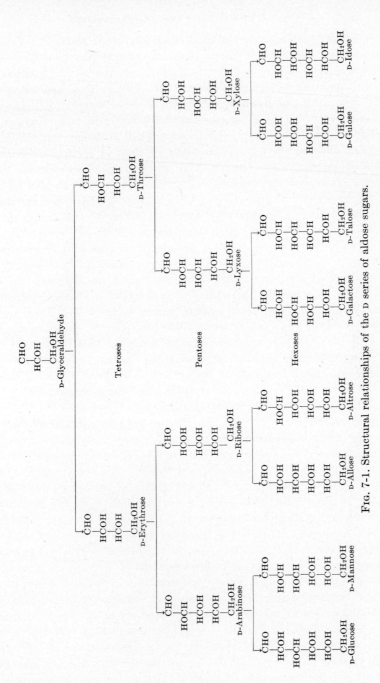

Fig. 7-1. Structural relationships of the D series of aldose sugars.

tion to the formation of the corresponding polyhydric alcohols. Various other changes occur when solutions of sugars are heated, and these at times in culture media lead to the formation of growth-inhibitory or growth-promoting substances, the activity being dependent upon the characteristics of the organism under study. For this reason it is often necessary to sterilize sugar solutions by filtration rather than by heating. Substitution in the sugar molecule may result in other compounds of biological importance, e.g., replacement of the OH group on the no. 2 carbon atom of glucose with an NH_2 group gives rise to glucosamine. Another example is the reaction of glucose with methyl alcohol to give methyl glucoside, $C_5H_{10}O_5$—CHO—CH_3. Monosaccharides can undergo condensation (substitution) reactions, two or more sugars uniting by means of glycosidic linkages with the formation of di- or polysaccharides. Certain of these reactions will be considered in appropriate sections of the text.

Three disaccharides of considerable importance in diagnostic bacteriology are sucrose, lactose, and maltose. A fourth disaccharide, cellobiose, is also of interest since it is a repeating unit in cellulose. These sugars are formed by means of a glycosidic union between two monosaccharides, one molecule of water, or of phosphate, being split off in the reaction. The scientific names of these sugars are derived from those of the component hexoses and indicate the carbon atoms involved in their linkages. The complete name for sucrose on this basis is α-D-glucopyranosido-1-2-β-D-fructofuranose. The structural formulas of these four disaccharides are given in Fig. 7-2. These sugars, before they are utilized by the cell, generally have to be degraded by their appropriate enzymes to their constituent hexoses, although disaccharides are utilized by some bacteria more readily than are their constituent sugars.

Carbohydrates are utilized by many species of organisms in a similar manner, as far at least as the stage of pyruvic acid. Deviation occurs at this point under anaerobic conditions; under aerobic ones pyruvate generally is oxidized via the Krebs tricarboxylic acid cycle. The evidence for this is not complete for many species of bacteria. The isolation from different species of various of the enzymes and of intermediates involved in the separate reactions, or the demonstration of the utilization of the important intermediates, lends support to the concept of the fundamental unity of biochemical processes. We probably are on fairly secure ground if we conclude that the Embden-Meyerhof dissimilatory pathway is common to the majority of organisms as far as the formation of pyruvate, although other pathways may also be utilized, even in one species. Bacteria differ from each other in the hydrogen acceptors they employ for the anaerobic oxidation of pyruvic acid or compounds derived therefrom. It is also possible for deviations to occur before the pyruvate stage. A

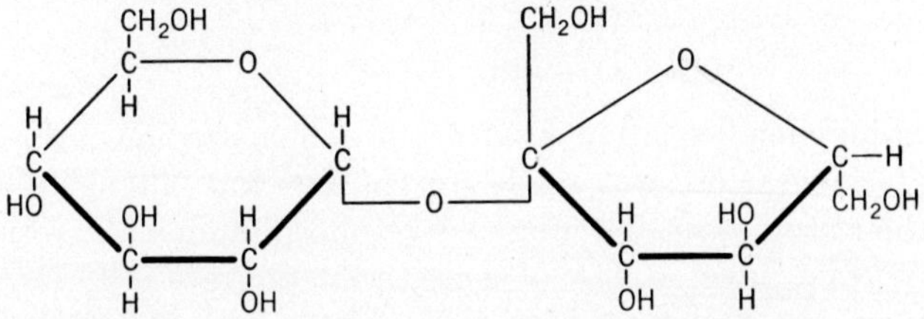

Sucrose (α-D-glucopyranosido-1-2-β-D-fructofuranose)

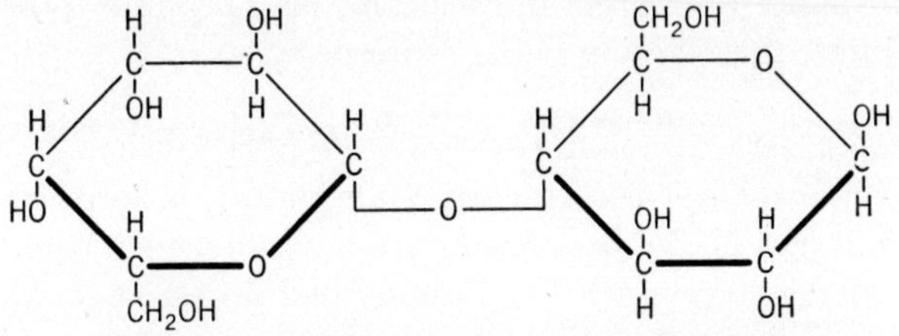

Lactose (β-D-galactopyranosido-1-4-β-D-glucopyranose)

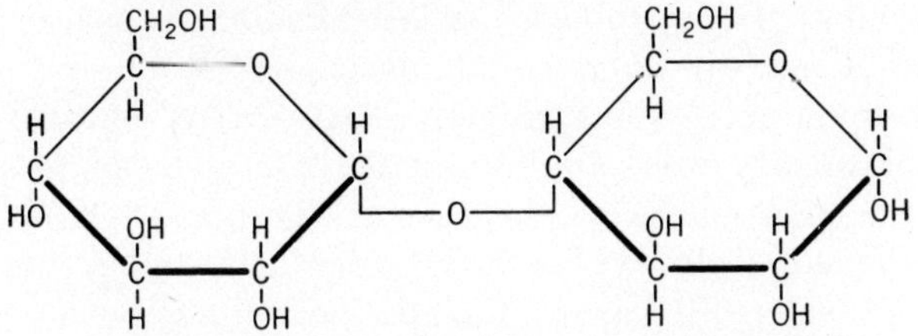

Maltose (α-D-glucopyranosido-1-4-α-D-glucopyranose)

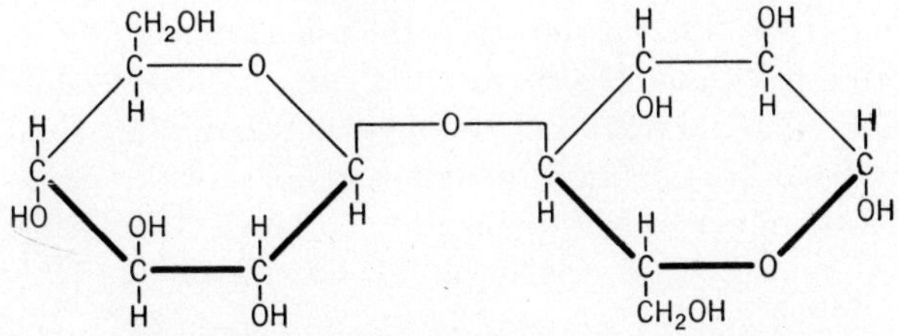

Cellobiose (β-D-glucopyranosido-1-4-β-D-glucopyranose)

FIG. 7-2. Structural formulas of four disaccharides of interest in bacteriology.

proper understanding of the bacterial fermentations requires a knowledge of the most completely studied fermentations, those induced by yeast and by muscle. Most of the enzymes involved in these fermentations have been isolated, and the individual reactions they catalyze have been studied in some detail.

Early Observations on Fermentation. In 1815 Gay-Lussac reported that the major chemical change in alcoholic fermentation can be represented as

$$C_6H_{12}O_6 \rightarrow 2C_2H_5OH + 2CO_2$$

The first major chemical advance, after the demonstration of the biological nature of fermentation, was made by Harden and Young in 1905 as a result of their studies on the influence of phosphate on the fermentation induced by yeast juice. They observed that the rate of fermentation of glucose by zymase decreased with time and that it could be restored by the addition of phosphate. During fermentation the concentration of inorganic phosphate decreased and a hexose diphosphate ester accumulated in the juice, the reaction being represented as

$$2C_6H_{12}O_6 + 2H_3PO_4 \rightarrow 2C_2H_5OH + 2CO_2 + C_6H_{10}O_6(PO_3H_2)_2 + 2H_2O$$

This hexose diphosphate, the Harden-Young ester, is fermented slowly by zymase and gradually disappears from the fermentation mixture. Phosphate added to yeast-cell suspensions had no effect on the rate of fermentation by intact cells, a behavior we now know is due to the activity of the adenylic acid system in the cells and the continuous transfer of phosphate groups. Later Robinson isolated a monophosphate ester now recognized as a mixture of glucose-6-phosphate (Robinson ester) and fructose-6-phosphate (Neuberg ester). These early observations suggested that phosphate esters are intermediates in alcoholic fermentation and raised the question as to the role of phosphates in the process. Another fundamental observation by Harden and Young, one that we have already considered (Chap. 5), was that yeast-juice zymase contained at least two different components, a heat-labile, nondialyzable portion and a heat-stable, dialyzable cozymase fraction.

The next major clues to the nature of the reactions leading from hexose diphosphate to ethyl alcohol (ethanol) and carbon dioxide came from the studies of Neuberg in the 1910's. He observed that when sodium sulfite was added to a fermentation mixture little alcohol was formed, and instead equal amounts of an acetaldehyde-bisulfite complex ($CH_3CHOHSO_3Na$), carbon dioxide, and glycerol (glycerine) accumulated, or

Glucose → acetaldehyde-sulfite + carbon dioxide + glycerol

This reaction is generally spoken of as Neuberg's second form of fermentation, the first being the true alcoholic one. These observations suggested that acetaldehyde is the precursor of ethanol in the regular fermentation and that glycerol could arise from a similar reduction of a 3-carbon compound. It appeared that the aldehyde and carbon dioxide could arise from a common source, a 3-carbon compound which Neuberg identified as pyruvic acid. He was able to demonstrate that pyruvic acid is decarboxylated by yeast with the formation of acetaldehyde and carbon dioxide. Neuberg concluded that glucose is phosphorylated with the formation of hexose diphosphate, this ester undergoes cleavage with the formation of methyl glyoxal (CH_3COCHO), the glyoxal is converted to pyruvic acid, and pyruvate is decarboxylated with the production of acetaldehyde which can be reduced to ethanol. In the presence of sulfite the acetaldehyde is trapped and methyl glyoxal, substituting for acetaldehyde in the reduction reaction, is reduced to glycerol.

Neuberg also observed that in an alkaline medium fermentation proceeded according to the third form of fermentation, which can be described by the equation

$$2 \text{ Glucose} \rightarrow 2 \text{ glycerol} + 2 \text{ carbon dioxide} + \text{acetic acid} + \text{ethyl alcohol}$$

Under alkaline conditions acetaldehyde undergoes a dismutation or Cannizzaro type of reaction in which one aldehyde molecule is reduced, the other oxidized, with the formation of ethanol and acetic acid, respectively. The production of acetic acid tends to lower the pH of the mixture, and unless the acid is neutralized, the tendency is for the normal course of fermentation to be resumed. Here we have another example of alterations occurring in the metabolism of microorganisms of such a nature as to neutralize the disturbing influence, an illustration of Le Châtelier's principle. It is worthy of noting in passing that the second and third forms of fermentation have been employed under First World War conditions of glycerol shortage in Germany for the production of this compound.

These various observations in the early 1900's clearly indicated the complexity of the fermentation process and the necessity for considering the various observed factors in any attempt to establish an acceptable scheme of fermentation. It was also noted that similar chemical events occurred during the anaerobic utilization of glucose by muscle, although this fermentation deviated from the alcoholic one in that lactic acid was the reduction product and no carbon dioxide was formed. The various factors that had to be considered can be summarized as follows:

1. The role of phosphate and phosphate esters.
2. All the compounds produced in the three forms of alcoholic fermentation (and in glycolysis by muscle) can arise from 3-carbon compounds derived from the cleavage of phosphorylated hexoses. It had been demonstrated that the fusel oil (higher alcohols) found in fermented liquors was a product of amino acid fermentation.
3. Pyruvic acid is an intermediate of fermentation and can be decarboxylated with the formation of equimolar amounts of acetaldehyde and carbon dioxide.
4. Acetaldehyde can be reduced to ethyl alcohol.
5. Traces of glycerol are always formed, much more being produced under certain unfavorable conditions.

Neuberg's scheme was supported fairly well by the known facts but did not offer explanations for the reaction mechanisms and how fermentation was coupled with other metabolic activities of the cell. Numerous studies in the 1930's, utilizing enzyme preparations from yeast and muscle, cellular poisons, and trapping agents, provided many of the details upon which the Embden-Meyerhof scheme of alcoholic fermentation and of lactic acid production (glycolysis) by muscle was founded. The basic foundation, however, was established by the earlier work of Harden and Young, of Neuberg, and others. This anaerobic pathway or main line of respiration will be considered in detail in the following pages since it has been well established and beautifully illustrates the intricate coupling of reactions and enzyme systems involved in the life of a cell. Many or all of these reactions are utilized in the respiratory activities of numerous species of bacteria and other organisms. It has also been established that other carbohydrates are ultimately converted into the phosphate esters of fermentation, and from this stage their pathways of utilization follow that of glucose oxidation or fermentation. Furthermore, other substances are frequently degraded with the formation of compounds found along the main line of respiration. The ethanol fermentation is summarized in Figs. 7-3 and 7-4. This scheme also illustrates one pathway of aerobic respiration up to the stage of pyruvate, with the exception that reduced DPN (CoI) transfers hydrogen and electrons to the pathway leading to oxygen.

Glucose-6-phosphate. The first step in the dissimilation of glucose involves phosphorylation at the no. 6 carbon, the hydroxyl hydrogen being replaced with a phosphate group. The reaction is mediated by hexokinase in the presence of Mg^{++} ions and ATP as a coenzyme or cofactor and may be represented as

This can be considered as the first preparatory reaction, glucose being activated by transfer of a phosphate group from ATP. This reaction involves the loss of a high-energy phosphate bond by the cell since an ordinary phosphate ester linkage exists in glucose-6-phosphate. The free energy of the reaction is about $-9,000$ cal. It illustrates a principle applicable to many biological reactions, i.e., a synthesis occurring in a coupled reaction in that one product has a higher free-energy content than its precursor, although there is a decrease in free energy for the over-all reaction.

Hexokinase has been obtained in crystalline form from yeast and has a molecular weight near 97,000.   It catalyzes the phosphorylation with ATP and Mg^{++} of glucose, fructose, or mannose with the formation of the corresponding -6-phosphates.   The maximum rate of glucose phosphorylation is around 13,000 molecules per enzyme molecule per minute. The Michaelis constant K_m [equation (5-8)] indicates that the enzyme

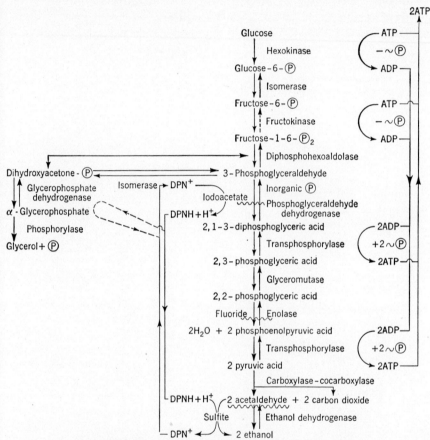

Fig. 7-3. Flow sheet for alcoholic fermentation by yeast.

is one-half-saturated at a glucose concentration of 1.5×10^{-4} M at the optimum pH.   The reaction is irreversible, or practically so, since the equilibrium constant as calculated with the aid of equation (2-8) ($\Delta F = -RT \ln K$) has a value near 3×10^6.   In other words, there would be 3 million molecules of glucose-6-phosphate per molecule of glucose at equilibrium.   This is one of the three irreversible reactions in alcoholic fermentation, the others being the formation of fructose-1-6-diphosphate and the decarboxylation of pyruvic acid.

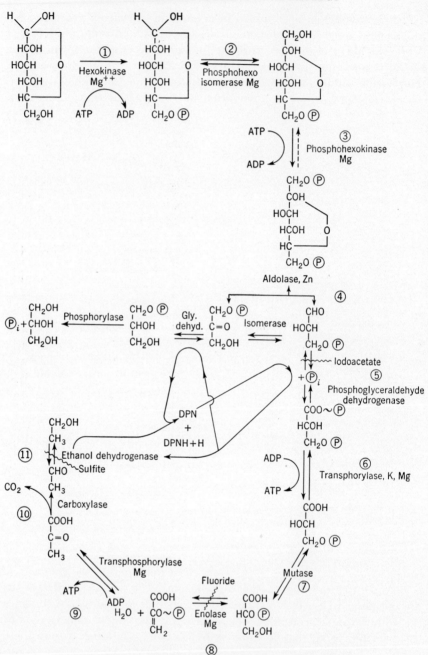

Fig. 7-4. Major steps in the fermentation of glucose by yeast.

Fructose-6-phosphate. The second preparatory step in the dissimilation of glucose is an isomerization, glucose-6-phosphate being converted to fructose-6-phosphate in a reversible manner, about 70 per cent of the glucose ester being present at equilibrium. The reaction, catalyzed by phosphohexoisomerase, can be represented as

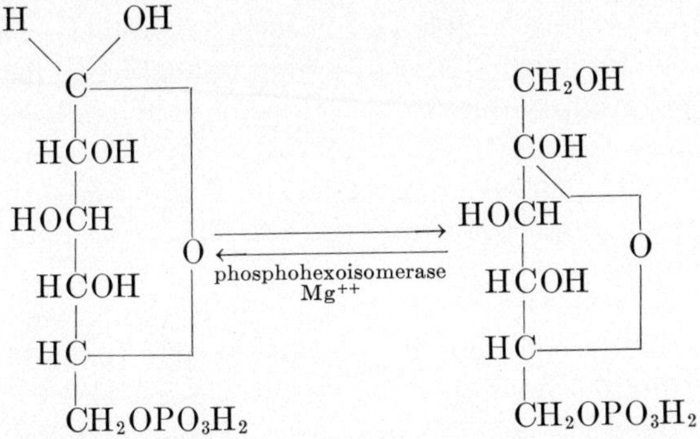

$$
\begin{array}{c}
\overset{H}{\underset{|}{\overset{\diagdown}{C}}} \overset{OH}{\diagup} \\
HCOH \\
HOCH \\
HCOH \\
HC \\
CH_2OPO_3H_2
\end{array}
\quad O
\xrightarrow[\underset{Mg^{++}}{\text{phosphohexoisomerase}}]{\;}
\begin{array}{c}
CH_2OH \\
COH \\
HOCH \\
HCOH \\
HC \\
CH_2OPO_3H_2
\end{array}
\quad O
$$

Fructose-1-6-diphosphate. The third preparatory step is similar to the first, fructose-6-phosphate being phosphorylated at the no. 1 carbon under the influence of a phosphohexokinase together with ATP and Mg^{++} ions. This involves the loss of a second high-energy phosphate bond by the cell and $\Delta F =$ about $-8,000$ cal. This reaction, therefore, like the first, is not truly reversible. It appears that the reverse reaction yields fructose-6-phosphate but not ATP, probably inorganic phosphate instead.

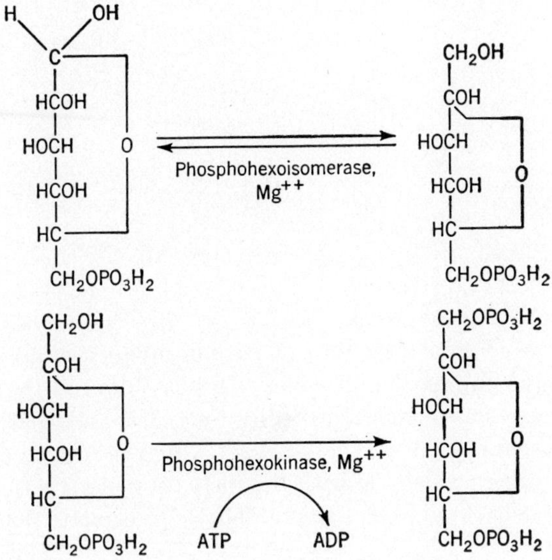

$$
\begin{array}{c}
\overset{H}{\underset{|}{\overset{\diagdown}{C}}} \overset{OH}{\diagup} \\
HCOH \\
HOCH \\
HCOH \\
HC \\
CH_2OPO_3H_2
\end{array}
\quad O
\xrightleftharpoons[\underset{Mg^{++}}{\text{Phosphohexoisomerase,}}]{\;}
\begin{array}{c}
CH_2OH \\
COH \\
HOCH \\
HCOH \\
HC \\
CH_2OPO_3H_2
\end{array}
\quad O
$$

$$
\begin{array}{c}
CH_2OH \\
COH \\
HOCH \\
HCOH \\
HC \\
CH_2OPO_3H_2
\end{array}
\quad O
\xrightarrow[\underset{ATP \quad ADP}{\text{Phosphohexokinase, } Mg^{++}}]{\;}
\begin{array}{c}
CH_2OPO_3H_2 \\
COH \\
HOCH \\
HCOH \\
HC \\
CH_2OPO_3H_2
\end{array}
\quad O
$$

Dihydroxyacetone-Glyceraldehyde Phosphates. The fourth reaction involves the cleavage of the hexosediphosphate molecule, with the formation of a molecule each of the triose phosphates, dihydroxyacetone phosphate and D-glyceraldehyde-3-phosphate (3-phosphoglyceraldehyde). This cleavage between carbon atoms 3 and 4 was demonstrated in 1934 by Meyerhof and Lohman. The responsible enzyme is termed an aldolase. The reaction is reversible and in reverse involves an aldol condensation between the aldehyde group of phosphoglyceraldehyde and the terminal alcohol group of dihydroxyacetone phosphate. The equilibrium constant, around 1×10^{-4}, would indicate the existence of about 5,000 hexosediphosphate molecules per molecule of the trioses if equilibrium were established. Since the trioses are utilized very rapidly, cleavage of the hexosediphosphate continues.

The triose phosphates formed by cleavage of the hexose are isomeric, and an enzyme, triosephosphate isomerase or phosphoglyceroisomerase, catalyzes the interconversion of the two isomers. The isomerization of phosphoglyceraldehyde to form dihydroxyacetone phosphate involves a free-energy decrease of around 2,000 cal., and hence an equilibrium mixture of about 6 molecules of the glyceraldehyde to 94 of the dihydroxyacetone phosphate. Equilibria such as this and the one with hexosediphosphate might serve as balance wheels in the dynamic equilibrium of respiration as a whole. The two enzymes involved in the cleavage and the isomerization frequently are spoken of as the zymohexase complex, the reactions they catalyze being

$$
\begin{array}{ll}
\begin{array}{l}
\text{CH}_2\text{OPO}_3\text{H}_2 \\
|\\
\text{COH} \\
|\\
\text{HOCH} \\
|\\
\text{HCOH} \\
|\\
\text{HC} \\
|\\
\text{CH}_2\text{OPO}_3\text{H}_2
\end{array}
&
\begin{array}{l}
\text{CH}_2\text{OPO}_3\text{H}_2 \\
|\\
\text{C}{=}\text{O} \quad \text{Dihydroxyacetone—(P)} \\
|\\
\text{CH}_2\text{OH} \\
\\
\text{CHO} \\
|\\
\text{HOCH} \quad \text{Glyceraldehyde—(P)} \\
|\\
\text{CH}_2\text{OPO}_3\text{H}_2
\end{array}
\end{array}
$$

(aldolase Zn^{++}; isomerase)

1-3-Diphosphoglyceric Acid. Either of the two triose phosphates formed by cleavage of hexosediphosphate conceivably could be converted into ethyl alcohol and carbon dioxide. It was observed that glyceraldehyde-3-phosphate was fermented readily by yeast, and Warburg demonstrated the presence of an enzyme in yeast which catalyzed the dehydrogenation of the glyceraldehyde with the formation of glyceric acid. This enzyme, triose dehydrogenase, glyceraldehyde phosphate dehydrogenase, or phosphoglyceraldehyde dehydrogenase, catalyzes the fifth reaction in the direct dissimilation chain with the aid of DPN^+ and with the uptake of inorganic phosphate to form 1,3-diphosphoglyceric acid. This enzyme is inhibited by iodoacetate. A high-energy phosphate bond is formed as a result of the oxidative change, and the attachment is to the carboxyl group, or

$$
\begin{array}{ccc}
\underset{\substack{\text{HOCH} \\ | \\ \text{CH}_2\text{OPO}_3\text{H}_2}}{\overset{\overset{O}{\underset{\text{H}}{\diagup\!\!\!\!\diagdown}}C}{|}} \; + \; \text{HOPO}_3\text{H}_2 & \xrightarrow{\hspace{1cm}} & \underset{\substack{\text{HOCH} \\ | \\ \text{CH}_2\text{OPO}_3\text{H}_2}}{\text{COO}\!\sim\!\text{PO}_3\text{H}_2}
\end{array}
$$

(DPN$^+$ → DPNH + H$^+$, Phosphoglyceraldehyde dehydrogenase)

(In these reactions the phosphate groups are pictured as being undissociated; actually, ionization occurs to an extent controlled by pH. Also in the discussions pH and temperature have not been considered as regards equilibria and free-energy changes. Most values are from data obtained near 30°C. and neutrality and must be considered as approximations, not as absolute values.)

The equilibrium constant for the above reaction is near unity, and the free-energy change around -500 cal. with a purified dehydrogenase preparation. Redox-potential data lead to a calculated $\Delta F = +13,500$ cal. for the reaction $DPN^+ + 2H \rightarrow DPNH + H^+$. These two ΔF values considered together indicate that the ΔF of the reaction 3-phosphoglyceric acid + phosphate $\rightarrow$ 1,3-diphosphoglyceric acid must be near $-14,000$ cal. In other words, although 14,000 cal. theoretically is made available as a result of the oxidation of aldehyde to acid, yet 13,500 of these is chemically bound in the reduction of DPN^+, and hence the over-all free-energy change is only -500 cal. The energy chemically bound in DPNH is later employed for the reduction of acetaldehyde to ethanol.

Since two moles of phosphoglyceric acid are ultimately produced per mole of glucose dissimilated it should be evident that two high-energy phosphate bonds are formed at this stage, and these two, on transfer to ADP to form ATP, cancel the two utilized in the preparatory stages of fermentation.

3-Phosphoglyceric Acid. In the sixth reaction the high-energy phosphate bond is transferred under the catalytic influence of a transphosphorylase to ADP with the formation of 3-phosphoglyceric acid and ATP. It might be well to mention again that usage of the phrase "transfer of a high-energy phosphate bond" is not strictly correct. The phosphate group is transferred, and in this reaction a high-energy bond is also found in the product ATP. The phrase is a descriptive one for the over-all result and is widely, if not wisely, used. The reaction may be expressed as

$$\begin{array}{cc}
\text{COO}\sim\text{PO}_3\text{H}_2 & \text{COOH} \\
| & | \\
\text{HOCH} \qquad + \text{ADP} \underset{\substack{\text{transphos-}\\\text{phorylase}\\\text{K}^+,\ \text{Mg}^{++}}}{\overset{}{\rightleftarrows}} \text{HOCH} \qquad + \text{ADP}\sim\text{\textcircled{P}(ATP)} \\
| & | \\
\text{CH}_2\text{OPO}_3\text{H}_2 & \text{CH}_2\text{OPO}_3\text{H}_2
\end{array}$$

This transphosphorylase-catalyzed reaction has an equilibrium constant of about 1×10^3, or an over-all ΔF near $-4,000$ cal., the reaction, therefore, proceeding toward an equilibrium far to the right. This reaction, together with the previous one, illustrates mechanisms of storage and transfer of energy in coupled reactions and serves to illustrate as well the application of thermodynamic reasoning to biological reactions. If we consider the two reactions together, a somewhat clearer insight into the problem can be obtained.

Energetics of the Coupled Oxidation-Phosphorylation Reaction. When the two preceding reactions are considered together, we obtain

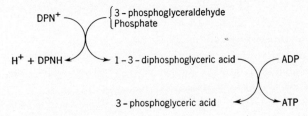

or, for the over-all reaction at constant pH,

3-Phosphoglyceraldehyde + phosphate + DPN$^+$ + ADP
$$\rightleftarrows \text{3-phosphoglyceric acid} + \text{DPNH} + \text{H}^+ + \text{ATP}$$

Substitution of experimental data into equation (2-13) and solving for the equilibrium constant K give a value of 3×10^3, where

$$K = \frac{[\text{PGA}][\text{DPNH}][\text{ATP}][\text{H}^+]}{[\text{PGAld}][\text{P}][\text{DPN}^+][\text{ADP}]}$$

The standard free-energy change for this reaction is $-4,700$ cal.

In order to facilitate thermodynamic calculations, and since the energy change for a reaction is the same regardless of the pathway, it is possible to consider that three distinct reactions could occur. These may be represented as an exergonic one:

3-Phosphoglyceraldehyde + H$_2$O $\rightleftarrows$ 3-phosphoglyceric acid + 2H, $- \Delta F_1$

and two endergonic ones:

$$\text{DPN}^+ + 2\text{H} \rightleftarrows \text{DPNH} + \text{H}^+, + \Delta F_2$$

and

$$\text{ADP} + \text{H}_3\text{PO}_4 \rightleftarrows \text{ATP} + \text{H}_2\text{O}, + \Delta F_3$$

The value of ΔF_1 has been estimated to be around $-30,200$ cal., that for ΔF_2 has been calculated from oxidation-reduction data and equation (6-1) ($\Delta F = -nFE$) to be $+13,500$ cal., and the hydrolysis of ATP to ADP and phosphate yields about $-12,000$ cal.; hence $\Delta F_3 = +12,000$ cal. This means that of the 30,200 cal. available from the oxidation of phosphoglyceraldehyde to phosphoglyceric acid, 13,500 are associated with the reduction of DPN$^+$ and 12,000 with the development of a high-energy phosphate bond in ATP from ADP and phosphate, thus leaving around 4,700 unavailable for doing work and expendable as heat energy. The energy stored in the reduced coenzyme is later used for the reduction of acetaldehyde to ethanol and therefore is not available to the cell. This leaves only the energy associated with the high-energy group added to ADP available to the cell for doing chemical work in coupled reactions. Syntheses appear to be accomplished to a considerable extent through the agency of such coupled reactions and others that may be encountered, e.g., of the nature of coupled reactions between oxidation and carbon dioxide fixation reactions.

2-Phosphoglyceric Acid. The seventh reaction involves the conversion of the 3-ester to the 2-ester, a substance postulated to be an intermediate in the formation of the enol form of phosphopyruvic acid. This reaction was demonstrated by the Meyerhof group around 1935. The transphosphorylation is similar to that of glucose-1-phosphate to glucose-6-phosphate. An enzyme, phosphoglyceromutase, elicits the transfer from 2,3-phosphoglyceric acid (which is present in small amounts) of the phosphate group on carbon atom 3 to the no. 2 atom in 3-phosphoglyceric acid, thus forming from the 2,3-ester a molecule of 2-phosphoglyceric acid and from the 3-ester a new molecule of 2,3-phosphoglyceric acid to continue the reaction.

2-Phosphoenolpyruvic Acid. The above step in fermentation and the eighth reaction are closely related and can be represented as

$$
\begin{array}{ccc}
\text{COOH} & \text{COOH} & \text{COOH} \\
| & | & | \\
\text{HCOH} \underset{\text{mutase}}{\overset{\longrightarrow}{\longleftarrow}} & \text{HCOPO}_3\text{H}_2 \underset{\substack{\text{enolase} \\ \text{Mg}^{++}}}{\overset{\longrightarrow}{\longleftarrow}} & \text{CO}\sim\text{PO}_3\text{H}_2 + \text{H}_2\text{O} \\
| & | & || \\
\text{CH}_2\text{OPO}_3\text{H}_2 & \text{CH}_2\text{OH} & \text{CH}_2
\end{array}
$$

The reaction leading from 2-phosphoglyceric acid to 2-phosphoenolpyruvic acid is a dehydration reaction, is inhibited by fluoride, and catalyzed by a phosphoglyceroenolase and Mg^{++} ions. Fermentation can be blocked by fluoride at this stage, magnesium being bound as magnesium fluorophosphate, and phosphoglyceric acid accumulates to some extent in the mixture. The equilibrium constant for the dehydration reaction has a value near unity, and therefore the free energy of the reaction is practically zero. This means that the energy of dehydration is not lost as heat, and instead it appears in the high-energy phosphate bond formed in the conversion of the glyceric ester to the enolpyruvate one.   Since two high-energy bonds per mole of glucose fermented are formed at this stage and two were formed during the oxidation of glyceraldehyde to glyceric acid it is evident (Fig. 7-3) that fermentation yields four of these energy-rich linkages and two are utilized in the process, thereby yielding two that the cell can employ for other purposes with the aid of ATP.

Pyruvic Acid.   The ninth reaction is analogous to the sixth in that there is a transfer of a high-energy phosphate group mediated by a trans-phosphorylase with the formation of ATP as indicated above.   It can be demonstrated with the aid of a dialyzed yeast enzyme preparation, phos-phoenolpyruvic acid being converted to pyruvic acid following the addition of Mg^{++} ions and ADP (which are lost on dialysis) or

$$
\begin{array}{c}
COOH \\
| \\
CO{\sim}PO_3H_2 + ADP \underset{\substack{transphosphorylase \\ Mg^{++}}}{\rightleftarrows} \\
\| \\
CH_2
\end{array}
\quad
\begin{array}{c}
COOH \\
| \\
C{=}O \quad + ATP \\
| \\
CH_3
\end{array}
$$

Acetaldehyde–Carbon Dioxide.   As pointed out earlier, Neuberg many years ago demonstrated that pyruvic acid can be decarboxylated by yeast with the formation of acetaldehyde and carbon dioxide, the tenth reaction in alcoholic fermentation.   This reaction can be employed in a quantitative test for the determination of pyruvic acid in a solution with a dried-yeast preparation.   This reaction is practically irreversible and can be represented as

$$
\begin{array}{c}
COOH \\
| \\
C{=}O \\
| \\
CH_2
\end{array}
\xrightarrow[\substack{carboxylase \\ Mg^{++}}]{}
\begin{array}{c}
CH_3 \\
| \\
CHO
\end{array}
+ CO_2
$$

It is catalyzed by the enzyme carboxylase (pyruvic decarboxylase would be a better name) together with Mg^{++} ions and cocarboxylase.   Cocarboxylase has been identified as thiamine pyrophosphate, a diphosphate ester of vitamin B_1.   This compound is involved in the decarboxylation of α-keto acids in general by many organisms with the participation of an oxidative enzyme, thus leading to an oxidative decarboxylation rather than the straight decarboxylation of the yeast–pyruvic acid type.   It will be shown (Chap. 8) that the CO_2 of alcoholic fermentation is derived from C atoms 3 and 4 of glucose.

Ethyl Alcohol.   In the eleventh and final step of alcoholic fermentation, acetaldehyde is reduced to ethanol with the aid of ethanol dehydrogenase acting in reverse and of DPNH formed during the oxidation of phospho-glyceraldehyde, or

$$\begin{array}{c} CH_3 \\ | \\ CHO \end{array} + DPNH^+ + H^+ \underset{\text{ethanol dehydrogenase}}{\rightleftharpoons} \begin{array}{c} CH_3 \\ | \\ CH_2OH \end{array} + DPN^+$$

In this reaction the oxidized form of CoI is regenerated and is ready to participate in the oxidation of other glyceric aldehyde molecules. Fermentation will continue in the manner described until all the sugar has been utilized or concentrations of ethyl alcohol are produced that are inhibitory to the yeast cells.

As mentioned earlier, DPNH is oxidized in muscle or in the lactic acid and other bacteria by transfer of hydrogen and electrons to pyruvic acid with the formation of lactic acid as the end product of fermentation rather than of ethyl alcohol and carbon dioxide. In the alcoholic fermentation a small amount of glycerol is always formed, DPNH reacting with dihydroxyacetone phosphate to give α-phosphoglycerol and to regenerate DPN^+. It is possible that the equilibria are of such a nature as to favor the reduction of acetaldehyde rather than of dihydroxyacetone. The equilibria may shift with pH in such a manner as to favor the reduction of the latter compound under alkaline conditions. Trapping of acetaldehyde with sulfite destroys its activity as a hydrogen acceptor and shifts the balance to glycerol formation.

Recapitulation. We have considered alcoholic fermentation as an orderly process, a series of reactions mediated by specific enzymes and in which the glucose molecule is so altered that some of the energy originally stored in it from light is made available to the heterotrophic cell. A number of preparatory reactions are involved during which the glucose molecule is degraded to a glyceraldehyde phosphate. The taking up of inorganic phosphate and a dehydrogenation at this point result in the formation of an energy-rich phosphate bond in the product of oxidation, 1,3-diphosphoglyceric acid. A second high-energy phosphate bond is produced during the conversion of glyceric acid phosphate by dehydration to the enol form of phosphopyruvic acid The energy so bound can be transferred by means of the adenylic acid system for use in the preparation of other glucose molecules for their entry into the fermentation process, while two of these bonds are formed in excess of those required for the fermentative process and can be employed by the cell for other work. Hydrogen and electrons derived from the one oxidative process involved in fermentation are disposed of by transfer through the agency of DPNH to an intermediate of the fermentation process, acetaldehyde, with the formation of ethyl alcohol and the regeneration of the oxidized form of the coenzyme, DPN^+.

It is apparent from Fig. 7-3 that fermentation can be likened to a flow process in an industrial plant, the various steps being dependent upon each other for their orderly continuance.   In the diagram three steps are indicated where specific cellular poisons can interfere with the regular course of events and lead to cessation or alteration of the respiratory pattern.   It is possible that in the yeast cell there exists a definite arrangement of the enzymes involved in fermentative respiration, thus imparting a higher degree of order and direction to the reactions they catalyze and at the same time through the agency of ATP facilitating the performance of useful work.   This is suggested by the fact that fermentation by yeast juice occurs at a rate considerably lower than that observed with intact cells and that in the latter about one-fourth of the utilized glucose can be converted into cellular material.   Two moles of ATP in excess of those utilized in the preparatory stages of fermentation are produced per mole of glucose fermented, and these represent an energy storage of 20,000 to 25,000 cal.   Since the free-energy decrease of alcoholic fermentation is around 55,000 cal. we can conclude that energy storage in fermentation occurs with a free-energy efficiency somewhat better than 40 per cent. How this energy is later utilized by the cell determines the over-all efficiency of metabolism and growth.

In the historical introduction it was considered that phosphate must be added to yeast juice to enable the fermentation to continue, while free inorganic phosphate is not essential for dissimilation by intact cells.   The reason for this behavior has been found in recent years, the excess ATP formed during fermentation in the cell being used in cellular activities with the liberation of phosphate that can be used over again.   Furthermore, there is a safety valve in the cell, an adenosine triphosphatase (ATPase) which hydrolyzes any excess of ATP and returns inorganic phosphate to the normal cycle.   This enzyme is readily inactivated in yeast juice.   Addition of a more stable phosphatase, such as is present in potatoes, to yeast juice enables the fermentation to continue without the further addition of phosphate.   This is another example of the various regulatory devices employed by the living cell, although they may have other functions than regulatory alone.

Harden and Young observed that fermentation by yeast juice continued without supplemental phosphate when arsenate was added to the fermentation mixture.   This arsenate effect can also be explained in the light of the modern scheme of fermentation.   Arsenate can replace phosphate in the fifth step of glucose dissimilation, the formation of 1,3-diphosphoglyceric acid, with the resultant formation of 1-arseno-3-phosphoglyceric acid.   This compound does not react with ADP but is somewhat unstable and breaks down slowly with the liberation of arsenate which can be used over again.   3-Phosphoglyceric acid is formed in this breakdown of the arsenate ester, and the fermentation continues. Since ATP is formed only from the pyruvate enolphosphate there is no excess, and no phosphate is tied up here; hence the fermentation can continue. Arsenate thereby creates an effective block at one stage of the fermentation process as regards ATP formation.

Fermentation is regarded as a wasteful process in that many times as much sugar must be utilized anaerobically to obtain the same mass of cells as would be produced under aerobic conditions. As we have just considered, the free-energy efficiency of anaerobic respiration can be quite high and possibly as great as or greater than that of aerobic respiration. Furthermore, there are around 600,000 cal. of free energy of oxidation stored in the two moles of ethanol produced from one mole of glucose. This energy can be made available by other organisms, or by yeast, under aerobic conditions, and hence is not lost under natural conditions. Fermentation is a wasteful process as far as sugar is concerned, but not necessarily as far as energy is concerned.

During the evolution of bacteria many species developed that apparently employ the same pathway of respiration as the one just considered for yeast, with the exception that they developed enzymes activating substances other than acetaldehyde as the final hydrogen acceptor or ones that introduced deviations from the main pathway. It is also possible that other pathways of sugar dissimilation could have evolved. These various deviations or departures have led to a number of distinct types of bacterial fermentations, which will be considered in the next chapter.

CHAPTER 8

BACTERIAL FERMENTATIONS

We have considered that anaerobic respiration or fermentation in yeast consists of a series of preparatory and alterative reactions during the course of which the substrate molecule is degraded. In certain of the reactions of alcoholic fermentation energy is made available, either as the result of an oxidative reaction or of a molecular rearrangement and dehydration, the transfer of energy being mediated through the agency of the ADP-ATP system. A similar course of reactions often is observed under aerobic conditions as far as the pyruvate stage, with the exception that hydrogen and electrons end up in union with oxygen rather than with an organic hydrogen acceptor. Many bacterial fermentations follow the same pathway to pyruvic acid as observed with yeast but diverge at this point.

A number of species of bacteria, as well as numerous other cells, have never become adapted to the use of terminal hydrogen acceptors other than molecular oxygen, and hence they are not able to respire and grow under anaerobic conditions. The majority of the different species of bacteria, the facultative anaerobes, have such abilities, and this could confer upon them distinct survival abilities under the various environmental conditions they might encounter in nature. On the other hand, a number of species are so adjusted to anaerobic life that their respiration is inhibited under aerobic conditions. The products of anaerobic life often are more numerous than in the fermentations induced by yeast or muscle and depend upon the nature of the organism, of the substrate, and of the medium.

More than one pathway of dissimilation of carbohydrates exists, and this together with the diversity of products that may be encountered rather complicates consideration of the bacterial fermentations. The fundamental purpose, however, remains the same: an orderly and controlled dissimilation of the substrate without molecular oxygen acting as a hydrogen acceptor and in such a manner that energy and building material are made available to the cell. The diversity of products, and also of utilizable foodstuffs, is of invaluable aid in the identification of species of both the facultative and the strict anaerobes. The types of fermentation appear to be scattered heterogeneously among the recognized species, and it is therefore more logical to approach bacterial fermentations from the standpoint of the end products formed rather than from a species or genus approach. Attention will be focused in this chapter on the anaerobic dissimilation of carbohydrates, and while the mechanisms are essentially the same, the fermentation of amino acids will be considered later. The major types of fermentation, together with typical organisms inducing them, can be summarized as follows:

1. Alcoholic fermentation.................... *Pseudomonas lindneri*
2. Lactic acid fermentation.................. Lactic acid bacteria
3. Propionic acid fermentation............... *Propionibacterium* sp.
4. Butyric acid fermentation................ *Clostridium butylicum*
5. Mixed acid fermentation.................. *Escherichia coli*
6. 2,3-Butyleneglycol fermentation........... *Aerobacter aerogenes*
7. Miscellaneous fermentations.............. Methane bacteria, SO_4^{--}, CO_2, and NO_3^- reducers

The general approach to the study of bacterial fermentations has been to determine the nature of the products derived from a particular substrate, to identify the products, to determine the quantitative relationships between the amount of substrate dissimilated and the amounts of the products recovered, and to verify the accuracy of the analyses on the basis of carbon, hydrogen, and oxygen recoveries and of oxidation-reduction balances. These will be illustrated as we proceed with our considerations. The next step frequently is one of mental gymnastics, an attempt to develop a plausible scheme or pathway for the fermentation. Studies to verify the scheme can be carried out on the fermentation of postulated intermediates, at times with the aid of washed cells or of enzyme preparations from the cells, and with labeled substrates. The use of specific poisons can also be of value either in stopping the fermentation at a definite stage or in altering the course of the fermentation. The most accurate results generally are obtained in experiments of short duration with washed-cell suspensions under closely controlled conditions since the formation of cell substance is decreased and the effect of endogenous respiration and side reactions is not so marked as in cultures. The major pathways of carbohydrate metabolism have been reviewed by Gunsalus, Horecker, and Wood (1955).

Alcoholic Fermentation. Ethanol is found as a minor product of many bacterial fermentations and as a major one in a few instances. *Clostridium botulinum* produces more than one mole each of ethanol and carbon dioxide, about one-third of a mole of lactic acid, and two-thirds of a mole of a mixture of acetic and butyric acids per mole of glucose fermented. *Pseudomonas lindneri* (*Termobacterium mobile* or *Zymomonas mobile*), *Leuconostoc mesenteroides*, and *Sarcina ventriculi* form as much or more ethanol and less of other products.   The *P. lindneri* fermentation of glucose gives rise to about 1.8 moles each of ethanol and carbon dioxide and 0.2 of lactic acid.   This fermentation is employed in the preparation of pulque, a Mexican alcoholic beverage.   *S. ventriculi* carries out a similar fermentation, traces of hydrogen, acetylmethylcarbinol (acetoin), and acetic and formic acids also being produced.   The *Leuconostoc* fermentation, which yields around one mole each of ethanol, carbon dioxide, and lactic acid, has been studied in most detail.   Typical results of a glucose fermentation at pH 7 by washed cells of *L. mesenteroides* are recorded in Table 8-1.

TABLE 8-1. GLUCOSE FERMENTATION BY *Leuconostoc mesenteroides**

	mM	C, mM	H, meq.
Glucose..	100.0	600.0	2,400
Lactate..	88.8	266.4	1,066
Ethanol..	95.7	191.4	1,148
Carbon dioxide....................................	103.8	103.8	
Recovery..	.....	561.6	2,214
Per cent recovery.................................	.....	93.6	
O/R balance.......................................	.....	.....	1.08

* Based on data from DeMoss, 1953.

The results summarized in Table 8-1 are expressed on the basis of millimoles (mM) of products produced per 100 mM of glucose fermented for convenience in establishing carbon and oxidation-reduction balances. The carbon balance is established by multiplying the number of millimoles of substrate fermented, or of each product produced, by the number of carbon atoms in each.   The total carbon in the products should equal that in the substrate utilized with the exception of a small amount that is assimilated.   A good recovery, 93.6 per cent, was obtained in this experiment.

The O/R balance can be established in a number of ways, the one utilized by Barker (1937) being employed here.   In column 3 of Table 8-1 the milliequivalents (meq.) of "available hydrogen" present in each compound are tabulated.   In a perfect balance the available hydrogen in the products would equal that in the substrate.   By available hydrogen is meant the number of hydrogen atoms which have to be removed from a compound to obtain complete dehydrogenation to carbon dioxide plus the hydrogen from the water needed to balance the equation.   The milliequivalents in column 3 are obtained by multiplying the available hydrogen by the number of millimoles of the substance.   The equations and the calculated values for available hydrogen for glucose, lactic acid, and ethanol are as follows:

$$C_6H_{12}O_6 + 6H_2O \rightarrow 6CO_2 + 24H$$
$$C_3H_6O_3 + 3H_2O \rightarrow 3CO_2 + 12H$$
$$C_2H_6O + 3H_2O \rightarrow 2CO_2 + 12H$$

The recovery of 2,214 meq. of hydrogen from a possible 2,400 is good, considering fermentation balances in general, and gives rise to an O/R index of 2,400/2,214, or 1.08. Satisfactory balances lend support to the accuracy of the experimental methods, but do not verify any postulated mechanism.

In view of the demonstration in a number of bacterial fermentation mixtures, or in enzyme preparations, of the presence of intermediates or of enzymes encountered in the Embden-Meyerhof (E-M) pathway for alcoholic fermentation by yeast, the existence of the same mechanism in bacteria has been suggested. Since lactic acid and ethanol are formed in equal amounts in the fermentation elicited by *Leuconostoc mesenteroides*, even at different hydrogen-ion concentrations, and particularly since no pyruvic acid decarboxylase activity can be demonstrated in *L. mesenteroides*, considerable doubt arose as to operation of the Embden-Meyerhof mechanism in this fermentation. On the other hand, certain of the enzymes and intermediates of this system have been detected in cell extracts or fermentation mixtures. DPN-linked dehydrogenases for ethanol, lactic acid, glyceraldehyde phosphate, and glucose-6-phosphate have been detected (DeMoss, 1953) in cell extracts together with hexokinase and phosphoglyceric transphosphorylase, but neither aldolase nor isomerase was present.

Gunsalus and Gibbs (1952) followed the fate of labeled carbon (C^{14} isotope) present in glucose in either the 1 or the 3 and 4 positions. Their results suggested the following pattern for the fermentation:

$$
\begin{array}{lll}
\text{H*C}=\text{O} & \rightarrow & \text{*CO}_2 \\
\text{HCOH} & & \text{CH}_3 \\
\text{HO**CH} & \rightarrow & \text{**CH}_2\text{OH} \\
\text{H**COH} & & \text{**COOH} \\
\text{HCOH} & \rightarrow & \text{CHOH} \\
\text{CH}_2\text{OH} & & \text{CH}_3
\end{array}
$$

where * indicates labeling of the no. 1 carbon atom in some tests, **labeling at both the 3 and 4 positions in others. The results summarized in the above equation indicate that C atom 1 gives rise to the CO_2-C and

C atoms 3 and 4 to carbinol-labeled ethanol and carboxyl-labeled lactic acid, respectively. This is an entirely different behavior than is noted in the yeast fermentation where CO_2 is formed from C atoms 3 and 4 (Koshland and Westheimer, 1950).

Other studies indicated that phosphorylation does occur in the *Leuconostoc* fermentation of glucose and that departure from the Embden-Meyerhof pathway occurs at the glucose-6-phosphate stage. *L. mesenteroides* possesses an active glucose-6-phosphate dehydrogenase, reactive with either DPN+ or TPN+, and oxidizes the sugar ester with the formation of 6-phosphogluconate. This oxidation has been described in a number of species of bacteria and will be considered later under aerobic metabolism as the hexose monophosphate shunt or the Warburg-Dickens pathway of oxidation. In this pathway dissimilation occurs with the formation, as the result of a decarboxylation, of a pentose phosphate which can be split into a 3C and a 2C compound. DeMoss could find no evidence for this cleavage with *L. mesenteroides* and suggested the formation of a keto-6-phosphogluconic acid. Cleavage of this molecule would give rise to two different trioses, one of which could be reduced to lactic acid and the other decarboxylated with the possible formation of acetic acid. This organism can reduce acetic acid to ethanol, but the final stages of the fermentation are obscure and details remain to be determined.

Pseudomonas lindneri, as indicated earlier, produces much more ethanol and carbon dioxide per mole of glucose fermented than is obtained in the *Leuconostoc* fermentation. This fermentation has not been studied extensively, but preliminary results (Gibbs and DeMoss, 1951) from both isotope and enzyme studies indicate an anaerobic hexosemonophosphate pathway. The isotope data suggest that CO_2 is formed from C atoms 1 and 4 of glucose, ethanol from the 2-3 and the 5-6 atoms. This organism does possess a pyruvate decarboxylating system. Gibbs and DeMoss proposed that glucose-6-phosphate is oxidized to phosphogluconic acid, which is then decarboxylated to yield a pentose phosphate. This compound then undergoes a C_2-C_3 cleavage, the 2C fragment being one precursor of ethanol and the 3C (pyruvic acid ?) the other after decarboxylation. DeMoss (1953) indicated that pentose phosphate does not accumulate and is not fermented; hence the mechanism of this fermentation is also somewhat uncertain.

Lactic Acid Fermentation. The lactic acid bacteria, particularly of the genera *Diplococcus, Streptococcus, Leuconostoc,* and *Lactobacillus*, are characterized by the production of considerable quantities of lactic acid from glucose or other sugars, and some species are employed for the commercial production of lactate. Different species in this group possess somewhat different enzyme systems, as regards both sugars fermented and pathways of fermentation, and these differences are employed as aids in species identification. Individual species are designated as *homofermentative* or *heterofermentative* on the basis of the products they produce from glucose. Homofermentative (homolactic) species such as *Lactobacillus casei* and *Streptococcus faecalis* ferment as much as 95 per cent of the glucose utilized to lactic acid. Traces of carbon dioxide, volatile acids, acetoin, or other substances may be produced. *L. casei* produces only the dextro, or L(+), form of lactic acid, *L. lactis* the levo, or D(−), form, while a few species such as *L. plantarum* yield an inactive mixture. No acceptable explanation for the specific differences in optical activity of the products has been advanced. The available evidence indicates that lactic acid production by homofermentative species utilizing hexoses, or higher sugars that can be split to form hexoses, is by way of the Embden-Meyerhof pathway. Some homolactics, particularly under alkaline conditions, shift their fermentation to a more heterofermentative one.

Heterofermentative lactic acid bacteria produce considerable quantities of other end products in addition to lactic acid. We have just considered a typical heterofermentative species, *L. mesenteroides*, which is a lactic acid bacterium, but its marked production of ethanol is more distinctive in that fewer species carry out this particular type of fermentation. Other species characteristically produce considerable quantities of acetic acid, acetoin, or other substances.

Both homo- and heterofermentative species ferment utilizable pentoses according to the equation

$$C_5H_{10}O_5 \rightarrow CH_3CHOHCOOH + CH_3COOH$$

Glycerol is oxidized anaerobically by certain species to lactic acid when an appropriate hydrogen acceptor is present in the fermentation mixture. Fumarate, for example, can act as the ultimate oxidant and is reduced to succinic acid which accumulates in the medium. Malic or oxalacetic acids are fermented with the production of lactic acid and CO_2. When pyruvate is the substrate, one molecule is reduced to lactic acid while a second is split with the production of acetic acid and CO_2, or

$$2CH_3COCOOH + H_2O \rightarrow CH_3CHOHCOOH + CH_3COOH + CO_2$$

Pyruvic Acid Dismutation and Coenzyme A. The observations of Lipmann (see reviews by Lipmann et al., and Lipmann, 1953, 1954) that pyruvic acid oxidation (aerobically or anaerobically) by enzyme systems from *Lactobacillus delbrueckii* is dependent on the presence of inorganic phosphate led to the discovery of acetyl phosphate and ultimately that of coenzyme A as well. It appears that there are two major pathways for the dismutation of pyruvic acid to lactic and acetic acids and CO_2 by the lactic acid bacteria: the *L. delbrueckii* type which is independent of lipoic acid, while the *Streptococcus faecalis* type requires lipoic acid as a coenzyme. Both types involve thiamine pyrophosphate and Mg^{++} ions for the decarboxylation of pyruvate (or other α-keto acids), a 2C complex (aldehyde or carbonyl) being formed with the thiamine coenzyme system. This complex probably is involved in an oxidation mediated by DPN^+, the reduced form of this coenzyme being oxidized by transfer of hydrogen and electrons to another pyruvate molecule in the *L. delbrueckii* fermentation, or

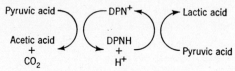

This scheme indicates that CoA does not enter into the oxidation of pyruvate directly, the experimental data suggesting that the acetic acid formed in the dismutation reacts with ATP to form acetyl phosphate and ADP. Acetyl phosphate can serve as a phosphate donor, reacting in this case with CoA in its reduced form (CoASH) to give acetyl-CoA and phosphate, or

$$CH_3COO^- + ATP \rightarrow ADP + CH_3COO\sim\textcircled{P}$$

$$CH_3COO\sim\textcircled{P} + HSCoA \rightarrow CH_3C\overset{\displaystyle O}{\underset{\displaystyle SCoA}{\diagdown\diagup}} + HO\textcircled{P}$$

In this manner an acyl-CoA complex is generated, and in conjunction with a transferring enzyme acyl groups $\left(RC\overset{\displaystyle O}{\diagup} \right)$ can be utilized in various synthetic reactions (see Fig. 8-1 and the butyric fermentation to follow). It should be noted that the energy-rich bond in acetyl phosphate is between an O and a P atom, in acetyl coenzyme A between the carboxyl-C and S. In yeast and animal tissues a similar type of generation of acetyl-CoA is observed with the exception that an enzyme-AMP complex and inorganic pyrophosphate are formed, CoA is substituted for the AMP, and the enzyme-CoA complex reacts with acetate to give acetyl-CoA and liberate the enzyme in its original state.

Pyruvate dismutation by *S. faecalis* (and by *E. coli*) differs from the *L. delbrueckii* one in that it is inhibited by arsenite and particularly in that is a requirement for lipoic acid (thioctic or 6,8-dithiooctanoic acid), a substance also known as factor II, acetate-replacing factor, pyruvate oxidation factor, and protogen before its chemical nature was established. The arsenite inhibits lipoic acid activity by forming a stable complex with it through the sulfhydryl groups, the active portion of the molecule. Lipoic acid,[1] as the pyruvate oxidation factor, was shown by O'Kane and Gunsalus to function in this oxidation as elicited by *S. faecalis*. There is some evidence that lipoic acid may be directly coupled with thiamine pyrophosphate, but Gunsalus (1954) concluded that pyruvic

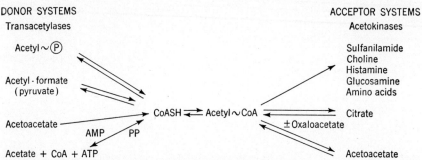

DONOR SYSTEMS   ACCEPTOR SYSTEMS

Fig. 8-1. Acetyl, or other acyl group, transfer and function of coenzyme A. (*After Lipmann*, 1954.) In the upper acceptor systems the carboxyl group of acetyl-coenzyme A unites with the acceptor molecule; in the second, or citrate, type of condensation with oxalacetate, union occurs with the methyl carbon; and in the acetoacetate type there is a methyl-to-carboxyl condensation.

acid, or other α-keto acids, is decarboxylated by *S. faecalis* with the formation of a carbonyl-thiamine-enzyme complex (TPP) as in *L. delbrueckii*.

This complex reacts with lipoic acid $\left(\begin{array}{c} S \\ | \quad L \\ S \end{array} \right)$ rather than directly with

DPN+. Both an acylation and a reduction of lipoic acid occur at this stage, which can be represented as

$$
\underset{\text{TPP}}{\overset{O}{\underset{||}{CH_3C}}} \quad + \quad \overset{S}{\underset{S}{|}} L \rightarrow \underset{\underset{HS}{S}}{\overset{O}{\underset{||}{CH_3C}}} L
$$

This acylated lipoic acid transfers the acyl group to CoA under the

[1] See papers of a symposium reported in *Federation Proc.*, vol. 13, no. 3 (1954).

influence of a transacetylase to give acetyl-CoA and reduced lipoic acid, or

$$CH_3C \overset{O}{\diagdown} S \diagdown L + CoASH \rightarrow CH_3C \overset{O}{\diagdown} SCoA + \overset{HS}{\diagup} L$$

The oxidized form of lipoic acid is regenerated on transfer of hydrogen and electrons to DPN⁺, and DPNH can be oxidized by reduction of pyruvate to lactate under the influence of lactic dehydrogenase. The acylated CoA can react as discussed earlier. The series of reactions is summarized in Fig. 8-2.

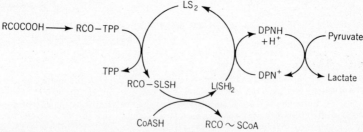

FIG. 8-2. Reaction steps observed during the dismutation of pyruvic and other α-keto acids by *Streptococcus faecalis* or *Escherichia coli*.

Propionic Acid Fermentation. A number of species of bacteria, particularly those of the genus *Propionibacterium*, ferment various carbohydrates, polyalcohols, and lactic acid with the formation of propionic and acetic acids and carbon dioxide. These organisms commonly are found in dairy products, particularly hard cheeses, and their activity was first noted by Fitz, who reported in 1876 that the fermentation of lactate can be represented as

$$3CH_3CHOHCOOH \rightarrow 2CH_3CH_2COOH + CH_3COOH + CO_2 + H_2O$$

It was generally considered (van Niel, 1953) that propionic acid was formed by loss of water from lactate to yield acrylic acid ($CH_2\!\!=\!\!CHCOOH$), which was then reduced to propionic acid. It became evident around 1940 that propionic acid bacteria are unable to reduce acrylic acid, although this reduction can be elicited by an entirely different bacterium, *Clostridium propionicum* (Johns, 1952). Since fluoride inhibits the formation of propionate from lactate but not from pyruvate, this suggests that lactic acid is not on the pathway of dissimilation of sugars by the propionic acid bacteria.

A new concept was introduced into bacterial physiology when Wood and Werkman (1936) demonstrated the uptake or fixation of CO_2 by a heterotrophic bacterium, *Propionibacterium pentosaceum*. They observed that the carbon content and redox index of the products of glycerol fermentation were greater than the theoretical and could be accounted for only on the assumption that there was an uptake of CO_2 during the fermentation. This uptake was observed only when the fermentation was carried out in the presence of carbonate. The main products were propionic and succinic acids. Propionic acid was formed in almost quantitative yield when the fermentation was carried out in the absence of carbonate and with phosphate as the buffer system. This behavior, together with the almost stoichiometric relationship between the amount of succinate formed and of CO_2 which disappeared, indicated that CO_2 fixation is not limited to the autotrophs and implicated succinate formation in the fixation process.

Further evidence for CO_2 fixation was obtained by Wood and his coworkers and by Carson and Ruben (1940) when they demonstrated that labeled carbon in CO_2 appeared in the carboxyl groups of propionic and succinic acids. (Determination of the position of labeled carbon in a compound is made in tests conducted during the stepwise and controlled degradation of the compound by specific methods.) CO_2 fixation was soon demonstrated to be a rather general phenomenon associated with the metabolism of heterotrophic bacteria and with that of mammalian cells as well.

Wood and Werkman advanced the hypothesis that CO_2 combined with pyruvic acid derived from glycerol to form a 4C compound, oxalacetic acid. This condensation is known as the Wood-Werkman reaction and was, together with subsequent reactions, pictured as

$$
\begin{array}{ccccccccc}
 & & \text{COOH} & & \text{COOH} & & \text{COOH} & & \text{COOH} \\
\text{CH}_3 & & | & & | & & | & & | \\
| & & \text{CH}_2 & & \text{CH}_2 & & \text{CH} & & \text{CH}_2 \\
\text{CO} & \xrightarrow{+CO_2} & | & \xrightarrow{+2H} & | & \xrightarrow{-H_2O} & \| & \xrightarrow{+2H} & | \\
| & & \text{CO} & & \text{CHOH} & & \text{CH} & & \text{CH}_2 \\
\text{COOH} & & | & & | & & | & & | \\
 & & \text{COOH} & & \text{COOH} & & \text{COOH} & & \text{COOH} \\
\text{Pyruvic} & & \text{Oxalacetic} & & \text{Malic} & & \text{Fumaric} & & \text{Succinic}
\end{array}
$$

Malic and succinic acid dehydrogenases, fumarase, and oxalacetic carboxylase have been demonstrated in the propionibacteria, but there is considerable doubt concerning the reversibility of oxalacetic decarboxylation, i.e., fixation of CO_2 by pyruvate to give oxalacetic acid. It appears more likely that CO_2 fixation occurs here with the formation of malic acid under the influence of the TPN-mediated malic enzyme (Ochoa, 1951). Carbon dioxide fixation will be considered in more detail later.

The next development regarding the propionic fermentation came from studies with *Veillonella gazogenes*, a gram-negative, anaerobic coccus that

cannot ferment sugars but does ferment lactic acid with the production
of acetic and propionic acids, hydrogen, and carbon dioxide.   This
organism was found (Johns, 1948) to decarboxylate succinic acid readily
with the formation of acetic and propionic acids.   Later studies with
P. pentosaceum by Delwiche (1948) showed that this bacterium can decarboxylate succinate slowly but at a rate sufficiently high to account for
the production of propionic acid, this decarboxylation having been suspected since studies of Shaw and Sherman in 1923.   Delwiche observed
that succinic acid decarboxylation (inhibited by malonic acid) occurs most

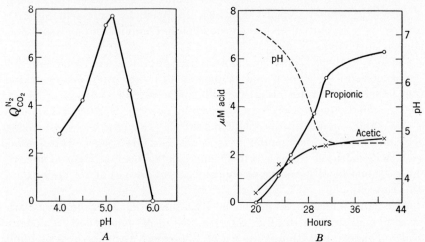

FIG. 8-3. Influence (*A*) of pH on CO_2 production and (*B*) of age of culture on acetic
and propionic acid production by *Propionibacterium pentosaceum*.   (*From Fig. 3 and
data of Delwiche, 1948, courtesy of The Williams & Wilkins Company.*)

readily in washed-cell suspensions prepared from cultures 32 to 38 hr. old
and at pH 5.1 to 5.2.   He analyzed aliquots of a glucose fermentation
broth for acetic and propionic acid at various intervals during growth of
P. pentosaceum, finding (Fig. 8-3) acetic acid production most marked
near neutrality, propionic acid formation below pH 6.5.   Some propionate was produced at higher pH levels than 6.5, the upper limit for decarboxylation as indicated in the graph for succinic acid decarboxylation.
He explained the production of propionic acid at higher pH values on the
basis of decarboxylation of intracellularly produced succinate, suggesting
that at the higher pH's the cell membrane was not permeable to succinate
supplied externally.   Hence it appears that the failure of early workers
to observe decarboxylation of succinic acid was due to the use of older
cells and to unfavorable pH levels.

The studies of Delwiche and of others indicate that the propionic acid
fermentation of pyruvic acid can be postulated as including an oxidative

decarboxylation of pyruvate to give acetic acid and carbon dioxide as well as reduced coenzyme. The hydrogen and electrons can be utilized in the formation of malic acid during carbon dioxide fixation and in the reduction of fumaric acid as indicated in the Wood-Werkman scheme considered above. Decarboxylation of the succinic acid so produced would give rise to propionic acid and carbon dioxide. Delwiche postulated that the formation of propionic acid from pyruvate includes the following six major reactions:

$$2CH_3COCOOH + 2H_2O \rightarrow 2CH_3COOH + 2CO_2 + 4H$$
$$CH_3COCOOH + CO_2 \rightarrow COOHCH_2COCOOH$$
$$COOHCH_2COCOOH + 2H \rightarrow COOHCH_2CHOHCOOH$$
$$COOHCH_2CHOHCOOH \rightarrow COOHCH{=}CHCOOH + H_2O$$
$$COOHCH{=}CHCOOH + 2H \rightarrow COOHCH_2CH_2COOH$$
$$COOHCH_2CH_2COOH \rightarrow CH_3CH_2COOH + CO_2$$

while the over-all transformation can be represented as

$$3CH_3COCOOH + H_2O \rightarrow CH_3CH_2COOH + 2CH_3COOH + 2CO_2$$

an equation that fits the experimental facts quite closely. The second and third steps should be modified since carbon dioxide fixation appears to occur via malic acid and with participation of the Ochoa enzyme rather than via oxalacetic acid. The end result, however, would be the same. In the fermentation of lactic acid or of glucose there is more hydrogen available than from pyruvate, and the tendency is for the ratio of volatile acids to be reversed, i.e., about two moles of propionate are formed to one of acetate. Traces of succinate are generally found in the fermentation mixtures.

It appears odd that carbon dioxide has to be added to a molecule, and subsequently a molecule of carbon dioxide is eliminated. This, however, may be a way of getting the substrate molecule, or a triose derived from it, into the Krebs or similar cycles. A number of studies (see Barker and Lipmann, 1949) have suggested that hexoses are utilized via the hexose diphosphate pathway to pyruvic acid, while pentoses are dissimilated by the monophosphate shunt with a 2-3 cleavage that results in the production of one mole of pyruvate by way of phosphoglyceric acid. Differences were noted between various sugars, and they were unsuccessful in attempts to detect acetyl phosphate formation. Most of the evidence today indicates that propionic acid is produced, except by *C. propionicum*, via succinic acid, although Leaver and Wood (1953) have presented data from labeled-C studies that indicate the possibility of another and unknown method of formation of propionic acid. There appears to be little or no evidence that propionic acid bacteria can synthesize succinic acid by condensation of two acetyl groups from acetyl-CoA complexes, a synthesis that has been demonstrated in certain species of bacteria and that will be considered soon.   Little is known as yet concerning the mechanism of decarboxylation of succinate, although CoA and carboxylase appear to be involved in the reaction.   It has been reported that certain species of propionic acid bacteria are able to reduce a portion of this acid to propyl alcohol, a reaction that occurs probably only when there is a paucity of hydrogen acceptors.   It is of interest to note that the diphtheria bacillus elicits a propionic acid type of fermentation.

Butyric Acid Fermentation.   A number of species in the genus *Clostridium* ferment carbohydrates and amino acids with the production of acetic and butyric acids along with other products, butyric acid being the most characteristic product of the fermentation.   It is quite possible that the fermentation of glucose follows the E-M pathway to pyruvate and diverges at that point.   Pyruvate can be fermented by many or all of the butyric acid bacteria and by other clostridia, *C. tetanomorphum* for example (Woods and Clifton, 1938) dissimilating it according to the equation

$$3CH_3COCOOH + H_2O \rightarrow CH_3(CH_2)_2COOH$$
$$+ CH_3COOH + 3CO_2 + H_2$$

The butyric acid fermentation was first observed by Pasteur, who also noted the accumulation of butyl alcohol in some fermentation mixtures. Some of the clostridia form, in addition to the above products, ethyl, isopropyl, and butyl alcohols, acetone, and acetoin, often with traces of formic and lactic acids.   It should be pointed out that the relative amounts of the various products depend upon the nature of the organism and of the medium and also to a considerable extent upon the age of the culture, primarily as this reflects pH as indicated in Fig. 8-4.   Little or no alcohols are formed when the pH is maintained around 7.

C. acetobutylicum is quite representative of the butyric acid–butanol group and has been used to a considerable extent for the industrial production of acetone and butanol (Prescott and Dunn, 1949).   The nature of this fermentation appeared to be quite complex, but the studies of Kluyver and his students (1931), Wood, Brown, and Werkman (1945), Davies and Stephenson (1941), Cohen (1949), and Stadtman and Barker 1949–1950) have clarified the picture (see also Cohen, 1950; Stadtman and Stadtman, 1953).

The studies of Kluyver and his school suggested that glucose is dissimilated to methyl glyoxal in the same manner as was believed to occur in yeast.   The glyoxal was postulated to undergo cleavage with the formation of acetaldehyde and formic acid, the latter being decomposed with the production of H_2 and CO_2.   A portion of the acetaldehyde formed was believed to condense with the formation of acetaldol which could be converted into butyric acid, and the latter to butanol under reducing conditions. Other molecules of acetaldehyde were assumed to be reduced to ethanol or oxidized to acetic acid, the latter condensing to yield aceto-acetic acid which could be converted by decarboxylation into acetone. Acetone under reducing conditions could be reduced to isopropanol. The Kluyver scheme was in agreement with the known experimental facts,

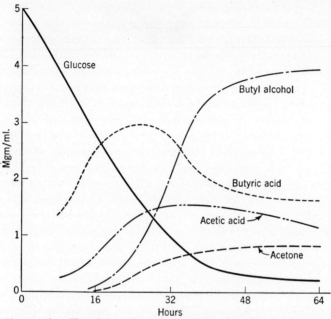

FIG. 8-4. Changes in pH and in end products of fermentation by *Clostridium aceto-butylicum* in a glucose medium. (*Based on data from Davies and Stephenson, 1941.*)

and satisfactory carbon and redox balances could be obtained. Furthermore, the scheme indicated that this and other fermentations can be pictured as an orderly series of phosphorylations, hydrolyses, dehydrogenations and hydrogenations, decarboxylations, and, at times, condensations. This concept of closely linked, orderly reactions can be considered as the major value of the early scheme, the details of which have undergone change with advances in knowledge of the biochemistry of fermentation and other cellular processes.

Actually, the equations we employ today to represent the butyric and other fermentations are not markedly different from those suggested in the earlier studies. Some of the postulated intermediates have been replaced by others; details of some of the reactions have been determined with enzymes extracted from the cells; more has been learned regarding the enzymes and their mode of action; and more is known of the mechanism of energy and of group transfer, so important in cellular syntheses.

The schemes accepted today may be modified at any time as the result of additional studies and consideration of the experimental data.   These remarks may appear out of place but are inserted here to indicate to the student that the validity of a concept is relative rather than absolute. The mechanisms remain the same, our ideas concerning them undergo change as our knowledge increases, and for this reason an open mind must be maintained if further progress is to be made.

The butyric acid fermentation has been a difficult one to study since washed suspensions readily lost their enzymatic activity and the reactions themselves frequently varied with variations in age of the cells, nature of the culture media, with pH, and with other factors, including bacterial variation.   Davies and Stephenson (1941; see also Fig. 8-4) were able to show that butanol formation depended primarily upon the development of a relatively high hydrogen-ion concentration, about pH 3.7, and once this level was reached both acetic and butyric acid concentrations decreased with concomitant increases in concentration of acetone and butanol.   Also cells harvested early in the growth period fermented glucose readily but produced no solvents, while those harvested later did so. This suggests that the formation of the enzymes involved is dependent upon some pH effect, although the nature of this has not been established definitely.

Wood, Brown, and Werkman (1945) studied the origin of products of fermentation of corn mash by *C. acetobutylicum* and *C. butylicum*, using heavy carbon (C^{13}) as a tracer.   When carboxyl-labeled acetic acid was added to the fermentation mixture, C^{13} was recovered in butanol, ethanol, isopropanol, acetone, acetic and butyric acids, and carbon dioxide.   This suggested that the above substances could be derived directly or indirectly from acetate.   Butanol contained much of the heavy carbon which was found in both the carbinol and the β positions, thus indicating synthesis from acetate.   Acetone and isopropanol contained the labeled carbon in the carbonyl and carbinol positions, respectively.   This finding is in agreement with formation of acetone by decarboxylation of acetoacetate and of isopropyl alcohol by reduction of the acetone.   Likewise, when carbonyl-labeled acetone was added to the mash, C^{13} was found in the carbinol group of isopropanol.

The addition of labeled butyric acid ($CH_3C^{13}H_2CH_2C^{13}OOH$) to the fermentation mixture resulted in the production of butanol labeled in the 1 and 3 positions as in the added acid and also of some labeled ethanol, isopropanol, and acetic acid.   This suggested that the reactions may be reversible, probably through acetoacetic acid.   Other studies (see reviews by Cohen, 1951; Stadtman and Stadtman, 1953) indicate that glucose is phosphorylated and the ester is split to form triose phosphates.   Pyruvic acid is formed and undergoes a phosphorolytic (phosphoroclastic) split with the formation of acetyl phosphate (or acetyl-CoA), carbon dioxide, and hydrogen, one of the types of pyruvate dissimilation considered earlier. It appears that hydrogen does not arise from formic acid as in the *E. coli* and similar fermentations.

Much of our information concerning the utilization of acetyl phosphate comes from the studies of Stadtman and Barker with *C. kluyveri*, a metabolically odd and intriguing anaerobe first described by Barker and Taha (1942). Some of the findings obtained with this organism have been confirmed by Cohen with true butyric acid bacteria and, therefore, appear to be applicable to them.

C. kluyveri was obtained from enrichment cultures in an ethanol-containing medium inoculated with mud. Its nutritional requirements are unique in that it will not develop (Barker, 1947) in ordinary media, does not utilize carbohydrates, and grows readily only with ethanol plus a small amount of acetic, propionic, or butyric acid as the substrate, biotin and *p*-aminobenzoic acid being required as growth factors. Butyric and caproic acids together with some hydrogen are the products of fermentation with ethanol and acetic acid as the substrates, valeric acid being produced when propionate is present. Only a small amount of acetic acid is needed in the medium to initiate growth, ethanol being oxidized to acetic acid and continuously producing it once growth is initiated. Acetic acid can, therefore, be considered as a "sparking" agent and as an example of other sparking compounds to be considered later. The basic reactions in the *C. kluyveri* fermentation (see details on p. 178) are

$$CH_3CH_2OH \rightarrow CH_3COOH + 4H$$
$$2CH_3COOH + 4H \rightarrow CH_3C^*H_2CH_2C^*OOH$$
$$CH_3(CH_2)_2C^*OOH + CH_3COOH \rightarrow CH_3(CH_2)_2C^*H_2CH_2COOH$$

the asterisks indicating the position of C^{14} in butyric acid when carboxyl-labeled acetic acid was added to the fermentation mixture (also found in the 1, 3, and 5 positions in caproic acid). The one asterisk in caproic acid indicates the position of the labeled carbon when it was present initially in the carboxyl group of butyric acid added to the medium.

Stadtman and Barker (1949, 1950) were able to study these reactions, actually syntheses of fatty acids ($\Delta F = -11,700$ cal. for the butyrate fermentation), with the aid of enzyme preparations from *C. kluyveri* as well as with labeled substrates. The oxidation of ethanol could be studied under either aerobic or anaerobic conditions with enzyme preparations, although oxygen is inimical to the intact cells. They observed that the amount of oxygen consumed, with methylene blue acting as a hydrogen carrier, depended upon the phosphate content of the suspending medium and that phosphate was taken up. In the presence of an excess of inorganic phosphate the over-all reactions can be represented as

$$CH_3CH_2OH + \text{P} + O_2 \rightarrow CH_3COO\sim\text{P} + 2H_2O$$

In the absence of phosphate only one atom rather than one molecule of oxygen was consumed per molecule of ethanol oxidized and acetaldehyde accumulated. They found that it is the oxidation of acetaldehyde to acetic acid that required phosphate. This oxidation yields acetyl phosphate in much the same manner as the oxidation of 3-phosphoglyceraldehyde to 1,3-diphosphoglyceric acid in the yeast fermentation. The organism possesses a phosphotransacetylase that could be involved in the formation of acetyl-CoA in the cell. Under anaerobic conditions hydrogen is presumably taken up by the coenzyme involved in these oxidations and transported to the organic oxidants as in the reactions to be considered next.

C. kluyveri possesses an active hydrogenase, and in enzyme preparations this activates hydrogen for the reduction of acetaldehyde to ethanol and particularly for the reductions involved in the formation of the higher fatty acids. These acids were pictured as being formed by the condensation of acetic acid with acetyl phosphate to form, on reduction, butyric acid. The latter compound on combination with acetyl phosphate and appropriate reduction would yield caproic acid. It now appears that CoA also is involved in the formation of these acids, and the mechanism can be illustrated with a consideration of the formation of butyrate as follows:

Ethanol
$\Updownarrow \mp 2H$
Acetaldehyde
$\Updownarrow \mp \text{P}_i \pm 2H$
Acetyl$\sim$P
$\Updownarrow \mp$ CoA (phosphotransacetylase)
Acetyl-CoA

$\Updownarrow \mp$ CoA $\mp$ H$_2$O

Acetoacetyl-CoA $\underset{\text{CoA transphorase}}{\overset{\mp \text{ acetate}}{\rightleftarrows}}$ acetoacetate + acetyl-CoA

$\Updownarrow \mp 2H$

Vinylacetyl-CoA $\overset{+ \text{ P}_i}{\longrightarrow}$ acetate + H$_2$ + CoA + acetyl$\sim$P

$\Updownarrow \mp 2H$

Butyryl-CoA $\underset{\text{CoA transphorase}}{\overset{\mp \text{ acetate}}{\longleftarrow\!\!\longrightarrow}}$ butyric acid + acetyl-CoA

There is still doubt regarding the intermediate reactions, but this scheme appears to fit the available facts. It appears that the hydrogen formed during the fermentation comes from a side reaction involving one of the postulated intermediates, vinylacetyl-CoA. Vinyl acetate (CH_2=$CHCH_2COOH$) can be oxidized to acetate and acetyl phosphate, but is not reduced readily to butyrate, the CoA complex probably being required for this reaction. ATP could be formed by a transphosphorylation reaction from acetyl-phosphate to ADP and employed for the energy-requiring reactions of the cell.

Another metabolically similar bacterium, *C. lacto-acetophilum* (Bhat and Barker, 1947), dissimilates lactate or glycerol only in the presence of acetate. The fermentation can be described as an oxidation of lactate to acetate and carbon dioxide coupled with a reductive condensation of acetate to butyrate, acetate acting as a primary oxidant.

The above scheme, starting at the acetyl-CoA stage, appears to be applicable to the mixed fermentations carried out by the butyric acid bacteria in general. Most or all of the hydrogen may come from the decomposition of pyruvate, but apparently without preliminary formation of formate, the mechanism of this reaction being obscure. It is probable that butyryl phosphate is the compound actually reduced rather than butyric acid to yield butanol via butyraldehyde. The origin of the various products (underlined) is depicted in the following scheme, the details of the reactions being omitted.

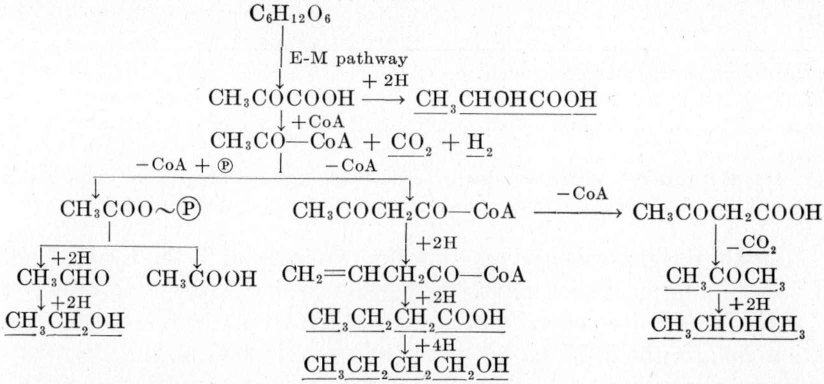

$$C_6H_{12}O_6$$

$$\downarrow \text{E-M pathway}$$

$$CH_3COCOOH \xrightarrow{+2H} CH_3CHOHCOOH$$

$$\downarrow +CoA$$

$$CH_3CO-CoA + CO_2 + H_2$$

$$-CoA + \text{\textcircled{P}} \mid \quad -CoA$$

$$CH_3COO{\sim}\text{\textcircled{P}} \qquad CH_3COCH_2CO-CoA \xrightarrow{-CoA} CH_3COCH_2COOH$$

$$\downarrow +2H \qquad \downarrow +2H \qquad \qquad \qquad \downarrow -CO_2$$

$$CH_3CHO \quad CH_3COOH \quad CH_2{=}CHCH_2CO-CoA \qquad CH_3COCH_3$$

$$\downarrow +2H \qquad \qquad \downarrow +2H \qquad \qquad \downarrow +2H$$

$$CH_3CH_2OH \qquad CH_3CH_2CH_2COOH \qquad CH_3CHOHCH_3$$

$$\downarrow +4H$$

$$CH_3CH_2CH_2CH_2OH$$

Mixed-acid Fermentation. The fermentation elicited by *Escherichia coli* is one of the most thoroughly studied fermentations and at the same time ranks among the least understood as far as certain of the reactions are concerned. Harden in 1901 represented the *E. coli* fermentation of glucose by the equation

$$2 \text{ Glucose} + H_2O = 2 \text{ lactate} + \text{acetate} + \text{ethanol} + 2CO_2 + 2H_2$$

Small amounts of succinic acid are also formed, and traces of formic acid ordinarily can be detected. It is readily apparent that organic acids constitute the bulk of the products of glucose fermentation (see Table 8-2).

The accumulation of these acids gives rise to an acidity in glucose-broth cultures sufficient to develop the acidic color of methyl red, and this behavior is utilized in a test designed to differentiate between *E. coli* and *Aerobacter aerogenes*. A similar acid fermentation is carried out by species of the genera *Salmonella* and *Shigella*, with the exceptions that more lactic acid and less volatile acids are generally formed and that *S. typhosa* and the dysentery bacilli do not produce hydrogen and carbon dioxide.

TABLE 8-2. INFLUENCE OF STRAIN, METHOD OF CULTIVATION, AND ENVIRONMENT ON GLUCOSE FERMENTATION BY *Escherichia coli*
(In moles per mole of glucose fermented)

Products	Cultures		Washed cells					
	1	2	3	4	5	6	7	8
Hydrogen............	0.39	0.54	0.56	0.57				
Carbon dioxide........	0.50	0.61	0.76	0.67	0.22			
Formic acid..........	0.01	0.02	0.03	0.01	0.84	0.75*	1.51*	1.21
Acetic acid..........	0.29	0.23	0.41	0.18	0.23			0.78
Ethanol..............	0.42	0.43	0.43	0.27	0.44	0.50	0.81	0.77
Lactic acid...........	1.09	0.84	0.72	1.46	1.10	0.74	0.10	0.20
Succinic acid.........	0.16	0.15	0.30	....	0.10	0.19	0.26	0.39
pH.................	....	....	6.2	6.2	6.2	6.0	7.0	7.1

* Total of acetic and formic acids.
1 (Scheffer, 1928) and 2 (Tasman, 1935) are products found in glucose-broth cultures, 3–7 in phosphate buffer suspensions, and 8 in bicarbonate buffer (5% CO_2). Fermentations 3–5 (Tasman, 1935) are by cells from broth (3), glucose broth (4), and agar (5); 6–8 (Stokes, 1949) are also by cells from agar cultures. The same strain was used in 2–5, while a different strain was employed in 1 and a third in 6–8.

Many of the enzymes and reactions known to occur in the E-M scheme of alcoholic fermentation have been demonstrated with preparations of *E. coli*. It is quite generally accepted that the bulk of the coli fermentation follows the E-M pathway to the pyruvic acid stage. Pyruvate appears to be utilized in three ways in the glucose fermentation: reduction to lactic acid, phosphoroclastic split with the formation of acetyl phosphate and formic acid, and condensation with carbon dioxide (or a C_1 fragment) to yield succinic acid.

E. coli possesses a lactic acid dehydrogenase which, when working in reverse, will catalyze the reduction of pyruvic to lactic acid with DPN as the coenzyme. Reduced DPN is formed during the preliminary dissimilation of the glucose molecule and can be oxidized, as in the lactic acid bacteria or in muscle, by transfer of its hydrogen and electrons to pyruvate. It is evident from the studies of Stokes (1949; Fig. 8-5; Table 8-2) that lactic acid production is dependent upon the pH and upon the presence of phosphate in the medium, relatively little being formed at the same pH when cells are suspended in bicarbonate rather than in phosphate buffer. It appears that competition between acetyl phosphate and pyruvic acid as hydrogen acceptors controls the extent of lactate formation, ethanol formation tending to increase with increase in pH while lactic acid production decreases. For the same strain the relative amounts of these two substances will, to a considerable extent, be controlled by the nature, and particularly the pH, of the culture or suspending medium. Under ordinary conditions the tendency is for glucose

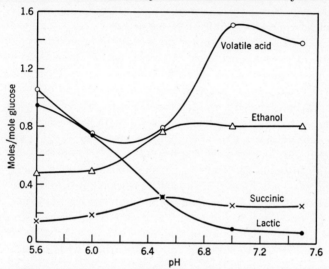

Fig. 8-5. Influence of pH on the production of volatile acids, succinic and lactic acids, and ethanol by *Escherichia coli*. (*From data of Stokes*, 1949.)

to be fermented by *E. coli* with the production of around one mole of lactate per mole of glucose utilized. When pyruvate, however, is the substrate rather than glucose, there is less hydrogen available for the reduction and only about 5 per cent is reduced to lactate, the bulk of the pyruvate being dissimilated to form acetic and formic acids.

Kalnitsky and Werkman (1943) obtained a cell-free extract from aerobically grown cells of *E. coli* which fermented pyruvate with the production in a typical experiment of 7.4 mM of carbon dioxide, 80.7 each of formic and acetic acids, 2.5 of lactic, and 8.4 of succinic acid. It has been suggested that lactic acid could be formed with formic acid acting as the reducing agent according to the equation

$$CH_3COCOOH + HCOOH \rightarrow CH_3CHOHCOOH + CO_2$$

since *E. coli* does possess a formic dehydrogenase. The evidence for this reaction is not convincing, and furthermore the amount of lactic acid formed can be increased by increasing the carbon dioxide content of the fermentation system.   This would not occur if the above reaction took place and was reversible.   Tracer studies with labeled carbon dioxide also indicate that this substance can be fixed and that some of the labeled carbon appears in the carboxyl group of lactic acid.

Studies by Nutting and Carson (1952) have shown that lactic, succinic, formic, and acetic acids and ethanol are formed from the pentose sugar, xylose.   When the fermentation was conducted at a low pH, about 5.3, neither ethanol nor succinic acid was produced, while about 1.4 moles of lactic acid were formed per mole of xylose utilized.   Since xylose appears to be utilized via a C_2-C_3 rupture of the pentose chain, some of the lactate must have been formed from a C_2 fragment in order to account for the production of more than a mole of lactic acid per mole of xylose.   This would suggest that it arose from a condensation of C_2 fragments with subsequent decarboxylation or from a C_2 molecule and carbon dioxide or formate.   When labeled formate was added to the fermentation mixture the lactic acid recovered later was found to be labeled in the carboxyl group.   Acetate or ethanol labeled in the methyl group gave rise to lactic acid labeled only in the methyl group.

These authors, on the basis of various considerations, concluded that lactic acid was not formed from a C_4 intermediate produced either by condensation of two C_2 compounds or through the Krebs cycle.   Likewise the tracer studies indicated that a C_2-formate condensation similar to the glycine-formate condensation of Sakami (1948) could not be responsible, for this would lead to labeling of the β-carbon with labeled formate. They suggested condensation of the type

$$
\begin{array}{ccc}
\text{C*H}_3 & & \\
| & & \\
\text{CO}-X & & \text{C*H}_3 \\
& & | \\
\text{``active C}_2\text{''} \rightarrow & \text{CHOH} \\
& & | \\
+ & & \text{C**OOH} \\
\end{array}
$$

$$\text{HC**OOH or C**O}_2$$

where the X probably represents CoA and the asterisks indicate labeled C. This condensation probably would involve a C_1-CoA complex in addition to the acetyl one.   Since Stokes (1949) also found that lactic acid production was enhanced and production of succinic acid was depressed at low pH, it thus appears that a C_2-C_1 condensation is favored by acidic conditions, a C_2-C_2 type, if it occurs, by less acidic or alkaline conditions.

When one attempts to establish a balanced series of equations for the xylose fermentation giving rise to more than one mole of lactate per mole of sugar, it becomes apparent that the reactions are much more complex than indicated above. Fixation of formate added to the medium could occur by reversal of the phosphoroclastic split, but the uptake of carbon dioxide (by hydrogenlyase-deficient cells) is more difficult to picture as occurring directly with a C_2 compound. Also the formation of up to 1.4 moles of lactate per mole of xylose would require the decomposition of at least 0.2 mole of a C_2 compound, or the fixation of 0.4 mole of carbon dioxide or formate. The latter value does not agree with the carbon balances of the fermentations.

Korkes et al. (1951) observed that extracts of *E. coli* catalyze the dismutation of two moles of pyruvate to one each of lactate, acetyl phosphate, and carbon dioxide. Two protein fractions were obtained which, together with lactic acid dehydrogenase, transacetylase, orthophosphate, Mg^{++}, and the coenzymes DPN, CoA, thiamine pyrophosphate, and α-lipoic acid (or lipothiamin pyrophosphate), are required for the dismutation. Replacement of transacetylase and orthophosphate with condensing enzyme and oxalacetic acid led to the synthesis of citric acid in amounts equal to the carbon dioxide produced. Carbon dioxide production, however, generally is not observed to any appreciable extent in the *E. coli* fermentation except when an equivalent amount of hydrogen is formed. It is doubtful, therefore, if this reaction occurs to any marked extent in the living cell. The observation does, however, illustrate the fact that care must be exercised in interpreting results obtained with artificial systems in terms of activity in the cell itself. This again suggests that spatial arrangement of the enzymes within the cell may control to a considerable extent the course of dissimilation, and of assimilation as well.

The second mode of utilization of pyruvate formed by *E. coli* during the fermentation of glucose results in the formation of acetic and formic acids. The latter acid is decomposed by the gas-producing enteric bacteria with the formation of hydrogen and carbon dioxide under ordinary conditions of anaerobic fermentation, but not by washed cells which were cultivated under highly aerobic conditions. The original concept was that pyruvate is hydrolytically split into the two fatty acids in what was termed the hydroclastic reaction. In more recent years it became apparent that phosphate enters the reaction and that it, rather than water, is involved in the breakdown of pyruvate, hence the term phosphoroclastic split. Now it appears that CoA is a participant in the reaction which yields formic acid and acetyl-CoA and that phosphate enters into the picture only when acetyl phosphate is formed as considered under the lactic acid fermentation. Ethanol can be formed by reduction of acetyl phosphate, probably with CoA-acetyl as a participant in the reaction, or the latter can be employed directly as it is formed. Little or no ethanol is formed when pyruvate itself is the fermentation substrate since there is less hydrogen available than in the glucose fermentation for this reduction.   Acetyl phosphate can enter into condensation reactions considered above and to be discussed later.   It also can be hydrolyzed or transfer its phosphate to ADP with the liberation of acetic acid which accumulates in the fermentation mixture.

When *E. coli* is cultivated under anaerobic conditions, particularly in the presence of a fermentable sugar, the cells are capable of decomposing formic acid into hydrogen and carbon dioxide.   This reaction is a reversible one, Woods (1936) having reported an observed ΔF of -171 cal. for the reaction

$$H_2 + HCO_3^- \rightleftarrows HCOO^- + H_2O$$

This reversibility accounts for the decreased gas production and accumulation of formic acid observed when the fermentation is carried out in a closed system, particularly in the presence of added hydrogen, carbon dioxide, or a mixture of the two gases.   The production of these two gases was ascribed by Stephenson and Stickland to the activity of an adaptive enzyme they termed hydrogenlyase.   The existence of such an enzyme is questioned by many workers who ascribe the gas production to the combined activity of formic dehydrogenase and hydrogenase.   Gest (1952) concludes, "Hydrogenlyase appears to be a complex composed of formic dehydrogenase, hydrogenase, dissociable cofactors, and possibly additional enzymes."   A number of reports indicate that both hydrogenase and formic dehydrogenase can be present in a cell without detectable hydrogenlyase activity.   The system is a complex one, and the use of the term hydrogenlyase here will be without reference to whether it is a single enzyme or a complex system.   Hydrogenlyase activity is lost when the cells are cultivated under aerobic conditions (see Table 8-2 and the xylose fermentation above).   Hydrogenlyase production is inhibited by the presence of nitrates in the culture medium or by low concentrations of iron and is stimulated by glutamic acid or by several groups of amino acids (Lichstein, 1952).

The third type of utilization of pyruvate by *E. coli* involves the fixation of carbon dioxide with the formation of succinic acid as mentioned under the propionic acid fermentation.   Elsden (1938) was the first to demonstrate this reaction with *E. coli*, pointing out that the rate of formation of succinate and the total amount produced from pyruvate, glucose, or galactose were directly related to the amount of carbon dioxide in the medium.   Earlier suggestions concerning the origin of succinic acid were that it was derived from a 4-carbon compound produced by a 2-4 split of the glucose molecule or by a condensation (Thunberg reaction) of two molecules of acetate.

We have already considered that Wood and Werkman advanced the hypothesis that carbon dioxide combines with pyruvic acid to form oxal-acetic acid which can be converted via malic and fumaric acids to succinic acid, four hydrogen atoms being required for the reductions.   Oxalacetate is readily decarboxylated by its decarboxylase with the formation of pyru-vate and carbon dioxide, but this reaction is not readily reversible.   There is some evidence that the Wood-Werkman reaction does occur with the participation of ATP, a hypothetical intermediate X being formed that can be converted to oxalacetic or to malic acid, depending upon the conditions of the test.

Much of the available data suggest that carbon dioxide is generally fixed by pyruvate (or lactate) with the aid of the malic enzyme of Ochoa and that some of the malic acid formed can be oxidized to oxalacetate with the aid of malic dehydrogenase.   Biotin appears to be involved in the formation or activity of the malic acid enzyme which is a carboxylase, reversible in its activity.   The formation of malate from pyruvate and carbon dioxide involves both the malic enzyme and lactic acid dehydro-genase together with TPN (or DPN depending on source of enzyme), the reaction being represented as

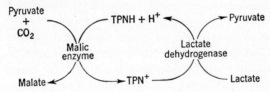

Malate can then be converted to succinate.

Another coupled reaction involving carbon dioxide fixation is the taking up of this substance by α-ketoglutaric with the formation of oxalosuccinic acid.   The equilibrium constant for the decarboxylation of oxalosuccinate has a value near 2,500, the ΔF, therefore, being close to $-4,600$ cal. With such a high equilibrium constant the reaction would tend to go practically to completion.   Oxalosuccinic acid can be reduced to isocitric acid, and thereby the former acid is removed, thus tending to favor carbon dioxide fixation if an energy source is available.   The oxidation of glucose-6-phosphate to 6-phosphogluconic acid can provide the requi-site energy in a reaction coupled through TPN^+ as follows:

α-Ketoglutaric acid $+ CO_2 \rightarrow$ oxalosuccinic acid $\Delta F = +4,600$ cal.
Oxalosuccinic acid $+ TPNH + H^+ \rightarrow$
$\qquad\qquad$ isocitric acid $+ TPN^+$ $\Delta F = +700$ cal.
Glucose-6-phosphate $+ TPN^+ \rightarrow$
$\qquad\qquad$ 6-phosphogluconic acid $+ TPNH + H^+$ $\Delta F = -6,900$ cal.

α-Ketoglutaric acid $+ CO_2 +$ glucose-6-phosphate $\rightarrow$
$\qquad$ isocitric acid $+$ 6-phosphogluconic acid $\Delta F = -1,600$ cal.

This reaction may be of little or no importance in the *E. coli* fermentation.

We have considered the work of Carson and Nutting in which they demonstrated carbon dioxide (or formate) condensation with acetate to yield lactic acid. It is apparent that a variety of methods exists for the fixation of carbon dioxide, and there is disagreement as to the actual mechanism employed by *E. coli* and other bacteria. For the time being we can consider this fixation to be an established phenomenon and that it may occur in a variety of reactions, either directly in some or after reduction to formate in other processes.

Actually, carbon dioxide fixation may be of little quantitative significance if the gas is removed as rapidly as it is formed. The study of Stokes (1949), in which hydrogenylase-deficient cells were employed, indicated that little or no carbon dioxide was fixed even when the fermentation was conducted under an atmosphere of this gas. Succinic acid production was accounted for by a condensation of formic acid with a 3-carbon intermediate. He reasoned that pyruvate was split with the formation of one mole each of formic and acetic acids, some of the latter being reduced to ethanol. The sum of the C_2 products, therefore, should equal the molecular quantities of formic acid produced in the fermentation. The moles of C_2 compounds present in the fermentation mixtures exceeded those of formic acid by values approximately equal to those of succinic acid formed, thus indicating that the difference is due to the amount of formate fixed. Bearing in mind that the relative amounts of the various compounds formed in the *E. coli* fermentation will vary with environmental conditions and with the strain employed, a general scheme for the fermentation can be established as follows:

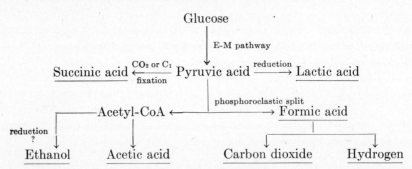

Doubt exists as to the actual mechanism of ethanol formation, and its formation by reduction of acetyl-CoA (or phosphate) must be considered as tentative only. Revision of the general scheme would be required if a part of the glucose were fermented over the hexose monophosphate pathway.

2,3-Butylene Glycol Fermentation. Harden and Walpole in 1906 demonstrated the production of acetylmethylcarbinol (acetoin) and

2,3-butylene glycol during the fermentation of glucose by *Aerobacter aerogenes*. *E. coli* does not produce these substances, and this difference in fermentation is employed in the Voges-Proskauer (VP) test for differentiating between these organisms. Acetoin is also formed during the fermentation of glucose by species other than those of *Aerobacter*, e.g., of *Aeromonas, Streptococcus, Bacillus*, and *Clostridium*. It can be reduced to 2,3-butylene glycol, the extent of this reduction depending upon the species and strain and upon environmental conditions.

The production of acetoin is favored by acidic conditions. *A. aerogenes* carries out a fermentation of glucose similar to that elicited by *E. coli* until the pH of the culture medium falls below 6.5. The fermentation then shifts in the direction of acetylmethylcarbinol production. Some acetic acid may be converted into acetoin, and either the first or both reactions lead to reduced acid production, or accumulation, in the medium. This neutralization mechanism results in a final higher pH in glucose-broth cultures of *A. aerogenes* as contrasted with *E. coli* and serves, as previously mentioned, in the MR test for differentiation between the two species.

At present there appear to be two mechanisms for acetoin production by microorganisms: the one in yeast for which one mole each of pyruvate and of acetaldehyde are required and the one in *Aerobacter* where two molecules of pyruvate act as the substrate to form α-acetolactate and carbon dioxide, the former compound being decarboxylated to yield acetoin. Juni (1952) has demonstrated this with extracts of *A. aerogenes* which catalyze the two separate reactions:

$$2\text{-Pyruvate} \rightarrow \text{acetolactate} + CO_2$$

$$\text{HO}-\underset{\underset{\text{CH}_3}{|}}{\overset{\overset{\text{COOH}}{|}}{\text{C}}}-\text{COCH}_3 \rightarrow \text{CH}_3\text{COCHOHCH}_3 + CO_2$$

α-Acetolactate   Acetoin

Here we find that carbon dioxide is released in reactions in addition to the one involved in the decomposition of formate, and hence the ratio of carbon dioxide to hydrogen liberated is greater than unity with *Aerobacter* while it is approximately unity with *E. coli*. The carbon dioxide produced should exceed the hydrogen by twice the number of moles of acetylmethylcarbinol produced, except for any acetoin that might arise from the condensation of acetate and pyruvate. This latter reaction would give rise to only one molecule in excess of that derived from formate. This quantitative relationship appears to be supported by the studies of Slade and Werkman (1943) with *A. indologenes*, this species reducing the acetoin completely to 2,3-butylene glycol (Table 8-3). These results also indicate the incorporation of acetate carbon into succinic acid and the glycol. They also further indicate the similarity between the *E. coli* and the *Aerobacter* fermentations, the latter having the additional mode of utilization of pyruvate resulting in the formation of acetoin and 2,3-butylene glycol. It is of interest to record that acetoin can be oxidized to yield diacetyl ($CH_3COCOCH_3$), a substance giving rise to the odor characteristic of butter, and that 2,3-butylene glycol can be converted by chemical means to butadiene ($CH_2{=}CH—CH{=}CH_2$), one of the starting materials for the production of synthetic rubber of the buna type.

TABLE 8-3. PRODUCTS OF GLUCOSE FERMENTATION BY *Aerobacter indologenes* AND UPTAKE OF LABELED ACETATE*

	CO_2	H_2	Formate	Acetate	Lactate	Succinate	Ethanol	2,3-Butylene glycol	Carbon recovered, %	O/R index
Glucose only..........	149.0	48.5	18.7	3.4	1.2	18.1	56.0	58.6	99.5	1.00
+ $CH_3C^{13}OOH$........	186.0	50.1	4.0	35.3	3.5	11.0	51.4	70.1	94.1	1.10
						(1.21)	(1.64)	(1.21)		
+ $C^{13}H_3C^{13}OOH$......	179.8	45.3	4.3	26.2	2.0	12.2	54.3	69.6	92.7	1.04
						(1.33)	(2.19)	(1.24)		

* From data of Slade and Werkman, 1943.

Products are expressed as millimoles per 100 mM of glucose fermented, and the values in parentheses indicate excess abundance of C^{13}.

Miscellaneous Fermentations—Carbon Dioxide Reduction. In the fermentations we have considered the organic substrates are oxidized, following appropriate changes, by loss of hydrogen and electrons to other molecules formed during the course of dissimilation. Fermentations also occur in which the hydrogen is accepted by other molecules, organic or inorganic, present in the original medium. Lactate, for example, can be oxidized to pyruvate with fumarate acting as the oxidant and being reduced to succinate. Carbon dioxide, sulfate, or nitrate can also act as hydrogen acceptors in fermentations induced by a number of bacteria and are reduced to characteristic products such as methane, sulfide, and ammonia.

The microbiological production of methane from cellulose in mud was recognized as early as 1875 and about ten years later as also occurring in the intestinal tract of cattle. Söhngen, by 1910, had shown that the decomposition of cellulose provided fatty acids which served as the substrate for methane production, the simplest reaction observed in enrichment cultures being

$$4HCOOH \rightarrow CH_4 + 3CO_2 + 2H_2O$$

He also observed that methane could be produced by the reduction of carbon dioxide with molecular hydrogen, or

$$CO_2 + 4H_2 \rightarrow CH_4 + 2H_2O$$

It was not until 1936 that the methane-producing bacteria were isolated in pure culture, thus enabling fermentation by these organisms to be studied in greater detail (Barker, 1936a,b). Barker employed simple enrichment media containing 1 to 2 per cent of the lower fatty acids or alcohols as the substrate, sulfates being omitted to prevent appreciable growth of sulfate-reducing bacteria. These media were inoculated with samples of mud and incubated for considerable periods of time under anaerobic conditions, the methane bacteria having relatively low rates of multiplication and being strict anaerobes. Serial transfers were made to the same media, and finally to the same media solidified with agar, care being taken to prevent the access of oxygen. Colonies could be picked from the agar shake cultures, and the isolates so obtained were cultivated in appropriate media. Four different species, *Methanosarcina methanica, Methanococcus mazei, Methanobacterium söhngenii*, and *Methanobacterium omelianskii*, were recognized on the basis of morphological and physiological characteristics.

Since methane was the only hydrocarbon produced, regardless of the number of carbon atoms in the substrate, Barker tested the suggestion of van Niel (based on comparative biochemical considerations and the earlier observation by Söhngen of carbon dioxide reduction by hydrogen) that this occurred because methane arose from carbon dioxide serving as an oxidizing agent. The role of the organic substrate was pictured as that of a hydrogen donor according to the equation

$$4H_2A + CO_2 \rightarrow 4A + CH_4 + 2H_2O$$

When ethanol was the substrate Barker observed an almost quantitative dehydrogenation of it to acetic acid, together with the reduction of amounts of carbon dioxide indicated by the equation

$$2C_2H_5OH + 2H_2O + CO_2 \rightarrow 2CH_3COOH + CH_4 + 2H_2O$$

a reaction quite similar to the reduction of sulfate by *Vibrio desulfuricans* as described earlier by Baars (1930). Butanol was dehydrogenated to butyric acid with simultaneous reduction of carbon dioxide to methane, the butyric acid then being dehydrogenated to acetic acid with further production of methane. Some species were capable of fermenting acetic acid, carbon dioxide and methane being produced in a fermentation indicated as

$$CH_3COOH + 2H_2O + CO_2 \rightarrow 2CO_2 + CH_4 + 2H_2O$$

Barker pointed out that it was highly improbable that acetic acid was reduced directly to methane, although it was impossible to prove this point from fermentation balances, more carbon dioxide being present at the end than at the start of the fermentation. Furthermore, it could be possible for the methane to arise from a split of the acetic acid molecule directly to give the same balance as indicated by the equation.

The application of the isotope technique of following the fate of a compound enabled Barker, Ruben, and Kamen (1940) to demonstrate that labeled carbon dioxide was reduced to methane and also that some of the carbon dioxide–carbon was assimilated by the cells. T. C. Stadtman and Barker (1949), employing C^{14}-labeled carbon dioxide, observed that in the methane fermentation of acetic acid by a *Methanococcus*, the methane was practically unlabeled. This did not agree with the results obtained with other species. Additional studies, with both methyl- and carboxyl-labeled acetate, indicated that this species produced methane from the methyl group of acetate and carbon dioxide from the carboxyl group, only a little of the methane being derived from the reduction of carbon dioxide. The methane formed in the fermentation of ethanol by *Methanobacterium omelianski*, however, was derived from carbon dioxide and not from ethanol or acetic acid.

The problem was further complicated (Stadtman and Barker, 1951a,b) when it became apparent that methane was also derived from the methyl group of acetate by a strain of *Methanosarcina*, while other evidence indicated that it did arise from carbon dioxide with other species using higher fatty acids or alcohols as the substrate. *Methanobacterium suboxydans* and *M. propionicum* were characterized by their incomplete oxidation of fatty acids. Various isotope studies with *M. suboxydans* offered evidence that this bacterium is unable to oxidize acetate or propionate but could oxidize higher fatty acids, even-carbon ones such as caproic and butyric being dissimilated to acetic acid with concurrent reduction of carbon dioxide to methane while the odd-carbon acid, valeric, was oxidized and split to form propionic and acetic acids. *M. propionicum* did oxidize propionic acid to carbon dioxide and acetate and in such a manner that the carboxyl group gives rise to carbon dioxide and the alpha and beta carbons to acetic acid. Acetate was not utilized by either species, and hence it appears that the methane produced came from the reduction of carbon dioxide. This indicates that methane may arise from two sources, carbon dioxide or the methyl group of acetate, depending upon the species under study and the substrate. Further observations indicated that the

Methanosarcina could convert methanol to methane. The following scheme, based on the assumption that there is only one general mechanism of methane formation, was advanced:

$$\text{Methyl group of acetate} \rightarrow X \rightarrow CH_4$$
$$\uparrow$$
$$CH_3OH \rightarrow Y \rightleftarrows CO_2$$

It is postulated in the above scheme that methanol is transformed by oxidation to a substance Y which is an intermediate in the formation of methane from either methanol or carbon dioxide. X can be derived from either Y or the methyl group of acetate and is distinguished by the fact that it cannot be converted to carbon dioxide, while Y can be converted either to X or to carbon dioxide. This scheme indicates that some methane can be formed from carbon dioxide during the fermentation of acetate or methanol but that the reduction is inhibited by the accumulation of X or Y, which, presumably, can be formed more readily from the organic substrates than from carbon dioxide. This inhibition might be regarded as analogous to the inhibition of nitrogen fixation by ammonia. No information is available concerning the nature of the postulated intermediates X and Y, but Stadtman and Barker suggested that they might be multicarbon compounds since other C_1 compounds tested (CO, HCOOH, and HCHO) were not reduced directly to methane.

Schnellen (1947) did show, however, that carbon monoxide can be reduced to methane in the presence or absence of free hydrogen by two species of methane bacteria, *Methanosarcina barkerii* and *Methanobacterium formicicum*. He suggested that in the absence of gaseous hydrogen the carbon monoxide reacted with water to yield carbon dioxide and hydrogen, the latter subsequently reducing carbon dioxide to methane. *Methanosarcina barkerii* is of considerable interest since it can bring about the reduction in an atmosphere of carbon monoxide, a rather potent cellular poison in general, and the fermentation

$$4CO + 2H_2O \rightarrow CH_4 + 3CO_2$$

is one of the simplest fermentations known.

Carbon dioxide can serve as an oxidant with still other species of bacteria, being reduced to acetic acid in the process. Wieringa isolated a *Clostridium* from mud which reduced carbon dioxide according to the equation

$$2CO_2 + 4H_2 \rightleftarrows CH_3COOH + 2H_2O$$

Certain clostridia carry out this reduction with hydrogen obtained from the oxidation of purines or other substances. Barker (1944) suggested that the formation of three moles of acetic acid from one mole of glucose fermented by *C. thermoaceticum* is due in part to this type of carbon dioxide reduction according to the equations

$$C_6H_{12}O_6 + 2H_2O \rightarrow 2CH_3COOH + 2CO_2 + 8H$$
$$2CO_2 + 8H \rightarrow CH_3COOH + 2H_2O$$

Later studies indicated that labeled carbon dioxide added to a fermentation mixture gave rise to acetic acid labeled in both carbons. *Diplococcus glycinophilus*, an organism characterized by its high specificity for glycine, also fixes some carbon dioxide as acetate during the fermentation of glycine. Utter and Wood (1951) raise doubt as to the validity of the concept of a total net synthesis of acetate from carbon dioxide, suggesting that an exchange of carbon dioxide occurs with the acetic acid carboxyl, the doubly labeled acetate arising largely as a result of this exchange reaction. Stadtman and Stadtman (1953) interpret Wood's results in favor of total synthesis of some acetate from carbon dioxide. The mechanism of the formation of acetate by the reduction and condensation of carbon dioxide remains obscure. The possibility of exchange reactions complicates the use of tracers in the study of bacterial metabolism.

Bacteria can, in addition to the reduction of oxygen, organic compounds, and carbon dioxide, bring about the oxidation of organic matter by concomitant reduction of sulfate, tetrathionate, or nitrate, utilizing the energy released for growth. They can also reduce selenite and phosphate, but these reductions appear to be of more diagnostic value than of use in the economy of the cell.

Desulfovibrio desulfuricans can bring about the reduction of sulfate, or of sulfur, hydrosulfite, thiosulfate, or sulfite, to hydrogen sulfide, the hydrogen for the reduction coming from the simultaneous oxidation of organic compounds for which the cells contain the appropriate dehydrogenases. Van Niel (1953) suggests that the reduction involves the participation of organic sulfate esters although little is known concerning the mechanism of the reaction. Sulfate reduction appears to be limited to a very small number of bacterial species, yet sulfate is assimilated by most or all species, being reduced with the ultimate formation of sulfhydryl compounds so essential for cellular activity. There appear, therefore, to be two types of sulfate reduction, just as in the case of nitrate reduction, one assimilatory, the other dissimilatory in character.

Van Niel also discussed the ability of a *Pseudomonas* to oxidize glycerol under anaerobic conditions with tetrathionate as the oxidant, tetrathionate being reduced to thiosulfate. Addition of oxygen-regenerated tetrathionate from thiosulfate and the anaerobic oxidation of more glycerol could follow, a large amount of the organic substrate being oxidized by a small amount of tetrathionate periodically regenerated. Tetrathionate appeared to act in a mediating role, much like coenzymes of oxidation, in

a manner that can be represented as

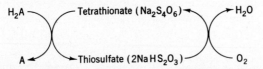

This organism can also bring about the oxidation of glycerol in the absence of tetrathionate, the latter not being essential for the reaction but being capable of entering into it.   Tetrathionase is an adaptive enzyme (Knox and Pollock, 1944).

The dissimilation or reduction of nitrate (denitrification) is characterized by the production of nitrous oxide, nitrite, nitrogen, or ammonia depending upon the bacterial species and the nature of the test conditions. Kluyver (1953) recognized three types of nitrate utilization.   In the first type nitrate is used solely for the formation of cellular nitrogenous matter, the majority of the assimilated nitrate molecules being reduced to the stage of ammonia existing in amino groups of cell proteins.   He designated this type of utilization as *assimilatory nitrate reduction* or *nitrate assimilation*.   It is analogous to the assimilation of sulfate mentioned above.

The second type was designated as *incidental dissimilatory nitrate reduction* and is characterized by the reduction of nitrate to nitrite or to ammonia, the nitrate competing with other hydrogen acceptors for hydrogen derived from the oxidation of organic substrates, much as methylene blue might do.   It might be considered as an interference reaction and is not essential for cellular activity.   This type of reaction serves as the basis for differentiation between certain species on the basis of their ability to produce nitrites from nitrates.   Nitrate will, by competing with other hydrogen acceptors in sugar fermentations, shift the fermentation balance toward the formation of more oxidized end products than are found in its absence.

The third type postulated by Kluyver was designated as *true dissimilatory nitrate reduction* since certain species are unable to survive in the absence of oxygen unless the oxygen is replaced with nitrates as an oxidant. This property of true dissimilatory nitrate reduction is exhibited by several species of *Pseudomonas*, particularly *P. stutzeri, aeruginosa*, and *denitrofluorescens*, by *Micrococcus denitrificans*, and by several species of *Spirillum* and *Bacillus*.

Kluyver and his students (see also Verhoeven, 1952) have reported that the organic substrate for nitrate reduction is generally oxidized to carbon dioxide and water, except for the amounts assimilated by the cells.   Complete dehydrogenation appears to be the fate of the organic molecule in nitrate reduction, while reduction of the latter may be incomplete, i.e., nitrites, nitrous oxide, or nitrogen rather than ammonia may be formed.

In sulfate or carbonate reduction the reverse appears to be true since incomplete oxidation of the substrate and complete reduction of the oxidant tend to occur. Molecular hydrogen can also be utilized by the cell for the reduction of nitrates. Hydrogenase and nitrase are adaptive enzymes.

Of most interest is the fate of the nitrate molecule in true dissimilatory nitrate reduction, Kluyver picturing a reaction chain as indicated below:

$$
\begin{array}{l}
\text{Nitric acid} \quad HNO_3 \\
\qquad 2H \rightarrow \downarrow \\
\text{Nitrous acid} \quad HNO_2 \\
\qquad 2H \rightarrow \downarrow \qquad \begin{array}{c}\text{Dimer of} \\ \text{nitroxyl}\end{array} \quad \begin{array}{c}\text{Nitrous} \\ \text{oxide}\end{array} \\
\text{Nitroxyl} \quad HNO \rightarrow 0.5H_2N_2O_2 \rightarrow 0.5N_2O + 0.5H_2O \\
\qquad 2H \rightarrow \downarrow \qquad\qquad\qquad \leftarrow H \rightarrow \searrow \\
\text{Hydroxylamine} \quad H_2NOH \qquad\qquad 0.5N_2 + 0.5H_2O \\
\qquad 2H \rightarrow \downarrow \\
\text{Ammonia} \quad NH_3
\end{array}
$$

Allen and van Niel (1952) observed that the dimer of nitroxyl (hyponitrous acid, $HON{=}NOH$) was not utilized, while nitramid, $H_2N\text{-}NO_2$ or

$$HN\underset{}{\overset{O}{\diagup\diagdown}}NOH$$

, was converted to nitrogen. They advanced the hypothesis that two organic complexes, R' and R'', were involved in the reaction chain which might in part be expressed as

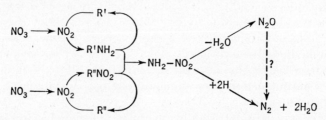

The nature of these postulated intermediate carriers is unknown, but the ideas presented in the schemes are suggestive for further studies on denitrification.

Why is ammonia the end product of nitrate reduction at times, nitrous oxide and nitrogen at others, even with the same organism? It has long been known that oxygen inhibits nitrate reduction, being preferably utilized as a hydrogen acceptor. Kluyver and Verhoeven found that in shallow-layer cultures of *Denitrobacillus licheniformis* subject to surface aeration only, nitrate was dissimilated with the production of the ultimate reduction product, ammonia. Under anaerobic conditions it was dissimilated to nitrous oxide and nitrogen. It was not attacked when the cultures were strongly aerated. It is known that in stationary cultures oxygen tension is low in the bulk of the medium, and this allows for the substitution of some nitrate for oxygen as a hydrogen acceptor. Under reduced oxygen tension nitrate goes to ammonia, while in the absence of oxygen, nitrous oxide and nitrogen are formed. Offhand, one might suspect that the reverse would hold true. The results suggest that in some manner free oxygen interferes with the union between two nitrogen atoms which is required in the pathway for the formation of nitrous oxide or nitrogen and instead the common intermediate is reduced to ammonia.

We have considered typical fermentations of various substrates by different species. Other pathways of fermentation may exist, and modifications of the schemes summarized will no doubt be advanced. These schemes, with modification, are applicable to the fermentation of still other substrates, many of which are hydrolyzed or otherwise dissimilated with the production of intermediates encountered in the schemes discussed in the preceding pages. Fermentations have this property in common: the major energy-providing reactions are dehydrogenations in which substances other than molecular oxygen are the ultimate hydrogen and electron acceptors and make possible life without air. The various types of reduction can be represented as

$$A + 2H \rightarrow AH_2$$
$$H_2CO_3 + 8H \rightarrow CH_4 + 3H_2O$$
$$H_2SO_4 + 8H \rightarrow H_2S + 4H_2O$$
$$HNO_3 + 8H \rightarrow NH_3 + 3H_2O$$
$$O_2 + 4H \rightarrow 2H_2O$$

The last, or aerobic oxidation, will be considered in subsequent chapters.

Industrial Applications. Microbial fermentations are employed for the industrial production of a number of agents. Around 200 million proof gallons of industrial ethyl alcohol is produced in the United States annually by the fermentation of carbohydrates, the cost of the substrate influencing the amount produced in this manner as compared with the amount produced by synthetic processes. It is estimated that 100 million lb. of butanol can be produced by the fermentation industries per year, the actual production in recent years being around 30 million lb., while over 100 million lb. is produced synthetically. Again economics is the controlling factor. Relatively little acetone is produced today by the application of microbial activity. Acetic acid (20 million lb.) in vinegar is produced by the partial oxidation of ethanol by the acetic acid bacteria. Other organic acids (gluconic, ketogluconic, α-ketoglutaric, itaconic, etc.) also can, be or are, produced by partial oxidations induced by acetic acid bacteria or molds. Lactic acid (5 million lb.) is produced by fermentation of appropriate carbohydrates by lactic acid bacteria and citric acid

(50 million lb.) by mold fermentations. Dextrans for use as plasma expanders are now being produced by biosynthetic methods as well as large quantities of riboflavin and some cortisone, in one procedure a fermentation step being utilized in its synthesis. Well over 1 million lb. of antibiotics is produced by various microorganisms harnessed for industrial purposes. A considerable proportion of these products is employed as an animal-feed supplement, both as growth stimulants and in the control of livestock infections. Other substances are produced in lesser amounts, the balance between synthetic and biosynthetic processes being controlled by economic factors.

Yeast is an important commodity, millions of pounds being utilized in the production of bakery products and lesser amounts as fodder supplements. Considerable interest in, and some use of, yeast as a human food exists at the present time, and it is a relatively cheap source of protein and fat. Another type of fungus, edible mushrooms, is produced to the extent of over 10 million lb. dry weight. The production of these fungi involves aerobic rather than anaerobic processes. Amylases, proteases, and other enzymes are obtained to a limited extent on an industrial scale from yeasts, molds, or bacteria. Microbic fermentations are also of considerable economic importance in the production of foodstuffs, e.g., butter, cheese, sauerkraut, pickles, and, for farm animals, ensilage.

REFERENCES

Allen, M. B., and C. B. van Niel: Experiments on bacterial denitrification, *J. Bacteriol.*, **64**, 397–412 (1952).

Baars, J. K.: Over sulfaatreductie door bacteriën, Dissertation, Delft, 1930.

Barker, H. A.: On the biochemistry of the methane fermentation, *Arch. Mikrobiol.*, **7**, 404–419 (1936).

———: Studies upon the methane-producing bacteria, *Arch. Mikrobiol.*, **7**, 420–438 (1936).

———: On the fermentation of glutamic acid, *Enzymologia*, **2**, 175–182 (1937).

———: On the role of carbon dioxide in the metabolism of *Clostridium thermoaceticum*, *Proc. Natl. Acad. Sci. U.S.*, **30**, 88–90 (1944).

———: *Clostridium kluyveri*, *Antonie van Leeuwenhoek*, **12**, 167–176 (1947).

——— and F. Lipmann: The role of phosphate in the metabolism of *Propionibacterium pentosaceum*, *J. Biol. Chem.*, **179**, 247–257 (1949).

———, S. Ruben, and M. D. Kamen: The reduction of radioactive carbon dioxide by methane-producing bacteria, *Proc. Natl. Acad. Sci. U.S.*, **26**, 426–429 (1940).

——— and S. M. Taha: *Clostridium kluyveri*, an organism concerned in the formation of caproic acid from ethyl alcohol, *J. Bacteriol.*, **43**, 347–363 (1942).

Bhat, J. V., and H. A. Barker: *Clostridium lacto-acetophilum* nov. spec. and the role of acetic acid in the butyric acid fermentation of lactate, *J. Bacteriol.*, **54**, 381–391 (1947).

Carson, S. F., and S. Ruben: CO₂ assimilation by propionic acid bacteria studied by the use of radioactive carbon, *Proc. Natl. Acad. Sci. U.S.*, **26**, 422–426 (1940).

Cohen, G. N.: Nature et mode de formation des acides volatils trouvés dans les cultures de bactéries anaérobies strictes, *Ann. inst. Pasteur*, **77**, 471–511 (1949).

———: Metabolism of bacteria, *Ann. Rev. Microbiol.*, **5**, 71–100 (1951).

Davies, R., and M. Stephenson: Studies on the acetone-butanol fermentation, *Biochem. J.*, **35**, 1320–1331 (1941).

Delwiche, E. A.: Mechanism of propionic acid fermentation by *Propionibacterium pentosaceum*, *J. Bacteriol.*, **56**, 811–820 (1948).

DeMoss, R. D.: Routes of ethanol formation in bacteria, *J. Cell. Comp. Physiol.*, **41**, suppl. 1, 207–224 (1953).

Elsden, S. R.: The effect of CO_2 on the production of succinic acid by *Bact. coli commune*, *Biochem. J.*, **32**, 187–193 (1938).

Gest, H.: Decomposition of $HCOOH$ to CO_2 and H_2 in cell-free systems, *Bacteriol. Proc.*, p. 144 (1952).

Gibbs, M., and R. D. DeMoss: Ethanol formation in *Pseudomonas lindneri*, *Arch. Biochem. and Biophys.*, **34**, 478–479 (1951).

Gunsalus, I. C.: Oxidative and transfer reactions of lipoic acid, *Federation Proc.*, **13**, 715–722 (1954).

——— and M. Gibbs: Position of C^{14} in the products of glucose dissimilation by *Leuconostoc mesenteroides*, *J. Biol. Chem.*, **194**, 871–875 (1952).

———, B. L. Horecker, and W. A. Wood: Pathways of carbohydrate metabolism in microorganisms, *Bacteriol. Rev.*, **19**, 79–128 (1955).

Johns, A. T.: The production of propionic acid by decarboxylation of succinic acid in a bacterial fermentation, *Biochem. J.*, vol. 42, *Proc. Biochem. Soc.*, ii–iii (1948).

———: The mechanism of propionic acid fermentation by *Clostridium propionicum*, *J. Gen. Microbiol.*, **6**, 123–127 (1952).

Juni, E.: Mechanisms of formation of acetoin by bacteria, *J. Biol. Chem.*, **195**, 715–726, 727–734 (1952).

Kalnitsky, G., and C. H. Werkman: The anaerobic dissimilation of pyruvate by a cell-free extract of *Escherichia coli*, *Arch. Biochem.*, **2**, 113–124 (1943).

Kluyver, A. J.: "The Chemical Activities of Microorganisms," University of London Press, Ltd., London, 1931.

———: Some aspects of nitrate reduction, in "Symposium on Microbial Metabolism," pp. 71–91, Istituto Superiore di Sanità, Rome, 1953.

Knox, R., and M. R. Pollock: Bacterial tetrathionase: adaptation without demonstrable cell growth, *Biochem. J.*, **38**, 299–304 (1944).

Korkes, S., A. del Campillo, I. C. Gunsalus, and S. Ochoa: Enzymatic synthesis of citric acid, *J. Biol. Chem.*, **193**, 721–735 (1951).

Koshland, D. E., Jr., and F. H. Westheimer: Mechanism of alcoholic fermentation: the fermentation of glucose-1-C^{14}, *J. Am. Chem. Soc.*, **72**, 3383–3388 (1950).

Leaver, F. W., and H. G. Wood: Evidence from fermentation of labeled substrates which is inconsistent with present concepts of the propionic acid fermentation, *J. Cell. Comp. Physiol.*, **41**, suppl. 1, 225–240 (1953).

Lichstein, H. C.: Metabolism of microorganisms, *Ann. Rev. Microbiol.*, **6**, 1–28 (1952).

Lipmann, F.: Development of the acetylation problem: a personal account, *Science*, **120**, 855–865 (1954).

———, M. E. Jones, S. Black, and R. M. Flynn: The mechanism of the ATP-CoA-acetate reaction, *J. Cell. Comp. Physiol.*, **41**, suppl. 1, 109–112 (1953).

Nutting, L. A., and S. F. Carson: Lactic acid fermentation of xylose by *Escherichia coli*. I. Fermentation studies, *J. Bacteriol.*, **63**, 575–580 (1952). II. Tracer studies: evidence for $C_2 + C_1$ condensation, *J. Bacteriol.*, **63**, 581–589 (1952).

Ochoa, S.: Enzymatic mechanisms of carbon dioxide fixation, in J. B. Sumner and

K. Myrbäck (eds.), "The Enzymes," vol. 2, pt. 1, pp. 929–1032, Academic Press, Inc., New York, 1951.

Prescott, S. C., and C. G. Dunn: "Industrial Microbiology," 2d ed., McGraw-Hill Book Company, Inc., New York, 1949.

Sakami, W.: The conversion of formate and glycine to serine and glycogen in the intact rat, *J. Biol. Chem.*, **176**, 995–996 (1948).

Scheffer, M. A.: De suikervergistung door Bacteriën der coli-groep, Dissertation, Delft, 1928.

Schnellen, C. G. T. P.: Onderzoekingen over de methaangisting, Dissertation, Delft, 1947.

Slade, H. D., and C. H. Werkman: Assimilation of acetic and succinic acids containing heavy carbon by *Aerobacter indologenes*, *Arch. Biochem.*, **2**, 97–111 (1943).

Stadtman, E. R., and H. A. Barker: Fatty acid synthesis by enzyme preparations of *Clostridium kluyveri*, *J. Biol. Chem.*, I, **180**, 1085–1093, II, 1095–1115, III, 1117–1124, IV, 1169–1186 (1949); V, **181**, 221–235 (1949); VI, **184**, 769–793 (1950).

—— and T. C. Stadtman: Metabolism of microorganisms, *Ann. Rev. Microbiol.*, **7**, 143–178 (1953).

Stadtman, T. C., and H. A. Barker: Tracer experiments on the mechanism of methane formation, *Arch. Biochem.*, **21**, 256–264 (1949).

—— and ——: Tracer experiments on fatty acid oxidation by methane bacteria, *J. Bacteriol.*, **61**, 67–80 (1951a).

—— and ——: The origin of methane in the acetate and methanol fermentations by *Methanosarcina*, *J. Bacteriol.*, **61**, 81–86 (1951b).

Stokes, J. J.: Fermentation of glucose by suspensions of *Escherichia coli*, *J. Bacteriol.*, **57**, 147–158 (1949).

Tasman, A.: The formation of hydrogen from glucose and formic acid by the so-called "resting" *B. coli*, *Biochem. J.*, **29**, 2446–2457 (1935).

Umbreit, W. W.: "Metabolic Maps," Burgess Publishing Co., Minneapolis, 1952.

Utter, M. F., and H. G. Wood: Mechanisms of fixation of carbon dioxide by heterotrophs and autotrophs, *Advances in Enzymol.*, **12**, 41–151 (1951).

van Niel, C. B.: Introductory remarks on the comparative biochemistry of microorganisms, *J. Cell. Comp. Physiol.*, **41**, suppl. 1, 11–38 (1953).

Verhoeven, W.: Aerobic sporeforming nitrate reducing bacteria, Dissertation, Delft, 1952.

Wood, H. G., R. W. Brown, and C. H. Werkman: Mechanisms of the butyl alcohol fermentation with heavy carbon acetic and butyric acids and acetone, *Arch. Biochem.*, **6**, 243–260 (1945).

—— and C. H. Werkman: The utilization of CO_2 in the dissimilation of glycerol by the propionic acid bacteria, *Biochem. J.*, **30**, 48–53 (1936).

—— and ——: The relationship of bacterial utilization of CO_2 to succinic acid formation, *Biochem. J.*, **34**, 29–33 (1940).

Woods, D. D.: Hydrogenlyase: the synthesis of formic acid by bacteria, *Biochem. J.*, **30**, 515–527 (1936).

—— and C. E. Clifton: The decomposition of pyruvate and 1-(+) glutamate by *Clostridium tetanomorphum*, *Biochem. J.*, **32**, 345–356 (1938).

CHAPTER 9

THE METABOLISM OF NITROGENOUS COMPOUNDS

In the early days of bacteriology it became apparent that material derived from proteins could serve as a source of carbon, nitrogen, and energy for the growth of many species of bacteria. It was observed, as with the carbohydrates, that only a relatively few species could attack the more complex compounds, such as native proteins, breaking these down into simpler compounds that could be utilized within the cell. We still employ liquefaction of proteins such as gelatin, casein, or serum proteins as diagnostic criteria in the identification of certain species of bacteria. This liquefaction or partial digestion in the medium is induced by extracellular proteinases which can be separated from the cells and shown to be active by themselves. Relatively little is known about the nature of these proteinases. In some species they appear to be virulence factors, the kappa toxin of *Clostridium perfringens* being a gelatinase which can attack collagen, the trypsin-insoluble framework of muscle. As a result of this breakdown the invasion of deeper tissues by this or other organisms is facilitated. Certain types of *C. perfringens*, *B*, *E*, and sometimes *D*, produce another proteinase called the lambda toxin which does not attack collagen. One peculiarity of the latter proteinase is that it is inhibited by normal serum proteins while the kappa toxin is not. A similar behavior is noted with other proteinases, the main ones of *C. histolyticum*, *C. septicum*, and *C. chauvoei* not being inhibited by normal serum while those of *C. tetani*, *C. sporogenes*, *C. botulinum*, and *C. oedematiens* are inhibited. Such differences, and also relative susceptibility to inhibition by oxygen, heavy metals, and cysteine, have been used in attempts to classify the bacterial proteinases (Maschmann, 1943). Some of the proteinases observed in older cultures may be intracellular enzymes released upon dissolution of the cell. In the cell these enzymes may be involved in synthesis of proteins, extracellular equilibrium conditions generally favoring hydrolysis rather than synthesis.

As a general rule native proteins are not attacked by bacteria unless sufficient amounts of simpler nitrogenous substances which will support the initiation of growth are present. Once growth has started the extracellular proteinases are elaborated by the cells and make their appearance in the culture media. The formation of proteinases is inhibited by the presence of utilizable carbohydrate in the medium, the so-called protein-sparing effect. This may be a phenomenon similar to diphasic growth (diauxie; see Monod, 1949) in which an adaptive enzyme such as galacto-zymase does not become evident in a glucose-galactose medium until after the disappearance of glucose from the medium. The proteinases, how-ever, appear to be constitutional rather than adaptive enzymes, but in the competition for protein components, the systems involved in the syn-thesis of carbohydrate-utilizing enzymes may have some peculiar advan-tage over those for the protein-utilizing ones resulting in formation of less of the latter enzymes.

The majority of bacterial species do not attack proteins but utilize more readily protein-degradation products such as peptones. Naegeli introduced the use of peptones for the cultivation of bacteria in 1879, and since then they have become one of the more or less standard components of culture media. Proteins, when subjected to hydrolysis by proteolytic en-zymes or by chemical agents, are broken down into simpler units known as metaproteins, proteoses, peptones, and polypeptides, the complexity of these compounds decreasing in the order indicated. No sharp line of de-marcation exists between these groups, and continued hydrolysis leads to the liberation of the component amino acids. Many or most species of bac-teria possess peptidases, enzymes involved in the dissimilation of the protein digest products, but little is known concerning the nature of these enzymes.

One type, carboxypeptidase, is characterized by its attack at the car-boxyl end of the peptide chain, the rate of action being greatest when the terminal amino acid group R is L-phenylalanine, lower rates being observed with other amino acid residues such as tyrosine and tryptophan. Carboxypeptidase may also hydrolyze certain peptide linkages adjacent to α-carboxyl groups in the peptide chain of proteins.

$$\text{R}$$
$$|$$
$$\text{R}'\text{CO--NHCHCOOH}$$
$$\uparrow$$

Linkage hydrolyzed by carboxypeptidase

Aminopeptidases catalyze the hydrolysis of peptide linkages adjacent to free α-amino groups of peptides, one aminopeptidase acting preferen-tially on peptides in which the free amino acid residue is that of L-leucine, or

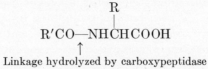

Linkage hydrolyzed by an aminopeptidase

Other aminopeptidases exist, and most or all of these enzymes require Mn, Mg, Co, Fe, or Zn ions as cofactors, those of the clostridia requiring cysteine in addition to the metal ion. Some peptidases may be limited in their action to attack upon di- or tripeptides. The end result of the activity of proteinases and peptidases is that amino acids are formed, some of which can be utilized by the cell in its metabolic activities. These enzymes, like the complex carbohydrate-splitting ones, may be regarded as preparatory enzymes for the most part, although it is possible, particularly with the participation of phosphate and of CoA rather than of water, that they may also act in the synthesis of cellular protein. The peptidases of most species apparently exhibit specificity for the L- or natural form of the peptide, although some bacterial peptidases, particularly of *Leuconostoc mesenteroides*, do attack the unnatural isomers.

In general, amino acids are utilized by the cell for synthetic purposes and as sources of oxidative energy much like the carbohydrates, removal of the amino group frequently leading to the formation of compounds such as pyruvic or α-ketoglutaric acids commonly encountered in carbohydrate metabolism. Species of bacteria may differ quite markedly in the deamination mechanism they employ. Decarboxylation of amino acids is induced by many species, sometimes both decarboxylation and deamination, and in other instances the amino acid is first split before being further dissimilated (Gale, 1940).

Deamination. Deamination of amino acids occurs most readily in an alkaline medium, decarboxylation in an acidic one, and the respective enzymes are formed most readily under the conditions indicated. Gale (1951) points out that *E. coli* forms glutamic decarboxylase when grown at pH 5, glutamic deaminase when cultivated at pH 8, and suggests that this serves as a neutralization mechanism enabling the organism to achieve some degree of internal pH stabilization in environments away from the pH optimum for its growth. Deamination in an alkaline medium results in the production of an acid which would tend to lower the pH, and vice versa. He suggests that the variation in enzyme formation and activity with pH is due to a great extent to the ionization of the amino acid, the un-ionized (relatively) group being the controlling factor. Ionization of the carboxyl group is suppressed in an acidic medium, and this leads to decarboxylation; conversely, in an alkaline environment ionization of the amino group is less, and this form, $RCHNH_2COO^-$, is attacked by deamination. When both deamination and decarboxylation of an amino acid are observed it is quite possible that deamination (or decarboxylation) might occur first, the resulting product no longer being an amino acid, and its utilization could involve a different pH optimum than for the intact amino acid.

There appear to be four general mechanisms for deamination, depending upon the concomitant changes, and these can be summarized as follows:

1. Oxidative deamination, formation of a keto acid
2. Reductive deamination, formation of a fatty acid
3. Desaturation deamination, formation of an unsaturated acid
4. Dehydration deamination, formation of a keto acid

E. coli is able to oxidatively deaminate amino acids such as glycine, L-alanine, and L-glutamic acid with the aid of specific enzymes, the products of the reaction being glyoxylic, pyruvic, and α-ketoglutaric acids, respectively. The products of these oxidations can then be further oxidized by the cells. The oxidative deamination of alanine to yield pyruvic acid can be demonstrated with the aid of toluene-treated cells, deamination proceeding with the accumulation of pyruvate in the medium and with an oxygen consumption equivalent to the oxidation of alanine to pyruvate. Oxidative deamination of this type will also occur under anaerobic conditions if an appropriate hydrogen acceptor is present, while other amino acids can be deaminated anaerobically without the participation of specific acceptors.

L-Glutamic acid is oxidatively deaminated to α-ketoglutaric acid via iminoglutaric acid as in mammalian tissues, with the exception that TPN^+ rather than DPN^+ is required with the *E. coli* system. The reaction can be represented as

$$
\begin{array}{cccc}
\text{COOH} & & \text{COOH} & \text{COOH} \\
| & TPN^+ \quad TPNH & | & | \\
\text{CH}_2 & +H^+ & \text{CH}_2 & \text{CH}_2 \\
| & \curvearrowright & | & \quad +H_2O \quad | \\
\text{CH}_2 & \xrightarrow{\text{Glutamic}} & \text{CH}_2 & \rightleftharpoons \quad \text{CH}_2 \; + \; NH_3 \\
| & \text{dehydrogenase} & | & | \\
\text{CHNH}_2 & & \text{C}=\text{NH} & \text{CO} \\
| & & | & | \\
\text{COOH} & & \text{COOH} & \text{COOH}
\end{array}
$$

Both reactions are reversible and in reverse could serve as a pathway of biosynthesis of glutamic acid in the cell.

In other species of bacteria aerobic deamination may involve an amino acid oxidase rather than a dehydrogenase. *Proteus vulgaris*, for example, is able to oxidatively deaminate 11 common natural amino acids with the formation of keto acids, apparently the same oxidase being involved and being quite unspecific in its action. The specificity of these deaminating oxidases appears to be dependent upon the source of the enzyme. D-Amino acid oxidases bring about the oxidative deamination of unnatural isomers.

The Stickland Reaction. In certain species of clostridia, e.g., *C. sporogenes* and *C. botulinum*, oxidative deamination of one amino acid can occur in what is known as the Stickland reaction, with a second amino acid acting as the oxidant. This reaction will be considered after an example of reductive deamination. In reductive deamination hydrogen is added to the amino acid according to the equation

$$RCHNH_2COOH + 2H \rightarrow RCH_2COOH + NH_3$$

One example is the reduction of aspartic acid to succinic acid and ammonia by *Mycobacterium phlei*, or

$$HOOCCH_2CHNH_2COOH + 2H \rightarrow HOOCCH_2CH_2COOH + NH_3$$

This may be an oxidative or desaturation deamination since it is possible that fumaric acid is an intermediate.

Stickland (1934) observed that certain amino acids, e.g., glycine, proline, and hydroxyproline, were reduced under anaerobic conditions by *C. sporogenes* in the presence of reduced dyes such as methyl or benzyl viologen, the dye being oxidized to its colored or oxidized form. Other amino acids, e.g., alanine, valine, or leucine, were not reduced but instead acted as hydrogen donors to suitable dyes, one molecule of alanine reducing two molecules of cresyl blue and being deaminated during the first stage of the reaction. Stickland observed that deamination of alanine and glycine occurred when the two were present in a suspension of *C. sporogenes*, but not when these amino acids were present singly. He also noted that acetic acid and carbon dioxide accumulated in the mixture, and quantitative analyses indicated a reaction that can be expressed by the equation

$$2CH_2NH_2COOH + CH_3CHNH_2COOH + 2H_2O \rightarrow$$
$$3CH_3COOH + 3NH_3 + CO_2$$

The various results led to the conclusion that *C. sporogenes* obtains energy from coupled reactions between pairs of appropriate amino acids, one amino acid being oxidized while the other is reduced. In the above reaction glycine is reductively deaminated to give acetic acid and ammonia, or

$$CH_2NH_2COOH + 2H \rightarrow CH_3COOH + NH_3$$

the hydrogen coming from the oxidative deamination of alanine. This reductive deamination of glycine can be demonstrated using hydrogen gas as the source of hydrogen since the organism possesses hydrogenase.

Stickland (1935) studied the reduction of proline by *C. sporogenes*, using alanine as the reductant, and observed that proline was reduced but not deaminated, giving rise to the formation of δ-amino-*n*-valeric acid, or

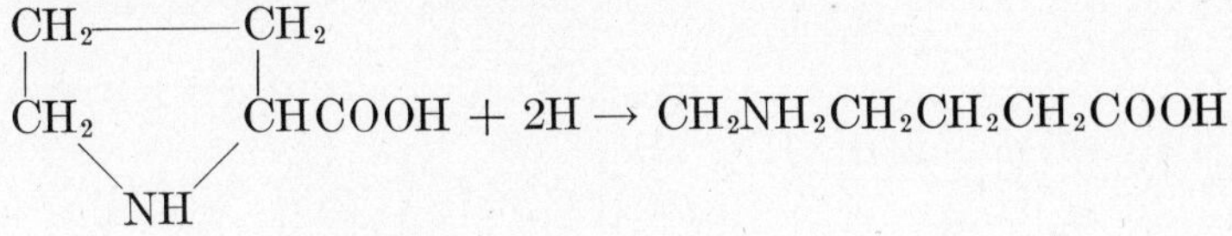

$$
\begin{array}{c}
CH_2 \!\!-\!\!-\!\!-\!\! CH_2 \\
| \qquad\qquad | \\
CH_2 \qquad\ CHCOOH + 2H \rightarrow CH_2NH_2CH_2CH_2CH_2COOH \\
\diagdown\quad\diagup \\
NH
\end{array}
$$

Clifton (1939) reported that amino acids are utilized by *C. botulinum* primarily by means of the Stickland reaction, and Nisman, Raynaud, and Cohen (1948) reported its occurrence in a number of other anaerobes. Many, however, are unable to carry out this type of coupled oxidation-reduction, frequently accompanied by deamination, between pairs of amino acids and instead ferment single, utilizable amino acids directly.

Nisman and Vinet (1950), Nisman (1954), and Mamelak and Quastel (1953) have studied the Stickland reaction in more detail, particularly the oxidation of alanine, which will occur under either aerobic or anaerobic conditions. The first authors suggest the following scheme for the oxidative deamination of alanine:

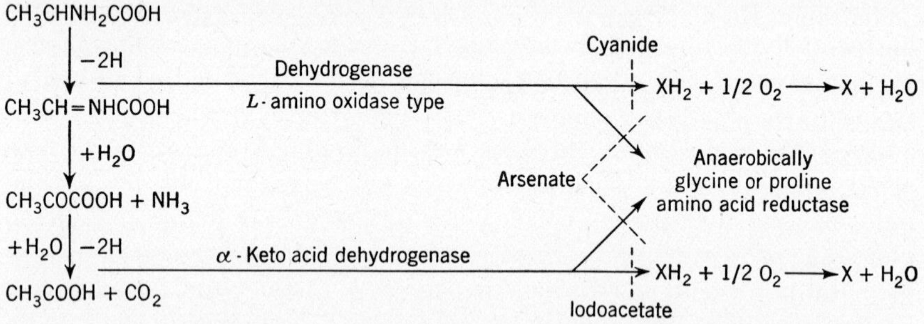

CH_3CHNH_2COOH

$$\downarrow -2H$$

Dehydrogenase

Cyanide

$CH_3CH=NHCOOH$ L-amino oxidase type $XH_2 + 1/2\ O_2 \longrightarrow X + H_2O$

$$\downarrow +H_2O$$

$CH_3COCOOH + NH_3$ Arsenate

Anaerobically glycine or proline amino acid reductase

$$+H_2O \downarrow -2H$$ α-Keto acid dehydrogenase

$CH_3COOH + CO_2$ $XH_2 + 1/2\ O_2 \longrightarrow X + H_2O$

Iodoacetate

the point at which various poisons inhibit the reaction being indicated by the broken vertical lines. The scheme suggests that the amino acid undergoing oxidation is activated by an enzyme of the L-amino acid oxidase type, the hydrogen being transferred by a carrier X to oxygen aerobically or to a second amino acid anaerobically, the latter being activated by its reductase. The imino acid formed is spontaneously converted, with the participation of water in the reaction, into the corresponding keto acid with the liberation of ammonia. The keto acid in turn is oxidatively decarboxylated with the participation of the keto acid dehydrogenase, this hydrogen also being transferred to oxygen or to an activated, hydrogen-accepting amino acid.

Mamelak and Quastel, working with cell suspensions and extracts, found that DPN+ serves as a coenzyme, and they obtained evidence for the production of pyruvic acid as an intermediate from alanine. According to their results we can picture the anaerobic oxidation of alanine and reduction of glycine as

$$CH_3CHNH_2COOH + DPN^+ + H_2O \rightarrow$$
$$CH_3COCOOH + NH_3 + DPNH + H^+$$
$$CH_3COCOOH + CoA + DPN^+ \rightarrow$$
$$\text{acetyl-CoA} + CO_2 + DPNH + H^+$$
$$2CH_2NH_2COOH + 2DPNH + 2H^+ \rightarrow$$
$$2CH_3COOH + 2NH_3 + 2DPN^+$$

Amino acid hydrogen donors and hydrogen compete with each other, and amino acid hydrogen acceptors likewise compete with each other, in mixtures for the common hydrogen carrier DPN. Lipoic acid may also be involved in the reactions associated with pyruvate as well as cocarboxylase.

Under aerobic conditions hydrogen peroxide is formed during the oxidation of an oxidizable amino acid such as alanine, its inhibitory effect on the amino acid activating enzymes being neutralized to a great extent by nonenzymic interaction with pyruvate or α-ketoglutarate. The inhibitory effect of air or peroxide can be reduced by the addition of thiol compounds. Mamelak and Quastel suggested that the amino acid dehydrogenases and reductases of *C. sporogenes* contain thiol systems that are readily converted into —S—S— forms by oxygen or hydrogen peroxide and that these are reduced to the active —SH form on addition of appropriate thiol compounds.

Other Deaminations. Aspartic acid undergoes a desaturation type of deamination in suspensions of *E. coli* and other bacteria, a reaction demonstrated in 1926 by Quastel and Woolf. The enzyme involved, aspartase, was one of the first intracellular bacterial enzymes to be studied in a cell-free state (Virtanen and Tarnanen, 1932) and catalyzes the reversible reaction

$$HOOCCH_2CHNH_2COOH \rightleftarrows HOOCCH{=}CHCOOH + NH_3$$

In suspensions or cultures of *E. coli* fumarate is reduced to succinate or hydrated to form malic acid as rapidly as it is produced and accumulates only when the cells are treated with an inhibitor such as toluene. Various studies suggest that biotin and adenylic acid are present in the prosthetic group of aspartase. The reversibility of this reaction provides a mechanism for the synthesis of an amino acid by bacteria.

E. coli can also deaminate histidine by means of a desaturation reaction to give urocanic acid, or

$$
\begin{array}{ccc}
\text{HC}{=\!=\!=}\text{CCH}_2\text{CHNH}_2\text{COOH} & \text{HC}{=\!=\!=}\text{CCH}{=}\text{CHCOOH} \\
| \qquad\qquad | & | \qquad\qquad | \\
\text{HN} \qquad\quad \text{N} & \rightarrow \text{HN} \qquad\quad \text{N} \qquad\qquad + \text{NH}_3 \\
\ \backslash \quad\ \ /\!/ & \ \backslash \quad\ \ /\!/ \\
\text{CH} & \text{CH}
\end{array}
$$

Pseudomonas fluorescens and *C. tetanomorphum* (Stadtman and Stadtman, 1953) elicit the same reaction, the enzyme involved being called histidase. In these organisms the reaction is carried further, the urocanic acid being dissimilated by urocanase and possibly other enzymes with the formation of a mole each of glutamic acid, formic acid, and ammonia.

Serine is hydrolytically deaminated by *E. coli*, Chargaff and Sprinson

(1943) showing with toluene-treated cells that the reaction proceeds through pyruvic acid under the influence of serine dehydrase, or

$$\begin{array}{cccc} CH_2OH & CH_2 & CH_3 & CH_3 \\ | & \| & | & | \\ CHNH_2 - H_2O \rightarrow & CNH_2 \rightleftharpoons C=NH + H_2O \rightarrow & C=O + NH_3 \\ | & | & | & | \\ COOH & COOH & COOH & COOH \end{array}$$

The coenzyme for this enzyme appears to be identical with that for aspartase and to require Zn^{++} ions as a cofactor.   An entirely similar reaction, with the exception that hydrogen sulfide rather than water is split from the molecule, is involved in the deamination of cysteine by a desulfurase in *E. coli*, or

$$\begin{array}{cccc} CH_2SH & CH_2 & CH_3 & CH_3 \\ | & \| & | & | \\ CHNH_2 - H_2S \rightarrow & CNH_2 \rightleftharpoons C=NH + H_2O \rightarrow & C=O + NH_3 \\ | & | & | & | \\ COOH & COOH & COOH & COOH \end{array}$$

Decarboxylation.   The amino acid decarboxylases of bacteria are most active in acidic solutions, the pH optima ranging from 3 for histidine decarboxylase to 6 for lysine decarboxylase, with little or no activity above pH 7.   Under optimum conditions decarboxylation of the natural isomers goes to completion and specific enzymes can be employed for the quantitative determination, on the basis of the amount of carbon dioxide released, of the particular amino acid activated by the enzyme.   Specific enzymes for the decarboxylation of arginine, aspartic acid, glutamic acid, histidine, lysine, ornithine, phenylalanine, and tyrosine have been reported (Gale, 1951).   Pyridoxal phosphate appears to be the coenzyme for these various enzymes, with the possible exception of the histidine decarboxylase.   It is characteristic of these enzymes that they will decarboxylate the natural isomers only and that the amino acid must possess a polar group in addition to the terminal carboxyl and the α-amino groups normally present in amino acids.   These decarboxylases are randomly distributed in the bacteria, even in strains of the same species, and, with the possible exception of glutamic acid decarboxylase, are adaptive enzymes.   In some species only one decarboxylase may be present and the organism can be employed directly for the quantitative determination of that amino acid.

Decarboxylation of the amino acid leads to the production of amines or diamines, vile-smelling compounds characteristically found in putrefying materials, or ω-amino acids, depending upon the nature of the compound decarboxylated.   Histamine, produced by the decarboxylation of histidine, is a "depressor substance" and may be responsible, if formed, for certain physiological reactions in bacterial infections.   Some of the diamines, e.g., putrescine and cadaverine, were at one time believed to be the cause of "ptomaine," or food, poisoning.   These compounds are formed from ornithine and lysine, respectively:

$$H_2NCH_2(CH_2)_2CHNH_2COOH \rightarrow H_2NCH_2(CH_2)_2CH_2NH_2 + CO_2$$
$$H_2NCH_2(CH_2)_3CHNH_2COOH \rightarrow H_2NCH_2(CH_2)_3CH_2NH_2 + CO_2$$

Decarboxylation of aspartic acid leads to the formation of β-alanine, which is a component of pantothenic acid.

Splitting of Amino Acids.   An old and common diagnostic test employed in the bacteriology laboratory is testing for the production of indole by cultures of bacteria grown in protein-digest media.   Hopkins and Cole in 1901 showed that indole is formed from tryptophan.   Peptones rich in this amino acid are desirable for media employed in testing for indole production.   Indole production is an aerobic reaction, tryptophan being reductively deaminated to β-indolepropionic acid under anaerobic conditions, and this substance is not utilized further, even under aerobic conditions, by *E. coli* and related species.

Tryptophan is reversibly converted to indole and serine by *Neurospora*, but serine does not appear to be an intermediate in the bacterial oxidation of tryptophan.   Wood, Gunsalus, and Umbreit (1947) have shown that the tryptophan-utilizing enzyme of *E. coli* requires pyridoxal phosphate as a coenzyme and catalyzes the decomposition of tryptophan, possibly by way of an imino acid, to indole, ammonia, and pyruvic acid, or

In the intact cell the pyruvate is oxidized in the normal manner.   It is worth pointing out here that pyruvate, and less often α-ketoglutarate, are frequently encountered as products of amino acid utilization and, once formed, then enter into the general pathway of metabolism.   Neither serine nor alanine is utilized by the *E. coli* tryptophanase and neither appears to be involved in the bacterial formation of indole.   Other bacteria, e.g., species of *Pseudomonas*, may attack the indole nucleus of tryptophan, the oxidation leading to the formation of kynurenine (Chap. 15).

In animals arginine is hydrolyzed to urea and ornithine, urea being broken down by urease to give carbon dioxide and ammonia.   A number of bacteria such as staphylococci, streptococci, lactobacilli, and certain clostridia dissimilate arginine to yield the same products.   These organisms, however, generally do not possess urease activity.   The dissimilation is catalyzed by an enzyme system termed arginine dihydrolase which now appears (Stadtman and Stadtman, 1953) to be composed of two enzymes, arginine desimidase or metarginase and citrulline ureidase or citrullinase, which catalyze, respectively, the deamination of arginine to form citrulline and the deamination and decarboxylation of the latter to yield ornithine as follows:

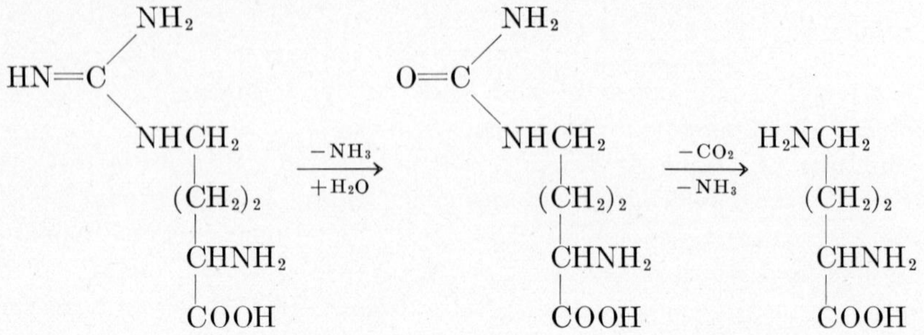

$$
\underset{\substack{\text{COOH} \\ | \\ \text{CHNH}_2 \\ | \\ (\text{CH}_2)_2 \\ | \\ \text{NHCH}_2 \\ | \\ \text{HN}=\text{C} \\ | \\ \text{NH}_2}}{} \xrightarrow[+\text{H}_2\text{O}]{-\text{NH}_3} \underset{\substack{\text{COOH} \\ | \\ \text{CHNH}_2 \\ | \\ (\text{CH}_2)_2 \\ | \\ \text{NHCH}_2 \\ | \\ \text{O}=\text{C} \\ | \\ \text{NH}_2}}{} \xrightarrow[-\text{NH}_3]{-\text{CO}_2} \underset{\substack{\text{COOH} \\ | \\ \text{CHNH}_2 \\ | \\ (\text{CH}_2)_2 \\ | \\ \text{H}_2\text{NCH}_2}}{}
$$

Arginine is one of the few amino acids readily attacked by various staphylococci and streptococci and may thus serve as a source of ammonia and of carbon dioxide for these organisms.

In the above reactions we see formation of one amino acid from another, a reaction which if reversible would lead to the synthesis of a more complex amino acid from a simpler one.   A number of interconversions have been reported in recent years, and some progress (e.g., see Fig. 9-1) is being made in understanding the pathways of biosynthesis of amino acids (Davis, 1955; Harper, 1955; Stadtman and Stadtman, 1953; Umbreit, 1952).   The use of biochemical mutants is of value in tracing these pathways (Chap. 15).

Some of the clostridia, as we have seen, utilize amino acids by means of the Stickland reaction.   Others by more or less unknown mechanisms bring about a splitting or dissimilation of an amino acid with the formation of a variety of end products.   *C. tetanomorphum*, for example, ferments glutamic acid with the production of butyric and acetic acids, carbon dioxide, hydrogen, and ammonia (Woods and Clifton, 1938) in amounts approximating the equation

$$5\text{HOOC(CH}_2)_2\text{CHNH}_2\text{COOH} + 6\text{H}_2\text{O} \rightarrow$$
$$6\text{CH}_3\text{COOH} + 2\text{CH}_3(\text{CH}_2)_2\text{COOH} + 5\text{CO}_2 + \text{H}_2 + 5\text{NH}_3$$

Glutamic and aspartic acids are fermented by *C. tetani* (Clifton, 1942) with the production of end products similar (no hydrogen) to those given above, lactic acid also being formed in appreciable amounts when aspartic acid is the substrate.   Essentially the same products (no ammonia) are formed by the two species, with pyruvate as the substrate, so it would appear that the amino acids might be deaminated, the deamination products yielding pyruvate and other intermediates.   Cardon and Barker

(1947) have reported a similar reaction with *C. propionicum*, this organism fermenting alanine as follows:

$$3CH_3CHNH_2COOH + 2H_2O \rightarrow$$
$$CH_3COOH + 2CH_3CH_2COOH + CO_2 + 3NH_3$$

It is possible that the oxidation of one mole of alanine via pyruvic acid to carbon dioxide and acetic acid provides the hydrogen required for the

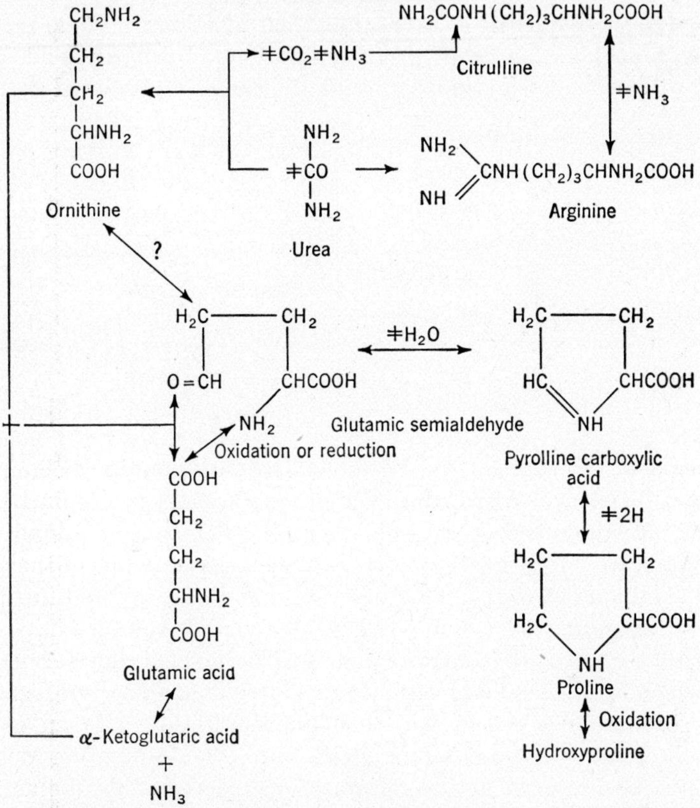

FIG. 9-1. Possible pathways for the formation or interconversion of different 5- and 6-carbon amino acids. Not all reactions have been definitely established, and pathways may differ somewhat between different organisms.

reductive deamination of two moles of alanine to propionic acid. This might be regarded as a variant of the Stickland reaction, one amino acid molecule being oxidized while two molecules of the same rather than of a different amino acid are reduced.

Transamination. Transaminases, enzymes involved in the transfer of an amino group from an amino to a keto acid with the formation of a new amino acid, were first reported by Braunstein and Kritzman in 1937 and were demonstrated to be active in bacteria by Lichstein and Cohen (1944). These enzymes, with the aid of pyridoxal phosphate as the coenzyme, catalyze the reversible transfer of an amino group from glutamic acid to a keto acid or from any one of a large number of amino acids to α-ketoglutaric acid to yield glutamic acid, this substance always appearing to be involved in transamination reactions. Since pyruvic and oxalacetic acids, as members of the tricarboxylic acid cycle, are so commonly present in the cell, it may be that these keto acids are the ones involved most frequently in transamination reactions. These transaminations from glutamic acid, yielding alanine and aspartic acid, respectively, with the aid of pyridoxal phosphate, can be represented as follows:

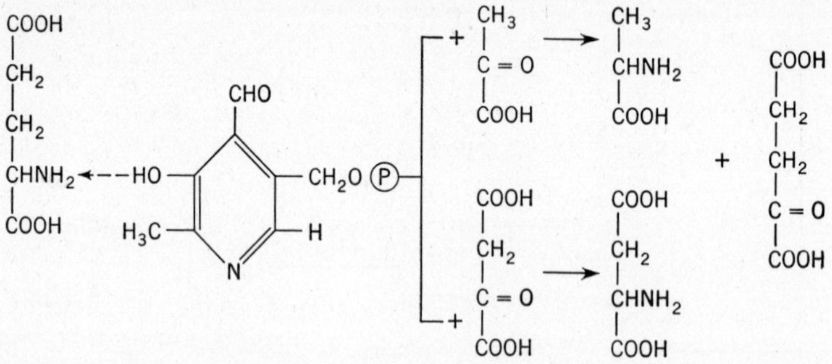

Racemase.   Certain of the lactic acid bacteria require D-alanine, the unnatural isomer, as a growth factor in the absence of vitamin B_6 (pyridoxine).   In the presence of D-alanine and the absence of B_6, pyridoxine compounds are not formed (Holden and Snell, 1949), while in the reverse case D-alanine is formed.   This suggests that B_6 is involved in the synthesis of the unnatural amino acid, and Wood and Gunsalus have shown (1951) that *Streptococcus faecalis* possesses an enzyme they termed racemase which catalyzes the racemization of L- to D-alanine, pyridoxal phosphate serving as a coenzyme.   The unnatural isomer is an essential metabolite, but its function is unknown.   Transamination does not appear to be involved in the racemization reaction.   D-Alanine in the growth medium (or B_6) is essential for the growth of *Lactobacillus casei*, but it inhibits the utilization of L-alanine, L-alanine peptides then being essential for growth (Kihara and Snell, 1952).   It was postulated that the inhibitory effect of the unnatural isomer is exerted at the cell surface, preventing the entrance of the free natural isomer but not that of its peptides.

Nucleic Acids.   The metabolism of nucleic acids and of their component purine and pyrimidine bases, particularly their biosynthesis, is receiving considerable attention.   The nucleoproteins, as we have seen, make up a high proportion of the organic content of bacteria, and one of the bases, adenine, is an important constituent of coenzymes of trans-phosphorylation and hydrogen transfer. Another base, uracil, is found in the uridine component of the coenzyme involved in the conversion of galactose-1-Ⓟ to glucose-1-Ⓟ. As we have seen, the nucleic acids are composed of nucleotides and can be hydrolyzed to these compounds by appropriate nucleases. The nucleotides are dephosphorylated by phosphatases to nucleosides (ribose or deoxyribose plus a purine or pyrimidine base) which can be cleaved to yield the free base and the sugar molecules. In the intact cell the equilibria (steady state) probably favor synthesis of the more complex compounds. Nucleic acids, or their derivatives, are not common foods for bacteria.

As far as is known the bacteria that can oxidize purines or pyrimidines aerobically do so in a manner analogous to that observed with mammalian cells. Purines can be oxidatively dissimilated through xanthine and uric acid, pyrimidines through a number of acids to yield urea and glyoxylic, or oxalic, acids, respectively. These products could be further decomposed by the same or by different species. Possible pathways of dissimilation (pyrimidines assumed to be converted to the uracil form) are indicated in Figs. 9-2 and 9-3.

Lara (1952) found that thymine and uracil are oxidized by soil corynebacteria through barbituric acid as an intermediate, this compound then being degraded to urea and malonic acid. Malonic acid is not generally considered as an intermediate in bacterial metabolism, but some of the nonsulfur purple bacteria can use it as an oxidizable substrate. The details of the oxidation of the pyrimidines or of malonic acid were not established.

Barker and Beck (1941) described two anaerobes, *C. acidi-urici* and *C. cylindrosporum*, that are able to decompose only a few organic compounds, all of which, with the exception of glycine, are purine derivatives. Uric acid, xanthine, and guanine are fermented rapidly and completely, hypoxanthine less so. These anaerobes form ammonia, carbon dioxide, and acetic acid from purines; *C. cylindrosporum* also produces some glycine. Glycine is activated as a hydrogen donor, in contrast to its role as a hydrogen acceptor in the Stickland reaction. They suggested that acetic acid formed in the fermentation of purines comes from a reduction of carbon dioxide. Barker (1943) also reported that *Streptococcus allantoicus* can grow in a medium containing allantoin as the major organic constituent, the fermentation of this compound giving rise to the formation of carbon dioxide, urea, ammonia, and formic, acetic, lactic, and oxamic acids. Young and Hawkins (1944) reported that a number of common bacteria, including members of the enteric group, staphylococci and streptococci, are able to ferment allantoin, but they gave no indication of the nature of the products formed in these fermentations.

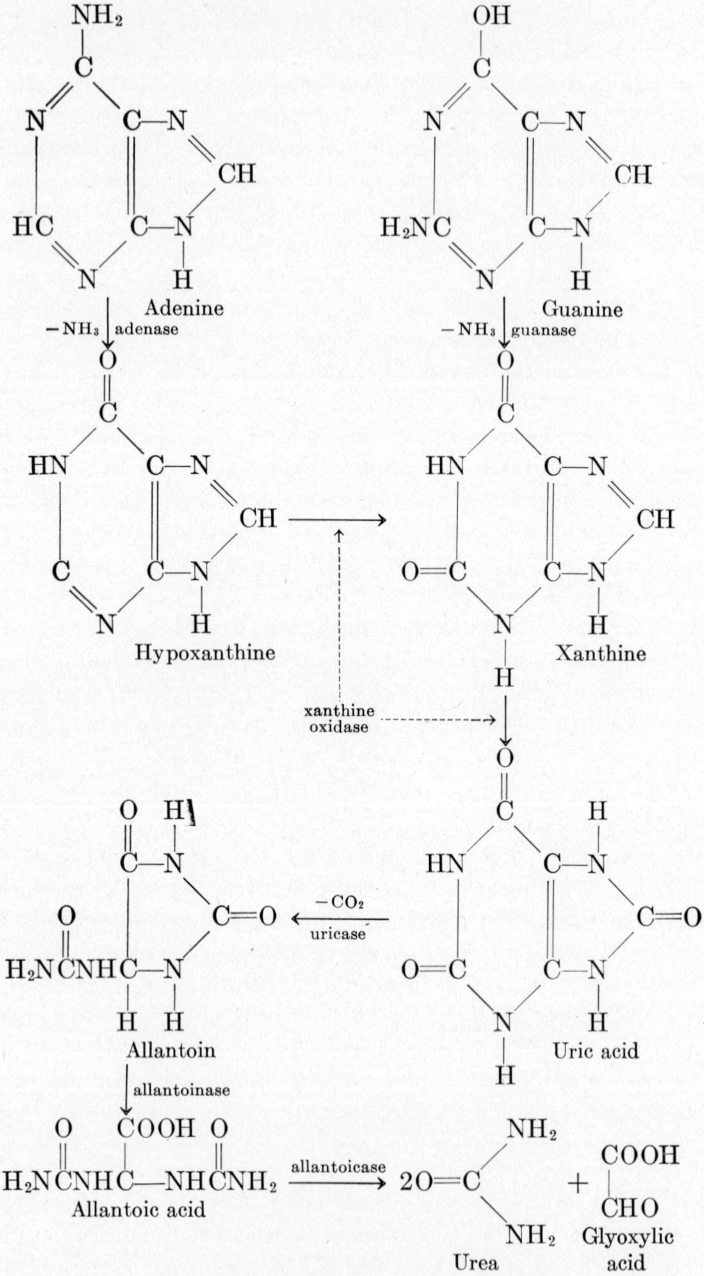

FIG. 9-2. Possible pathway for the degradation of purines.

It is apparent that, with the exception of ammonia, the products of amino acid fermentation for the most part are similar to or identical with those of carbohydrate fermentation. In some instances the amino acids are not degraded very far and more complex end products accumulate than are produced from other amino acids. Such dissimilations may have little or no energetic value for the cell but could serve as sources of essential ammonia or carbon dioxide. Under aerobic conditions the amino

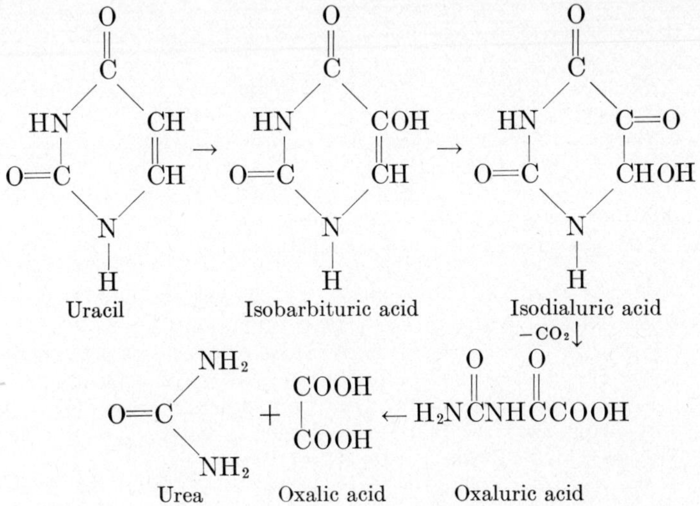

FIG. 9-3. Possible pathway for the degradation of a pyrimidine.

acids appear to be dissimilated along pathways similar to the anaerobic ones, the intermediates frequently being the same as encountered in carbohydrate metabolism and being disposed of ultimately over a common route. Other nitrogenous compounds are utilized along pathways similar to those observed with the amino acids, or feed into them. Amino acids in the medium may also be used as such in the synthesis of proteins, either directly or after conversion to other forms, and specific ones must be provided preformed in the medium to support growth of some of the more exacting species of bacteria.

REFERENCES

Barker, H. A.: *Streptococcus allantoicus* and the fermentation of allantoin, *J. Bacteriol.*, **46**, 251–259 (1943).

——— and J. V. Beck: The fermentative decomposition of purines by *Clostridium acidi-urici* and *Clostridium cylindrosporum*, *J. Biol. Chem.*, **141**, 3–27 (1941).

Cardon, B. P., and H. A. Barker: Amino acid fermentation by *Clostridium propionicum* and *Diplococcus glycinophilus*, *Arch. Biochem.*, **12**, 165–180 (1947).

Chargaff, E., and D. B. Sprinson: Mechanism of deamination of serine by *Bacterium coli*, *J. Biol. Chem.*, **148**, 249–255 (1943).

Clifton, C. E.: The utilization of amino acids and of glucose by *Clostridium botulinum*, *J. Bacteriol.*, **39**, 485–497 (1939).

———: The utilization of amino acids and related compounds by *Clostridium tetani*, *J. Bacteriol.*, **44**, 179–183 (1942).

Davis, B. D.: Intermediates in amino acid biosynthesis, *Advances in Enzymol.*, **16**, 247–312 (1955).

Gale, E. F.: Enzymes concerned in the primary utilization of amino acids by bacteria, *Bacteriol. Rev.*, **4**, 135–176 (1940).

———: Organic nitrogen, in C. H. Werkman and P. W. Wilson (eds.), "Bacterial Physiology," chap. 13, Academic Press, Inc., New York, 1951.

Harper, H. A.: "Review of Physiological Chemistry," Lange Medical Publications, Los Altos, Calif., 1955.

Holden, J. T., and E. E. Snell: The relation of D-alanine and vitamin B₆ to growth of lactic acid bacteria, *J. Biol. Chem.*, **178**, 799–809 (1949).

Kihara, H., and E. E. Snell: L-Alanine and growth of *Lactobacillus casei*, *J. Biol. Chem.*, **197**, 791–800 (1952).

Lara, F. J. S.: Studies on the oxidation of pyrimidines by bacteria, Dissertation, Stanford University, Stanford, Calif., 1952.

Lichstein, H. C., and P. P. Cohen: Transamination in bacteria, *J. Biol. Chem.*, **157**, 85–91 (1944).

Mamelak, R., and J. H. Quastel: Amino acid interactions in strict anaerobes (*Cl. sporogenes*), *Biochim. et Biophys. Acta*, **12**, 103–120 (1953).

Maschmann, E.: Bakterien-Proteasen, *Ergeb. Enzymforsch.*, **9**, 155–192 (1943).

Monod, J.: The growth of bacterial cultures, *Ann. Rev. Microbiol.*, **3**, 371–394 (1949).

Nisman, B.: The Stickland reaction, *Bacteriol. Rev.*, **18**, 16–42 (1954).

———, M. Raynaud, and G. N. Cohen: Extension of the Stickland reaction to several bacterial species, *Arch. Biochem.*, **16**, 473–474 (1948).

——— and G. Vinet: Le mécanisme enzymatique de la réaction de désamination couplée chez les bactéries anaérobies strictes du groupe *Cl. sporogenes*, *Ann. inst. Pasteur*, **78**, 1–18 (1950).

Stadtman, E. R., and T. C. Stadtman: Metabolism of microorganisms, *Ann. Rev. Microbiol.*, **7**, 143–178 (1953).

Stickland, L. H.: The chemical reactions by means of which *Cl. sporogenes* obtains its energy, *Biochem. J.*, **28**, 1746–1759 (1934).

———: The reduction of proline by *Cl. sporogenes*, *Biochem. J.*, **29**, 288–290 (1935).

Umbreit, W. W.: "Metabolic Maps," Burgess Publishing Co., Minneapolis, 1952.

Virtanen, A. I., and J. Tarnanen: Die enzymatische spaltung und synthese der asparaginsäure, *Biochem. Z.*, **250**, 193–211 (1932).

Wood, W. A., and I. C. Gunsalus: D-Alanine formation: a racemase in *Streptococcus faecalis*, *J. Biol. Chem.*, **190**, 403–416 (1951).

———, ———, and W. W. Umbreit: Function of pyridoxalphosphate: resolution and purification of the tryptophanase enzyme of *Escherichia coli*, *J. Biol. Chem.*, **170**, 313–321 (1947).

Woods, D. D., and C. E. Clifton: The decomposition of pyruvate and 1-(+) glutamate by *Clostridium tetanomorphum*, *Biochem. J.*, **32**, 345–356 (1938).

Young, E. G., and W. W. Hawkins: The decomposition of allantoin by intestinal bacteria, *J. Bacteriol.*, **47**, 351–353 (1944).

CHAPTER 10

AEROBIC RESPIRATION

The Citric Acid Cycle. In the preceding chapters we have considered the anaerobic pathways of carbohydrate and amino acid dissimilation by various species of bacteria. A portion of these pathways may be utilized during the aerobic oxidation of carbohydrates, amino acids, and fats, with the exception that the reduced coenzymes are oxidized by the systems (Chap. 6) involved in the transfer of hydrogen (protons) and electrons to oxygen. Many of the bacterial fermentative pathways appear to be similar up to, or to converge at, the stage of pyruvate or of "active-acetate" formation and to diverge again from these compounds. Under aerobic conditions the major pathway for dissimilation of pyruvic acid and "active acetate" appears to be one shared in common by many, or possibly all, of the aerobes and facultative anaerobes. Along this pathway, the Krebs, citric acid, or tricarboxylic acid cycle, pyruvic acid is oxidized to carbon dioxide and water with an uptake of five atoms of oxygen, or

$$CH_3COCOOH + 2.5O_2 \rightarrow 3CO_2 + 2H_2O$$

Considerable doubt existed in recent years regarding the participation of this cycle in bacterial respiration, primarily because citric acid or other intermediates in the cycle were not oxidized readily or at all by many species. Various workers have shown that permeability factors prevent some species from oxidizing exogenous tricarboxylic acids, oxidation of these acids occurring readily in dried cells or in cellular extracts. This indicates that the requisite enzymes are present in the cells, and it is assumed that they participate in pyruvate oxidation via the citric acid cycle in the viable cell.

The term cycle implies that in the first stage of the series of reactions involved, a process is initiated which leads ultimately to the formation of a product which participates in the first step, and so on. In other words, the system operates in such a manner that a very small amount of a key substance (or substances which can give rise to its formation) is sufficient to start the cycle, and this key substance, oxalacetic acid in the citric acid cycle, is reformed at the end of the cycle.

The citric acid cycle (Ochoa, 1954), illustrated in Fig. 10-1, involves a

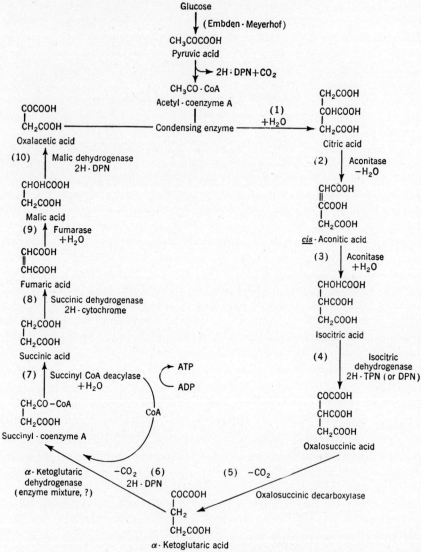

FIG. 10-1. The citric acid cycle.

complex of many enzymes intervening between pyruvic acid and the ultimate disposal of carbon as carbon dioxide and of hydrogen and electrons as water. The integrated series of enzymes which make up the citric acid cycle together with the systems involved in the oxidation of reduced coenzymes (DPNH and TPNH) and the transfer of hydrogen and electrons to oxygen constitute the cyclophorase system. This system (Chap. 6) is associated with mitochondria in animal cells and possibly with mitochondria, or metabolic equivalents thereof, in bacteria. The citric acid cycle has three main results: (1) together with the hydrogen and electron transfer systems, it provides for stepwise degradation of the pyruvate molecule and transfer of hydrogen and electrons in such a manner that energy is liberated in small amounts rather than in destructive ones; (2) in these stepwise and orderly processes energy is made available to the cell in the form of a considerable number of high-energy phosphate bonds; and (3) certain intermediates of the cycle can be utilized in syntheses essential for maintenance and growth of the cell.

An important step in our understanding of the oxidation of pyruvic acid was made by Szent-Gyorgi in 1935 when he observed that small amounts of any one of the four-carbon dicarboxylic acids had a catalytic effect on oxidations by pigeon breast muscle. It was known from the work of Keilin that succinic acid dehydrogenase was linked with the cytochrome system and from that of Thunberg and others that muscle possesses the enzymes succinic acid dehydrogenase, fumarase, and malic acid dehydrogenase. These observations led Szent-Gyorgi to the conclusion that a compound such as fumaric acid could act as a hydrogen carrier, being reduced to succinic acid which could be oxidized by the cytochrome system with the regeneration of fumaric acid. Oxalacetic acid can be reduced to malic acid, and this in turn dehydrated with the formation of fumaric acid, thereby maintaining a reservoir of fumaric acid for the catalytic cycle.

The major advance was made by Krebs in 1937 when he showed that oxalacetic acid could be converted into citric acid by pigeon breast muscle. This conversion involves the addition of two carbon atoms from a metabolite, and Krebs suggested that they could come from pyruvic acid which is decarboxylated in the condensation process. This reaction was known to occur spontaneously in alkaline solution, one molecule of oxalacetic acid condensing with one of pyruvic acid in the presence of hydrogen peroxide to yield citric acid and carbon dioxide. Numerous studies with various enzyme preparations from tissues and microorganisms and with the aid of labeled carbon have verified this hypothesis and the conversions of citric acid as postulated by Krebs. Other studies have indicated that citric acid is formed from oxalacetic and acetic acids with the participation of the condensing enzyme together with ATP, Mg^{++}, and CoA, which are required along with the essential enzymes for the conversion of acetate to acetyl-CoA. All of these agents can be obtained from bacteria such as *E. coli*.

If we could follow the oxidation of a typical substrate such as glucose, we would probably find that it generally is dissimilated aerobically over the Embden-Meyerhof anaerobic pathway with the formation of pyruvic acid and water. The pyruvic acid then is oxidatively decarboxylated by a decarboxylase requiring (in *E. coli* and probably in many other cells) lipothiamide pyrophosphate, a complex in which α-lipoic acid and thiamin pyrophosphate appear to be joined by an amide bond, as the cocarboxylase. Decarboxylation leads to the formation of acetyl-CoA, which serves as an acetyl donor for the acetylation of oxalacetic acid to form citric acid. These reactions can be represented as follows:

$$
\begin{array}{c}
\text{CH}_2\text{COOH} \\
|\\
\text{COHCOOH} \\
|\\
\text{CH}_2\text{COOH}
\end{array}
$$

DPN$^+$ — CH$_3$COCOOH — CoA ← ... → CH$_2$COOH   Condensing enzyme

DPNH +H$^+$ → CH$_3$CO·CoA → COCOOH, CO$_2$, CH$_2$COOH

If acetyl-CoA is formed by mechanisms other than indicated above, it can enter the cycle directly by condensation with oxalacetic acid.

In the acetylation of oxalacetic acid, an exergonic reaction with a ΔF about $-7,700$ cal., the condensing enzyme (an acetyl transferase) catalyzes the attachment of the methyl group of acetyl-CoA to the keto-carbon of oxalacetate. In other acetyl-transfer reactions, the formation of acetylsulfonamides or of acetylcholine, union is established between the carbonyl-carbon and the acetyl acceptor. The carbon involved in the acetyl-transfer reactions is determined by the nature of the enzyme systems.

Once the formation of citrate has occurred, a series of reactions follows during the course of which the remainder of the carbon atoms of pyruvate (or their equivalent) are disposed of as CO_2 by decarboxylations. Oxygen is brought into union with hydrogen and electrons to form water, the excess formed over that utilized in the cycle being equivalent to that which could be formed from the first oxidation product of pyruvate. The details of the citric acid cycle reactions are summarized in Fig. 10-1.

The first reaction in the citric acid cycle proper is the condensation between oxalacetic acid and acetyl-CoA to yield citric acid and CoA, a reaction considered above. If the regeneration of oxalacetic acid in the cycle is inhibited by utilization of intermediates for synthetic or other purposes, more can be formed to continue the cycle by carbon dioxide fixation with pyruvate and the Ochoa enzyme to give malic acid. In reactions 2 and 3 (Fig. 10-1) we note dehydration of citric acid to give *cis*-aconitic acid and hydration of the latter to form *d*-isocitric acid, both reactions being catalyzed by aconitase. An equilibrium is established between the amounts of these three substances in the presence of aconitase.

Reaction 4, the oxidation of isocitric acid to oxalosuccinic acid with the participation of isocitric dehydrogenase and TPN$^+$ (or in some species it may be DPN$^+$), is the first energy-providing reaction in the cycle. Actually, the energy made available comes primarily from outside the cycle in the transfer of hydrogen and electrons via the flavin-cytochrome pathway to oxygen. It has been estimated that three high-energy phosphate bonds can be generated in this oxidation of DPNH or TPNH, 36,000 cal. approximately being made available in ATP from about 50,000 cal. that would be liberated if no energy were stored in the oxidation.

Reaction 5 is pictured as a decarboxylation of oxalosuccinic acid to yield α-ketoglutaric acid, the equivalent of a second carbon atom of the original pyruvate being eliminated as CO_2 in this step. There is uncertainty as to the actual participation of oxalosuccinic acid, except possibly as a fleeting intermediate, in the Krebs cycle. Isocitric dehydrogenase and oxalosuccinic acid decarboxylase activity have not been separated from each other, and it is possible that reactions 4 and 5 are catalyzed by the same enzyme.

Reaction 6 is undoubtedly more complex than illustrated in Fig. 10-1 and probably involves a series of reactions. The net result is an oxidative decarboxylation of α-ketoglutaric acid to yield CO_2 and succinyl-CoA, DPN$^+$ mediating the oxidation. Lipothiamide pyrophosphate apparently is involved as cocarboxylase in the decarboxylation which eliminates the final carbon equivalent of the acetate carbon introduced into the cycle. CoA participates in the series of reactions which yields succinyl-CoA. The latter compound is converted to succinic acid in reaction 7, and CoA is regenerated, succinyl $\sim$Ⓟ probably being an intermediate in the regeneration. This high-energy phosphate-bond energy is transferred to the adenylic acid system with the formation of ATP, the only energy-providing reaction in the cycle itself. Succinyl-CoA, like acetyl-CoA, is a high-energy compound and could serve as a source of succinyl groups in transfer reactions leading to the synthesis of compounds requiring this structure.

The remaining three reactions, 8, 9, and 10, regenerate oxalacetic acid, 8 and 10 being oxidations which serve to bring succinic acid up to the oxidation state of the key substance, oxalacetic acid, of the cycle.

In the citric acid cycle, or in the pyruvate-introductory step, compounds are available that can serve in the synthesis of amino acids. Pyruvate itself can be aminated to form alanine, while α-ketoglutarate can be converted in a similar manner to glutamic acid and fumaric (or oxalacetic) to aspartic acid. Acetyl-CoA or succinyl-CoA can serve as sources of acetyl or succinyl groups, and hence the cycle not only serves as an oxidative mechanism but also as a source of key intermediates for synthetic purposes. Assimilatory reactions will be considered in Chap. 12.

In summarizing the reactions considered above we find that one carbon of pyruvate is eliminated outside the cycle along with a pair of hydrogens and of electrons. Within the cycle two other carbons are eliminated as carbon dioxide, thus disposing of the three carbons, or their equivalents, in the original molecule of pyruvic acid. Four more pairs of hydrogen and of electrons are eliminated in the cycle, the net result being the disposal of three carbon atoms as carbon dioxide and ten hydrogens and electrons started on the way to union with oxygen. Four molecules of water are utilized in the cycle (reactions 1, 3, 7, and 9) and one is formed (2), so the over-all reaction is

$$CH_3COCOOH + 4H_2O + 2.5O_2 \rightarrow 3CO_2 + 6H_2O$$

On the assumption that three (two from the succinate oxidation) high-energy bonds are formed during the transfer of each pair of hydrogen and electrons, and considering the energy changes in reaction 7 as well as those involved in the formation of pyruvate, we can set up the following energetic balance sheet for the oxidation of glucose:

	$\sim$Ⓟ bonds formed
Glucose → 2 phosphoglyceraldehyde → 2 phosphoglyceric acid	2
2DPNH + 2H$^+$ + O$_2$ → 2DPN$^+$ + 2H$_2$O	6
2 Phosphoglycerate → 2 phosphopyruvate + 2H$_2$O	2
2 Pyruvate → 2 acetyl-CoA + 2CO$_2$	
2DPNH + 2H$^+$ + O$_2$ → 2DPN$^+$ + 2H$_2$O	6
2 Isocitrate → 2 oxalosuccinate	
2TPNH + 2H$^+$ + O$_2$ → 2TPN$^+$ + 2H$_2$O	6
2 α-Ketoglutaric acid → 2 succinyl-CoA	
2DPNH + 2H$^+$ + O$_2$ → 2DPN$^+$ + 2H$_2$O	6
2 Succinyl-CoA → 2 succinic acid	2
2 Succinate → 2 fumarate	
4H$^+$ + 4e via cytochrome directly	4
2 Malic → 2 oxalacetic	
2DPNH + 2H$^+$ + O$_2$ → 2DPN$^+$ + 2H$_2$O	6
Total	40
$\sim$Ⓟ used in phosphorylating glucose	2
$\sim$Ⓟ available to the cell	38

When glycogen is the substrate being oxidized, only one $\sim$Ⓟ is required (and one inorganic phosphate) in the formation of hexose diphosphate; hence 39 rather than 38 high-energy bonds would be available. Variable amounts of this energy may be lost because of phosphorylase activity which could act as a controlling factor on respiration. ATPase activity is particularly noticeable in enzyme preparations.

Since many species of bacteria do not possess all of the cytochromes (*a*, *b*, and *c*, or similar ones), it may be that less than 38 ATP molecules are generated during the oxidation of glucose via the Embden-Meyerhof and the Krebs cycle pathways and the concomitant hydrogen-electron transfers to oxygen. If a substrate is oxidized via flavoprotein to oxygen or if glucose is oxidized over the Warburg-Dickens route and the Krebs cycle, the energy yield in terms of $\sim$ⓅP groups could be different. It is also possible, although the probability is low, that some species utilize the dicarboxylic acid or Thunberg-Weiland cycle in their terminal respiration, pyruvate being oxidized to acetate and acetic acid molecules condensing to form succinic acid which is oxidized to oxalacetate. This compound can be decarboxylated to yield pyruvic acid, from which acetate, the key intermediate, can be generated by decarboxylation. This cycle can be represented as follows:

$$
\begin{array}{c}
CH_3 \\
| \\
CO \qquad \text{from substrate} \\
| \\
COOH \\
\downarrow \rightarrow CO_2
\end{array}
$$

$$
\begin{array}{ccccc}
COCOOH & CO_2\ CH_3 & CO_2 & CH_3COOH \\
| & \uparrow\ | & \uparrow & + \\
CH_2COOH & \xrightarrow{\ }\ CO & \xrightarrow{\ } & CH_3COOH \\
\uparrow & | & & | \\
\ & COOH & & \downarrow \\
CHOHCOOH & CHCOOH & & CH_2COOH \\
| & \rightleftarrows\ || & \rightleftarrows & | \\
CH_2COOH & CHCOOH & & CH_2COOH
\end{array}
$$

the net result being, as in the Krebs cycle,

$$CH_3COCOOH + 2.5O_2 \rightarrow 3CO_2 + 2H_2O$$

Umbreit (1953) presents a discussion indicating the possible existence of other respiratory cycles in bacteria, none, however, having been definitely established as terminal respiratory cycles.

If amino acids are dissimilated to yield pyruvic or acetic acids or any of the acids encountered in the Krebs cycle, these amino acid residues can then be disposed of in the cycle in the manner considered for carbohydrate-dissimilation residues. Fats can also be oxidized through the Krebs cycle, after hydrolysis of the fat by lipase to yield glycerol and fatty acids, glycerol being oxidized to pyruvic acid, and the fatty acid residues to acetic acid.

Oxidation of Fatty Acids. Knoop, and also Dakin, early in this century observed that fatty acids were oxidized in such a manner that two carbon atoms were removed from the carboxyl end of the fatty acid chain at one time, a new carboxyl group being formed at what was the β-carbon atom. This process became known as beta oxidation. In more recent years, as a result of studies by Quastel, Leloir, Lipmann, and others, the mechanism of fatty acid oxidation by tissues has been established in some detail. The studies of Barker and Stadtman with *C. kluyveri* (actually with fatty acid synthesis, see Chap. 8) showed the importance of CoA in the oxidation of fatty acids and also indicated the similarity between the reactions as carried out in tissues and in bacteria. The oxidation of a fatty acid can be represented as follows:

$$RCH_2CH_2COOH \underset{\text{fatty-acid (acyl) dehydrogenase}}{\overset{\text{CoA}}{\rightleftharpoons}} RCH{=}CHCO{-}CoA$$

$$RCH{=}CHCO{-}CoA + H_2O \underset{\text{hydrase}}{\rightleftharpoons} RCHOHCH_2CO{-}CoA$$

$$RCHOHCH_2CO{-}CoA \underset{\text{cleavage enzyme}}{\overset{\text{CoA}}{\rightleftharpoons}} RCO{-}CoA + CH_3CO{-}CoA$$

Acetyl-CoA can enter the Krebs cycle, and the oxidation and cleavage of the fatty acid will continue to completion in the manner pictured above. High-energy phosphate bonds are spent in making the CoA derivatives, much as they are expended in the initiation of glucose dissimilation, but they are recovered manyfold in the oxidations that follow. Relatively few species of bacteria are active in attacking fats, of either the simple or the more complex lipid types, but lipoidal matter does make up a considerable portion of their organic content. Fatty acids, however, frequently are formed by bacteria under anaerobic conditions and can be disposed of, as indicated above, when oxygen becomes available to the cells.

The Warburg-Dickens Pathway of Oxidation—the Pentose Cycle. Although the Embden-Meyerhof scheme for the dissimilation of carbohydrates describes the principal mode of conversion of phosphorylated glucose or fructose units to pyruvic acid in many cells, it became apparent that agents such as fluoride which block certain reactions in the scheme had relatively little influence on glucose utilization in some species. Furthermore, some organisms do not possess the enzyme aldolase involved in the splitting of fructose-1,6-diphosphate into the triose phosphates. Some organisms, e.g., *Acetobacter*, oxidize glucose directly rather than at the triose stage. Formation of pentose compounds from glucose has been demonstrated with a number of bacteria. Many bacteria ferment pentose as well as hexose sugars, and fermentation balances indicated that these compounds are utilized directly, i.e., without conversion to a hexose. Since these pentoses can be oxidized, as well as fermented, by many species it was postulated that they undergo a 2-3 carbon split with the formation of a molecule each of a di- and of a tricarbon compound.

As a result of numerous studies (see Horecker, 1953; Wood and Schwert, 1953; Lampen, 1953; Cohen, 1954; Racker, 1954; Gunsalus, Horecker, and Wood, 1955), three major pathways for the aerobic oxidation of glucose appear to exist and more than one may be operative in the same cell. These can be summarized as follows:

1. Embden-Meyerhof pathway to pyruvate followed by oxidation of the latter through the Krebs cycle.
2. Oxidation through glucose-6-P and possibly phosphorylated ketogluconic acids (Warburg-Dickens pathway or hexosemonophosphate shunt), the ketogluconic acid being decarboxylated in many species to yield a pentose. In some species the phosphoketogluconic acid is split to form trioses.
3. Oxidation of nonphosphorylated sugars and alcohols, phosphorylation and the Krebs cycle possibly being involved in later reactions in some species.

Warburg and Christian showed in 1935 that 6-phosphogluconic acid was produced on oxidation of glucose-6-phosphate with enzyme preparations from yeast or from animal tissues. Yeast enzymes also induced oxidation of the gluconate with the evolution of carbon dioxide. Dickens studied this oxidation further and noted the formation of a pentose which he concluded to be ribose-5-phosphate, a compound which could be oxidized further. There is evidence (Horecker, 1953) that 3-keto-6-phosphogluconic acid and ribulose-5-phosphate are intermediates on this pathway of oxidation, which may be represented as

An enzymatically catalyzed equilibrium is also established between the ribulose phosphate and xylose- and arabinose-5-phosphates, thus providing other compounds that may be needed by the cells. Ribulose-5-phosphate can be split with the formation of glyceraldehyde-3-phosphate and "active glycolaldehyde," this reaction being catalyzed by a thiamine-pyrophosphate-requiring transketolase according to the equation

$$
\begin{array}{c}
\text{H}_2\text{COH} \\
| \\
\text{C}{=}\text{O} \\
| \\
\text{HCOH} \\
| \\
\text{HCOH} \\
| \\
\text{H}_2\text{CO}{-}\text{(P)} \\
\text{Ribulose-5-(P)}
\end{array}
\; + \; \text{ThPP-Enz} \; \rightleftarrows \;
\begin{array}{c}
\text{H}_2\text{COH} \\
| \\
\text{HC}{=}\text{O} \\
\vdots \\
\text{ThPP-Enz} \\
\text{"Active} \\
\text{glycoaldehyde"}
\end{array}
\; + \;
\begin{array}{c}
\text{HC}{=}\text{O} \\
| \\
\text{HCOH} \\
| \\
\text{H}_2\text{CO}{-}\text{(P)} \\
\text{Glyceral-} \\
\text{dehyde-3-(P)}
\end{array}
$$

Active glycoaldehyde may be converted to glycolaldehyde itself in some species (*Acetobacter* sp.), but apparently the glycoyl moiety is transferred to an acceptor molecule by many bacteria, yeasts, and mammalian tissues. The fate of the triose phosphate depends upon the species and whether aerobic or anaerobic conditions prevail. Not all of the reactions have been determined, and therefore only a general picture can be considered here.

In some organisms the glycolaldehyde-enzyme complex is involved in a transfer of the glycoyl moiety to ribose-5-(P) with the formation of a 7-carbon sugar, sedoheptulose-7-(P), and the regeneration of the free transketolase. This reaction can be represented as

$$
\begin{array}{c}
\text{HC}{=}\text{O} \\
| \\
\text{HCOH} \\
| \\
\text{HCOH} \\
| \\
\text{HCOH} \\
| \\
\text{H}_2\text{CO}{-}\text{(P)} \\
\text{Ribose-5-(P)}
\end{array}
\; + \;
\begin{array}{c}
\text{H}_2\text{COH} \\
| \\
\text{HC}{=}\text{O} \\
\vdots \\
\text{ThPP-Enz}
\end{array}
\; \rightleftarrows \;
\begin{array}{c}
\text{H}_2\text{COH} \\
| \\
\text{C}{=}\text{O} \\
| \\
\text{HOCH} \\
| \\
\text{HCOH} \\
| \\
\text{HCOH} \\
| \\
\text{HCOH} \\
| \\
\text{H}_2\text{CO}{-}\text{(P)} \\
\text{Sedoheptulose-7-(P)}
\end{array}
\; + \; \text{ThPP-Enz}
$$

Sedoheptulose-7-(P) can react with glyceraldehyde-3-(P) under the influence of a transaldolase, a dihydroxyacetone group being transferred from sedoheptulose to the triose yielding fructose-6-Ⓟ and a 4-carbon compound tentatively identified as erythrose-4-Ⓟ. Fructose-6-Ⓟ can be converted to glucose-6-Ⓟ to continue the cycle, while the tetrose can react under the influence of the transketolase with ribulose-5-Ⓟ to form fructose-6-Ⓟ and glyceraldehyde-3-Ⓟ. These reactions can be represented as

$$
\begin{array}{l}
\text{H}_2\text{COH} \\
\text{C}{=}\text{O} \\
\text{HOCH} \\
\text{HCOH} \quad + \quad \text{HC}{=}\text{O} \\
\text{HCOH} \qquad\quad \text{HCOH} \\
\text{HCOH} \qquad\quad \text{H}_2\text{CO}{-}\text{Ⓟ} \\
\text{H}_2\text{CO}{-}\text{Ⓟ}
\end{array}
\xrightleftharpoons[\text{transaldolase}]{}
\begin{array}{l}
\text{HC}{=}\text{O} \\
\text{HCOH} \\
\text{HCOH} \quad + \\
\text{H}_2\text{CO}{-}\text{Ⓟ}
\end{array}
\begin{array}{l}
\text{H}_2\text{COH} \\
\text{C}{=}\text{O} \\
\text{HOCH} \\
\text{HCOH} \\
\text{HCOH} \\
\text{H}_2\text{CO}{-}\text{Ⓟ}
\end{array}
$$

Sedoheptulose-7-Ⓟ
Glyceraldehyde-3-Ⓟ   Erythrose-4-Ⓟ (?)   Fructose-6-Ⓟ

and

$$
\begin{array}{l}
\text{HC}{=}\text{O} \\
\text{HCOH} \\
\text{HCOH} \quad + \\
\text{H}_2\text{CO}{-}\text{Ⓟ}
\end{array}
\begin{array}{l}
\text{H}_2\text{COH} \\
\text{C}{=}\text{O} \\
\text{HCOH} \\
\text{HCOH} \\
\text{H}_2\text{CO}{-}\text{Ⓟ}
\end{array}
\xrightleftharpoons[]{\text{transketolase}}
\begin{array}{l}
\text{H}_2\text{COH} \\
\text{C}{=}\text{O} \\
\text{HOCH} \\
\text{HCOH} \\
\text{HCOH} \\
\text{H}_2\text{CO}{-}\text{Ⓟ}
\end{array}
\begin{array}{l}
\text{HC}{=}\text{O} \\
\text{HCOH} \quad + \\
\text{H}_2\text{CO}{-}\text{Ⓟ}
\end{array}
$$

Erythrose-4-Ⓟ   Ribulose-5-Ⓟ   Fructose-6-Ⓟ   Glyceraldehyde-3-Ⓟ

Reactions of this nature also are involved in the photosynthetic fixation of carbon dioxide (Chap. 11).

Racker (1954) has suggested a cycle starting with glucose-6-Ⓟ in which ribose-5-Ⓟ acts as an intermediate, being used and re-formed much like oxalacetic acid in the Krebs cycle. This pentose cycle is depicted in Fig. 10-2. Three major reactions are represented in this scheme, and these can be described as follows: (1) oxidative decarboxylation of glucose-6-Ⓟ to form ribulose-5-Ⓟ, which reacts, under the influence of a transketolase, to form sedoheptulose-7-Ⓟ and glyceraldehyde-3-Ⓟ; (2) reaction between the heptulose and the triose, under the influence of a transaldolase, to yield erythrose-4-Ⓟ and fructose-6-Ⓟ, which can be converted to glucose-6-$\textcircled{P}$; and (3) decarboxylation of the glucose-6-$\textcircled{P}$ to ribulose-5-$\textcircled{P}$, which reacts with a transketolase in the transfer of glycolaldehyde from the ribulose to erythrose, giving a triose-$\textcircled{P}$ and fructose-6-$\textcircled{P}$. The fructose so formed is converted to the glucose phosphate. The triose can be oxidized, or more probably condenses with the formation of hexose diphosphate. This latter substance can be converted by some, but not by all, bacteria to the monophosphate which could reenter the cycle.

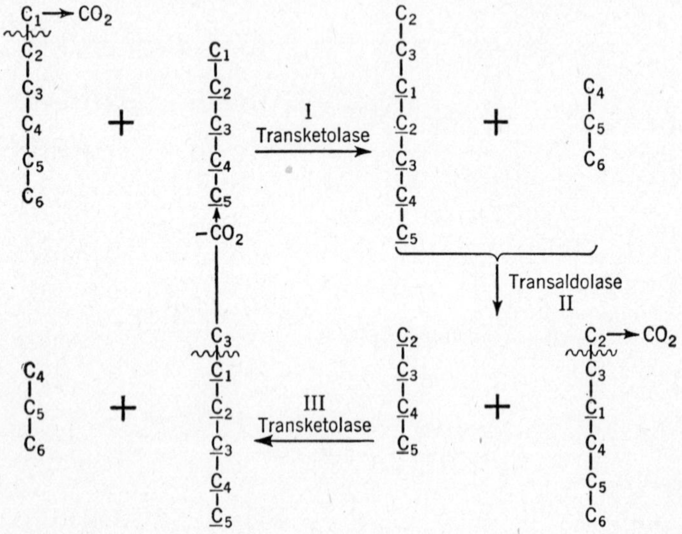

FIG. 10-2. The pentose cycle (after Racker, 1954), showing the catalytic activity of ribose 5-$\textcircled{P}$ on the utilization of glucose-6-$\textcircled{P}$. Only the carbon skeletons are indicated in the diagram, and the ribose carbons are underscored in order to follow the fate of the original glucose carbons, C_1, C_2, and C_3, which are disposed of as CO_2 in one turn of this cycle.

The fate of the triose mentioned above has not been established definitely, and the scheme should be considered only as a tentative one until further work establishes its validity. Cheldelin[1] has developed a somewhat more complete picture of the pentose cycle (Horecker cycle), which is summarized in Fig. 10-3. This scheme indicates that for every six molecules of glucose entering the cycle the equivalent of one molecule is oxidized to carbon dioxide and water, while five molecules of hexose phosphate are regenerated. According to these concepts the Warburg-Dickens pathway is not a shunt mechanism providing an alternate route for feeding material into the Krebs cycle, but rather it is a distinct cycle for the oxidation of glucose. This cycle appears to function in organisms such as yeast (aerobically), molds, various bacilli (Dedonder, 1953), *Strep-*

[1] Personal communication.

tomyces (Cochrane, Peck, and Harrison, 1953), and *E. coli*. Scott, McNair, and Cohen (1953) have calculated by indirect methods (subject to some question) that as much as 40 per cent of the glucose oxidized by *E. coli* may go through the monophosphate pathway or cycle. Thermodynamic data on this pathway of oxidation are not so complete as for the Embden-Meyerhof one and the Krebs cycle. The total energy change would be the same regardless of the pathway, but it is possible that fewer high-energy bonds would be generated.

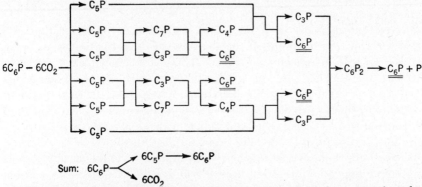

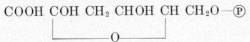

FIG. 10-3. A balanced flow sheet for the oxidation of one mole of glucose per six moles entering into the pentose cycle.   (*After Cheldelin, personal communication.*)

Entner and Doudoroff (1952) described a somewhat different pathway for the oxidative metabolism of glucose in *Pseudomonas saccharophila*. Glucose is phosphorylated and oxidized to 6-phosphogluconic acid, which is split with the formation of pyruvic acid and glyceraldehyde-3-$\textcircled{P}$ in equimolar amounts. The triose molecules appear to be utilized in the normal manner in the cells. MacGee and Doudoroff (1954) have presented evidence that an enzyme they termed phosphogluconic dehydrase converts the phosphogluconate to 2-keto-3-deoxy-6-phosphogluconic acid, an intermediate which appears to possess a furanoid structure of the type

$$\text{COOH COH CH}_2 \text{ CHOH CH CH}_2\text{O}-\textcircled{P}$$
$$\underline{\hspace{2cm} \text{O} \hspace{2cm}}$$

A splitting enzyme converts this keto-gluconic acid into pyruvic acid and glyceraldehyde-3-$\textcircled{P}$. A similar or identical mechanism appears to function in *Pseudomonas fluorescens* (Wood and Schwerdt, 1954; Wood, 1955).

Campbell and his colleagues (Warburton, Eagles, and Campbell, 1951; Campbell, 1954) have reported that *Pseudomonas aeruginosa* oxidizes glucose without phosphorylation through gluconic acid to 2-ketogluconate. The latter compound is split with the ultimate formation of two molecules of pyruvate, one mole probably being formed via a triose phosphate.

Acetate was shown to be an intermediate of glucose oxidation which proceeds, at least to the triose stage, without participation of the Embden-Meyerhof system.   Claridge and Werkman (1954) have presented evidence that two types of glucose dissimilation may occur in *P. aeruginosa*, one type involving oxidation of nonphosphorylated compounds while the other might be the Embden-Meyerhof pathway.   Oxidative phosphorylation coupled to hydrogen transport, however, might be involved in the first type of glucose utilization, formation of as many as four to six moles of ATP being possible in the transport of the hydrogen derived from the oxidation of glucose to ketogluconic acid.

Aerobic mechanisms of dissimilation of glucose and other hexoses also appear to operate in species of the genus *Acetobacter*, the first steps being carried on without phosphorylation.   It has been known since the early days of bacteriology that certain species, e.g., *suboxydans*, of the genus *Acetobacter*, oxidize primary alcohols and aldohexoses to the corresponding acids and secondary alcohols to the corresponding ketones.   Ethyl alcohol is oxidized to acetic acid, glucose to gluconic acid, glycerol to dihydroxyacetone, and sorbitol to the keto sugar sorbose, this latter reaction being one step in the commercial synthesis of vitamin C.   These products accumulate in large amounts in cultures developing under even highly aerobic conditions but are oxidized further quite readily by washed-cell suspensions and with liberation of CO_2.   King and Cheldelin (1953) have shown that while compounds such as dihydroxyacetone and sorbose are oxidized, these compounds cannot serve as sources of carbon for growth, while the parent compounds, glycerol and sorbitol, can support growth.   The phosphate esters encountered in the Embden-Meyerhof scheme and members of the citric acid cycle were also unable to support growth.   2,4-Dinitrophenol, which appears to "uncouple" phosphorylation from respiration, in concentrations inhibitory to the oxidation of dihydroxyacetone or sorbose by resting cells did not affect oxidation of or growth on glycerol or sorbitol.   King and Cheldelin concluded that phosphate esterification occurs at the substrate level (dihydroxyacetone or sorbose phosphates) and that such phosphorylations are not influenced by 2,4-dinitrophenol, while further phosphorylations involving coenzyme phosphorylation are sensitive to this agent.   Furthermore, Cheldelin, Hauge, and King (1953) have shown that the oxidation of alcohol to acetic acid, of glycerol to dihydroxyacetone, and of glucose to gluconic acid proceeded with equal velocity in coenzyme A–deficient and normal cells.   This indicates noninvolvement of coenzyme A in these reactions.   Subsequent oxidations are inhibited in deficient cells.   Addition of coenzyme A to the deficient cells increased their ability to oxidize dihydroxyacetone.   These and earlier studies indicated that neither a C_6 nor a C_4 cycle operates to a significant extent in *A. suboxydans* and leaves the role of coenzyme A in this organism, as well as the mechanism of energy trapping, to be established. Likewise, the reason for the relative inability of the organism to oxidize a compound such as dihydroxyacetone in aerobic cultures while washed cells do affect the oxidation remains to be determined.

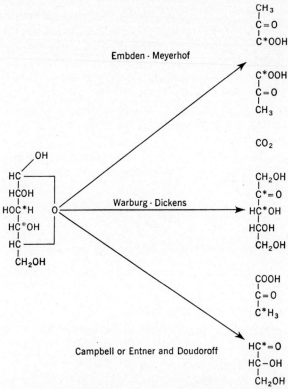

FIG. 10-4. The intermediate fate of glucose (phosphate esters not shown) and the distribution of labeled glucose carbons* 3 and 4 dissimilated via the three pathways indicated.

Katznelson, Tanenbaum, and Tatum (1953) observed the accumulation of 2,5-diketogluconic acid during the oxidation of glucose by "old" cells and cell-free extracts of *Acetobacter melanogenum*, the oxidation proceeding through gluconic and 2-ketogluconic acids. The diketo acid is rather unstable, especially above pH 4.5, and changes to a brown-colored product probably responsible for the color observed in cultures of this organism in glucose media. Young cells carry out a more complete oxidation of glucose with CO_2 evolution; in the presence of 2,4-dinitrophenol, however, their metabolism resembles that of older cells.

It is apparent that a number of pathways (Fig. 10-4) for the dissimilation of sugars exist, even in the same organism. It is difficult to evaluate their relative importance. The Warburg-Dickens pathway appears to be second in importance to the Embden-Meyerhof one. In the Warburg-Dickens scheme, decarboxylation of phosphogluconic acid gives rise to a pentose which may be utilized through the pentose cycle. We have seen, e.g., the *Leuconostoc* fermentation, that such a mechanism can be involved under anaerobic conditions as well as under aerobic ones. It has been suggested also that a pentose could be oxidized with the formation of a pentose acid which could be decarboxylated to yield a tetrose, and so on. There is little experimental evidence for such a mechanism of dissimilation. A departure from the Warburg-Dickens pathway occurs when a phosphorylated sugar acid is split into two trioses as in the Entner-Doudoroff scheme. Another pathway, as we have seen, involves the oxidation of nonphosphorylated sugars and their derivatives. We must recognize that alternate or different pathways for oxidative dissimilatory reactions do exist and that it is extremely difficult, on the basis of our present knowledge, to interpret the events which take place in cells containing the enzymes involved in more than one pathway.

REFERENCES

Campbell, J. J. R.: Metabolism of microorganisms, *Ann. Rev. Microbiol.*, **8**, 71–104 (1954).

Cheldelin, V. H., J. G. Hauge, and T. E. King: Oxidative dissimilation in pantothenate-deficient *Acetobacter suboxydans* cells, *Proc. Soc. Exptl. Biol. Med.*, **82**, 144–147 (1953).

Claridge, C. A., and C. H. Werkman: Evidence for alternative pathways for the oxidation of glucose by *Pseudomonas aeruginosa*, *J. Bacteriol.*, **68**, 77–79 (1954).

Cochrane, V. W., H. D. Peck, and A. Harrison: The metabolism of species of streptomyces. VII. The hexosemonophosphate shunt and associated reactions, *J. Bacteriol.*, **66**, 17–23 (1953).

Cohen, S. S.: Other pathways of carbohydrate metabolism, in D. M. Greenberg (ed.), "Chemical Pathways of Metabolism," vol. 1, chap. 4, Academic Press, Inc., New York, 1954.

Dedonder, R.: Étude de la glycolyse chez certaines bactéries du genre *Bacillus*, *Ann. inst. Pasteur*, **85**, 71–81 (1953).

Entner, N., and M. Doudoroff: Glucose and gluconic acid oxidation of *Pseudomonas saccharophila*, *J. Biol. Chem.*, **196**, 853–862 (1952).

Gunsalus, I. C., B. L. Horecker, and W. A. Wood: Pathways of carbohydrate metabolism in microorganisms, *Bacteriol. Rev.*, **19**, 79–128 (1955).

Horecker, B. L.: The metabolism of pentose phosphate, *J. Cell. Comp. Physiol.*, **41**, suppl. 1, 137–164 (1953).

Katznelson, K., S. W. Tanenbaum, and E. W. Tatum: Glucose, gluconate, and 2-ketogluconate oxidation by *Acetobacter melanogenum*, *J. Biol. Chem.*, **204**, 43–59 (1953).

King, T. E., and V. H. Cheldelin: Sources of energy and the dinitrophenol effect in the growth of *Acetobacter suboxydans*, *J. Bacteriol.*, **66**, 581–584 (1953).

Lampen, J. O.: Pentose and desoxypentose metabolism in bacteria, *J. Cell. Comp. Physiol.*, **41**, suppl. 1, 183–205 (1953).

MacGee, J., and M. Doudoroff: A new phosphorylated intermediate in glucose oxidation, *J. Biol. Chem.*, **210**, 617–626 (1954).

Ochoa, S.: Enzymic mechanisms in the citric acid cycle, *Advances in Enzymol.*, **15**, 183–270 (1954).

Racker, E.: Alternate pathways of glucose and fructose metabolism, *Advances in Enzymol.*, **15**, 141–182 (1954).

Scott, D., B. McNair, and S. S. Cohen: The oxidative pathway of carbohydrate metabolism in *Escherichia coli*, *Biochem. J.*, **55**, 33–36 (1953).

Umbreit, W. W.: Respiratory cycles, *J. Cell. Comp. Physiol.*, **41**, 39–66 (1953).

Warburton, R. H., B. A. Eagles, and J. J. R. Campbell: The intermediate metabolism of *Pseudomonas aeruginosa*. V. The identification of pyruvate as an intermediate in glucose oxidation, *Can. J. Bot.*, **29**, 143–146 (1951).

Wood, W. A.: Pathways of carbohydrate degradation in *Pseudomonas fluorescens*, *Bacteriol. Rev.*, **19**, 222–233 (1955).

—— and R. F. Schwert: Alternate pathways of hexose oxidation in *Pseudomonas fluorescens*, *J. Cell. Comp. Physiol.*, **41**, suppl. 1, 165–182 (1953).

—— and ——: Carbohydrate metabolism by *Pseudomonas fluorescens*. II. Mechanism of hexosephosphate oxidation, *J. Biol. Chem.*, **206**, 625–635 (1954).

CHAPTER 11

AUTOTROPHIC BACTERIA

The idea that microorganisms might bring about the oxidation of inorganic matter such as ammonia was advanced quite early by Pasteur. It was not until 1877, however, that rather conclusive evidence was advanced by Schloesing and Muntz in support of the biological nature of nitrification, the oxidation of ammonia to nitrate. These workers demonstrated that in time ammonia disappeared from sewage circulating through a column of sand and chalk and that nitrate, together with traces of nitrite, appeared in the effluent. They also noted that chloroform or heat stopped the nitrification process as they did other biological reactions. Nitrification was resumed within a few days following the addition of soil washings to the perfusing liquid, thus indicating the presence of nitrifying organisms in the soil. These workers also noted that nitrification was favored by a slightly alkaline perfusate.

About ten years after the first report by Schloesing and Muntz, Winogradsky reported the presence of large filamentous bacteria (*Beggiatoa*) in water from hot springs and that these colorless organisms were capable of oxidizing hydrogen sulfide to sulfur which accumulated in the cells. When the supply of sulfide was depleted these cells oxidized their internal stores of sulfur, sulfate accumulated in the medium, and the cells in time lost their ability to multiply unless sulfide was added to the medium. Winogradsky also noted that carbon dioxide was essential for growth of these sulfur bacteria and concluded that he was studying a unique type of microorganism, one differentiated from the green plant by its ability to grow in the dark and from heterotrophic or animal life both by its utilization of energy obtained from the oxidation of inorganic rather than organic matter and by its apparent use of carbon dioxide.

Winogradsky lent further support to his rather radical concept of autotrophic (self-sufficient), chemosynthetic forms of life by his observations on the iron bacteria and particularly by his isolation in 1890 of pure cultures of nitrifying bacteria from soil-enrichment cultures. He found these bacteria grew in a water-salts-bicarbonate medium free of organic matter and that some isolates oxidized ammonia to nitrites, others nitrites to nitrates. Other bacteria capable of growth at the expense of sulfide or

232

other reduced compounds of sulfur, of ammonia, of nitrites, of hydrogen, or of reduced iron compounds were reported in the years immediately following Winogradsky's pioneer studies.

A classification of bacteria into various nutritional groups was presented in Chap. 1. This classification was considered as a spectrum rather than as a number of absolute groups since no sharp lines of demarcation can be drawn between the different groups. Likewise, trouble has been encountered in the attempts to classify the autotrophic bacteria into rigid groups, on the basis of either morphological or physiological characteristics, or both. Winogradsky's concept of chemoautotrophic bacteria, and the later concept of photoautotrophic bacteria, as organisms that do not require and cannot use exogenous organic matter for growth, and for which such compounds are generally toxic, is too rigid a definition. Only a few species of sulfur-oxidizing bacteria in the genus *Thiobacillus*, the nitrifying bacteria, and the iron bacteria *Gallionella* appear to fulfill the primary requirement imposed by the definition. We considered the chemosynthetic and photosynthetic autotrophic bacteria as members of group 1, which was characterized on the basis of carbon assimilation from carbon dioxide and of nitrogen from inorganic sources, the chemosynthetic cells obtaining energy from the oxidation of inorganic matter, the photosynthetic ones from light. It is better for our purpose to consider the autotrophs as a broad spectrum of organisms of widely different characteristics for which carbon dioxide does, or may, constitute the main (bulk) ultimate source of carbon. Such a definition enables us to include in our discussion those species which require one or more growth factors in trace amounts, the photosynthetic "heterotrophs" which utilize organic matter primarily as a source of hydrogen, and the facultative autotrophs. These latter bacteria grow most readily in heterotrophic media but are capable of growth in appropriate inorganic solutions.

By a slight stretch of the imagination we might also include in the autotrophic spectrum those bacteria which obtain energy from the oxidation of compounds such as carbon monoxide, formate, and oxalate. Formate and oxalate can be converted to carbon dioxide by the removal of two electrons, and it appears possible (van Niel, 1954), although adequate evidence is lacking, that carbon dioxide can serve as the main carbon source for these bacteria, the energy for its reduction to cellular material coming from the oxidation of these simple carbon compounds.

The strict autotrophs are self-reliant or are independent of other forms of life, as are the green plants, until the supplies of carbon dioxide and of inorganic nutrients in an available form become limiting factors for growth. The heterotrophs, or dependents, are dependent upon other forms of life for the synthesis of organic compounds in appropriate molecular forms.   Carbon dioxide as such constitutes only a limited source of carbon in their chemical structures.   Foster (1951) has said, "Autotrophs generate organic matter and heterotrophs interconvert it."   Bacteria on the border line between the strict autotrophs and the strict heterotrophs may lead either type of existence or may compromise by using organic matter as a source of hydrogen and of energy of oxidation while employing carbon dioxide as their main source of carbon, even though the carbon dioxide arose from their utilization of organic matter.   The broad definition of autotrophs as organisms possessing the ability to live and multiply in an environment in which carbon dioxide is the main source of carbon stresses the ability of the autotrophic bacteria rather than the necessity for these cells to live autotrophically.

The autotrophic bacteria have been considered by many as a peculiar group of organisms possessing "odd" characteristics.   They were believed to differ from the heterotrophic species, not only in their carbon and energy sources, but also in the difficulties encountered in cultivating them in the laboratory, the at times detrimental influence of organic matter on their growth and activity, their powers of synthesis akin to those of the green plants, and their position in the evolutionary system. Recent improvements in culture methods and increased knowledge of the nature of these bacteria render the task of isolating and cultivating most species little or no more difficult than that encountered with many heterotrophic species.   Organic matter as such has been found not to be so detrimental as once believed.   Certain compounds, e.g., methionine, may be inhibitory, but then certain amino acids by themselves may be inhibitory for certain heterotrophic species.   The position of the autotrophic bacteria in the evolutionary scheme is still debatable, but they are far from being "simple forms" both in a morphological and in a biosynthetical sense.   They fix carbon dioxide, possibly in a manner analogous to the green plant, and reduce the fixed material with the formation of new, endogenous organic matter.   It now appears that they interconvert the organic matter formed endogenously much like heterotrophs do with organic compounds of exogenous origin.

In a few species enzymes, coenzymes, and intermediates of metabolism known to be present in heterotrophic species have been detected.   It is quite likely that similar enzymes and metabolites will be found in other autotrophic species when the appropriate studies are carried out.   Furthermore, the facultative autotrophs do possess the ability to use exogenous organic matter for growth.   Possibly under the appropriate environmental conditions even a strict autotroph might be able to assimilate organic substrates, and it could be that permeability factors play the controlling role.   The uniqueness of the autotrophic, chemosynthetic bacteria consists only in their marked ability to use carbon dioxide and in their possession of enzyme systems enabling them to use energy sources not tapped by other forms of bacterial life.

Schemes that have been advanced for the classification of the autotrophic bacteria are not entirely satisfactory. In the Bergey system the majority of the autotrophic species are included in the family Nitrobacteriaceae, and a few are found in other families of the Eubacteriineae and in other orders. Problems concerning the identification of bacteria as autotrophic species, determination of their physiological characteristics, and their classification have been discussed recently by van Niel (1954) and in a symposium edited by Fry and Peel (1954). References to earlier studies and reviews can be found in these papers.

The Nitrifying Bacteria. These autotrophs, defined as bacteria dependent for growth upon the energy obtained from the oxidation of ammonia to nitrite by some species and of nitrite to nitrate by others, are divided into seven genera in the tribe Nitrobacterieae. The validity of some of the genera is in doubt. Most work has been done with the ammonia oxidizer *Nitrosomonas europea* and the nitrite oxidizer *Nitrobacter winogradskyi*. The energy-providing reactions can be represented as

$$NH_4^+ + 1.5O_2 \rightarrow 2H^+ + H_2O + NO_2^- \qquad \Delta F = -66,000 \text{ cal.}$$

and

$$NO_2^- + 0.5O_2 \rightarrow NO_3^- \qquad \Delta F = -17,500 \text{ cal.}$$

Winogradsky isolated nitrifying bacteria in 1890 with the aid of a silica-gel medium impregnated with essential minerals. Silica-gel plates are still commonly employed for the isolation of these organisms. The nitrifiers are very common and very active in mixed populations under natural conditions (for general accounts see Foster, 1951; Quastel and Scholefield, 1951; and chapters by Meikeljohn and by Lees in Fry and Peel, 1954), even in the presence of large quantities of organic material as in sewage and in compost heaps. In fact, they were employed unknowingly for the conversion of ammonia in manures to nitrates for use in gunpowder in France during the Napoleonic wars. Yet gelatin or agar plates appear to be inhibitory to them, or at least to their isolation in pure culture. Nährstoff-Heyden, a hydrolyzed egg albumin preparation, will stimulate growth of *Nitrosomonas* and *Nitrobacter* but is not essential. It could either neutralize the inhibitory action of some material present in the medium or serve as the source of an essential metabolite. Washed cells, in the absence of ammonia, do exhibit an endogenous oxygen uptake, their respiration being stimulated by the addition of soil, yeast, or meat extracts and by a number of simple compounds such as acetic or lactic acids. It has not been determined if any of these compounds are assimilated.

Much of our lack of knowledge concerning the more detailed aspects of the metabolism of these bacteria is due to their slow rate of growth and to low crop yields in pure culture. Chemically, they, and the other autotrophs, appear to be no different from the other bacteria, and they are inhibited by the same general cellular poisons. Considerable information regarding nitrification, and factors influencing it, has been collected from studies using a soil-perfusion apparatus introduced by Lees and Quastel (see reviews cited above). Soil is perfused with a solution which is continuously circulated through the system under relatively constant experimental conditions. Samples of the perfusate can be collected and analyzed when desired, or materials can be added during the course of an experiment.

Quastel and his associates noted that nitrification in a fresh-soil column occurs at a low rate, the rate increasing with time and reaching a maximum and steady value when the soil becomes saturated with the organisms. The nitrifiers remain attached to the soil particles, very few being found in the perfusate. Nitrification appears to occur wholly at the particle surfaces, the bacteria adhering to or multiplying at those points where ammonia ions are adsorbed. The rate of nitrification is increased by factors which increase the base-exchange capacity of the soil and is decreased by agents such as calcium ions which compete with ammonium ions for the soil's colloidal surfaces.

Lees and his associates have studied in some detail the oxidation of ammonia to nitrite. They concluded that this oxidation must take place in several steps if the energy of oxidation is to be bound in an efficient manner and transferred through the agency of high-energy phosphate bonds. This would also require intimate coupling of the reducing power generated in the oxidation with the reduction of carbon dioxide fixed by the cells. No good evidence for these energy-transfer reactions has been obtained, their occurrence being assumed as possible owing to the demonstration of such reactions in *Thiobacillus*.

The simplest scheme for the stepwise oxidation of ammonia to nitrite, advanced by Kluyver and Donker in 1926, can be summarized as follows:

1. Ammonia → hydroxylamine
2. Hydroxylamine → hyponitrite (or dihydroxyammonia)
3. Hyponitrite → nitrite

Lees and his coworkers presented evidence that the oxidation probably occurs through hydroxylamine. The latter compound, in low concentration, can be oxidized by *Nitrosomonas*, and its oxidation is inhibited by hydrazine. Ammonia oxidation proceeds in the presence of hydrazine, but without nitrite formation and with the accumulation of hydroxylamine. Thiourea, on the other hand, specifically inhibits the oxidation of ammonia, but not that of hydroxylamine. These observations indicate that the first reaction probably occurs. The thioureas are chelating agents with a high affinity for copper, thus suggesting the possibility of a copper-containing enzyme active at this stage. Low nitrifying power was noted in copper-deficient soils, and activity was enhanced following the addition of copper to them. Furthermore, a number of copper-containing enzymes react directly with oxygen, the free energy of oxidation of ammonia to hydroxylamine is low, and such an enzyme might promote a preparatory rather than an energy-providing reaction.

Nitrosomonas does not appear to be readily permeable to ammonium ions, and Lees suggests that the first reaction might be carried out at the cell surface with the formation of electrically neutral hydroxylamine molecules to which the cells could be readily permeable. Oxidation of the hydroxylamine, and the subsequent reactions, could occur within the cell where suitable energy-coupling systems are located. The evidence for such a scheme is scanty, but it does appear that the first stage of the reaction can be represented as

$$NH_4^+ + 0.5O_2 \rightarrow NH_2OH + H^+$$

Reactions 2 and 3 have not been demonstrated conclusively. Both dihydroxyammonia ($NH(OH)_2$) and nitroxyl (NOH) are extremely unstable and cannot be tested. Hyponitrite (HON:NOH) supplied extracellularly is not oxidized, but it may not penetrate into the cells. Lees favors the possible transient formation of dihydroxyammonia which could be dehydrogenated directly with the formation of nitrite.

Since the oxidation of nitrite to nitrate involves an energy change only slightly greater than that associated with a high-energy phosphate bond, it appears that the oxidation is a one-step process, possibly a dehydrogenation of a hydrated ($O:NH(OH)_2$) molecule of nitrous acid. Reduction of nitrate to nitrite with the participation of TPNH has been shown to occur in *Neurospora*, indicating the possibility of the reverse reaction in *Nitrobacter*. Practically nothing is known, however, about the oxidation elicited by *Nitrobacter* or the enzymes involved. Quastel and Scholefield (1951) have demonstrated specific blocking of the reaction by nitrourea.

The free-energy efficiency of the nitrifying bacteria has been estimated to be of the order of 5 to 10 per cent. The measurements upon which these values depend were carried out over long periods of time and may not reflect the true efficiency of assimilation by these bacteria.

The Colorless Sulfur Bacteria. Organisms capable of obtaining energy for growth from the oxidation of sulfur or sulfur compounds are scattered widely among the bacteria (Bisset and Grace; and Baalsrud, in Fry and Peel, 1954), some being classified in the Nitrobacteriaceae, others (*Thiospira*) in the Spirilleae of the family Pseudomonadaceae, and the larger forms in the Beggiatoaceae. Some of the latter organisms are more closely related to the algae than to the bacteria and are considered as colorless algae by many workers. The majority of the physiological studies on the sulfur-oxidizing bacteria have been conducted with species of Nitrobacteriaceae. The five species recognized in the 1948 Bergey Manual can be characterized as follows:

Thiobacillus thioparus. Optimum pH for growth near 7.0
Thiobacillus thiooxidans. Optimum pH for growth near 3.0, some strains active below pH 0
Thiobacillus novellus and *T. coproliticus.* Facultative autotrophs
Thiobacillus denitrificans. Can grow either aerobically or anaerobically, under the latter condition using nitrate as the oxidant

All are small, gram negative, asporogenous rods generally motile by means of a polar flagellum. Morphologically, they closely resemble the pseudomonads.

The thiobacilli, like the nitrifying bacteria, have not been cultivated on an organic source of carbon, although certain observations suggest that various organic compounds may be stimulatory to growth and be taken up to a limited extent by the cells. Mutants of *T. thiooxidans* have been isolated which do require growth factors in an otherwise inorganic medium. The thiobacilli grow somewhat more readily than do the nitrifying bacteria. Carbon dioxide, ammonia, phosphate, potassium, and magnesium, together with the trace elements generally found in tap water, suffice to support growth in the presence of an oxidizable substrate, either hydrogen sulfide or sulfur under natural conditions or on thiosulfate which is frequently employed with laboratory cultures. *T. denitrificans*, although it can use nitrate as the oxidizing agent under anaerobic conditions, requires ammonia as a nitrogen source for growth. The cytochrome system appears to be involved in the terminal respiration of these autotrophs.

One interesting problem is the mechanism by which sulfur, which is highly insoluble in water, gains entrance into the cell. Sulfur is soluble in fats and oils. Vogler and Umbreit (Umbreit, 1947) reported sulfur is transported through fat globules located at the ends of cells of *T. thiooxidans*, the cells aligning themselves around sulfur particles with the droplet in contact with the sulfur particle. Knaysi (1943) was unable to confirm this report, reporting instead the presence of a marked slime layer and intact cell wall around each cell. A large vacuole could be observed within the cell, but it was intraprotoplasmic in location and hence could not come into contact with extracellular sulfur. The mechanism for uptake of sulfur remains obscure.

Very little is known about the mechanism of oxidation of sulfur although it may occur by way of thiosulfate. Vishniac (1952) has studied the oxidation of thiosulfate by *T. thioparus* and supports the view that it is oxidized through polythionates, a pathway questioned by some of the earlier workers.   Vishniac noted that 60 per cent of the total growth in a thiosulfate medium occurred after disappearance of thiosulfate from the medium.   Tetrathionate could be detected in the medium, and by itself supported good growth of the bacteria.   Trithionate was observed in fluids from tests conducted in Warburg flasks in respiration studies. Synthetic trithionate was oxidized when added to washed-cell suspensions. The chemical events involved in the transformation of thiosulfate by *T. thioparus* are often expressed by the equation (Starkey, 1935)

$$5Na_2S_2O_3 + H_2O + 4O_2 \rightarrow 5Na_2SO_4 + H_2SO_4 + 4S$$

Sulfur is deposited extracellularly during the growth of this organism on thiosulfate, but Vishniac concludes that it is of nonbiological origin, excess thiosulfate in the medium catalyzing the dismutation of tetrathionate to trithionate and pentathionate, the latter decomposing to yield sulfur and tetrathionate.   No sulfur was deposited by washed cells oxidizing thiosulfate in concentrations lower than those commonly employed in growth media.   Vishniac pictured the enzymatic oxidations and the thiosulfate-catalyzed dismutation observed in cultures as follows:

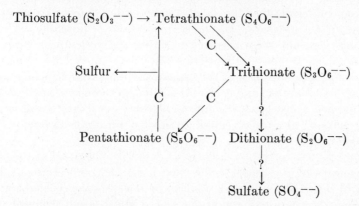

The unlabeled arrows indicate biological oxidations, and those labeled with a C, conversions catalyzed by an excess of thiosulfate.

A considerable number of studies have been carried out with *T. thiooxidans*, an organism commonly found in mine waters and to a great extent responsible for their high acidities.   Vogler, Umbreit, and LePage (Umbreit, 1947) demonstrated the presence of various common enzymes and coenzymes in this organism, intermediates of heterotrophic metabolism, and a storage polysaccharide which could be oxidized in the absence of an oxidizable sulfur substrate.   These observations suggested a close relationship between the endogenous metabolism of this species and the metabolism of heterotrophic ones.   They further claimed to have demonstrated a separation in time between the oxidation of sulfur and the assimilation of carbon dioxide.   Cells oxidizing sulfur in the absence of carbon dioxide were reported to be capable of assimilating it after removal of the sulfur and subsequent introduction of carbon dioxide, even under anaerobic conditions.   They believed this was accomplished through the agency of energy stored in high-energy phosphate bonds.   The oxidation of sulfur in the absence of carbon dioxide was reported to be accompanied by a decrease in inorganic phosphate; subsequent exposure of the cells in the absence of sulfur to carbon dioxide resulted in liberation of the phosphate and uptake of carbon dioxide.   An adenosine-3'-triphosphate, rather than the ordinary adenosine-5'-triphosphate, was also reported to be present in considerable amounts in the cells.   This latter report could not be confirmed by Barker and Kornberg (1954).

The concept that high-energy phosphate bonds are the energy-coupling agents between sulfur oxidation and carbon dioxide assimilation and that energy could be stored in such bonds for fixation of carbon dioxide under conditions precluding sulfur oxidation and concomitant phosphorylation has been questioned by the Baalsruds (see the Baalsruds in Fry and Peel, 1954) and by Newburgh (1954).   The Baalsruds, using manometric techniques and thiosulfate as the substrate, could not detect carbon dioxide fixation in the absence of thiosulfate oxidation.   Phosphate exchanges were observed, but these occurred in either the presence or absence of carbon dioxide.   Newburgh, using $C^{14}O_2$ as a tracer, did observe an uptake of carbon dioxide, but the uptake was only slightly higher in cells previously kept under aerobic conditions than in those kept anaerobically.   Exchange reactions could not entirely be ruled out.   No release of phosphate, using P^{32} as a tracer, could be detected during the delayed fixation of carbon dioxide.

Umbreit (1954) presented additional evidence in support of the earlier conclusions, isotopic tracer studies indicating that at least some of the energy of separate sulfur oxidation can be stored in the cells and used to fix carbon dioxide under conditions where sulfur is not oxidized.   The amounts of carbon dioxide fixed were lower than originally reported, "energy storage" decaying with time and apparently varying with the condition of the cells.   Vishniac and Ochoa (1952) have suggested that the oxidation of sulfur may be coupled with the reduction of electron carriers (TPN), which in turn could reduce carbon dioxide fixed within the cells.   Oxidation of electron carriers could also lead to the formation of high-energy phosphate compounds, and subsequent utilization of these compounds could result in the liberation of phosphate.   The actual mechanism of fixation of carbon dioxide and its subsequent reduction by autotrophic organisms remains obscure, and more work will be required before a picture satisfactory to all is established.

Desulfovibrio desulfuricans (*Sporovibrio desulfuricans*) catalyzes the reverse reaction, the reduction of sulfates under anaerobic conditions. This bacterium is primarily heterotrophic in character, but it can grow autotrophically if provided with hydrogen, sulfate, and carbon dioxide. In the presence of hydrogen, autotrophic reduction of sulfate occurs along with heterotrophic reduction. Biological corrosion of iron pipes in the soil is believed to be due to the activity of this organism, its hydrogenase system utilizing hydrogen produced when iron is polarized under anaerobic conditions. The reactions involved in corrosion have been represented (Starkey and Wight, 1945) as

$$\left.\begin{array}{l} 8H_2O \rightarrow 8H^+ + 8OH^- \\ 4Fe + 8H^+ \rightarrow 4Fe^{++} + 8H \end{array}\right\} \text{Anodic solution of iron}$$

$$H_2SO_4 + 8H \rightarrow H_2S + 4H_2O \text{ Depolarization}$$

$$\left.\begin{array}{l} Fe^{++} + H_2S \rightarrow FeS + 2H^+ \\ 3Fe^{++} + 6OH^- \rightarrow 3Fe(OH)_2 \end{array}\right\} \text{Corrosion}$$

or, in a summarized form, as

$$4Fe + H_2SO_4 + 2H_2O \rightarrow 3Fe(OH)_2 + FeS$$

The third reaction is induced by *D. desulfuricans*, which removes the cathodic hydrogen by oxidizing it with sulfate, the latter being reduced to sulfide. Under aerobic conditions hydrogen is depolarized chemically by oxygen with the formation of ferrous hydroxide alone.

The true sulfur bacteria, those oxidizing reduced sulfur compounds or sulfur itself to sulfate, are of importance in agriculture since sulfuric acid production in the soil aids in the production of soluble phosphates, in improving the condition of alkaline soils, and even in the control of a plant disease. The lowering of the pH of soil following the heavy application of sulfur inhibits *Actinomyces scabies*, the causative agent of potato scab. Corrosion of stone and of concrete may be caused in part or entirely by the action of sulfur bacteria, hydrogen sulfide of either chemical or biological origin being oxidized by these bacteria with the production of sulfuric acid. *T. thiooxidans* has been considered as a potential agent for the commercial production of this acid. The manner in which an apparently normal pH of the protoplasm is maintained in the presence of very high hydrogen-ion concentrations in the exterior milieu is unknown.

An interesting sulfur bacterium, *Thiobacillus ferrooxidans*, has been described by Temple and Colmer (1951). This bacterium, which grows autotrophically on thiosulfate but not on sulfur, can also grow autotrophically upon ferrous iron under acidic conditions which exclude iron oxidation by atmospheric oxygen directly. Temple and Colmer reported that iron oxidation and cell growth are mutually interdependent in the absence of oxidizable sulfur compounds and that iron oxidation results in a measurable, although small, increase in carbon.

The Iron Bacteria. Many bacteria oxidizing ferrous and manganous compounds have been described; most deposit the iron or manganese oxides (or hydroxides) around themselves in the form of a sheath which may be almost entirely inorganic in character in some species or consists of ferric compounds deposited in or upon an organic matrix around others. There is very little evidence that these organisms can utilize the energy of oxidation of iron or manganese compounds alone for growth, with the exception of *T. ferrooxidans* mentioned above and possibly species of *Gallionella*. This genus is characterized by the secretion of ferric hydroxide in the form of a stalk at right angles to the long axis of the cell; hence it is classified in the Caulobacteriineae, or stalked bacteria. If these bacteria are unable to lead a complete autotrophic existence, they can grow in the presence of extremely low amounts of organic matter and do deposit relatively large amounts of iron. Some of the problems concerning the iron bacteria have been discussed by Pringsheim (1949).

The Hydrogen Bacteria. The hydrogen-oxidizing bacteria are facultative autotrophs that are widely distributed in nature. They frequently lose their ability to grow autotrophically when passed a number of times on heterotrophic media, apparently by mutation and selection. *Micrococcus denitrificans*, however, retained the ability to grow at the expense of hydrogen after over forty years' cultivation on organic media. Many of the hydrogen bacteria are closely related to the pseudomonads; others are spore-forming rods. Many heterotrophic species are able to oxidize hydrogen but cannot grow with hydrogen as the only oxidizable substrate. The hydrogen bacteria can be classified for discussion here according to the oxidizing agent they employ, some using oxygen as the hydrogen acceptor, others reducing carbon dioxide, carbon monoxide, sulfate, or nitrate.

Kaserer in 1906 isolated from soil an organism now termed *Hydrogenomonas pantotropha* which could grow either heterotrophically or autotrophically, autotrophic growth involving the oxidation of hydrogen, or

$$H_2 + 0.5O_2 \rightarrow H_2O \qquad \Delta F = -56,000 \text{ cal.}$$

Other hydrogen-oxidizing bacteria (Knallgasbakterien) were observed, and it was established that the amounts of hydrogen consumed during growth were somewhat greater than predicted by the above equation, the excess being used for the reduction of carbon dioxide to cellular material. It has been established that these bacteria do not reduce carbon dioxide in the absence of concomitant oxidation of hydrogen, a behavior which differentiates the Knallgasbakterien from similar species capable of growth with carbon dioxide as the oxidant of hydrogen.

Washed suspensions of hydrogen bacteria grown heterotrophically often are unable to oxidize hydrogen readily or at all unless cultivated under conditions favorable to the production of hydrogenase. Some question still exists as to the constitutive or adaptive nature of this enzyme in certain species. Organic substrates, on the other hand, may be oxidized by autotrophically grown cells without any period of adaptation. In some species hydrogen and an organic substrate such as lactic acid may be oxidized at the same time by autotrophically grown cells (Kluyver and Manten, 1942), the observed rate of oxygen consumption with both substrates present approximating the sum of the rates with each substrate alone. This observation would suggest that the oxygen activating system(s) have a capacity greater than that utilized with either substrate alone. It is not known if the energy made available by the combined oxidations is utilized in the same manner as would occur with the cells using hydrogen or organic substrate separately.

Hydrogenomonas facilis has been studied rather extensively in recent years, Schatz (1952) reporting the following reactions as being elicited by washed cells:

$$4H_2 + 2O_2 \rightarrow 4H_2O$$
$$\underline{2H_2 + CO_2 \rightarrow H_2O + (CH_2O)}$$
$$6H_2 + 2O_2 + CO_2 \rightarrow 5H_2O + (CH_2O)$$

Marino and Clifton (1955) obtained similar results, noting a slightly higher assimilation of carbon dioxide per mole of hydrogen utilized in actively proliferating cultures. Autotrophically grown cells were found in general to assimilate less carbon from organic substrates than did heterotrophically grown ones and to be more limited in their range of substrates utilized without adaptive enzyme formation. It is of interest that autotrophically grown cells oxidized acetic and lactic acids readily, while they appeared unable to oxidize glucose or pyruvic acid immediately. Schatz and Bovell (1952) found that *H. facilis* can oxidize hydrogen anaerobically with either methylene blue or nitrate, the latter being reduced only as far as nitrite. No growth occurred with nitrate as the oxidant, the accumulation of nitrite possibly being inhibitory. Schatz (1952), however, was unable to demonstrate any fixation of carbon dioxide during the oxidation of hydrogen by nitrate, even before nitrite accumulated to any extent.

Kistner in 1953 described a carbon monoxide–oxidizing bacterium (*Hydrogenomonas carboxydovorans*) which he reported (1954) capable of growth at the expense of either carbon monoxide or hydrogen oxidation.

Carbon dioxide is of particular interest as the oxidant of hydrogen in some species since it acts in them both as a hydrogen acceptor and as the bulk source of carbon. *Clostridium aceticum* (Wieringa, 1940) reduces carbon dioxide with the production of acetic acid according to the equation

$$4H_2 + 2CO_2 \rightarrow CH_3COOH + 2H_2O$$

Methanobacterium formicicum, M. omelianskii, and *Methanosarcina barkerii* oxidize hydrogen with the simultaneous reduction of carbon dioxide to methane, or

$$4H_2 + CO_2 \rightarrow CH_4 + 2H_2O$$

The first and third of the species of methane bacteria named above can use carbon monoxide in place of hydrogen (Kluyver and Schnellen, 1947), apparently by means of reactions which can be summarized as

$$CO + H_2O \rightarrow H_2 + CO_2$$
$$CO_2 + 4H_2 \rightarrow CH_4 + 2H_2O$$

The methane bacteria, which are strict anaerobes, also reduce carbon dioxide to methane, employing organic substrates as the hydrogen donor as indicated by the results of tracer studies (Stadtman and Barker, 1949), the carbon dioxide requirement appearing to be strictly specific for growth. The autotrophic status of the opposite type of bacteria, ones such as *Methanomonas methanica* that are capable of growth at the expense of methane oxidation, is uncertain.   It is possible that these bacteria obtain all their carbon from carbon dioxide, as is also possible for organisms such as *Vibrio oxaliticus* (Bhat and Barker, 1948) that can grow with oxalate as the sole carbon and energy source (the removal of two electrons from oxalate results in its conversion to carbon dioxide).

The oxidation of hydrogen with sulfate acting as the oxidizing agent was discussed under the sulfur bacteria (*Desulfovibrio desulfuricans*) and will not be considered here.

Since carbon dioxide and sulfate can serve some species as the oxidizing agent for hydrogen and since nitrate can be reduced by many species of bacteria, it seemed feasible that bacteria capable of autotrophic growth with nitrate as the oxidizing agent for hydrogen should exist.   Kluyver and Verhoeven (1954) have reported that *Micrococcus denitrificans* can grow in an inorganic medium containing a trace of yeast autolysate, hydrogen being oxidized by oxygen aerobically or by nitrate anaerobically. Both hydrogenase and nitrase were found to be adaptive enzymes in this bacterium.   Autotrophically grown cells oxidized various organic compounds aerobically or anaerobically with nitrate without noticeable adaptation and could oxidize hydrogen and an organic compound simultaneously and independently.   The anaerobic oxidation of glucose can be expressed by the equation

$$5C_6H_{12}O_6 + 24KNO_3 \rightarrow 30CO_2 + 12N_2 + 24KOH + 18H_2O$$

Cells capable of reducing nitrates were also adapted to the reduction of nitrite or nitrous oxide. The various oxidations of hydrogen can be represented as follows:

$$2H_2 + O_2 \rightarrow 2H_2O$$
$$5H_2 + 2KNO_3 \rightarrow N_2 + 4H_2O + 2KOH$$
$$3H_2 + 2KNO_2 \rightarrow N_2 + 2H_2O + 2KOH$$
$$H_2 + N_2O \rightarrow N_2 + H_2O$$

Nitrite was found to be much less suitable as a hydrogen acceptor than either nitrate or nitrous oxide, the conclusion being that nitrite in appreciable concentrations is inhibitory to hydrogenase. Kluyver and Verhoeven further concluded that their results present a clear demonstration of the homology of respiration and denitrification.

Photosynthetic Bacteria. The existence of photosynthetic bacteria was suspected since 1883 when Engelman reported that certain red-colored or "purple" bacteria tended to collect in particular regions of the spectrum (phototaxis) and that possibly they evolved oxygen when illuminated, behaviors similar to those exhibited by certain algae with which he was familiar. Somewhat later Winogradsky, in a cursory study of these organisms, found that hydrogen sulfide was utilized during their growth with the deposition of droplets of sulfur in the cells and that this sulfur was oxidized to sulfate in the absence of sulfide. Hence he concluded that these colored bacteria were similar in their metabolism to the colorless sulfur bacteria he had been studying. Molisch in 1907 reported the isolation and cultivation of purple, sulfur-free bacteria that grew most readily in the light but required organic compounds for growth. He concluded that light was involved in the activities of these organisms, but was not certain of its true function. Some information concerning these various purple bacteria accumulated during the next two decades, but a rational explanation of the role of light and of the metabolism of these organisms was not established until the studies of van Niel around 1930 (van Niel, 1941, 1952, 1954).

Van Niel demonstrated that both light and reduced compounds of sulfur are required for the growth of the purple and green sulfur bacteria and that they can use carbon dioxide as the only source of carbon. He pointed out that autotrophic sulfur bacteria use up to forty or more moles of sulfide per mole of carbon dioxide assimilated, at the same time consuming about twice as many moles of oxygen as of sulfide. The purple or green sulfur bacteria, however, grew anaerobically exposed to light, and the amounts of sulfide consumed were found to bear simple stoichiometric relationships with the amounts of carbon dioxide assimilated, relationships which can be expressed by the equations

$$2CO_2 + H_2S + 2H_2O + light \xrightarrow[\text{S-bact.}]{\text{purple}} 2(CH_2O) + H_2SO_4$$

$$CO_2 + 2H_2S + light \xrightarrow[\text{S-bact.}]{\text{green}} CH_2O + 2S + H_2O$$

Since the reactions expressed above occurred only in the light and energetically are dependent upon an external source of energy, van Niel concluded that these organisms must be photosynthetic species although he could observe no evolution of oxygen. This led him to picture photosynthesis as a more general type of reaction than is expressed by the classical equation of photosynthesis and one that can be better represented by the general equation

$$CO_2 + 2DH_2 + light \rightarrow (CH_2O) + H_2O + D$$

where DH_2 is a reducing agent (H donor) which is water in the case of the green plant and sulfide in the purple or green sulfur bacteria. The respective reactions yield waste products dependent upon the nature of the reductant and of the organism, D being oxygen in the green plant, sulfate with the purple bacteria, and sulfur for the green bacteria. Shortly thereafter it was shown that the purple sulfur-free bacteria carry out a similar type of carbon dioxide reduction anaerobically in the light, simple organic compounds acting as the electron donor DH_2, carbon dioxide generally being the ultimate oxidation product D. Later it was shown that water is the source of the hydrogen utilized in the reduction of fixed carbon dioxide, the ultimate reducing agent, however, for the photosynthetic bacteria being reduced sulfur compounds or organic substrates, as will be considered shortly. Hydrogen gas can also be used as the ultimate reductant by many species.

Three major physiological groups of photosynthetic bacteria are recognized, and they are classified as the families Thiorhodaceae, Athiorhodaceae, and Chlorobacteriaceae in the suborder Rhodobacteriineae of the Eubacteriales. Species in the first two families contain bacteriochlorophyll and generally one or more carotenoids, the combination being responsible for the red, purple, or brown colors exhibited by masses of the cells. The third family possesses only a chlorophyllous pigment different from that of the other two families or of the green plants. The Athiorhodaceae do not utilize reduced compounds of sulfur in the photosynthetic reaction and instead require organic hydrogen donors. Those species of photosynthetic bacteria capable of growth in the presence of air can be cultivated in heterotrophic media aerobically in the dark. Various growth factors are required by the Athiorhodaceae, the same factors being essential for either photosynthetic or heterotrophic growth. The present classification into genera and species in the three families is recognized generally as being of tentative value only, since pure culture studies are not of sufficient extent to provide any satisfactory basis for classification.

Bacterial Photosynthesis. At the time of van Niel's early studies it was generally believed that the oxygen evolved in green-plant synthesis came from carbon dioxide. He pointed out that the oxygen could come from the photolysis of water, evidence for which was provided by others in subsequent studies. Later van Niel in various studies presented evidence that the photosynthetic bacteria could oxidize the ultimate electron donors in the dark, provided an electron acceptor other than carbon dioxide was available. Oxygen, methylene blue, quinone, and other readily reducible substances could function as the acceptor. This suggested that the electron donor reacted in a dark reaction and not in the photochemical one. Evidence also accumulated that the reduction of carbon dioxide, fixed in an organic molecule, also is a dark reaction. This leaves water as the reactant involved in the photochemical reaction in either the green plant or the photosynthetic bacteria. Water could be split photolytically into a reducing component, a hydrogen radical having a strong tendency to give up its electron and hence being a powerful reducing agent, and into an oxidizing component, a hydroxyl radical having a strong tendency to take up an electron. This concept leads to a general view of photosynthesis which can be represented as follows, assuming that an enzyme system E' is reduced and a second system E'' is oxidized by the photolytic decomposition products of water:

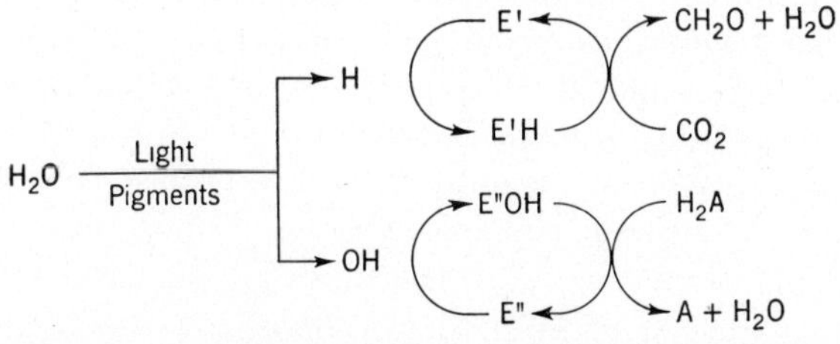

In the green plant the liberation of oxygen can best be considered as the result of the decomposition of a peroxide, possibly an organic one arising from the $E''OH$ complex in some manner. This mechanism for the regeneration of E'' is not available to the photosynthetic bacteria, and instead they reduce the $E''OH$ system with hydrogen and electrons derived from the reductant H_2A, e.g., sulfide, hydrogen, or an organic substrate.

Bacterial chlorophyll is present in small bodies called grana or chromatophores in the photosynthetic bacteria, absorbs light energy directly or through the carotenoid pigments, and becomes "excited." This excitation energy is utilized in the photolytic decomposition of water. It has been determined (Larsen, 1953) that about nine quanta of light energy are absorbed per molecule of carbon dioxide reduced to cellular material, either in the green plant or in the bacteria. The amounts of light energy required by the photosynthetic bacteria appear to be the same regardless of the nature of the reducing agent employed. This suggests that the oxidation of the ultimate reductant H_2A does not contribute energy for the assimilation of carbon dioxide. Since this energy is lost, photosynthesis in the bacteria appears to have a lower thermodynamic efficiency than in the green plants.

Numerous hypotheses have been advanced concerning the mechanisms of the first steps in photosynthesis. A recent one (Duysens, 1955) proposes that chlorophyll, directly or indirectly excited by light, reacts with a pyridine nucleotide PN^+ and an unknown agent ZH to yield reduced nucleotide PNH and Z, the latter being considered as a strong oxidant. Z was considered to react in part as an oxidant for water, in part also for the oxidation of cytochrome f. Duysens further postulated that the reduced coenzyme was utilized primarily for the reduction of fixed carbon dioxide, a smaller portion being used for the reduction of cytochrome f via the appropriate systems and with the formation of ATP. The agents PN^+ and Z could be considered as being related to the systems E' and E'' in the scheme of van Niel.

Lipoic acid has been implicated as a factor in photosynthesis. One hypothesis (Levitt, 1953) considers that energy from light-excited chlorophyll is involved in the transfer of an electron from this molecule (Chl') to the disulfide linkage of lipoic acid, the chlorophyll with a missing electron (Chl*) then reacting to accept an electron from water. This scheme can be represented as follows:

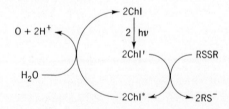

The oxidation of water generates reducing power for the reduction of fixed carbon dioxide. There is considerable question as to a possible role of lipoic acid in photosynthesis. The above hypotheses must be considered as suggestive of the ideas being advanced regarding the mechanism of conversion of light energy to chemical-bond energy. They have not been confirmed and represent ideas for further consideration. Gaffron recently has summarized the more commonly considered concepts regarding photosynthesis in general, while Larsen and Elsden have considered certain aspects of the bacterial photosyntheses (articles in Fry and Peel, 1954).

Pathway of Carbon Assimilation. Before the advent of tracer carbon little was known concerning the first products of photosynthesis, the formula $(CH_2O)_n$ being employed to denote that the analytical data indicated material with the empirical composition of carbohydrate was formed. The use of long-lived, radioactive carbon (C^{14}) as a tracer in pioneer studies by Ruben, Benson, Calvin, and their coworkers at Berkeley and then by the Gaffron-Fager group at Chicago helped break the deadlock.

Calvin and Benson (1949) exposed illuminated algae to radioactive carbon dioxide for short periods of time (5 sec. to 5 min.), killed and extracted the cells immediately with hot ethanol, and separated various components in the extract by paper chromatography. Various areas on the chromatograms exhibited marked radioactivity. Compounds in these areas were identified in part by comparison with the behavior of known substances in similar chromatograms. In a 5-sec. period of photosynthesis most of the label appeared in phosphoglyceric acid. Labeling became noticeable in triose phosphate, phosphates of the higher sugars, malic acid, and amino acids following longer periods of photosynthesis.

From the various studies that have been reported it has become evident that during photosynthetic assimilation of carbon dioxide the tracer carbon enters the metabolic machinery of the cell primarily in the form of the carboxyl group of phosphoglyceric acid. This suggests that a 2-carbon compound might act as the carbon dioxide acceptor. The α- and β-carbon atoms of phosphoglyceric acid also become radioactive during the course of photosynthesis, but much less rapidly than does the carboxyl carbon. This suggests a regeneration of the acceptor compound from assimilated carbon and, therefore, a cyclic mechanism. It is possible that the 2-carbon acceptor does not exist as such but only as a 2-carbon fragment of a larger molecule. Identification of pentose and heptulose phosphates in extracts suggested the participation of these compounds, possibly in some manner similar to their participation in the pentose cycle considered in Chap. 10. Various schemes have been advanced (Brown and Frenkel, 1953) concerning the pathway of assimilation of fixed carbon dioxide, one of the most recent being that of Bassham et al. (1954) of the Berkeley group. This scheme, outlined in Fig. 11-1, suggests that carbon dioxide is fixed by ribulose diphosphate with the formation of a C_6 β-keto acid which is split immediately to form two molecules of phosphoglyceric acid. Reduction of the acid to triose phosphates follows, and the triose molecules can be utilized in a number of reactions suggested in the scheme.

In short-term experiments labeling is most pronounced in the 3 and 4 positions in hexose molecules, suggesting their formation from labeled triose. Labeled carbon soon appears in malic acid, alanine, glutamic acid, and other compounds in secondary reactions. Some compounds may enter the Krebs cycle. Carbon dioxide fixation in the dark by photosynthetic organisms appears to occur primarily through this cycle, fixation of carbon dioxide occurring with the participation of pyruvic acid to form malic acid. Light appears to be inhibitory to this dark-fixation

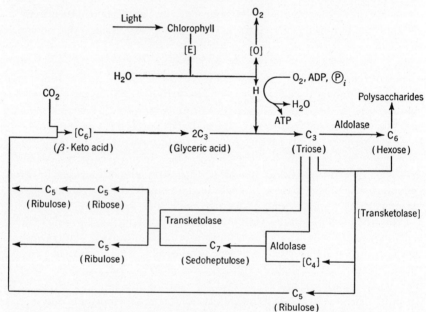

FIG. 11-1. The path of carbon assimilation in photosynthesis, together with cyclic regeneration of the carbon dioxide acceptor. (*After Bassham et al.*, 1954.)

mechanism in some unknown manner. Some doubt exists regarding certain of the steps depicted in Fig. 11-1, but the proposed scheme does summarize fairly well various ideas concerning the basic steps of photosynthetic assimilation of carbon dioxide.

The pathway of carbon dioxide assimilation in the photosynthetic bacteria has not been studied to any extent with most species. Stoppani, Fuller, and Calvin (1954) have reported results of their studies with the nonsulfur purple bacterium *Rhodopseudomonas capsulatus* which photoreduces carbon dioxide with organic hydrogen donors or with hydrogen. The same substances can be employed by this bacterium for the assimilation of carbon dioxide in the dark under aerobic conditions. The percentage distribution of labeled carbon in various compounds following both light- and dark-fixation periods, with hydrogen gas providing the final reducing power, is indicated in Table 11-1. These results are quite similar to those noted with algae and with higher plants. The above workers concluded that *R. capsulatus* assimilates carbon dioxide in the light mainly through the phosphoglyceric acid cycle and only slowly through the malic acid–Krebs cycle pathway, the reverse behavior being noted for dark fixation with hydrogen oxidation as the energy source.

TABLE 11-1. DISTRIBUTION OF RADIOACTIVITY AFTER $C^{14}O_2$ FIXATION BY THE PHOTOSYNTHETIC BACTERIUM *Rhodopseudomonas capsulatus**

Compound	Distribution of activity in methanol-water-soluble fraction, %	
	2 min. light fixation	10 min. dark fixation
Sugar phosphates and allied compounds:		
Hexose and pentose monophosphates (glucose, fructose, ribose, and ribulose)................	43.2	19.6
Pentose diphosphates (ribose and ribulose).....................	1.3	0.0
Phosphoglyceric acid.............	4.6	8.4
Phosphoenolpyruvic acid.........	0.7	0.8
Triose phosphate...............	1.9	4.0
Phosphoglycolic acid.............	0.6	0.0
Di- and tricarboxylic acids:		
Citric.........................	0.6	2.1
α-Ketoglutaric.................	0.6	0.8
Malic.........................	5.5	1.8
Amino acids:		
Glutamic......................	20.6	34.5
Glutamine.....................	0.9	3.2
Aspartic......................	6.7	5.6
Alanine.......................	4.5	2.3
Glycine.......................	4.8	8.6
Threonine.....	0.4	2.6
Methionine sulfoxide............	0.8	2.6

* From Stoppani, Fuller, and Calvin (1954), courtesy of M. Calvin.

The basic pathway of assimilation appears to be the same in photosynthetic bacteria and in higher photosynthetic forms of life. If we compare photoreduction of carbon dioxide in green plants or bacteria and chemoreduction in general, we note a very marked similarity. This can be illustrated by the over-all equations

$$CO_2 + 4H{-}OH \xrightarrow{\text{light}} (CH_2O) + 3H_2O + O_2$$
$$CO_2 + 4H{-}OH + 2DH_2 \xrightarrow{\text{light}} (CH_2O) + 5H_2O + 2D$$
$$CO_2 + 4H_2D + O_2 \rightarrow (CH_2O) + 3H_2O + 4D$$

REFERENCES

Barker, H. A., and A. Kornberg: The structure of the adenosine triphosphate of *Thiobacillus thiooxidans, J. Bacteriol.*, **68**, 655–661 (1954).

Bassham, J. A., A. A. Benson, L. D. Kay, A. Z. Harris, A. T. Wilson, and M. Calvin: The path of carbon in photosynthesis. XXI. The cyclic regeneration of carbon dioxide acceptor, *J. Am. Chem. Soc.*, **76**, 1760–1770 (1954).

Bhat, J. V., and H. A. Barker: Studies on a new oxalate-decomposing bacterium, *Vibrio oxaliticus, J. Bacteriol.*, **55**, 356–368 (1948).

Brown, A. H., and A. W. Frenkel: Photosynthesis, *Ann. Rev. Plant Physiol.*, **4**, 23–58 (1953).

Calvin, M., and A. A. Benson: The path of carbon in photosynthesis. IV. The identity and sequence of the intermediates in sucrose synthesis, *Science*, **109**, 140–142 (1949).

Duysens, L. N. M.: Role of cytochrome and pyridine nucleotide in algal photosynthesis, *Science*, **121**, 210–211 (1955).

Foster, J. W.: Autotrophic assimilation of carbon dioxide, in C. H. Werkman and P. W. Wilson (eds.), "Bacterial Physiology," Academic Press, Inc., New York, 1951.

Fry, B. A., and J. L. Peel (eds.): "Autotrophic Microorganisms," Cambridge University Press, London, 1954.

Kistner, A.: Conditions determining the oxidation of carbon monoxide and of hydrogen by *Hydrogenomonas carboxydovorans, Koninkl. Ned. Akad. Wetenschap., Proc.* (C), **57**, 186–195 (1954).

Kluyver, A. J., and A. Manten: Some observations on the metabolism of bacteria oxidizing molecular hydrogen, *Antonie van Leeuwenhoek*, **8**, 71–85 (1942).

——— and C. G. T. P. Schnellen: On the fermentation of carbon monoxide by pure cultures of methane bacteria, *Arch. Biochem.*, **14**, 57–70 (1947).

——— and W. Verhoeven: Studies on true nitrate reduction. IV. On adaptation in *Micrococcus denitrificans, Antonie van Leeuwenhoek*, **20**, 337–358 (1954).

Knaysi, G.: A cytological and microchemical study of *Thiobacillus thiooxidans, J. Bacteriol.*, **46**, 451–461 (1943).

Larsen, H.: On the microbiology and biochemistry of the photosynthetic green sulfur bacteria, *Kgl. Norske Videnskab. Selskabs, Skrifter*, no. 1 (1953).

Levitt, L. S.: Photosynthesis as a photoelectric phenomenon, *Science*, **118**, 696–697 (1953).

Marino, R. J., and C. E. Clifton: Oxidative assimilation in suspensions and cultures of *Hydrogenomonas facilis, J. Bacteriol.*, **69**, 188–192 (1955).

Newburgh, R. W.: Phosphorylation and chemosynthesis by *Thiobacillus thiooxidans, J. Bacteriol.*, **68**, 93–97 (1954).

Pringsheim, E. G.: Iron bacteria, *Biol. Rev. Camb. Phil. Soc.*, **24**, 200–245 (1949).

Quastel, J. H., and P. G. Scholefield: Biochemistry of nitrification in soils, *Bacteriol. Rev.*, **15**, 1–53 (1951).

Schatz, A.: Uptake of carbon dioxide, hydrogen, and oxygen by *Hydrogenomonas facilis, J. Gen. Microbiol.*, **6**, 329–335 (1952).

——— and C. Bovell: Growth and hydrogenase activity of a new bacterium, *Hydrogenomonas facilis, J. Bacteriol.*, **63**, 87–98 (1952).

Stadtman, T. C., and H. A. Barker: Tracer experiments on the mechanism of methane fermentation, *Arch. Biochem.*, **21**, 256–261 (1949).

Starkey, R. L.: Products of the oxidation of thiosulfate by bacteria in mineral media, *J. Gen. Physiol.*, **18**, 325–349 (1935).

—— and K. M. Wight: "Anaerobic Corrosion of Iron in Soil," American Gas Association, New York, 1945.

Stoppani, A. O. M., R. C. Fuller, and M. Calvin: Carbon dioxide fixation by *Rhodopseudomonas capsulatus*, *Univ. Calif. Radiation Lab. Paper* 2745 (1954).

Temple, K. L., and A. R. Colmer: The autotrophic oxidation of iron by a new bacterium, *Thiobacillus ferroxidans*, *J. Bacteriol.*, **62**, 605–611 (1951).

Umbreit, W. W.: Problems of autotrophy, *Bacteriol. Rev.*, **11**, 157–166 (1947).

——: Phosphorylation and carbon dioxide fixation in the autotrophic bacterium, *Thiobacillus thiooxidans*, *J. Bacteriol.*, **67**, 387–393 (1954).

van Niel, C. B.: The bacterial photosyntheses and their importance for the general problem of photosynthesis, *Advances in Enzymol.*, **1**, 263–328 (1941).

——: Bacterial photosyntheses, in J. B. Sumner and K. Myrbäck (eds.), "The Enzymes," vol. 2, pt. 2, Academic Press, Inc., New York, 1952.

——: The chemoautotrophic and photosynthetic bacteria, *Ann. Rev. Microbiol.*, **8**, 105–132 (1954).

Vishniac, W.: The metabolism of *Thiobacillus thioparus*. I. The oxidation of thiosulfate, *J. Bacteriol.*, **64**, 363–373 (1952).

—— and S. Ochoa: Reduction of pyridine nucleotides in photosynthesis, in W. D. McElroy and B. Glass (eds.), "Phosphorus Metabolism," vol. 2, Johns Hopkins Press, Baltimore, 1952.

Wieringa, K. T.: The formation of acetic acid from carbon dioxide and hydrogen by anaerobic spore-forming bacteria, *Antonie van Leeuwenhoek*, **6**, 251–262 (1940).

CHAPTER 12

NUTRITION OF BACTERIA

When an oxidizable substrate is added to a washed suspension of bacteria a relatively definite proportion of the compound is oxidized aerobically or anaerobically, while the remainder is assimilated as cellular material. This leads to an increase in the organic content of the cell, i.e., to growth and ultimately to multiplication if all essential raw materials are available. We have considered metabolism as the sum of all the chemical activities occurring in the bacterial cell. It is difficult to draw a line between bacterial nutrition, or the formation of cellular substance, and bacterial metabolism, particularly since nutrition is commonly defined as "the sum of the processes by which an animal or plant absorbs, or takes in and utilizes, food substances." The energy-providing or catabolic activities of the bacterial cell are to a considerable extent directly involved in the utilization of nutrients, and it is realized today that there is no sharp line of demarcation between catabolic and anabolic activities. It might be more desirable to speak of the nutritional requirements of bacteria, i.e., their requirements for external sources of raw materials (nutrients), and not attempt to establish an arbitrary boundary between the nutrition and the metabolism of bacteria.

We have seen that there is a wide variety of physiological types among the bacteria as regards sources both of energy and of building material, particularly sources of carbon and of nitrogen. A culture medium for a particular bacterium must be designed to meet its nutritional requirements. These nutritional requirements may be divided into six main groups:

1. Water
2. Regulatory substances
3. The essential ions
4. Sources of energy
5. Sources of bulk-building material
6. Essential nutrilites, the "growth factors" or vitamins

Such a classification is an arbitrary one and is set up for purposes of discussion. It must be borne in mind that sharp distinctions between the groups do not exist and that one substance may exert two or more of the functions postulated in this classification.

Water. Water is the major component of culture media and of cells, making up 75 to 90 per cent of the total weight of the cell. It takes part, or is produced, in many of the chemical reactions essential to the synthesis of cellular material and to the maintenance of life. Water also serves as a source of some of the oxygen found in the organic matter of the cell, the oxygen consumed in respiration uniting with hydrogen rather than with carbon. Water is spoken of as the most universal solvent and serves as a vehicle for the transport of foodstuff into, and of waste materials out of, the cell. In addition, it has a high specific heat, thus tending to absorb the heat liberated during metabolism without too great an increase in temperature, and at the same time is a good conductor of heat, thus facilitating its dissipation. The growth of bacteria is markedly inhibited as the water content of their environment is decreased, the bacteria in general tending to be aquatic organisms as contrasted with the more terrestrial mode of life exhibited by many of the higher fungi.

Regulatory Substances. Substances exerting regulatory activities may serve a variety of purposes, their more important functions being the control of (1) osmotic pressure, (2) hydrogen-ion concentration, (3) permeability, and (4) oxidation-reduction potential of the medium.

In general the utilization of a foodstuff by bacteria is dependent upon possession of the requisite enzymes and the concentration of the foodstuff. The latter may vary from a lower limit below which the enzymes are no longer saturated and concentration becomes the limiting factor for growth to an upper limit above which osmotic-pressure effects are inhibitory. Actually, the osmotic pressure of a medium decreases during aerobic growth, primarily owing to utilization of the foodstuff, but salts are usually present in culture media in sufficient concentrations to prevent the development of such low osmotic pressures that swelling of the cells would occur. Fortunately most bacteria are not markedly inhibited by osmotic-pressure changes over a relatively wide range. It is necessary, however, that the concentration of organic foodstuffs and of electrolytes be so adjusted that the osmotic pressure is kept within limits conducive to the growth of the cells. Frequently, not only the total concentration of the constituents of a medium but also the relative amounts of the various ions must be taken into account, since ionic ratios can markedly influence permeability of the cell and other activities as well.

The studies of Ringer around 1880 indicated the importance of various ions in the maintenance of normal activity of perfused heart muscle and led to the development of Ringer's and other physiologically balanced isotonic salt solutions. Flexner, Lipman, and Eisler, in the early part of this century, noted that sodium chloride, even in dilute solution, is relatively toxic to bacteria and that this toxicity can be neutralized by the addition of potassium and calcium ions. Balanced salt solutions were found to be of value in maintaining viability and biochemical activity in suspensions of various bacteria. Many of the earlier studies are complicated, however, by the failure of the workers to control the hydrogen-ion concentration of their solutions.

Eisenberg in 1919 reported that the toxicity of the common cations tended to increase in the order

$$Na \rightarrow K \rightarrow NH_4 \rightarrow Li \rightarrow Mg \rightarrow Ca \rightarrow Mn \rightarrow Fe^{++}$$
$$\rightarrow Zn \rightarrow Fe^{3+} \rightarrow Cu \rightarrow Hg \rightarrow Ag$$

the order being influenced slightly by the nature of the anion and of the bacterial species. The anions were placed in the general order: $SO_4 < Cl < Br < SCN < I$ in respect to their toxicity. These orders closely follow the Hofmeister series so often encountered in colloidal chemistry and physiology. Many salts were found to stimulate bacterial growth when present in low concentrations and to inhibit it in more concentrated solutions. The earlier work is reviewed by Falk (1923).

Pasteur noted in 1879 that the relatively high acidity of must favored alcoholic fermentation in grape juice, while the low acidity of wort made the brewing of beer more susceptible to "disease" (undesirable fermentations). He also pointed out that the acidity of the medium was a determinative factor in the establishment of lactic or alcoholic types of fermentation and of the effective temperature for pasteurization. The importance of controlling the acidity in culture media, in the fermentation industries, in the preservation of food, in disinfection studies, in serological tests, and in general biological work was realized by many early workers. The discussion by Clark and Lubs (1917) of the importance of the actual hydrogen-ion concentration and of methods for adjusting media to definite hydrogen-ion concentrations is an important milestone in the study of bacteria and their activities under controlled conditions.

Winslow and Falk (1923) reported that the toxicity of sodium chloride toward E. coli is manifested in solutions in which the pH was regulated as well as in unregulated solutions, while the toxic effect of calcium chloride (0.145 M) was evident only on the alkaline side of neutrality. They suggested that the toxic effect of calcium was due to an inhibition of a mechanism by which cells tended to maintain the pH on the acid side. Shaughnessy and Winslow (1927) found that E. coli suspended in water was able to change the pH toward an optimum of 6.2 to 6.4 by liberation of carbon dioxide or of ammonia. Certain concentrations of sodium and calcium chlorides promoted the liberation of these substances, while higher concentrations inhibited the liberation of ammonia and increased diffusion of carbon dioxide from the cells. Sherman and Holm (1922) reported that sodium chloride in 0.2 M solution decreased the sensitivity (minimum time for turbidity to appear in cultures) of $E.\ coli$ to variations in pH of a 1 per cent peptone solution, while sodium citrate (0.2 M) increased the sensitivity. In plain peptone solution little difference in the time required for growth to become evident was noted over a pH range of 6.2 to 7.8; this range was increased to between 5.2 and 8.5 in the presence of sodium chloride and decreased to 6.3 to 7.3 in the presence of citrate. The optimal zones and limiting values of pH for bacterial growth and activities have been investigated by many workers. Summaries of typical studies are presented by Buchanan and Fulmer (1928), Porter (1946), and Rahn (1932).

Hydrogen-ion concentration and the nature and concentrations of other ions influence such a variety of reactions and substances or structures that it generally is impossible to ascertain the exact point of attack. For this reason it usually is necessary to determine directly the influence of these variables on the behavior of a given species under the particular test conditions, the tests being guided in part by information obtained under other conditions. One factor that frequently is involved is permeability of the cell, the state either of the cell membrane or of the solute molecules (or both) being influenced by changes in pH and often by changes in nature and concentrations of other ions as well. The cytoplasmic membrane is credited with being the selectively permeable barrier of the bacterial cell, although the cell wall and the slime layer may also exert an influence on the passage of materials into or out of the cell. Because of lack of information concerning the role played by these structures in controlling the permeability of the cell, some workers speak of an osmotic barrier rather than of a definite membrane or structure.

Fischer in 1897 demonstrated that bacteria are subject to osmotic forces, plasmolysis or shrinkage of cell contents being noted when cells were placed in solutions of high osmotic pressure. Plasmolysis is most evident in gram-negative species, shrinkage of the cytoplasmic membrane away from the cell wall being less evident in gram-positive ones. Plasmolysis may be followed by expansion of the cytoplasm to again fill the cell if the plasmolyzing agent can penetrate, but at a slower rate than water, the osmotic barrier. This illustrates the role of physically functioning salts as defined by Larson (Chap. 4). Plasmoptysis, an increase in volume frequently followed by bursting of the cell, was also noted by Fischer, but is not of common occurrence in bacteria because of structural stability imparted by the cell wall.

Permeability factors play an important role in the activities of bacteria and lead to many problems. For example, we have discussed the citric acid cycle in bacteria; the proof for this in many species was delayed owing to low permeability for various members of this cycle. Demonstration that the intact, living cell does not oxidize or utilize a particular substance in the medium is no proof that the substance is not utilized within the cell if it can gain entrance or is formed therein.

Various factors influencing permeability and theories concerning the mode of action of semipermeable membranes are discussed by Lamanna and Mallette (1953) and Mitchell (in Miles and Pirie, 1949). The former authors illustrated different permeability behaviors with examples of the penetration of the osmotic barrier of bacteria by sodium and potassium ions and by amino acids.

Sodium appears to cross the osmotic barrier of bacteria such as *E. coli* with ease and rapidity from a region of high to one of lower concentration. Penetration of this type, which follows the ordinary laws for passage of a solute through a membrane, is called permeation. As mentioned in Chap. 4, Larson and his coworkers found that both sodium and chloride ions passed freely from the cell into water, very little of these elements being bound in the protoplasm and apparently being involved primarily in the maintenance of osmotic equilibria.

Potassium penetrates the osmotic barrier by permeation, but it can also accumulate within the cell against a concentration gradient. This accumulation is associated with metabolism of the cell and can be inhibited by poisons which interfere with the coupling of oxidation with energy exchange by means of high-energy phosphate bonds. Potassium appears to be associated with cellular material (metabolites such as phosphate esters) but can be replaced to a considerable extent by hydrogen ions as the pH is decreased.

The studies of Gale and his coworkers (Gale, 1948) have indicated that permeability toward amino acids, particularly in the case of gram-positive bacteria, is a more complex phenomenon. They observed that various gram-positive bacteria (and yeast) have the ability to accumulate certain amino acids within the cell, gram-negative species lacking this ability. Lysine diffuses freely into cells of *Streptococcus faecalis* deficient in this amino acid, but does not pass out of these cells when they are placed in water unless an energy source such as glucose is also present. Since the highest rate of penetration into the cell was observed at pH 9.5, it appeared that lysine passes the osmotic barrier most readily at its isoelectric point (pH 9.47), and the possibility exists that lysine accumulates in its cationic form within the cell. Hence lysine would not diffuse readily from the cell if present primarily only in this ionic form.

Glutamic acid, on the other hand, did not diffuse into *S. faecalis* or *Micrococcus pyogenes* var. *aureus* (*Staphylococcus aureus*) but entered the cell only as the result of an active process, i.e., the oxidation of glucose, or in the presence of large amounts of adenosine triphosphate (30 to 50 molecules of ATP required per molecule of glutamic acid taken up). The equilibrium (steady-state) concentration of glutamic acid frequently was 50 to 60 times as high per unit volume of the cell as of the external environment, a ratio of internal to external concentration as high as 400 being obtained in at least one instance. The ratio for lysine was generally lower, but often as high as 15 to 20. In the case of *S. faecalis* no leakage of internal glutamic acid occurred in the absence of glucose, while there was leakage from the staphylococci, the addition of glucose checking rather than enhancing this leakage. These differences serve to point out the complexities of membrane permeability. It is possible that the passage of amino acids across the osmotic barrier of gram-negative species is similar to that observed with gram-positive ones, but this has not been established since amino acids do not accumulate as such within the gram-negative cells. The amino acids taken up by the cells are utilized in various syntheses to be considered later.

Detergents, or substances such as tyrocidine or phenol which exert similar activity, were found to modify permeability relationships to such an extent that amino acids and other cell constituents passed out of the cells. Gale suggested that the action of these agents was to strip material off the cell wall, this material consisting largely of lipoidal matter. One interesting aspect of these studies was that within certain limits a linear relationship was observed between the number of cells lysed in a suspension and the quantity of tyrocidine present. This all-or-none behavior is also observed in the denaturation of proteins by detergents. It is explained on the basis that once one or more molecules are taken up by the cell (or the protein molecule), that cell can combine more readily with more molecules of the detergent. In other words, the probability that a molecule of detergent will be taken up is much greater for those cells that have already combined with some molecules than for the cell that has not reacted. Gale calculated that about 10^8 molecules of tyrocidine are required to lyse (or kill) one *S. faecalis* cell.

There is little that can be done to control the permeability of bacteria other than to provide in culture media ratios and concentrations of salts found by test to be favorable for growth and also to regulate pH at a suitable level. Maintenance of pH within a favorable range may be accomplished with the aid of buffers or with relatively insoluble substances such as calcium carbonate which will react with and neutralize acidic products of metabolism.

The low permeability of the mycobacteria to dyes suggests a marked difference between the osmotic barrier of these cells and that of most bacteria. This may be responsible for the low rate of growth and metabolism associated with these organisms and could serve to reduce the amount of energy required to maintain the unstable state represented by a cell.

Fortunately the oxidation-reduction potential, actually the potential noted at a noble-metal electrode dipping into the culture media, has little influence on growth of most species. Growth of anaerobes, however, may require the establishment of reducing conditions. Germination of clostridia spores (Chap. 6) will not occur unless the potential is below a limit characteristic of the particular species.

The Essential Ions. Ions, in addition to their regulatory activities, are required as a source of the various inorganic elements found in the chemical components of the bacterial cell. Nitrogen and phosphorus, with carbon, oxygen, and hydrogen, are the major constituents, but the lesser quantities of other elements found in the cell do not reflect their true value. Potassium, calcium, magnesium, sodium, sulfur, and chlorine are present in variable amounts although their content in the fixed salts is relatively constant. Smaller and often only trace amounts of elements such as iron, manganese, cobalt, copper, boron, zinc, molybdenum, and aluminum are also present. Fortunately, the requirements for these, or for still other elements, are so small that generally they are present as impurities in sufficient amounts to meet the requirements of the cell. The amounts essential for growth may be too small to be detected by ordinary methods of analysis.

The trace-element nutrition of the higher fungi has been studied more extensively (Foster, 1949; Knight, 1951; Lilly and Barnett, 1951) than that of the bacteria. It was recognized quite early that certain elements were required in minute amounts for growth, and these were supplied at times from such diverse sources as cigar ashes and cellular extracts. The role of most of the essential elements is primarily functional rather than structural, many of the trace elements entering into the structure and function of enzymes or coenzymes. Some elements are absolutely essential, while the functions of others may be performed by closely related elements, e.g., manganese replacing magnesium or vanadium substituting for molybdenum.

A rather detailed study (Young et al., 1944) of the inorganic requirements for growth of *E. coli* in a basal medium containing NaCl, $(NH_4)_2SO_4$, KH_2PO_4, and Na_2HPO_4 indicated an absolute need for Fe and Mg. The effect of Fe was detectable at 5×10^{-4} μg per ml. and of Mg at 5×10^{-6}, optimum growth being obtained at concentrations around 1.0 and 0.5 μg per ml., respectively. Such small amounts appear rather insignificant but suffice to supply many millions of atoms of these elements per cell. The addition of other elements was found to exert no effect although it was not entirely ruled out that they were absolutely absent from the medium, traces of various elements often being present in glassware and other materials used in growth studies.

Waring and Werkman (1942) reduced the Fe content of their basal culture medium by a chloroform-8-hydroxyquinoline extraction to less than 0.003 part per million (p.p.m.). They observed relatively little growth of members of the Eschericheae in the iron-deficient medium and a requirement of 0.02 to 0.03 p.p.m. for maximal growth. A more complex relationship between growth and Fe concentration was noted with *Pseudomonas aeruginosa*, a species of bacteria containing a more complete cytochrome system than in the Eschericheae studied, with maximal growth around 0.09 p.p.m. *Aerobacter indologenes* was found (Waring and Werkman, 1944) to have its catalase, peroxidase, formic hydrogen-lyase, formic dehydrogenase, and hydrogenase activities suppressed by Fe deficiency, and cytochrome bands were not evident in iron-deficient cells. Almost (92 per cent) maximal growth of *Serratia marcescens* was obtained at 0.03 p.p.m. iron, with maximal growth occurring around 0.3 p.p.m. Prodigiosin formation was also dependent upon the Fe concentration (and amino nitrogen), becoming evident around 0.1 p.p.m. and maximal near 0.3 p.p.m. The slight additional growth observed over the range of 0.03 to 0.3 p.p.m. appears to be associated with pigment production. Pigment production fell off as the concentration of Fe was further increased, growth inhibition becoming apparent at still higher concentrations. Most ordinary ingredients of culture media were found to contain sufficient iron to meet the nutritional requirements of bacteria, although some iron may be made less available as a result of autoclaving the medium.

Traces of Cu and Zn have been reported to enhance growth of *Corynebacterium diphtheriae* and Mg for *Azotobacter*. The inhibitive effect of too low or too high concentrations of Fe on toxin production by *C. diphtheriae* is well known. The need for Co has become apparent in recent years with detection of it as a constituent of vitamin B_{12}. The effects of Mg on cellular division have been summarized by Webb (1953), gram-positive rods tending to form long filaments when a deficiency of this element exists. Gram-positive species appear to require about ten times as much Mg for maximal growth as do gram-negative ones. Foster and Heiligman (1949) have reported that potassium deficiency in some media inhibits sporulation of *Bacillus cereus* without having an observable effect on growth. The trace- or microelement nutrition of a wide range of species needs considerable study.

Many bacteria are able to use sulfate as their sole source of sulfur which is found in such compounds as cysteine, methionine, glutathione, biotin, lipoic acid, and coenzyme A. It is generally accepted that sulfate ions are reduced via sulfite to sulfide ions which can be incorporated into cysteine, possibly with the aid of cysteine desulfhydrase acting in reverse, according to the over-all equation

$$H_2S + NH_3 + CH_3COCOOH \rightarrow HSCH_2CHNH_2COOH + H_2O$$

Aminoacrylic acid ($CH_2{=}CNH_2COOH$) probably is an intermediate in the reaction and the acceptor of H_2S. Desulfhydrases are responsible for the liberation of H_2S from sulfur-containing amino acids, a reaction used in the identification of certain species of bacteria. It is also possible that cysteine could be formed by a route involving the formation of a sulfate ester such as cysteic acid, sulfate reduction in this case involving sulfate esters rather than inorganic sulfur compounds. Such a scheme can be represented as

$$
\begin{array}{ccccc}
& \text{OH} & \text{H} & \text{H} & \text{H} \\
& | & | & | & | \\
\text{CH}_3 & \text{O}{=}\text{S}{=}\text{O} & \text{O}{=}\text{S}{=}\text{O} & \text{S}{=}\text{O} & \text{S} \\
| & | & | & | & | \\
\text{CHNH}_2 \rightarrow & \text{CH}_2 \rightarrow & \text{CH}_2 \rightarrow & \text{CH}_2 \rightarrow & \text{CH}_2 \\
| & | & | & | & | \\
\text{SO}_4{}^{--} + \text{COOH} & \text{CHNH}_2 & \text{CHNH}_2 & \text{CHNH}_2 & \text{CHNH}_2 \\
& | & | & | & | \\
& \text{COOH} & \text{COOH} & \text{COOH} & \text{COOH}
\end{array}
$$

Alanine (?)   Cysteic acid   Cysteine sulfinic acid   Cysteine sulfenic acid   Cysteine

It is also possible that sulfate could be reduced to thiosulfate which reacts with alanine (or aminoacrylic acid) to give cysteine—S—sulfonate (serine thiosulfate, HSO_3—S—CH_2CHNH_2COOH), the latter being converted to cysteine. Since sulfate reduction occurs to a marked extent only in the genus *Desulfovibrio*, it is likely that the biosynthesis of cysteine by most bacteria involves reduction of sulfur esters rather than of sulfate itself. The reduction of sulfate and incorporation of sulfur in sulfhydryl groups are analogous to the utilization of nitrate as a sole source of nitrogen in the process Kluyver (Chap. 8) designated as assimilatory nitrate reduction or nitrate assimilation. Once cysteine is formed it can be converted to methionine by organisms such as *E. coli*, possibly over the pathway

$$
\begin{array}{cccc}
\text{SH} & \text{HO—CH}_2 & \text{S}\text{———}\text{CH}_2 & \\
| & | & | \quad\quad | \\
\text{CH}_2 & \text{CH}_2 & \text{CH}_2 \quad \text{CH}_2 \\
| \quad + & | & | \quad\quad | \\
\text{CHNH}_2 & \text{CHNH}_2 \xrightarrow{-\text{H}_2\text{O}} & \text{CHNH}_2 \quad \text{CHNH}_2 \\
| & | & | \quad\quad | \\
\text{COOH} & \text{COOH} & \text{COOH} \quad \text{COOH}
\end{array}
$$

Homoserine   Cystathionine

$$\downarrow{+\text{H}_2\text{O}}$$

$$
\begin{array}{ccc}
\text{CH}_2\text{OH} & \text{SH} & \text{SCH}_3 \\
| & | & | \\
\text{CHNH}_2 & (\text{CH}_2)_2 \xrightarrow{+\text{CH}_3} & (\text{CH}_2)_2 \\
| & | & | \\
\text{COOH} & \text{CHNH}_2 & \text{CHNH}_2 \\
& | & | \\
& \text{COOH} & \text{COOH}
\end{array}
$$

Serine   Homocysteine   Methionine

observed with mutants of *Neurospora* (Fling and Horowitz, 1951). The methylation of homocysteine probably involves choline as a methyl donor and vitamin B_{12} as a cofactor.

Cowie, Bolton, and Sands (1950) observed that the growth of *E. coli* is a function of the sulfur concentration for concentrations of sulfate, sulfite, or sulfide up to 0.005 to 0.01 mg. S per milliliter of synthetic medium. Sulfite appeared to give rise to slightly higher yields, but both sulfite and sulfide were inhibitory in concentrations above 0.01 to 0.1 mg. They further observed that (1) methionine- and homocysteine-requiring mutants also utilize some sulfate; (2) no sulfate-derived organic sulfur could be detected in cysteine-requiring mutants; and (3) sulfite or cysteine suppresses almost completely the utilization of sulfate. These observations suggest that cysteine is an important intermediate of sulfur utilization (see also Bolton, Cowie, and Sands, 1952).

Nitrates frequently can supply the nitrogen requirements of bacteria, but ammonia generally is the common source of nitrogen. As mentioned earlier, nitrate assimilation may be similar to sulfate assimilation and will be considered more fully under bulk-food requirements.

The Supply of Energy and Bulk-building Materials. Light, inorganic oxidizable matter, or oxidizable organic compounds, serve as sources of energy for the photosynthetic, the autotrophic, and the heterotrophic bacteria, respectively. The mechanisms of energy supply and utilization have been discussed in earlier chapters, and attention will be given here to the bulk sources of carbon and nitrogen for heterotrophic species. The enzymic constitution, both constitutive and adaptive, together probably with permeability factors determine the actual organic compounds that can be utilized by a bacterium as bulk sources of carbon and of energy. Some species are rather limited in substrate range, while others are able to grow with any one of dozens of different compounds as the sole source of carbon and of energy. Growth is generally proportional to the concentration of the carbon (or nitrogen) source at low concentrations, all other factors being optimal, while the growth rate depends to some extent upon the nature of the carbon source. Carbon dioxide, at least in trace amounts, is essential for the initiation of growth but does not serve as a bulk supply of carbon for the true heterotrophs.

Oxidative Assimilation. In the case of the nonexacting heterotroph all cellular constituents can be synthesized using one carbon and energy source together with the essential elements in appropriate form. Barker (1936) was the first to show that definite quantitative relationships hold between the amounts of foodstuff dissimilated and the amounts assimilated by nonproliferating cells of the colorless alga *Prototheca zopfii*. With acetate as the substrate, only one mole of oxygen was consumed and one mole of carbon dioxide produced per mole of acetate disappearing from the cellular suspension, rather than the two moles of each gas that would be involved in complete oxidation. On the assumption that one mole of water was produced per mole of oxygen consumed, and from the amounts of the other reactants involved, Barker advanced the balanced equation

$$CH_3COOH + O_2 \rightarrow (CH_2O) + CO_2 + H_2O$$

to express the experimental observations. Similar relationships were noted with other substrates. Barker concluded that this phenomenon of incomplete oxidation could best be explained on the basis of an accompanying assimilation by the cells of material with the empirical composition of carbohydrate, probably glycogen, which is synthesized and stored by *P. zopfii*. The stoichiometric relationships noted with various substrates suggested that definite quantitative relationships exist between the dissimilatory and assimilatory activities of this microorganism, a relationship difficult to interpret on the basis of energy exchange between independent catabolic and anabolic reactions.

These studies were confirmed and extended by other investigators (see Clifton, 1951) using bacteria, yeasts, molds, and algae as test agents under aerobic and anaerobic conditions, generally on the basis of amounts of substrate utilized and of the gaseous exchange noted in manometric studies. Increases in dry weight, in reducing sugar content, or of cellular carbon were also noted and found to be in general agreement with those postulated on the basis of data from the manometric observations. The same general stoichiometric relationships were also noted in growth studies, a tendency, however, being observed for somewhat higher ratios of carbon assimilated to carbon dioxide produced to hold in growth as contrasted with resting-cell experiments with *E. coli* (Siegel and Clifton, 1950). In other instances the opposite behavior may be noted.

The various studies point to differences in efficiency between organisms concerning their ability to assimilate a particular substrate. The algae *Chlorella pyrenoidesa* and *Prototheca zopfii*, a yeast, *Candida albicans*, and various *Spirillum* species have been reported to assimilate one mole of carbon per mole of acetate utilized; *E. coli* and *Pseudomonas calco-acetica*, one mole per two moles of acetate; and *Saccharomyces cerevisiae*, two moles per three moles of acetate. The extent of assimilation does not appear to have any direct relationship to the free energy of oxidation of the substrate, as much assimilation occurring from pyruvate as from lactate, or from fumarate compared with succinate, although the former compounds in each pair are oxidation products of the latter and have lower free energies of oxidation. Typical results of manometric and carbon-balance studies are recorded in Tables 12-1 and 12-2 and the efficiencies of synthesis by *E. coli* during growth on various substrates in

Table 12-3. Utilization of carbon during growth was most efficient with glycerol, next with the sugars, and least with the acids as substrates. These figures indicate a much higher efficiency of assimilation (40 to 70 per cent) during growth than the values of 10 to 20 per cent usually cited, particularly for studies of longer duration.

TABLE 12-1. MANOMETRIC OBSERVATIONS ON THE OXIDATIVE ASSIMILATION OF SEVERAL SUBSTRATES BY WASHED SUSPENSIONS OF *Escherichia coli**

Substrate	Succi-nate	Fuma-rate	Lac-tate	Pyru-vate	Gly-cerol
Mg. C utilized....................	0.883	0.680	0.672	0.726	0.803
μl. O_2 consumed..................	1,030	676	935	755	1,465
μl. CO_2 produced.................	1,152	974	960	950	1,175
% oxidized.......................	71.5	76.0	69.5	70.5	78.0
R.Q. observed....................	1.12	1.44	1.02	1.26	0.80
R.Q. for complete combustion.......	1.14	1.33	1.00	1.20	0.86
R.Q. for oxidative assimilation.......	1.20	1.50	1.00	1.33	0.80
C assimilated/CO_2-C†.............	0.43	0.35	0.31	0.43	0.28

* From Siegel and Clifton (1950b), courtesy of The Williams & Wilkins Company.
† Calculated by difference between mg. C utilized and mg. CO_2-C produced.

TABLE 12-2. COMPARATIVE CARBON BALANCES IN THE OXIDATIVE ASSIMILATION OF SEVERAL SUBSTRATES DURING THE GROWTH OF *Escherichia coli* FOR 4.5 HR.*

Substrate, mg C	Succi-nate	Fuma-rate	Lac-tate	Pyru-vate	Gly-cerol
Initial substrate C................	5.51	3.14	3.31	4.45	5.40
Cell C after assimilation...........	0.55	0.44	0.37	0.51	0.72
Cell C before assimilation..........	0.35	0.21	0.29	0.20	0.51
C stored.......................	0.20	0.23	0.08	0.31	0.21
Supernatant C at end of experiment	5.04	2.57	3.19	3.76	5.15
CO_2-C.......................	0.29	0.30	0.12	0.39	0.10
Total recovered..................	5.53	3.10	3.40	4.46	5.46
Total recovered, %..............	100.3	98.7	102.7	100.2	101.1
μl. CO_2 produced................	536	534	214	724	182
μl. O_2 consumed.................	380	274	222	394	266
R.Q. observed...................	1.41	1.95	0.97	1.84	0.70

* From Siegel and Clifton (1950b), courtesy of The Williams & Wilkins Company.

Clifton (1937) observed that oxidation tended to go to completion in the presence of suitable concentrations of sodium azide (NaN_3) or 2,4-dinitrophenol. This has been confirmed by a number of workers (see review by Simon, 1953a). It is believed that these poisons in some manner interfere with the utilization of high-energy phosphate, i.e., uncouple phosphorylations from oxidations by inhibiting the formation of energy-rich phosphate and/or catalyze the breakdown of ATP or ATPase activity. Gramicidin appears to act in a similar manner. The action of these agents, however, is more complex than indicated above. Pickett and Clifton (1943) reported that aerobic assimilation from glucose by yeast was inhibited by dinitrophenol, the sugar assimilated in its absence being dissimilated to ethanol and CO_2 in the presence of this poison. Simon (1953b) supports the concept that the phosphate cycle is the factor controlling the glycolysis rate (or Pasteur effect) in yeast,

TABLE 12-3. EFFICIENCIES OF SYNTHESIS BY *Escherichia coli* DURING GROWTH ON VARIOUS SUBSTRATES*

Substrate	Increase in cell C, mg.	CO_2-C, mg.	Increase in cell C / C consumed
Glucose	0.34	0.25	0.59
Lactose	0.12	0.10	0.55
Arabinose	0.34	0.19	0.64
Succinate	0.20	0.29	0.41
Fumarate	0.23	0.30	0.43
Lactate	0.08	0.12	0.40
Pyruvate	0.31	0.39	0.44
Glycerol	0.21	0.10	0.70

* Data from Siegel and Clifton (1950a,b,c).

uncoupling of phosphate energy utilization by nitrophenols leading to aerobic fermentation. Azide, on the other hand, inhibited both oxygen consumption and assimilation, glucose then being fermented to completion under aerobic conditions in the presence of suitable concentrations of this poison.

Taylor (1950) reported that the oxidation of glucose by the alga *Scenedesmus quadricauda* goes to about 16 per cent completion, the remainder of the sugar being converted into an acid-hydrolyzable polysaccharide. He concluded that there is no fixed relation between oxidation and assimilation and that once glucose saturates the oxidative mechanisms of the cell, the excess sugar phosphate is converted into a polysaccharide. His manometric data suggest that under fixed conditions assimilation occurs to a relatively constant extent, which is all that the equations for oxidative assimilation indicate. It may be that the bacterial cell synthesizes polysaccharide as the result of a process similar to that proposed by Taylor. Levine, Stevenson, and Bordner (1953) have reported the formation of glycogen in *A. aerogenes*. Fales (1951) noted differences in the type of carbohydrate formed during fermentative assimilation of glucose by yeast, a transient carbohydrate other than glycogen or trehalose being formed during the course of fermentations by washed cells. Reserve or transient materials of the nature of carbohydrate could serve as a uniform source of carbon for the cell in the various syntheses a species carries out on media containing different substrates.

The possibility that assimilated reserves are utilized by the actively respiring cell is suggested by studies on the endogenous respiration of bacteria. When bacteria are suspended in a buffer solution, respiration continues at a rate generally much lower than in the presence of a utilizable substrate, the only oxidizable material being in the cell itself, and hence the term endogenous respiration as contrasted with exogenous respiration, the utilization of externally supplied material. Whether or not one should correct total observed respiration values (generally spoken of as exogenous values) by subtracting a fraction or all of the values observed in the absence of a substrate has long been a debatable problem in various studies of bacterial metabolism. With bacteria having low endogenous and high exogenous rates of respiration, correction may not markedly influence the values obtained. Wilner and Clifton (1954) have reviewed the earlier studies dealing with this problem as it relates to oxidative assimilation. They found with *B. subtilis*, a species exhibiting relatively high rates of endogenous respiration and only several-fold increases in rates of oxygen consumption in the presence of utilizable substrates, that the percentages of assimilation varied markedly with the concentration of substrate employed. On correction for observed endogenous values (Fig. 12-1) the percentages of assimilation agreed quite closely. They interpreted this as indicating that endogenous respiration continues at about the same rate, in either the presence or absence of an oxidizable foodstuff. Santer and Ajl (1954) came to the same conclusion in studies with *Pasteurella pestis*. They reported that washed cells grown in the presence of labeled substrate evolved labeled CO_2 at about the same rate irrespective of the presence or absence of substrate. The observations that endogenous respiration does continue in many species, or in some may even be stimulated, lend further support to the concept of the necessity for a pool of intracellular organic matter needed by the organism, not only for the maintenance of the *status quo*, but also for use during growth. Other concepts are discussed by Lamanna and Mallette (1953).

Another problem concerning the conversion of substrate to cellular carbon is the fate of the carbon atoms in the substrate. Is the whole molecule, or only portions thereof, converted into cellular material? Taylor (1952) reported that 46 per cent of the acetate utilized by yeast was oxidized with an R.Q. of 1.0. The CO_2 liberated from carboxyl-labeled acetate was found to equal the specific activity of the original acetate carbon, thus indicating that it was derived from complete oxidation of the acetate. The fate of the nonoxidized fraction of acetate was not determined.   Fraser and Tolbert (1951), utilizing lactic acid singly labeled with C^{14} in either the 1, 2, or 3 position, found that the carboxyl carbon is largely converted to CO_2 by *E. coli*.   Some of the carbon in positions 2 and 3 was converted to CO_2, but most was utilized in synthetic reactions, although an appreciable amount of the C_2 fragment from decarboxylation of lactic acid (or possibly its oxidation product, pyruvic acid) was excreted into the medium.   Wiame and Doudoroff

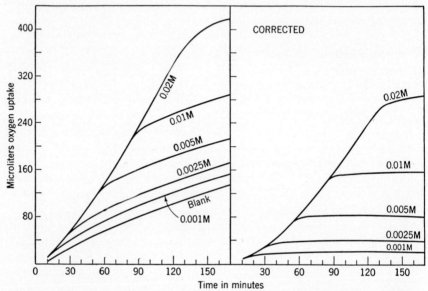

Fig. 12-1. Oxygen consumption by washed suspensions of *Bacillus subtilis* in different concentrations of glucose as observed directly and following correction for endogenous respiration.   The breaks in the corrected curves are sharper and fall within a narrower range as regards extent of oxidation.   (*From Wilner and Clifton, 1954, courtesy of The Williams & Wilkins Company.*)

(1951) concluded that *Pseudomonas saccharophila* utilizes 2-carbon fragments of the nature of "active acetate" as the fundamental building block during oxidative assimilation.   By the use of C^{14}-labeled substrates they showed that (1) both carbons of acetate are assimilated, the methyl carbon being favored; (2) the carboxyl carbon of lactate is almost completely converted to CO_2, the remaining C_2 fragment being largely assimilated; and (3) both carboxyl carbons of succinate are oxidized, while the methylene carbons are largely assimilated.   Studies of this nature will aid in the understanding of how substrate carbon is converted into cellular material, a problem that becomes more complex when bacteria are growing in a medium containing more than one source of carbon and of energy. The studies on oxidative assimilation indicate that a quantitative relationship exists between the energy-providing and the energy-requiring reactions. We know more concerning the nature of the oxidative reactions that supply the necessary energy but as yet relatively little concerning the intimate links between these reactions (except for high-energy phosphates) and the utilization of substrate and energy for cellular syntheses.

Pathways of Assimilation. Roberts et al. (1955) attempted to trace the major pathways of assimilation during growth of *E. coli* in a glucose–basic salts medium. During one generation time they observed utilization for synthetic purposes of approximately 30 per cent of the glucose

TABLE 12-4. GLUCOSE UTILIZATION BY *Escherichia coli**

Product	μM per g. per 100 sec.	Percentage of glucose carbon
Total glucose utilized............................	420 (C-6)	100
Incorporated in cells............................	252 (C-3)	30
Converted to CO_2.............................	1,135 (C-1)	45
Converted to acetate..........................	200 (C-2)	16
Converted to other products in culture fluid......	76 (C-3)	9
C-3 units required for synthesis of:		
Pentose....................................	30	
Serine products..............................	39	
Pyruvate products............................	400	
Miscellaneous................................	66	
Moles C-3 available from glucose.................	840	
Moles C-3 required for synthetic mechanisms.......	535	
Moles C-3 not accounted for.....................	305	

* From Roberts et al. (1955), courtesy of R. B. Roberts and the Carnegie Institution of Washington.

disappearing from the culture medium. With the aid of tracers and various fractionations of cellular material, they followed the distribution of glucose carbon used in the synthesis of new cellular material. Their results are summarized in Table 12-4 and Fig. 12-2 and are expressed on the basis of micromoles (μM) of glucose used, or of products formed, per gram of dry cells per 100 sec. Only 344 μM of carbon dioxide were accounted for as arising from reactions leading to the synthesis of cellular matter, the source of approximately 800 μM being unknown. A rather large amount of material, equivalent to about 25 per cent of the glucose utilized, was secreted into the culture medium. Acetate was the major waste product, comprising about 16 per cent of the glucose utilized. Whether this is due to particular growth conditions or the strain of *E. coli* employed remains undetermined. Results of studies of this nature will lead to a better understanding of the general flow of material and of energy through the multitude of reactions involved in the growth of a cell.

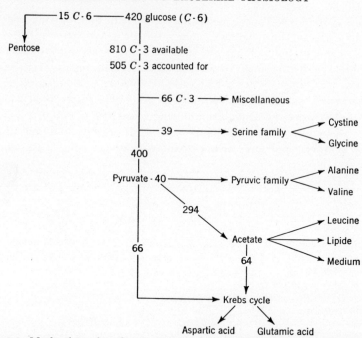

FIG. 12-2. Mechanisms for glucose incorporation in *Escherichia coli*, results being expressed in terms of micromoles per gram of dry cells per 100 sec. (*After Roberts et al., 1955, courtesy of R. B. Roberts and the Carnegie Institution of Washington.*)

Synthesis of Polysaccharides. Bacteria may assimilate (Barker and Hassid, 1951) a considerable portion of the substrate carbon in the form of polysaccharides present as reserve food within the cell or deposited as structural components, particularly in their cell walls or capsules. A number of species, including *Leuconostoc mesenteroides, Acetobacter viscosum,* and *Phytomonas tumafaciens,* form dextrans by condensation of glucose units through 1,6-glucosidic linkages. The dextran formed by the first-named bacterium is of considerable interest for use as a blood-plasma substitute, polymers of a molecular weight around 100,000 appearing to be the most desirable for this purpose. Glucose may be derived from a number of different sugars for these polymerizations. *Acetobacter xylinum* forms a bacterial cellulose in which the glucose units are joined by β-1,4-glucosidic linkages. *Clostridium butylicum* forms a starch-like complex termed granulose, and similar polysaccharides are formed by other bacteria such as *Neisseria perflava* and *Corynebacterium diphtheriae.*

A number of aerobic spore formers and of lactic acid bacteria condense fructose rather than glucose with the formation of levans (levulans) but are limited to utilization of sucrose or raffinose for this polymerization.

More complex polysaccharides are formed by other species, some, e.g., the pneumococcus, containing more than one basic sugar and, in addition, uronic acids, amino sugars, or acetyl groups.

Those organisms capable of utilizing a number of sugars as a glucose source for polymerization commonly do so following a preliminary conversion to common phosphate esters. Galactose, for example, is phosphorylated to yield galactose-1-phosphate, which, under the influence of appropriate enzymes and the coenzyme uridinediphosphoglucose (UDPG), is converted to glucose-1-phosphate, the Cori ester. A probable reaction scheme for this reversible reaction can be represented as

$$\text{Galactose-1-}®\ +\ \text{UDPG} \rightleftarrows \text{glucose-1-}®\ +\ \text{UDP}\quad\text{galactose}$$
$$\text{UDP galactose} \rightleftarrows \text{UDP glucose}$$

Glucose-6-phosphate, a common intermediate in the utilization of sugars, can be converted under the influence of phosphoglucotransferase (phosphoglucomutase) into glucose-1-phosphate with glucose-1,6-diphosphate acting in the role of a coenzyme.

In earlier days it was believed that the synthesis of polysaccharides from monosaccharides could occur by reversal of the hydrolytic splitting induced by enzymes such as invertase. Since ΔF for the hydrolysis of sucrose is around $-6,600$ cal., hydrolysis tends to proceed to completion for all practical purposes. Observations of Cori and Cori indicated that polysaccharides (glycogen) also can be dissimilated under the influence of a phosphorylase and with uptake of inorganic phosphate to yield glucose-1-phosphate. This type of reaction is analogous to hydrolysis but with phosphate substituting for water; hence it is termed a phosphorolytic reaction. It has been found to occur in many organisms and with different sugars. The phosphorolytic reaction involves only a slight change in free energy and is reversible, thus providing for synthesis as well as for dissimilation. The equilibrium in phosphorolysis is controlled primarily by the relative concentrations of glucose-1-phosphate and phosphate ions rather than by the concentration of water as in the hydrolytic reaction. Any decrease in concentration of phosphate, e.g., induced by oxidative phosphorylation, would favor polysaccharide synthesis.

Glucose-1-phosphate by itself is not converted into polymers such as starch in the absence of a primer or sparker. The ester molecules do not condense with each other but rather with terminal units of the primer such as glycogen or starch, or

$$(C_6H_{10}O_5)_x\ +\ C_6H_{11}O_5O\text{-}®\ \rightleftarrows\ (C_6H_{10}O_5)_{x+1}\ +\ ®$$

Ultimately, the chain formed by repetition of this condensation separates from the starter. In the branched polysaccharides an enzyme known as the "branching factor" induces departure from straight-chain formation.

Phosphorolytic cleavage of a polysaccharide such as glycogen leads, as we have seen, to the formation of glucose-1-phosphate with the uptake of inorganic phosphate. Utilization of glycogen rather than glucose as a substrate would be more efficient in that one less high-energy phosphate would be expended with the former in preparatory reactions for oxidation, the near equivalence of the energy of glucosidic and phosphate linkages rendering utilization of ATP unnecessary.

Phosphorylases can act on disaccharides as well as higher sugars in a reversible manner (Stacey, 1954), sucrose phosphorylase catalyzing the reaction

$$\text{Glucosido-fructoside} + Ⓟ \rightleftarrows \text{glucose-1-}Ⓟ + \text{fructose}$$
(Sucrose)

The sucrose phosphorylase is also able to catalyze the transfer of glucose moieties from one sugar to another, e.g.,

$$\text{Glucosido-fructoside} + \text{sorbose} \rightleftarrows \text{glucosido-sorboside} + \text{fructose}$$

thus acting as a transglucosidase without participation of phosphate ions. A reaction type of this nature provides possibilities for the synthesis of a variety of polysaccharides. Glucose can also be transferred to phosphate, or

$$Ⓟ + \text{glucose-enzyme} \rightleftarrows \text{glucose-1-}Ⓟ + \text{enzyme}$$

No free glucose is formed; hence the energy in the glucose-1-phosphate bond is preserved in the glucose-enzyme system, or vice versa. Sucrose phosphorylase, acting as a glucose transfer enzyme, can also transfer glucose to fructose according to the reaction scheme

$$\text{Fructose*} + \text{glucose-enzyme} \rightleftarrows \text{glucosido-fructose*} + \text{enzyme}$$

where the asterisk indicates radioactive fructose utilized as a tracer for the reaction. Transglucosidation is also involved in reactions such as the conversion of maltose by *E. coli* into a starch-like compound under the influence of amylomaltase, or

$$\text{Maltose} + \text{amylomaltase} \rightleftarrows \text{glucose} + \text{glucose-amylomaltase}$$
$$\text{Glucose-amylomaltase} + \text{maltose} \rightleftarrows \text{amylomaltase} + \text{trisaccharide, etc.}$$

Phosphate does not appear to be involved in this transfer of glucose to maltose or higher polysaccharides.

The various reactions outlined above can serve for the synthesis of a wide variety of carbohydrates, and other compounds can be formed from these as required by the species. The general types of carbohydrate utilization, other than oxidative and the formation of sugar derivatives, can be summarized as follows:

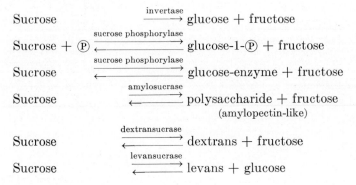

$$\text{Sucrose} \xrightarrow{\text{invertase}} \text{glucose} + \text{fructose}$$

$$\text{Sucrose} + \text{\textcircled{P}} \underset{\xleftarrow{\hspace{2cm}}}{\xrightarrow{\text{sucrose phosphorylase}}} \text{glucose-1-\textcircled{P}} + \text{fructose}$$

$$\text{Sucrose} \underset{\xleftarrow{\text{sucrose phosphorylase}}}{} \text{glucose-enzyme} + \text{fructose}$$

$$\text{Sucrose} \underset{\xleftarrow{\xrightarrow{\text{amylosucrase}}}}{} \text{polysaccharide} + \text{fructose}$$
$$\text{(amylopectin-like)}$$

$$\text{Sucrose} \underset{\xleftarrow{\xrightarrow{\text{dextransucrase}}}}{} \text{dextrans} + \text{fructose}$$

$$\text{Sucrose} \underset{\xleftarrow{\xrightarrow{\text{levansucrase}}}}{} \text{levans} + \text{glucose}$$

It can be seen that all of these reactions, with the exception of the first three, lead to the assimilation of carbohydrate, while the second and third in reverse do lead to synthesis of sucrose which could be assimilated by means of the latter reactions. The complex carbohydrates may be utilized as food under starvation conditions, degradation not necessarily having to follow the synthetic pathway in reverse.

Nitrogen Fixation. Most bacteria can obtain their nitrogen from ammonia (or nitrates), a considerable number require one or more specific amino acids in addition to the bulk supply of nitrogen, while many species can fix atmospheric nitrogen although only a limited number grow readily with nitrogen gas as the only source of this element. Winogradsky in 1894 isolated an anaerobe, *Clostridium pasteuranium*, which grew readily in a medium devoid of fixed nitrogen, fixing about 2 mg. of nitrogen per gram of glucose fermented. This fixation was inhibited by the addition of ammonium salts to the synthetic medium. Beijerinck in 1901 isolated two species of aerobic nitrogen-fixing bacteria designated as *Azotobacter chroococcum* and *A. agilis*. Certain blue-green algae have also been shown to possess marked nitrogen-fixing ability. Photosynthetic bacteria and a number of other bacteria are also capable of fixing nitrogen, many species of heterotrophs apparently fixing slight but significant amounts. The use of leguminous plants as a means of maintaining soil fertility has long been recognized, but it was not until 1886 that Hellriegel and Wilfarth demonstrated that this was due to nitrogen fixation associated with the development of nodules on the roots of these plants, no fixation occurring in sterile soil and no nodule formation as well. The "soil ferment" of Hellriegel and Wilfarth was isolated in pure culture by Beijerinck in 1888 and is now classified in the genus *Rhizobium*. Members of this genus fix nitrogen only when growing in symbiosis with the appropriate leguminous plants and do not do so in pure culture in the laboratory.   Only in recent years has it been possible to demonstrate consistent fixation of nitrogen by nodules removed from the roots of legumes, and this fixation by excised nodules decreases markedly with time.   Symbiotic relationships may also be involved in nitrogen fixation by the *Azotobacter* under natural conditions and could lead to greater efficiency of fixation in the soil than is observed in nonsymbiotic fixation in vitro. Various estimates indicate the magnitude of biological nitrogen fixation to be slightly over five million tons annually by the symbiotic species and around four million tons by the nonsymbiotic bacteria.

Much of our information concerning the physiology of nitrogen fixation comes from studies with *Azotobacter*, since species of this genus will grow readily in simple synthetic media practically devoid of nitrogenous compounds.   Fixation is associated with growth and so far has not been demonstrated with cell-free preparations.   In early studies nitrogen fixation was demonstrated primarily by increases (often small) in nitrogen content as determined by the Kjeldahl procedure, which has definite limitations.   In the 1920's Burk and his colleagues found that plots of the rate of growth of *Azotobacter* are practically superimposable on curves representing rates of oxygen consumption.   Since growth is proportional to nitrogen fixation in media free of combined nitrogen, the rate of respiration can be used as a measure of nitrogen fixation.   Plots of log O_2 uptake per hour or of log N_2 uptake (Kjeldahl analysis) per hour against time give straight-line relationships, both curves having the same slope and being expressed by the monomolecular equation, or

$$k = \frac{2.303}{t} \log \frac{\text{final } O_2}{\text{initial } O_2} = \frac{2.303}{t} \log \frac{\text{final } N_2}{\text{initial } N_2}$$

This relationship holds quite well in young, actively growing cultures. Oxygen consumption can be followed in Warburg respirometers, and by this indirect method nitrogen fixation can be followed quite readily, the method being particularly useful for comparative experiments.   It has been observed, for example, in such experiments that hydrogen competitively inhibits nitrogen fixation by *Azotobacter*.   Nitrogen isotopes have been utilized in more recent years in the study of nitrogen fixation, their use being limited by the short life of radioactive N_2 and the cost and complexity of the mass spectrograph required for studies with heavy nitrogen, N_2^{15}.   With the aid of the latter it is possible to detect nitrogen fixation in experiments of short duration and in bacteria fixing relatively little of this element.   For recent reviews on methods and results of nitrogen-fixation studies the reader is referred to Wilson and Burris (1953) and Virtanen and Rautanen (1952).

The rate of nitrogen fixation is dependent on the nitrogen tension, the rate decreasing below a pN_2 of 0.1 atm. and being half maximum (Michaelis constant) at 0.02 atm. for *Azotobacter* and the alga *Nostoc* and around 0.05 atm. for the red clover–*Rhizobium* system. It is usually stimulated by increasing the supply of air, although this effect may be the result of increased cellular activity and not on the fixation mechanism directly. Most species of *Azotobacter* grow and fix nitrogen most readily in the pH range of 7 to 8 with a lower limit of pH 6. Up to 20 mg. of nitrogen can be fixed per gram of carbohydrate oxidized under optimum conditions. *Clostridium* species are the chief nitrogen fixers in acid soils although acid-tolerant *Azotobacter* have been described. Calcium, iron, and molybdenum have been shown to be essential for nitrogen fixation although it has not been definitely established that these elements are involved in the nitrogen-fixing system itself.

In earlier experiments on the influence of pN_2 on nitrogen fixation, nitrogen was replaced in part with readily available, cheap, supposedly inert hydrogen. Nitrogen fixation by the red clover system was inhibited approximately 50 per cent at a pH_2 of 0.43 atm. and a pN_2 of 0.37 atm., no inhibition being noted at the same pN_2 with helium as the inert gas in a control system. This inhibition was found to be competitive and has also been observed with *Azotobacter*, but not with the clostridia (which liberate H_2). Photosynthetically grown cells of *Rhodospirillum rubrum* evolve hydrogen in an atmosphere of helium, argon, or hydrogen, this photoevolution being blocked by nitrogen or by ammonium ions. These observations suggested that this organism might be a nitrogen fixer, and fixation was soon established. The interrelationship between nitrogen and hydrogen in nitrogen fixation is unknown, the presence of hydrogenase in the highly aerobic *Azotobacter* and the inhibition by hydrogen of nitrogen fixation or of hydrogen evolution by nitrogen in *Rhodospirillum* suggesting a close tie.

Nitrous oxide and carbon monoxide also inhibit nitrogen fixation. Inhibition by carbon monoxide is primarily noncompetitive and occurs at much lower pCO's than required for marked inhibition of respiration.

When ammonia, nitrates, or nitrites are available, the uptake of nitrogen gas is competitively inhibited, almost completely in most instances, and no period of adaptation is required for the utilization of the ammonium ion. Ammonia containing labeled nitrogen in N-fixation tests can be isolated, it can replace nitrogen, the isotope studies indicate a similar distribution of N^{15} in cellular material derived from free or ammonium nitrogen, and many workers therefore consider ammonia to be a key intermediate in nitrogen fixation. Little is known of the intermediates between free nitrogen and ammonia, although Virtanen has supported the concept of hydroxylamine (NH_2OH) as the key intermediate. Studies with the symbiotic system suggested that hydroxylamine reacted with oxalacetic acid to yield aspartic acid. Most evidence supports ammonia as being the key substance and its reacting primarily with α-ketoglutaric acid to yield glutamic acid which through transamination reactions will give rise to other amino acids. Glutamic acid, therefore, represents the end of the fixation reaction and the starting point for assimilation of nitrogen into other organic compounds. Tracer studies of short duration indicate that glutamic acid is the predominant compound formed, although N^{15} may also be found in significant amounts in aspartic acid.

Utilization of Amino Acids. We have considered in previous chapters (see also Chap. 15) that ammonia can be taken up by keto acids with the formation of amino acids and that other amino acids can be formed by transamination and in various reaction chains. When an amino acid is added to a C^{14}–glucose–basal salt medium it may be utilized as such, or may serve as a source of ammonia. Britten (1954) has reported that *E. coli* will assimilate glutamic acid added to the glucose medium, continuing, however, to form considerable amounts of glutamate from C^{14}-glucose. Appreciable quantities of labeled glutamate appeared in the culture medium. A similar behavior was noted when aspartate, glycine, alanine, or valine was added as a supplement to the basal medium. When either proline, arginine, serine, methionine, or threonine was added as the supplement, the test amino acid was used for protein synthesis, but suppressed synthesis of itself, and no C^{14}-labeled amino acid of this group could be found in the medium.

Many species have lost the ability to synthesize one or more of the amino acids found in their cellular constituents, and the essential amino acids must be supplied as such (or as a utilizable precursor). Freshly isolated strains of *Salmonella typhosa* are unable to synthesize tryptophan, and either it or indol must be provided in the medium. This organism apparently lacks the ability to synthesize the indol structure rather than the amino acid itself. Mutants capable of synthesizing tryptophan appear readily, and most laboratory strains of *S. typhosa* are not exacting in their growth requirements. Other bacteria, particularly many grampositive species, require one or more amino acids in their diet. At this stage of synthetic ability, or lack thereof, a distinction between amino acids and growth factors (vitamins) begins to be less evident. In most instances the amino acids enter into the structure of cellular proteins, while many of the vitamins are found in coenzyme and other constituents of the cell. This may well be a minor difference, and for convenience the essential amino acids will be considered along with the growth factors as essential nutrilites required by the exacting heterotrophs.

Earlier in this chapter we considered the studies of Gale and his colleagues on the uptake by and concentration of glutamic and other amino acids within cells of gram-positive species. They found that glutamic acid is incorporated into cellular protein by at least two mechanisms: true incorporation into newly formed protein and exchange with glutamic acid residues in existing protein. They also presented evidence that the rate of synthesis of protein is correlated with the nucleic acid content of the cells and that protein synthesis by damaged cells in a complete mixture of amino acids is markedly accelerated by the presence of a nucleic acid fraction obtained from soluble cell contents. This suggests, as considered earlier, that nucleic acids may act as templates for certain cellular syntheses.

Essential Nutrilites. The term growth factor has been employed in many instances for any substance required for growth, although in more strict usage it implies any organic compound required only in minute amounts for growth. It is often used synonymously with vitamin, but here again trouble may be encountered since amino acids and other organic substances not regarded as vitamins are often essential in minute amounts for growth. The term *essential nutrilite* is employed here to encompass any organic compound required only in minute amounts for growth and serving, directly or as a precursor, for the provision of a chemical structure the strain is unable to synthesize for itself. Overlapping may occur, some essential nutrilites serving not only the implied purpose but also being used to some extent as sources of building material and energy in general. Substances exerting a stimulatory action but not being essential for growth are often excluded from the category of essential nutrilites. In the same manner we can define an *essential metabolite* as a substance utilized in a synthesis essential for the growth of a cell and without which, either formed within the cell or obtained from the environment, the cell cannot grow. An essential nutrilite, therefore, is an essential metabolite, but the reverse need not be true.

The concept that microorganisms may require organic substances other than those known to supply gross needs originated around 1901 with Wildier's failure to obtain growth of a strain of yeast from small inocula in a sucrose-salt medium. Growth occurred following the addition of a small amount of dead yeast cells or of yeast extract to the basal medium. The active principle was named bios and appears to have been a mixture of biotin, thiamin, pyridoxine, pantothenic acid, and inositol. The first recognition of the need for such factors by bacteria came around 1911 from observations by Twort and Ingram that *Mycobacterium paratuberculosis* (Johne's bacillus) would not grow, even in complex media, except in the presence of an extract of other acid-fast bacteria. The timothy bacillus (*M. phlei*) was a good source of the active principle (now recognized as phthiocol, the aromatic portion of vitamin K), and they suggested that it might be representative of the wild ancestor, concluding that

"Johne's bacillus has lived a pathogenic existence from such remote ages that it has lost the original power of its wild ancestor and can no longer build up all its necessary foodstuffs outside the animal body." This concept, modified and extended by more recent studies, still expresses in a general way the modern belief that the need for essential nutrilites is an expression of loss of synthetic abilities by an organism.

The stimulation of growth of *Hemophilus influenzae* by the addition of blood to nutrient agar and the additional stimulation (satellite-colony formation) induced by growth of other bacteria near the *H. influenzae* colonies led Davis in 1917 to conclude that a vitamin-like substance was required in addition to hemoglobin. Thjötta and Avery showed in 1921 that there are two substances in fresh blood essential for growth of the influenza bacillus. One, the X factor, was heat-stable and associated with hemoglobin; the other, the V factor (vitamin-like) was relatively heat-labile and could be obtained from red blood cells, yeast, and vegetables. The latter was identified by the Lwoffs in 1936 as cozymase or coenzyme I (DPN). Williams in 1919 reported that the substance (vitamin B_1) stimulating growth of yeast was identical with that preventing beriberi in animals; Warburg and Christian in 1932 identified as riboflavin what is now known as vitamin B_2; and the identity of nicotinic acid as a growth factor was established by Knight in 1936. Other agents were soon identified, and new ones are being discovered (for reviews, see Knight, 1936; Peterson and Peterson, 1945; yearly reviews in *Annual Review of Microbiology*). Many of the vitamins for man and other animals have been discovered or identified in studies with microorganisms.

Most of the nutritionally exacting bacteria belong in the fourth group, the exacting heterotrophs (Chap. 1). At first the accessory growth factors or vitamins were thought to be specific requirements of a limited number of bacteria and not essential for the activities of other species. It has become apparent that (1) they represent chemical structures essential for the activities of most or all bacteria; (2) they are found ultimately in molecules such as coenzymes and to a great extent serve functional rather than structural purposes; and (3) they are needed as essential metabolites by all bacteria but can be synthesized by many from relatively simple substrates. In some instances an organism may be able to synthesize a given component, but the rate of synthesis is too slow to allow normal multiplication. Addition of the component to the medium stimulates growth. This makes for a very vague border line between growth-stimulatory substances and essential nutrilites. Absolute differences are usually the exception.

To illustrate the differences in nutritional requirements of different bacteria let us consider the over-all picture of the need for DPN as an essential metabolite. This can be represented as a series of reactions such as

$$NH_3 \xrightarrow{(1)} \text{amino N} \begin{array}{c} \xrightarrow{(2)} \text{Nucleotide} \\ \\ \xrightarrow{(3)} \text{Pyridine} \end{array} \xrightarrow{(4)} DPN$$

Ammonia nitrogen can be incorporated into amino acids in stage 1 by organisms such as *E. coli*. Amino acids, or other nitrogenous organic compounds, are converted in stages 2 and 3 into the nucleotide and the pyridine structures which are ultimately combined in stage 4 to yield this coenzyme essential for the activity of bacteria. Some bacteria may be unable to utilize ammonia and require preformed amino acids, thus being deficient in synthetic abilities represented by stage 1. *Micrococcus pyogenes* var. *aureus* is an example of a bacterium requiring amino acids, but it also is deficient in a synthetic ability required in stage 3; hence nicotinic acid, or its amide, must be supplied in the growth medium. The staphylococcus can carry out reaction series 2 and combine the nucleotide with the preformed pyridine in stage 4. The influenza bacillus is unable to complete stage 4, and DPN must be supplied as such for this organism.

The study of essential nutrilites can be divided into four phases as follows:

1. Recognition of need, usually by the observation that the addition of small amounts of cellular extracts to a medium is necessary for growth
2. Concentration of the active principle
3. Isolation and identification of the substance (or substances)
4. Elucidation of its function when possible

Today, with many of these agents identified, it is generally possible to prepare a synthetic medium complete with the various essential amino acids and other factors. If growth occurs, amino acids or other factors can be omitted in turn, and by elimination the nutrilites essential for growth can be determined. Complications arise at times, as, for example, an amino acid being essential for growth but at the same time being inhibitory, its toxicity being neutralized by the addition of a second amino acid. The cause of this toxic effect and the antagonistic action of a second amino acid is unknown. If growth does not occur in a "complete medium" except following the addition of a tissue extract, it then becomes necessary to fractionate the extract and to attempt to isolate and identify the unknown factor. Studies of this latter type were predominant in earlier years and are well illustrated by the studies of Mueller and his colleagues (Mueller, 1943–1944) on the nutritional requirements of *Corynebacterium diphtheriae*.

Most strains of the diphtheria bacillus would not grow and produce toxin except on complex media, peptone and meat extract being essential with sugars serving as a bulk nutrient. Mueller found that casein hydrolysate, reinforced with tryptophan in which it is deficient, could be substituted for peptone. Tryptophan was thus established as an essential nutrilite, and by trial and error glycine, valine, leucine, glutamic acid, cystine, methionine, and tyrosine were also found to be essential amino acids. Methionine was found to exert an inhibitory effect in the absence of histidine and leucine, although histidine is not required in the mixture given above.

Liver extract was found to be a good source of the unknown factors which were soluble in alcohol. They could be adsorbed by charcoal and eluted from it with acid alcohol. The somewhat concentrated and purified material could be divided into two fractions by extraction with ether. The active substance in the ether-soluble material was finally identified as pimelic acid, more recent work showing that pimelic acid serves in the synthesis of, and could be replaced by, biotin. Five-thousandths of a microgram of pimelic acid per milliliter of medium served to support limited growth, the maximum effect being noted with 5 to 10 times this concentration.

The ether-insoluble fraction was eventually divided into various portions by vacuum distillation, nicotinic acid being identified in a low-boiling fraction and β-alanine in a high-boiling one. Synthetic compounds could be substituted for the extracted ones, and it was found that 1 μg. of each served to support good growth and toxin production. All three of these components of meat extract are required by many, but not by all, strains. Strain differences are frequently encountered in studies on bacterial nutrition. Mutations were also observed during the course of these extended studies, and they further complicate, yet at the same time often aid in the elucidation of, such studies. The work of Pappenheimer brought out the importance of iron concentration on toxin production, maximum yields being obtained around 1.5 μg. of iron per milliliter.

Further studies showed even more complex requirements for the tetanus bacillus, pantothenic acid, biotin, thiamine, riboflavin, folic acid, adenine, oleic acid, and uracil being essential, and probably nicotinic acid and pyridoxine. This indicates very marked deficiencies in the synthetic mechanisms of this species. Uracil is of interest in that it may be associated with anaerobiosis, staphylococci requiring it under anaerobic, but not under aerobic, conditions.

The list of essential nutrilities is a long and growing one, substances such as p-aminobenzoic acid and streptogenin being among those recognized in recent years. p-Aminobenzoic acid is of interest in the development of the concept of antimetabolites. Streptogenin is a low-molecular-weight peptide that can be replaced by L-serylglycyl-L-glutamic acid. Other peptides exert a streptogenin-like activity or may be required by different species. Even acetic acid has been identified as an essential nutrilite, being required (or stimulatory) in trace amounts if the organism is unable to produce this essential metabolite, or sparking agent, in amounts sufficient for growth. Another essential nutrilite, lipoic acid, was known as the "acetate-replacing factor."

Finally, there are those organisms in nutritional group 5 (Chap. 1), e.g., *Mycobacterium leprae*, *Treponema pallidum*, the rickettsiales, and the filtrable viruses, that are extremely difficult or impossible to cultivate at this time in media of known composition. They appear to be so lacking in synthetic ability as to be able to grow only upon or within cells of the host.

Not only have microorganisms been employed in studies on the identification of essential nutrilites and on their function, but they can also be employed in quantitative analyses for an essential nutrilite. Growth, over a limited range in an otherwise complete medium, is proportional to the concentration of the one missing essential nutrilite when it is added in appropriate amounts. A standard curve (Fig. 13-16) can be established with known amounts of the substance, and by comparing the growth response induced by the standard and the material under test, the concentration of the latter can be determined. Microbiological assays are employed for various amino acids and vitamins but must be rigidly controlled as they are subject to numerous errors.

It is readily apparent that bacterial growth and multiplication is a complex phenomenon embodying numerous synthetic reactions that must be closely correlated with the energy-providing ones if they are to proceed in an orderly manner. Loss of one or more synthetic abilities leads to a greater degree of dependence of the organism on other forms of life, and ultimately to parasitism and pathogenicity. Bit by bit information is being collected concerning the nutritional requirements of the various species and pathways of utilization of the nutrients. Ultimately this should lead to a better understanding, not only of each species, but also of the relationships between organisms as expressed by symbiotic effects and antagonisms in their natural habitats, whether the latter is animate or inanimate in character.

Nomenclature of Nutritional Types. We considered in Chap. 1 in a general way the nutritional and energy requirements of bacteria and classified the bacteria and closely related organisms into five relatively distinct groups. The major trend observed was an increase from group to group in nutritional requirements, or decrease in synthetic abilities, together with increasing dependence upon other forms of life. Knowing more about the energy sources, nutritional requirements, and synthetic abilities of bacteria, we can now better describe various nutritional types in a few words on the basis of a nomenclature suggested at a Cold Spring

Harbor Symposium on Quantitative Biology.[1]   There has been some confusion in the past in the use of certain terms, and these have been redefined and new ones introduced as follows:

I. Nomenclature based upon energy sources
    A. PHOTOTROPHY
       Energy chiefly provided by photochemical reaction
       1. *Photolithotrophy*
          Growth dependent upon exogenous inorganic H donors
       2. *Photoorganotrophy*
          Growth dependent upon exogenous organic H donors
    B. CHEMOTROPHY
       Energy provided entirely by dark chemical reaction
       1. *Chemolithotrophy*
          Growth dependent upon oxidation of exogenous inorganic substances
       2. *Chemoorganotrophy*
          Growth dependent upon oxidation or fermentation of exogenous organic substances
    C. PARATROPHY
       Energy apparently provided by the host cell
       1. *Schizomycetotrophy*
          Growth only in bacterial cells
       2. *Phytotrophy*
          Growth only in plant cells
       3. *Zootrophy*
          Growth only in animal cells
II. Nomenclature based upon ability to synthesize essential metabolites
    A. AUTOTROPHY
       All essential metabolites are synthesized
       1. *Autotrophy sensu stricto*
          Ability to reduce oxidized inorganic nutrients
       2. *Mesotrophy*
          Inability to reduce one or more oxidized inorganic nutrients = need for one or more reduced inorganic nutrients
    B. HETEROTROPHY
       Not all essential metabolities are synthesized = need for exogenous supply of one or more essential metabolites (growth factors or vitamins)
    C. HYPOTROPHY
       The self-reproducing units (bacteriophages, viruses, genes, and so on) multiply by reorganization of complex structures of the host

Composite names are used for the concise characterization of a nutritional type with respect to the chief energy source as well as to the capacity for the synthesis of all essential cell constituents.

Examples (see also Table 12-5):
    Photolithoautotrophic—*Rhodopseudomonas vannielli*
    Chemoorganomesotrophic—*Escherichia coli*
    Chemoorganoheterotrophic—*Streptococcus pyogenes*

[1] *Cold Spring Harbor Symp. Quant. Biol.*, vol. 11, p. 302 (1946).

TABLE 12-5. EXAMPLES OF VARIOUS NUTRITIONAL TYPES OF MICROORGANISMS ACCORDING TO THE COLD SPRING HARBOR SCHEME OF CLASSIFICATION

		Autotrophy		Heterotrophy	Hypotrophy
		Autotrophy *sensu strictu*	Mesotrophy		
Phototrophy	Photolithotrophy Photoorganotrophy	*Chlorella vulgaris*		*Rhodopseudomonas palustris* *Rhodospirillum rubrum*	
Chemotrophy	Chemolithotrophy Chemoorganotrophy	*Thiobacillus denitrificans* *Pseudomonas fluorescens*	*Escherichia coli*	*Saccharomyces cerevisiae*	
Paratrophy	Schizomycetotrophy Phytotrophy Zootrophy				Bacteriophages? Plant viruses? Animal viruses?

Isolation of Nutritional Types. Once we know the nutritional type of an organism we are in a better position to attempt to isolate it in pure culture and to devise a synthetic medium upon which we can cultivate it in the laboratory. Suppose we wish to isolate a bacterium that utilizes the oxidation of sulfur to sulfate as the energy source. We have seen that water and certain salts are essential constituents of all media. We therefore would select a basic salt medium and add sulfur to it. Since the organism is an aerobe and is autotrophic we would expose the culture to air and at the same time increase the carbon dioxide tension to a level above that of normal air. The medium could be inoculated with a sample of soil and incubated at a suitable temperature, preferably in the dark to eliminate growth of photosynthetic forms. A variety of organisms would be introduced in the inoculum along with some organic matter, thus making it possible for a number of heterotrophic species to multiply, at least to a limited extent. Ultimately conditions should develop conducive primarily to the growth of sulfur oxidizers. On transfer of a sample of this mixed culture to the basic, sulfur-containing medium, conditions become less favorable for the growth of other organisms.

On repeated transfer in this manner the culture will become enriched with sulfur-oxidizing bacteria, i.e., their proportion with respect to other species will be markedly increased. Hence such a procedure is known as the enrichment-culture technique, and the cultures as enrichment cultures. Once the relative numbers of the desired type of bacterium have increased, the chances of isolating the organism in pure culture on plating out on a semisolid medium are increased.

If we desired to isolate a hydrogen-oxidizing bacterium, we could follow the same general procedure, keeping the concentrations of all oxidizable inorganic compounds in the basal medium at as low levels as possible. Suitable tensions of hydrogen, oxygen, and carbon dioxide would have to be provided for in the gas phase. Similar procedures could be utilized for the isolation of a sterol oxidizer, a cellulose fermenter, or any other organism possessing a distinctive nutritional requirement or metabolic activity. In some instances it would be necessary to supply traces of essential amino acids or of growth factors to promote growth of exacting species. Isolation might be facilitated by adjustment of the pH of the culture medium, either to the optimum for growth of the species or to a pH inhibitory to the growth of many species while still suitable for the one desired. Examples of the latter type of adjustment of pH would be the alkaline media devised for the isolation of cholera vibrios and the acidic media for *Thiobacillus thiooxidans*. Isolation of a particular species can also be made easier at times by the addition of agents inhibitory to the growth of other species, even of the same metabolic or nutritional type. Examples would be the use of gentian violet to inhibit gram-positive species, azide to retard growth of gram-negative forms, or bile salts to inhibit coliforms in the isolation of salmonellas or shigellas from feces.

Various, often relatively complex media are employed in the isolation and identification of heterotrophic species, some of which may be quite fastidious in their nutritional requirements.[1] Some of these media are designed to serve as both enrichment and selective media and at the same time may also serve as differential media. Such media are used, often unknowingly, in the search for coliform bacteria in water and for the isolation of many pathogenic species in clinical laboratories.

Or, if we have isolated a particular species of bacteria, we can determine its basic nutritional requirements and devise a synthetic medium, one of known chemical composition, for its cultivation. This often enables us to study the metabolism of one compound by the species more accurately than when the substance is present in a complex broth which might provide other utilizable foodstuffs. A synthetic medium is also valuable for the production of toxins and other agents, the isolation of these substances being less difficult from a simple medium. Finally, as has been amply demonstrated, studies of specific nutritional requirements of bacteria and the role played by these agents have broadened our understanding of the nutrition of higher forms of life.

REFERENCES

Barker, H. A.: Oxidation of organic compounds by *Prototheca zopfii*, *J. Cell. Comp. Physiol.*, **8**, 231–250 (1936).

[1] For a general account and numerous examples see the "Difco Manual of Dehydrated Culture Media and Reagents," Difco Laboratories, Detroit.

———— and W. Z. Hassid: Degradation and synthesis of complex carbohydrates, in C. H. Werkman and P. W. Wilson (eds.), "Bacterial Physiology," Academic Press, Inc., New York, 1951.

Bolton, E. T., D. B. Cowie, and M. K. Sands: Sulfur metabolism in *Escherichia coli*. III. The metabolic fate of sulfate sulfur, *J. Bacteriol.*, **63**, 309–318 (1952).

Britten, R.: Extracellular metabolic products of *Escherichia coli* during rapid growth, *Science*, **119**, 578 (1954).

Buchanan, R. E., and E. I. Fulmer: "Physiology and Biochemistry of Bacteria," 3 vols., The Williams & Wilkins Company, Baltimore, 1928.

Clark, W. M., and H. A. Lubs: The colorimetric determination of hydrogen ion concentration and its applications in bacteriology, *J. Bacteriol.*, **2**, 1–34, 109–136, 191–236 (1917).

Clifton, C. E.: On the possibility of preventing assimilation in respiring cells, *Enzymologia*, **4**, 245–253 (1937).

————: Assimilation by bacteria, in C. H. Werkman and P. W. Wilson (eds.), "Bacterial Physiology," Academic Press, Inc., New York, 1951.

Cowie, D. B., E. T. Bolton, and M. K. Sands: Sulfur metabolism in *Escherichia coli*, *J. Bacteriol.*, **60**, 233–248 (1950).

Fales, F. W.: The assimilation and degradation of carbohydrates by yeast cells, *J. Biol. Chem.*, **193**, 113–124 (1951).

Falk, I. S.: The role of certain ions in bacterial physiology, *Abstr. Bacteriol.*, **7**, 33–50, 87–105, 133–147 (1923).

Fling, M., and N. H. Horowitz: Threonine and homoserine in extracts of a methionineless mutant of *Neurospora*, *J. Biol. Chem.*, **190**, 277–285 (1951).

Foster, J. W.: "Chemical Activities of Fungi," Academic Press, Inc., New York, 1949.

———— and F. Heiligman: Mineral deficiencies in complex organic media as limiting factors in the sporulation of aerobic bacilli, *J. Bacteriol.*, **57**, 613–615 (1949).

Fraser, D., and B. Tolbert: The utilization of the three singly-C^{14}-marked lactic acids by *Escherichia coli*, *J. Bacteriol.*, **62**, 195–197 (1951).

Gale, E. F.: The nitrogen metabolism of gram positive bacteria, *Bull. Johns Hopkins Hosp.*, **83**, 119–175 (1948).

Knight, B. C. J. G.: "Bacterial Nutrition," *Med. Research Council (Brit.), Spec. Rept. Ser.* 210 (1936).

Knight, S. G.: Mineral metabolism, in C. H. Werkman and P. W. Wilson (eds.), "Bacterial Physiology," Academic Press, Inc., New York, 1951.

Lamanna, C., and M. F. Mallette: "Basic Bacteriology," The Williams & Wilkins Company, Baltimore, 1953.

Levine, S., H. J. R. Stevenson, and R. H. Bordner: Identification of glycogen in whole bacterial cells by infrared spectrophotometry, *Science*, **118**, 141–142 (1953).

Lilly, V. G., and H. L. Barnett: "Physiology of the Fungi," McGraw-Hill Book Company, Inc., New York, 1951.

Miles, A. A., and N. W. Pirie (eds.): "The Nature of the Bacterial Surface," Charles C Thomas, Publisher, Springfield, Ill., 1949.

Mueller, J. H.: Nutrition of the single cell: its application in medical bacteriology, *Harvey Lectures, Ser.*, **34**, 143–161 (1943–1944).

Peterson, W. H., and M. S. Peterson: Relation of bacteria to vitamins and other growth factors, *Bacteriol. Rev.*, **9**, 49–109 (1945).

Pickett, M. J., and C. E. Clifton: The effect of selective poisons on the utilization of glucose and intermediate compounds by microorganisms, *J. Cell. Comp. Physiol.*, **22**, 147–165 (1943).

Porter, J. R.: "Bacterial Chemistry and Physiology," John Wiley & Sons, Inc., New York, 1946.

Rahn, O.: "Physiology of Bacteria," The Blakiston Division, McGraw-Hill Book Company, Inc., New York, 1932.

Roberts, R. B., P. H. Abelson, D. B. Cowie, E. T. Bolton, and R. J. Britten: Studies on biosynthesis in *Escherichia coli*, *Carnegie Inst. Wash. Publ.* 607 (1955).

Santer, M., and S. Ajl: Metabolic reactions of *Pasteurella pestis*. I. Terminal oxidation, *J. Bacteriol.*, **67**, 379–386 (1954).

Shaughnessy, H., and C.-E. A. Winslow: The diffusion products of bacterial cells as influenced by the presence of various electrolytes, *J. Bacteriol.*, **14**, 69–99 (1927).

Sherman, J. M., and G. E. Holm: Salt effects in bacterial growth. II. The growth of *Bact. coli* in relation to H-ion concentration, *J. Bacteriol.*, **7**, 465–470 (1922).

Siegel, B. V., and C. E. Clifton: Oxidative assimilation of glucose by *Escherichia coli*, *J. Bacteriol.*, **60**, 113–118 (1950a).

——— and ———: Energy relationships in carbohydrate assimilation by *Escherichia coli*, *J. Bacteriol.*, **60**, 573–583 (1950b).

——— and ———: Energetics and assimilation in the combustion of carbon compounds by *Escherichia coli*, *J. Bacteriol.*, **60**, 585–593 (1950c).

Simon, E. W.: The action of nitrophenols on respiration and on glucose assimilation in yeast, *J. Exptl. Bot.*, **4**, 377–392 (1953a).

———: Dinitrocresol, cyanide, and the Pasteur effect in yeast, *J. Exptl. Bot.*, **4**, 393–402 (1953b).

Stacey, M.: Enzymic synthesis of polysaccharides, *Advances in Enzymol.*, **15**, 301–318 (1954).

Taylor, F. J.: Oxidative assimilation of glucose by *Scenedesmus quadricauda*, *J. Exptl. Bot.*, **1**, 301–321 (1950).

———: The oxidation of labelled acetate by baker's yeast, *New Phytologist*, **51**, 256–257 (1952).

Virtanen, A. I., and N. Rautanen: Nitrogen assimilation, in J. B. Sumner and K. Myrbäck (eds.), "The Enzymes," vol. 2, pt. 2, Academic Press, Inc., New York, 1952.

Waring, W. S., and C. H. Werkman: Growth of bacteria in an iron-free medium, *Arch. Biochem.*, **1**, 303–310 (1942).

——— and ———: Iron deficiency in bacterial metabolism, *Arch. Biochem.*, **4**, 75–87 (1944).

Webb, M.: Effects of magnesium on cellular division in bacteria, *Science*, **118**, 607–611 (1953).

Wiame, J. M., and M. Doudoroff: Oxidative assimilation by *Pseudomonas saccharophila* with C^{14}-labeled substrates, *J. Bacteriol.*, **62**, 187–193 (1951).

Wilner, B., and C. E. Clifton: Oxidative assimilation by *Bacillus subtilis*, *J. Bacteriol.*, **67**, 571–575 (1954).

Wilson, P. W., and R. H. Burris: Biological nitrogen fixation: a reappraisal, *Ann. Rev. Microbiol.*, **7**, 415–432 (1953).

Winslow, C.-E. A., and I. S. Falk: Studies on salt action. IX. The additive and antagonistic effects of sodium and calcium chlorides upon the viability of *Bact. coli*, *J. Bacteriol.*, **8**, 237–244 (1923).

Young, E. G., R. W. Begg, and E. I. Pents: The inorganic nutrient requirements of *Escherichia coli*, *Arch. Biochem.*, **5**, 121–136 (1944).

CHAPTER 13

GROWTH OF BACTERIA

We have considered in the preceding chapter the general conditions essential for growth of bacteria, actually for increase in cell constituents and eventually multiplication of the cells. When the essential cellular constituents have been synthesized and arranged in requisite manner, the individual cell divides into halves, each one of which normally repeats the process in time, and so on. There may be some delay before separation is complete and chains of cells can be observed, particularly in some species or variants thereof. Growth and multiplication continue until the food supply, either bulk or a specific ingredient, becomes a limiting factor, or until metabolic products of an inhibitory nature begin to exert their effect. How the remarkable organization in time and space that leads to cellular multiplication is accomplished remains as one of the major problems of biology.

Cell growth and division in the over-all aspect can be considered as a cyclical process much like the metabolic cycles. The cell grows and divides according to a predetermined pattern imposed by its genetic structure and implemented by the enzymic apparatus of the cell which is also under genetic control ultimately. The potential enzyme pattern of a species is determined by the genetic structure of the cell, while formation and activity of the enzymes are influenced by physical and chemical factors in the environment. Influences of these factors (pH, temperature, etc.) are major determinants of growth, or lack thereof, and factors influencing enzyme activity are generally found to influence growth in a similar manner. Numerous studies have been carried out on the influence of physical and chemical factors on growth of bacteria in pure culture. In many instances results of such studies can be expressed in mathematical terms. Progress has been much less rapid in the study of factors influencing growth of bacteria in their natural environments where a species must compete with others for its food supply and be able to survive under conditions of constant biological warfare, the competition for survival. Somewhat less complex conditions are encountered in the relationship between a host and a parasite, but even here we know relatively little concerning the interplay between the two organisms involved.

Determination of Numbers of Bacteria. The quantitative determination of bacterial growth commonly involves measurements of increases in numbers of bacteria directly or indirectly, and much less frequently actual determination of increases in size of individual cells. The indirect methods for estimation of increases in bacterial populations depend upon measurements of protoplasmic content, of specific components or activities thereof, or of physical properties of the cell suspensions.

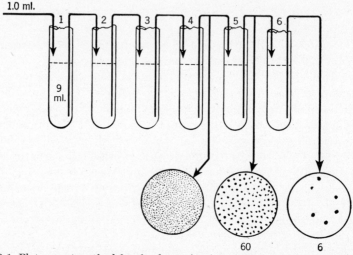

FIG. 13-1. Plate-count method for the determination of the number of viable bacteria in a culture. Decimal dilutions are made, and appropriate dilutions are plated out. In this example plating out 1.0 ml. from tube 6, a 1:1,000,000 dilution, gave rise to six colonies. This count times the dilution factor gives 6 million as the number of viable bacteria in the original culture. Sixty colonies from 1.0 ml. of dilution tube 5 also gives a count of 6 million since 60 × the dilution factor 100,000 = 6,000,000.

The number of viable cells, i.e., cells capable of multiplying in a favorable environment, is determined by cultural methods applied to appropriate dilutions of the test culture. By carrying out the dilutions, usually decimally, in a suitable medium and determining the highest dilution in which growth is evident upon incubation, an approximation of the number of bacteria in the original sample can be obtained. A large number of dilution tubes, and preferably serial dilution, must be employed when statistically valid results are desired. This technique, modified to use acid and gas production from lactose as an indicator rather than number of viable cells, is employed in the estimation of the most probable number of coliform bacteria in a water sample.

A more common method (Fig. 13-1) for the enumeration of viable bacteria is to mix measured dilutions of the culture or suspension with nutrient agar or gelatin in a petri dish or in roll tubes; a count of the number of colonies developing upon incubation gives an indication of the number of viable cells in the dilution plated out. This value, preferably in the range of 30 to 300 colonies, multiplied by the dilution factor gives the number present in the original sample. Actually, not all living cells necessarily multiply and give rise to colony formation during the period and conditions of incubation (a nonmultiplying cell may be living and be viable under other conditions), and some of the colonies may arise from clumps of bacteria rather than from individual cells. Some cells in the test sample may be damaged by the diluent or the dilution and plating procedure. In addition, mechanical errors of measurement are involved and the plate count, therefore, is subject to these errors besides being time-consuming and requiring considerable numbers of petri dishes, pipettes, and dilution blanks.

The plate count gives an indication of the number of viable cells under the conditions employed, but is of no value if one is interested in the total number of bacteria, both viable and nonviable, in the sample. Counts of the total number of cells in a definite volume of the sample can be made with the aid of a microscope, employing either a stained smear or a counting chamber. Knowing the area of the field of vision in the microscope and the total area of the smear, keeping the latter as uniform as possible, one can calculate the total number of bacteria in the smear by simple proportion from the average count per microscope field. Since the smear was made from a known volume of the culture, the total number per unit volume of the original test material can be estimated. Considerable error is involved in the total count because of uneven drying of the smear and consequent uneven distribution of organisms on the slide. This method is employed in determining numbers of bacteria in milk. The Petroff-Hauser counting chamber, similar in construction to a blood-cell counting chamber, can be employed for the direct enumeration of bacteria. The chamber is of known depth, and the bottom surface is ruled in squares of known area; hence counts can be made directly of the number of cells in a definite volume. Counts can be made only when fairly high numbers of bacteria are present in the sample. Various difficulties are encountered during actual use of this chamber, but with practice a fair degree of accuracy can be developed. Attempts have been made to differentiate between living and dead cells in the chamber by the use of vital stains, but these do not work well with bacteria.

Photomicrographic records of unstained or stained bacteria can be made, and from these pictures measurements can be made of the dimensions of individual cells. If the records are of a single cell and its progeny, one can follow directly changes in size of the cells with time in living, unstained cells, thus obtaining data on actual growth of a cell as well as following the increase in population. Studies of this nature are quite limited in number. Actual volume changes can be determined by measurements of volume of cells packed by centrifugation in calibrated tubes.

The indirect methods for the estimation of increases in bacterial populations involve determinations of changes in wet or dry (about 10 to 20 per cent of wet weight) weight in appropriate samples: of increases in carbon or nitrogen content or increases in oxygen consumption or the production of waste products such as carbon dioxide or lactic acid where these changes can be shown to be directly related to growth of the organisms. The physical property of cell suspensions most commonly employed in assays of bacterial populations is based upon light absorption and scattering by the cells. When a suspension of bacteria is placed in a beam of light of constant intensity, the amount of light transmitted by the suspension is inversely proportional to the density of the suspension over a fairly wide concentration range. Measurements of light transmission can be made with the aid of a photoelectric colorimeter. The instrument can be calibrated in terms of numbers of "normal" or "average" bacteria, of wet or dry weight of the cells, or of their carbon or nitrogen content. Deviations from a linear relationship may be noted, but frequently corrections for this can be applied. This method is widely employed but, like most of the methods other than the viable count, suffers from the inability to detect numbers of bacteria of an order less than several million per milliliter. A less commonly employed and somewhat more sensitive method involves measurement of the light scattered at right angles to the beam of light by the cells in a suspension. The various methods of assay usually yield results of the same general nature.

Phases of Growth. When bacteria are inoculated into a culture medium, or when they gain entrance into a suitable environment, they remain dormant as far as numbers of bacteria are concerned for a period of time. The duration of this period of apparent dormancy depends upon the nature of the organisms and their environment, the age of the cells, and the temperature. After some time an increase in numbers of bacteria can be detected, and somewhat later the cells multiply with great rapidity, division occurring at a relatively constant rate. Finally, the rate of reproduction diminishes, in time becomes zero, and in a closed system the cells eventually die. When logarithms of numbers of viable cells (for convenience in covering a range of numbers that may lie between 0 and 1×10^x per milliliter) or of total numbers are plotted against time, a so-called bacterial-growth curve is obtained. Studies of multiplication in bacterial cultures offer opportunities for studying population problems in general, similar behaviors being noted in time-population studies in plant and animal populations. Inspection of time-growth curves in Figs. 13-2 and 13-4 leads to the conclusion that definite points of inflection exist and that these tend to separate the growth curve into a series of relatively distinct, connected, and consecutive phases of growth characterized primarily by differences in rates of growth. The growth, and death, cycle has been divided into various phases by different workers,

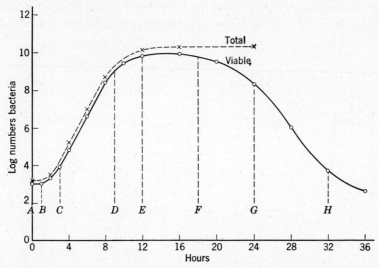

FIG. 13-2. Schematic representation of time-multiplication relationships in a culture of bacteria.

the descriptive terms proposed by Buchanan, Winslow, and Monod being used most frequently. These phases, together with factors influencing growth of bacteria, are discussed in books by Buchanan and Fulmer (1928), Henrici (1928), Rahn (1932), Monod (1942), Porter (1946), and Hinshelwood (1946) and in reviews by Winslow and Walker (1939) and Monod (1949). The phases (depicted in Fig. 13-2) can be compared with each other as follows:

Period	Buchanan	Winslow	Monod
A–B	Initial stationary	Adjustment	Lag
B–C	Lag, or + acceleration	. . . .	Acceleration
C–D	Logarithmic	Increase	Exponential
D–E	Negative acceleration	Crisis	Retardation
E–F	Maximum stationary	. . . .	Stationary
F–G	Accelerated death	Decrease	Decline
G–H	Logarithmic death		
H–	Negative acceleration of death*	Readjustment	

* Added by author.

These phases are illustrated in Fig. 13-2, in which the logarithms of the numbers of viable bacteria are plotted against time. The semilogarithmic plot of total numbers of bacteria against time gives rise to a similar curve slightly above the viable plot and one which diverges away from it if some of the cells die during the period of active growth.   The total count reaches a maximum value which generally is maintained relatively constant for a considerable period of time, the numbers eventually decreasing at a rate dependent upon the ability of the cells to undergo autolysis or to disintegrate because of other factors.

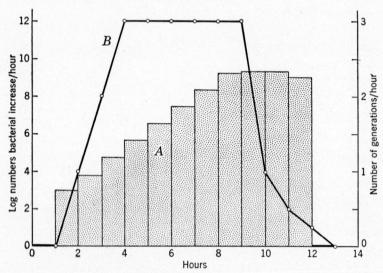

Fig. 13-3. Data from Fig. 13-2 plotted to show (A) logarithms of number of bacteria formed per hour and (B) number of generations per hour.

The data used for constructing Fig. 13-2 were used in the preparation of Fig. 13-3, in which plots of generations per hour and of the logarithms of the numbers of bacteria formed per hour are presented.   It is apparent that the number of generations per hour remains constant for several hours, i.e., during the logarithmic period of growth.   It is also apparent from Fig. 13-3 that the majority of the cells ultimately present in the culture are formed after the logarithmic period of growth.

Time-growth relationships in a culture of bacteria are also presented in Fig. 13-4.   Plots of logarithms to the base 10 and also to the base 2 (see p. 295) of the numbers of viable bacteria against time are given for comparative purposes.   Lactic acid accumulation with time is included in this figure to illustrate that production of this end product in this example is proportional to the bacterial concentration over a relatively wide growth period and can, therefore, be employed as a measure of growth.   A plot of generation time during the various time periods is also included to illustrate how this varies with phases of growth of the culture.

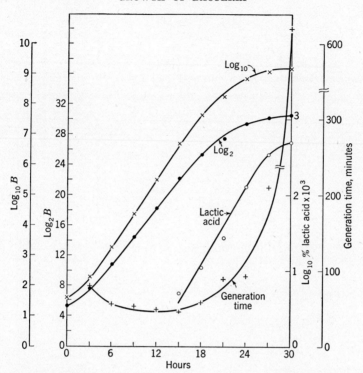

Fig. 13-4. Actual behaviors noted during the growth of a culture of lactic acid bacteria. (*Data from Rahn*, 1932.)

Mathematical Relationships. Since bacteria multiply primarily asexually it is possible for one cell to initiate development of a new population, the cell dividing to form two in one generation time, and so on. This geometrical progression, assuming that no cells die during the process (Fig. 13-5), can be represented as

$$1 \rightarrow 2 \rightarrow 4 \rightarrow 8 \rightarrow 16 \rightarrow 32 \cdots$$

or since

$$2^0 = 1,\ 2^1 = 2,\ 2^2 = 4,\ 2^3 = 8,\ \ldots$$

we can write

$$2^0 \rightarrow 2^1 \rightarrow 2^2 \rightarrow 2^3 \rightarrow \cdots \rightarrow 2^n$$

the exponents representing the number of generations. The same relationship holds if we start with any number of viable cells. At the end of n generations there will be $B2^n$ cells, or in other words

$$B_t = B_0 2^n \tag{13-1}$$

where B_0 = number of bacteria at beginning of time interval t

B_t = number at end of period of time

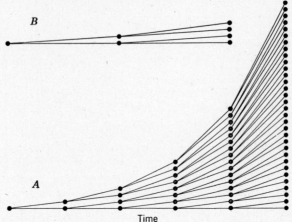

Fig. 13-5. Illustration of the relative change in numbers of bacteria with time during multiplication at a rate (A) of one generation per hour and (B) of one generation every 2 hr.

If we represent an average generation time by g, then

$$\frac{t}{n} = g \tag{13-2}$$

or

$$n = \frac{t}{g} \tag{13-3}$$

On substituting t/g for n in equation (13-1) we obtain

$$B_t = B_0 2^{t/g} \tag{13-4}$$

Equation (13-4) expressed in logarithmic form becomes

$$\log B_t = \log B_0 + \frac{t}{g} \log 2 \tag{13-5}$$

and, on solving for t/g, we obtain

$$\frac{t}{g} = \frac{\log B_t - \log B_0}{\log 2} \tag{13-6}$$

Or, on rearranging equation (13-6) and solving for g, we obtain

$$g = \frac{t \log 2}{\log B_t - \log B_0} \tag{13-7}$$

Time and numbers of bacteria can be determined experimentally, and the value of g can be calculated with the aid of equation (13-7). The slope of the viable count-time curve in Fig. 13-2 is 0.9 during the logarithmic period, or, in other words, $\log B_t - \log B_0 = 0.9$ per hour. Substituting this value in equation (13-7) along with the other known values and solving for g yields a value of $\frac{1}{3}$ hr., or 20 min., depending upon the time unit employed, for the generation time. Knowing t and g now, we can calculate n directly with the aid of equation (13-3) and find it to be 3. Hence a slope of 0.9 for the growth curve indicates a generation time of 20 min. and three generations per hour. The value of n can be calculated directly with the aid of equation (13-6) since $n = t/g$, or

$$n = \frac{\log B_t - \log B_0}{\log 2} \qquad (13\text{-}8)$$

We have seen that $B_t = B_0 2^n$. This means that during multiplication of bacteria, the number of bacteria is an exponential function of 2. Logarithms are the exponents of the base figure, and Monod (1949) has stressed that growth curves can be presented best if this is taken into account. In other words, he advocates plotting logarithms to the base 2 of numbers of bacteria against time rather than using $\log_{10}$. Plots of both $\log_{10}$ and of $\log_2$ values ($\log_2 = 3.322 \times \log_{10}$ values) against time are included in Fig. 13-4. One unit increase on the $\log_2$ scale represents one generation (doubling of population). The number of divisions that have occurred during any time interval can be determined directly from the graph, being equal to the difference of the ordinates of the corresponding points. Likewise, the generation time can be read directly from the plot to the base 2 against time. These graphical relationships hold because we can write equation (13-1) as $B_t = B_0 2^d (t_1 - t_0)$, where d equals the number of divisions per unit time and $t_1 - t_0$ represents the elapsed time, since $n = d(t_1 - t_0)$. On converting to logarithms to the base 2 we obtain

$$d = \frac{\log_2 B_t - \log_2 B_0}{t_1 - t_0} \qquad (13\text{-}9)$$

The mathematical relationships presented above are fundamental to a consideration of multiplication of bacteria and of factors influencing this process. Other equations will be considered as the need for them arises. The terminology that will be employed in the consideration of growth phases will be for the most part that of Buchanan, which differs relatively little from that proposed later by Monod. The Winslow terminology is somewhat more general in character; it can be applied at times when growth curves depart from the ideal behavior indicated in Fig. 13-2; but it does not lend itself so well to a consideration of the smaller changes in rates of growth that are indicated by the other terminologies.

Initial Stationary Period of Growth. A cell can be likened to a factory in which raw materials are broken down and converted, some into energy and others into various forms in a series of stages. Once adjusted to a favorable environment, a bacterial cell grows (increases in size) continuously, and during division, a distribution of material occurs of such a nature that the two daughter cells are able to continue the processes. Growth and division continue for a time at a constant rate. What appears to be an equilibrium is established, but actually it is a steady state in which all components of the cell increase at rates such that their relative proportions remain unchanged, or practically so. Once unfavorable conditions develop, whether caused by accumulation of waste products or depletion of essential materials, the steady state can no longer be maintained and both the growth and the division rates decrease. Ultimately, growth and division come to a standstill, and the culture is then in the maximum stationary period. During and after this time the activities of various enzymes decline, or actual enzyme destruction occurs, the concentrations of intermediates of metabolism decrease, and structural or functional units begin to break down. In other words, without a continuous supply of raw materials and of energy the thermodynamically improbable state represented by a cell cannot be maintained. Cells from cultures in or beyond the maximum stationary phase are unable to establish a steady state in a new medium immediately upon transfer to it, and this, basically, is responsible for the initial stationary period of growth or, more specifically, of cell division.

Instead of the population being stationary during the first minutes (even hours in some instances), it may show a decrease in numbers of viable cells. The course and length of the initial stationary period depend on the nature of the cells and of the medium and on the temperature. The essence of this phase is adjustment of the cells to a new environment, an adjustment first evidenced by an increase in cell size and later by cellular division. The initial increase in cell volume frequently is due primarily to an uptake of water by the cells, and this is followed by a general increase in cellular material. The dissimilatory or energy-providing reactions can start at once in the new medium, if adaptive enzyme formation is not involved, while the synthetic processes frequently require compounds not present as such in the medium but arising during the course of dissimilation. The formation of essential metabolites in appropriate concentrations and the trapping of the energy required for the syntheses arising from these compounds are essential for the adjustment of the cell to its new environment and for rejuvenation of the cell, i.e., development of steady-state conditions. The initial stationary period has not been studied in great detail and most frequently is included in considerations of the lag or positive acceleration in growth phase.

The Period of Positive Acceleration in Growth. Numerous studies concerning this period of growth have been carried out, usually, however, with inclusion of the initial stationary phase. Some authors use the term lag phase in the Buchanan sense; most, however, use it to include both the initial stationary and the positive acceleration in growth periods. The term lag phase or period will be used here to cover the period from A to C in Fig. 13-2 and corresponds to the phase of adjustment of Winslow. The various early studies concerning it were summarized in a review by Winslow and Walker (1939). These authors described five different characteristics exhibited by cells or cultures in the "phase of adjustment," which can be summarized as follows:

1. The phenomenon of lag has a biological basis since the age of the cells in the inoculum has a direct effect on the extent of the lag phase, cells from the logarithmic period of growth showing little or no lag when transferred to the same medium under the same conditions, while a marked lag is observed with cells from older cultures as the inoculum.
2. Metabolic activity per cell increases during this period and reaches a maximum value late in this period or early in the logarithmic one.
3. Cells in cultures late in the lag and early in the logarithmic periods of growth are generally more sensitive to heat treatment and to chemical agents in general than are cells from mature cultures, a behavior ascribed by Sherman and Albus in 1923 to "physiological youth" of the cells.
4. Various demonstrations that cells are generally much larger during this early phase of growth than are cells from the parent culture.
5. Cells in young cultures are more resistant to acid agglutination than those from older cultures and also exhibit a lower electrophoretic charge.

These, and other considerations, led Winslow and Walker to support Henrici's concept that bacteria in a culture exhibit changes analogous to those observed during the growth and development of multicellular forms of life, i.e., embryonic, youthful, adult, and senescent forms. It is difficult, however, to ascribe an age to cells in a rapidly developing culture, those formed late in the logarithmic period being as young at the moment of division as those formed earlier in the logarithmic phase. Aging occurs primarily when division comes to a standstill, and resting forms as postulated by Bisset and others may develop. There are, however, definite and observable changes that do occur in cell size, metabolic activity, sensitivity to inimical agents, and so on with changes in age of the culture. It would be more accurate to speak of physiological age of the culture rather than of the cells.

Henrici (1928) summarized the studies of his group and those of others on changes in size of cells with age of the culture. Many species showed a two- to threefold increase in average cell size during the late-lag and early-log phases of growth, the average cell size decreasing from then on to the characteristic one ordinarily seen in 24-hr. smear preparations. Henrici also concluded that a greater lag occurs in multiplication than in actual growth, i.e., increase in size, of the cells.

Various workers, particularly in the 1930's, demonstrated increased metabolic activity per cell (heat production, oxygen consumption, carbon dioxide liberation, etc.) during the late-lag and early-log periods of growth. Cell size increased two- to threefold, whereas metabolic activity increased as much as tenfold during the lag period. Hence the increase in metabolic rate could not be accounted for by increased cell size alone. Hershey and Bronfenbrenner (1938), however, presented evidence that the rate of metabolism (O_2 consumption) remained constant per unit of cellular nitrogen. Their studies, unfortunately, did not cover oxygen consumption during the first 2 to 3 hr. More recent ones do indicate increased metabolic rates, whether expressed per cell, per unit volume of the cells, or per unit of nitrogen or other cellular constituent, during the early-log period. Monod (1949) points out that changes in concentration of intracellular reactants and in enzymatic activity per cell do occur when older cells are transformed to a fresh medium. Changes in metabolic rates would be expected until the cells were adapted to the new environment and the steady state had been established. Changes in rate also occur with changes in concentration of foodstuffs and of hydrogen ions.

Evidence of an adaptation of cells in the inoculum to the new environment and to multiplication has been presented in recent years by Hinshelwood (1946) in studies on "early" and "late" lag, by Malmgren and Hedén (1947) on the nucleotide metabolism of bacteria, by Monod (1949) on enzymatic adaptation, and by others in various studies. Hinshelwood and his coworkers have proposed a convenient lag time constant which can be represented as T_1 and defined as the difference between the observed time t_r required for the culture to reach a certain density x_r and the "ideal" time at which the same density would have been established had the logarithmic rate prevailed from the time of inoculation. This constant is significant for comparative purposes only when cultures having the same exponential rate of growth are compared. A more general constant L (Monod, 1949) can be defined as a growth-lag constant indicating the difference between the number of generations occurring between observed and ideal growth, or

$$L = T_1 n \qquad (13\text{-}10)$$

where n is the number of generations per unit time [equation (13-9)] during exponential growth. T_1 and L values can be determined graphically (Fig. 13-6). The lag phase involved in the use of these constants includes both the initial stationary and the positive acceleration growth phases and can be considered as a measure of the physiological distance between the times at which the medium was inoculated and the steady state was developed. L values are useful in comparing results obtained in studies on the influence of various foodstuffs or of inhibitory agents on growth and on enzyme activation or formation.

One, several, or, most likely, very many reactions may control the extent of the building-up process, and each reaction may be affected by change in amount or activity of the requisite enzyme(s) or in concentration of metabolites. The necessity for small amounts of carbon dioxide, or metabolites able to replace it, is well known, a pronounced growth lag being noted when concentrations below the optimum are employed. Another example is provided by studies of Hinshelwood and his coworkers (Hinshelwood, 1946). They found that *Aerobacter aerogenes* would grow without lag when transferred during the logarithmic phase of growth from complex media or a glucose-asparagine medium to another portion of the same medium. The time lag increased within limits as the age of the culture used for inoculation increased, as graphically indicated in Fig. 13-7.

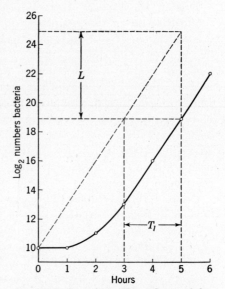

FIG. 13-6. Lag time (T_l) and growth lag (*L*) in a culture of bacteria. (*After Monod*, 1949.) The diagonal dashed line represents "ideal" growth, i.e., without lag.

An entirely different behavior was noted in a glucose–ammonium salt medium (Fig. 13-7), a marked lag being noted on transfer of cells in the early logarithmic phase in this medium to the same, but fresh, medium. Duration of this time lag decreased with increase in age of the parent culture to a minimum, and then increased with further age. This increase occurred in a manner similar to the increase noted with asparagine as the nitrogen source. The marked time lag observed with cells from early phases of growth in the ammonium medium was designated as early lag in contrast to the normal behavior, late lag, generally

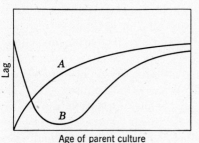

FIG. 13-7. Lag-age relationships in (*A*) an amino acid medium and (*B*) a glucose–ammonium sulfate medium. (*Redrawn from Hinshelwood*, 1946.)

noted with cells from parent cultures late in the growth cycle. Early lag was ascribed to the need for essential metabolites present in older cultures and carried over with the inoculum from older cultures. They found that it could be abolished by the addition of filtrates from older cultures to the glucose-ammonium medium, along with cells from young cultures.

Dagley, Dawes, and Morrison (1950) obtained similar results and also found that the method employed in maintaining the cultures affects the relationship between duration of the lag phase and the age of the inoculum in a glucose-ammonium medium. The fact that glutamic, aspartic, succinic, or oxalacetic acid added to the basal medium decreased lag time lends support to the concept that glutamate is a key intermediate which, when present in sufficient amounts, enables growth as such to proceed more rapidly. These compounds had little or no effect on rate of growth once exponential growth was evident in the glucose-ammonium medium. According to the Hinshelwood concept late lag is due to factors other than, or in addition to, the concentration of essential metabolites, or precursors thereof, in the medium.

Britten (1954) studied the release from the cell of metabolic products formed during the rapid growth of *E. coli* in a synthetic medium with C^{14}-labeled glucose as the principal carbon source. In the absence of organic supplements, a complex pattern of metabolic products, including amino acids, was noted. When unlabeled glutamate was added to the medium, it was used by the cells, but they also synthesized glutamate from glucose and secreted more labeled glutamate into the medium than in the absence of this amino acid as a supplement. A similar behavior was noted with aspartate, glycine, alanine, or valine as a supplement. When unlabeled proline was added to the basal medium it was also used, but C^{14}-labeled proline was no longer secreted into the medium. Arginine, serine, methionine, or threonine elicited a similar response. More complicated effects were also noted. These observations are suggestive of the need of the cell for essential metabolites and also of the complex relationships that must exist between diffusion of substances into and out of the cell, the synthetic reactions, and the formation of cellular elements.

Malmgren and Hedén (1947) measured the nucleotide content of bacteria indirectly from the photographic density of cells in photomicrographs taken with ultraviolet light in the region at which nucleotides absorb the light maximally. They also calculated the mean volume of cells at different ages of the culture from measurements of the photographic images. Typical results of measurements of relative increase in numbers of bacteria and of nucleotide content per cell for a gram-negative and a gram-positive species are presented in Fig. 13-8. A marked increase in light-absorbing material per cell is noted during the lag phase. The onset of rapid division is accompanied by a decrease in cellular content of this material, which further decreases in amount per cell as the exponential phase is approached. The second peak in the curve for *B. cereus* was also noted with other gram-positive species and may be due to the formation of material associated with gram positivity. Other studies have indicated a marked increase in RNA content of cells early in the growth cycle, the content per cell of DNA and of protein tending to remain relatively constant. Results of this nature (see also discussion of nucleic acid

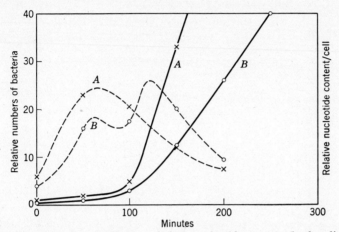

FIG. 13-8. Time-growth (solid lines) and time–nucleotide content (broken lines) relationships in cultures of (A) *Escherichia coli* and (B) *Bacillus cereus*. (*Redrawn from Malmgren and Hedén*, 1947.)

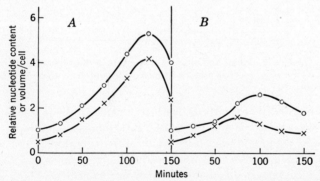

FIG. 13-9. Influence of size of inoculum ($A = 107 \times 10^6$, $B = 918 \times 10^6$ bacteria per milliliter) on volume (O——O) and nucleotide content (×——×) of cells during growth of *Proteus vulgaris*. (*Redrawn from Malmgren and Hedén*, 1947.)

structure in Chap. 15) suggest that RNA controls protein synthesis in the cell.

In the last study in their series Malmgren and Hedén noted that the total volume of the cells increased much more rapidly than did the dry weight of *Proteus vulgaris* in the early phases of growth. The curves (Fig. 13-9) more or less run parallel to each other. The changes are less pronounced when larger inocula are employed, a similar behavior having been reported in volume-change studies by other workers. In another experiment (Fig. 13-10) a portion of a broth medium was inoculated with cells of *P. vulgaris* from an 18-hr. culture and incubated for 75 min., at which time the nucleotide maximum per cell should almost have been reached. The cells were removed by centrifugation and then transferred to fresh broth, while the supernatant fluid was filtered and inoculated with cells from the 18-hr. culture. The nucleotide content per cell

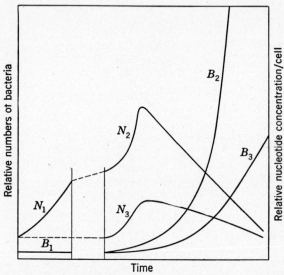

Fig. 13-10. Nucleotide content and number of bacteria in three associated experiments, 1, 2, and 3, where B = bacteria and N = nucleotide content. (*Redrawn from Malmgren and Hedén*, 1947. See text for details.)

increased markedly in the fresh broth to a peak at about the time multiplication was initiated, and decreased with increase in growth rate. A much shorter lag period was observed in this culture than in the one where cells were added to the semi-used medium. The nucleotide content of the cells in the latter culture did not increase to nearly so high a level as observed in the fresh medium, the lag period was about normal, and a lower growth rate was noticed. They interpreted these findings as indicating that in bacterial growth an essential substance appears in the medium, the formation of which is linked with nucleotide metabolism. It would appear, however, that this substance should be in the used broth and would favor a decreased lag phase. They further concluded that the increase in size of the cells during the lag phase can be ascribed mainly to an uptake of water which might be associated in some manner with nucleotide metabolism. More work should be carried out on this problem, but the various studies do indicate that the formation of essential metabolites could be an important factor in determining duration of the lag phase.

Mitchell and Moyle (1951) also followed (chemically) changes in the nucleic acid content of cells during growth. They concluded that the rate of cell growth (dry weight) of *Micrococcus pyogenes* var. *aureus* appears to be controlled by the percentage of RNA in the cells. The rate of synthesis and the percentage of DNA were related to the size of the cells in such a manner as to maintain the DNA content per cell constant. The total nucleotides produced increased more rapidly than cellular dry weight (mostly protein increase) at first. Their studies indicated that RNA synthesis was accelerated to the greatest extent. The maximum rate of cell growth was noted after a maximum rate of nucleic acid synthesis had been established, but occurred almost simultaneously with the period at which a maximum percentage of nucleic acids was observed. The rate of cell-protein synthesis appeared to be controlled by the percentages by weight of nucleic acids in the cells.

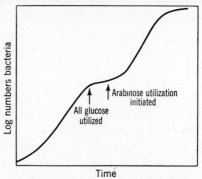

FIG. 13-11. The phenomenon of diauxie, or diphasic growth. (*Redrawn from Monod*, 1949).

Monod (1942, 1949) described behaviors during the growth of various bacteria in a mixed-sugar medium that well illustrate adaptation by bacteria to the environment. *E. coli*, for example, in a glucose-arabinose medium exhibited a double growth cycle (Fig. 13-11) consisting of two exponential phases of growth separated by a phase during which the growth rate passes through a minimum. He presented evidence (see also Chap. 15) that each growth cycle corresponds to the exclusive utilization of one of the sugars in the medium. After a period of lag *E. coli* grew in the glucose-arabinose medium until all of the glucose had been utilized. A second period of lag was observed, and then growth was reinitiated and arabinose was utilized, the concentration of the sugars being such that the extent of growth upon each substrate was limited by this factor. He termed this phenomenon "diauxie," or diphasic growth, and explained it on the basis of one sugar (or other substrate) inhibiting in some manner the formation of the enzyme attacking the other. A more recent hypothesis (Monod, in Davies and Gale, 1953) proposes that, for example, since glucose is an essential metabolite, the glucose-utilizing enzymes are always formed regardless of the presence of glucose in the medium. Glucose in the medium is inhibitory to the uptake of a second sugar such as sorbitol. The reason for this inhibition is unknown.   Once glucose is utilized completely, the cells become permeable to sorbitol, and after a phase during which the sorbitol-activating enzyme is formed, growth is reinitiated. The glucose enzyme is regarded as a normal constituent of the cell formed as a response to an essential intracellular metabolite, while the sorbitol-activating system is considered as an adaptive enzyme formed only in response to an extracellular stimulus.   It is evident that conditions were favorable for growth during the first exponential phase and also later on, the only detectable difference being in the ability of the cells to utilize sorbitol.   Here is a simple example of adaptation to substrate utilization that is induced by an environmental factor.   Time relationships and other considerations rule out mutation and selection as the causative factor for the phenomenon of diauxie, enzymatic adaptation being simply the formation of a specific enzyme under the influence of its substrate. This formation (Chap. 15) primarily occurs from constituents of the medium rather than from enzyme precursors in the cell.

Late in the positive acceleration in growth phase the over-all rate of the numerous linked reactions essential for growth and multiplication reaches a maximum and constant value, i.e., a steady state is established, and the culture passes into the logarithmic (exponential) phase of growth.

Logarithmic Period of Growth.   We have seen that during this phase the numbers of bacteria increase exponentially with time, and therefore a plot of logarithms of numbers of cells against time yields a straight-line relationship.   This means that the rate of cellular division remains constant during this period of growth.   The actual numbers of bacteria, or amounts of bacterial protoplasm, formed per unit of time during this phase, however, increase with time since growth is proportional to the number of cells present at any given time.   This behavior is depicted in Figs. 13-2 and 13-4, but is not self-evident in the ordinary semilogarithmic plots.   During a statistical-generation time, as many additional cells are produced, assuming that none dies, as were present at the beginning of the generation.   With the development of each new generation the demand for building materials and energy theoretically doubles.

One would assume that during the logarithmic period of growth the steady-state conditions that prevail would be such that the rate of metabolism per cell would remain relatively constant.   The rate per cell, however, tends to decrease during this phase of growth, as evidenced by many reports in the literature.   This could be due in part to experimental factors, the relatively high populations required for accurate determinations of respiratory activity creating an oxygen demand that is difficult to fulfill under the common methods of observation.

As we shall see, the total crop produced is proportional to the concentration of the nutrient, when this is the growth-limiting factor, over a relatively wide concentration range. The exponential-growth behavior is noted when increases either in numbers or in dry weights of the cells are considered. These observations would suggest that a constant amount of the nutrient is utilized per cell, or per unit mass, formed during the lag period, and therefore a constant amount of oxygen should be consumed (or carbon dioxide produced) per cell. The relationship between total crop and nutrient concentration generally has been determined on the basis of optical density of the cultures or the dry weights of cells produced, while metabolic studies ordinarily have been reported per cell.

TABLE 13-1. Oxygen Consumption and Growth per Milliliter of a Glucose–Basic Salt Culture of *Escherichia coli**

Time, hr.	Oxygen consumption, mm.³			Bacterial count × 10⁷		Bacterial C, mg	
	/ml.	× 10⁻⁸ /cell/hr.	/mg C/hr.	Viable	Total	× 10⁻²	× 10⁻¹⁰ /cell
0	...	....	...	16	18	5.8	3.6
1	7	3.8	107	19	31(?)	7.0	3.7
2	20	6.7	162	23	29	9.4	4.1
3	50	10.4	281	37	39	12.1	3.3
4	104	11.1	353	64	75	20.2	3.2
5	221	14.7	482	97	117	26.9	2.8
6	326	7.8	358	175	200	32.3	1.9

* From Siegel and Clifton (1950), courtesy of The Williams & Wilkins Company.

We have seen that Hershey and Bronfenbrenner (1938) noted marked changes in rate of oxygen consumed per cell during growth, while oxygen consumption per unit of cellular nitrogen was relatively constant. Siegel and Clifton (1950), on the other hand, noted about the same extent of change in oxygen consumed (Table 13-1) per cell or per milligram of cellular carbon per hour in young cultures of *E. coli* in a glucose medium. Both the rate of oxygen consumption (Fig. 13-12) and the amount of carbon per cell began to decrease with time before any decrease in rate of cell multiplication was noted. They also found (Table 13-2) remarkably constant ratios of carbon assimilated to carbon utilized during the early stages of growth, an efficiency of assimilation of 56 to 60 per cent being noted. It is evident that complex phenomena that are not as yet clearly understood are involved in the relationships among growth, multiplication, and metabolism in a bacterial culture.

It should be noted that in the early or late stages of growth, during which changes in numbers of cells are not pronounced, we can obtain a close approximation of metabolic activity per cell if we divide the total

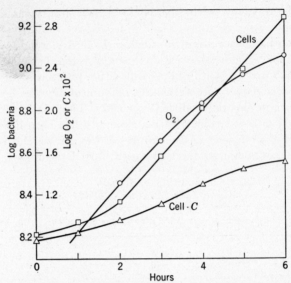

Fig. 13-12. Semilogarithmic plots of growth (□———□), oxygen consumption (○——○), and cellular carbon × 10² (△———△) per milliliter of medium as determined during the growth of *Escherichia coli* in a glucose–basic salt medium. (*From Siegel and Clifton, 1950, courtesy of The Williams & Wilkins Company.*)

TABLE 13-2. OXIDATIVE ASSIMILATION OF GLUCOSE DURING THE EARLY STAGES OF GROWTH OF *Escherichia coli**

	0–1.5	1.5–3.0	3.0–4.5	0–4.5
Time interval, hr....................	0–1.5	1.5–3.0	3.0–4.5	0–4.5
Initial substance carbon, mg..........	5.18	5.12	4.86	5.18
Cell carbon after assimilation of glucose, mg.....................	0.55	0.67	0.88	0.88
Cell carbon before assimilation of glucose, mg..........................	0.50	0.55	0.67	0.50
Carbon stored, mg..................	0.05	0.12	0.21	0.38
Supernatant carbon at end of interval..	5.12	4.86	4.53	4.53
Carbon dioxide carbon, mg..........	0.03	0.08	0.16	0.28
Total recovered, mg................	5.20	5.06	4.90	5.19
Total recovered, %.................	100.4	98.8	100.8	100.2
R.Q.............................	1.50	1.23	1.19	1.23
Ratio C assimilated/C utilized........	0.56	0.60	0.57	0.58

* From Siegel and Clifton (1950), courtesy of The Williams & Wilkins Company.

metabolic activity exhibited by the culture by the average number of cells present during the test period. A large error is involved when this type of calculation is used for changes observed during the log period of growth. Rahn (1932) discussed this problem and presented the derivation of an equation that can be employed for the more accurate calculation of the metabolic activity per cell.   This equation can be represented as

$$m = \frac{2.303 \, \Delta M (\log B_t - \log B_0)}{\Delta t (B_t - B_0)} \qquad (13\text{-}11)$$

where m = metabolic activity per cell per unit time

ΔM = increase in metabolic product, or amount of oxygen or of foodstuff consumed, during a short period of time Δt

B_0, B_t = number of bacteria at beginning and at end, respectively, of test period

The rate of growth of a bacterial culture is an expression of the over-all velocity of the numerous reactions involved in the synthesis of cellular substance.   It can be expressed by the equation representing the velocity of a unimolecular chemical reaction (Chap. 2) in the form

$$K = \frac{2.303}{t} \log \frac{B_t}{B_0} \qquad (13\text{-}12)$$

The value of K, the velocity constant of growth, is the resultant of hundreds of reactions linked in a complex network and is of general value for comparing the effect of various conditions on the rate of multiplication of bacteria. K values of 0.103, 0.069, and 0.034 correspond to generation times of 20, 40, and 60 min., respectively.   In a few instances growth may be arithmetical (linear) rather than logarithmic with time, being limited by one enzyme or enzyme system the activity of which is constant. In general, however, growth is exponential, and no one master reaction controls its rate.

The law of exponential growth is a good approximation but is not absolute in character.   The concentration of foodstuffs in the medium changes during growth, products of metabolism may accumulate, not all cells survive, and even though they did, a constantly changing environment could have an effect on the rate of division.   These factors appear to be relatively unimportant over a fairly wide range, and the law holds quite well over this range.

The phase of truly exponential multiplication at a maximum rate generally does not last more than 2 to 4 hr. in ordinary test-tube or flask cultures, but it can be prolonged by aeration.   Rahn and Richardson (1942) have pointed out that with most oxygen-consuming bacteria, the oxygen dissolved in the medium is exhausted by the time 2 to 10 million cells have developed per milliliter.   Oxygen may diffuse into the medium in stationary vessels at a rate sufficient to supply the demand of the cells in the first few millimeters near the surface, and they continue to multiply at the aerobic rate.   Anaerobic mechanisms can supply energy for many species, but generally not at a rate sufficiently high to support a maximum rate of growth.   The rate of growth in the bulk of the culture will, therefore, decrease, and a departure from the logarithmic relationship becomes evident.   Aeration does not necessarily increase the rate of multiplication, but it maintains it constant for a longer time and thereby induces a much larger crop.   Cultures aerated from the start often exhibit a longer lag phase than nonaerated cultures, an excess of oxygen possibly inducing more oxidations than are required for the nonadapted cells whose enzyme systems are not yet in balance.   A vigorous current of air through the medium is not enough to keep it saturated with oxygen when high popu- lations have been established.   It is necessary to employ physical

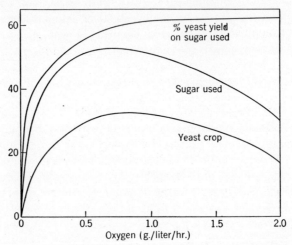

FIG.13-13. Variation of yeast crop, sugar used, and percentage of yeast yield on sugar used during 15 hr. with different rates of oxygen supply.   (*From White and Munns,* 1951, *courtesy of Wallerstein Laboratories.*)

methods for the production of smaller bubbles, and hence greater areas of air-medium contact to ensure an adequate oxygen supply.   Aeration in the right amount and of the right nature is highly important in indus- trial applications such as vinegar production by constant-flow procedures, the growth of molds for the production of penicillin and other agents, and for the production of baker's yeast.   White and Munns (1951) have studied aeration and yeast growth in detail (Fig. 13-13).   They recorded the strange behavior that although increasing aeration beyond a certain point reduces the total quantity of yeast produced during a test period, the efficiency of sugar transformation into yeast is increased.   Oxygen plus traces of carbon dioxide is at times inhibitory rather than stimulatory to the growth of some aerobic species.

    The exponential growth rate is determined to a great extent by three factors: temperature of incubation, nature of the medium, and the species of bacteria.   Relatively little is known concerning the reasons why species such as *E. coli* may multiply as rapidly as once every 20 min., the tubercle bacillus has a generation time of many hours, and many other species exhibit intermediate rates of multiplication, all under optimal conditions, as far as these have been established, for the individual species.

Influence of Temperature on Growth. The temperature of incubation determines, to a large extent, the rate of growth of a species. The classical study of Barber in 1908 well demonstrated (Fig. 13-14) the influence of temperature on rate of multiplication. The rate of multiplication generally increases rapidly at first with increase in temperature above the lower limit for growth; the increase in rate decreases as the temperature is further increased and levels off near the optimal temperature for growth. Above the optimal temperature for growth the growth rate decreases abruptly, owing to the high Q_{10} (Chap. 2) of protein denaturation. The Q_{10} for cell multiplication is commonly 2 to 3 over a fairly wide temperature range but may be higher at the lower temperatures at which growth can occur. The optimum temperature appears to be a compromise between the stimulatory effect of heat on many chemical reactions involved in cellular metabolism and the destructive action of heat as exhibited by decreased enzyme activity, probably due to protein denaturation. This compromise is at times reflected in the production of a maximum cell crop at a temperature slightly below that at which cellular division occurs at a maximum rate. The actual optimum temperature, or temperature range, for maximum rate of growth depends on the characteristics of the organism and particularly whether it is a psychrophilic, mesophilic, or thermophilic bacterium.

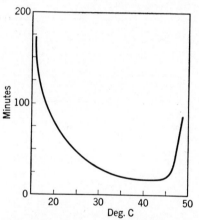

Fig. 13-14. Influence of temperature on generation time. (*After Barber, J. Infectious Diseases*, **5**, 396, 1908.)

Influence of Nutrients on Growth. As a general rule most heterotrophic species grow at a more rapid rate in complex rather than in chemically simple media. The rate of growth in a synthetic medium frequently increases during repeated transfers in the medium, thus suggesting adaptation and selection of cells best suited to the medium. In adapted cultures, however, different rates may be noted with different substrates. The rate of growth is relatively independent of the concentration of the growth-limiting factor (concentration of bulk foodstuff, of growth factors, or of essential elements) over a relatively wide concentration range. It varies directly with the concentration only at low levels (Fig. 13-15) for most species, the proportional response falling off at a concentration of glucose around $M/5{,}000$ or of 1×10^{-5} M phosphate for *E. coli*. The concentration of glucose required for one-half maximum rate of growth is considerably higher for some organisms, e.g., around $M/45$ for *M. tuberculosis*.

Monod (1949) concludes that the relationship between the rate of growth and the concentration of the limiting factor can be most conveniently and logically expressed by the hyperbolic equation

$$R = R_K \frac{C}{C_1 + C} \tag{13-13}$$

where R_K = rate limit for increasing concentrations of C
$\quad$ C_1 = concentration at which rate is half maximum
This equation is similar to an adsorption isotherm or to the Michaelis equation (Chap. 5).

The rate of growth is also influenced by the pH of the medium, the optimum pH and range of pH over which growth can occur being determined by the nature of the organism. The rate of growth frequently decreases in ordinary cultures in sugar-containing broths owing to the decrease in pH induced by the accumulation of acidic-fermentation products once the oxygen supply becomes a limiting factor. We shall see (Chap. 15) that the cell may compensate for unfavorable hydrogen-ion concentrations by increased activity or increased production of particular enzymes or by the production of different enzymes. This is another example of the adaptability of bacteria and an illustration of Le Châtelier's theorem. As a general rule, the rate of growth of facultative anaerobes is higher under aerobic than under anaerobic conditions.

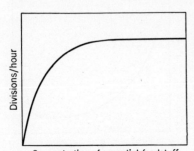

Fig. 13-15. Effect of concentration of foodstuff on rate of division of bacteria. (*After Monod*, 1949.)

Under the stable-state conditions evidenced by a logarithmic rate of multiplication it is possible that growth and division of single cells may occur in a manner similar to that observed with *Amoeba proteus* (Mazia, 1956). The increase in weight of single cells, after formation from their parent cell, was followed with the aid of a Cartesian diver. No appreciable lag in growth was noted following the original division, but growth slowed down and came to a halt when the mass of an amoeba was twice its original mass. A lapse of time was then noted between the completion of growth in mass and the onset of cellular division. The extent to which a cell increases in volume or mass appears to be controlled to a considerable extent by some trigger mechanism. Once a definite size has been reached processes of division are initiated, or at least become evident. It is possible that growth and division may be separate in time with bacteria as well as with protozoa. Use of synchronously multiplying cultures of bacteria (Novick, 1955) may enable study of this problem to be carried on.

Negative Acceleration of Growth Phase. Under as favorable conditions for growth as can be provided, the rate of multiplication will decrease once a relatively large population has developed and the exponential relationship between growth and time no longer is evident. The duration of this phase of progressive decrease in the rate of multiplication depends upon the nature both of the species and of the environment. During this period, however, the majority of the cells ultimately present in the culture are formed (Fig. 13-3). Even one doubling of the population would result in twice as many cells as were present at the start of the phase. Generally several generations are produced before multiplication comes to a virtual standstill. The development of unfavorable conditions is the factor generally considered to be responsible for the progressively decreasing rate of multiplication observed during this period of negative acceleration. The major factors involved can be considered most readily in conjunction with factors influencing the maximum crop yield or stationary period.

Maximum Stationary Period. The total population of a species which develops per unit volume of a culture in a given medium tends to be one of the most constant values noted in the study of bacteria. The number of viable cells tends to remain relatively constant for a time, the duration of this stationary phase depending upon the nature both of the species and of the medium. It has been suggested that a certain minimum volume (M space) of medium per cell is required if growth is to occur. This concept of a biological space requirement generally is not believed to be a limiting factor for bacterial growth. It appears more plausible that certain critical concentrations of those substances serving as sources of energy and of building materials and also of oxygen (for aerobic growth) *per cell* are required if multiplication is to continue.

That concentration relationships are a factor is indicated by the observation that it is often possible to remove the cells from a fully developed culture and to observe growth anew from a fresh inoculum. The maximum population that develops in the secondary culture is generally much lower than in the primary culture. This behavior can be noted also if unfavorable conditions are induced by the accumulation of waste products such as organic acids, multiplication occurring again upon neutralization of the toxic material.

The amount of any material required for the doubling of a population of 1 million cells is one-thousandth that required for a twofold increase starting with 1 billion cells. The amount of any essential substance per cell, therefore, in the latter case is one-thousandth that available per cell in the former population. It would be desirable to have more quantitative studies carried out on this problem and to apply the Michaelis equation to the data. Rahn and Richardson (1942) stressed the heavy oxygen demand for aerobic growth and pointed out that this is frequently a growth-limiting factor. An oxygen demand of hundreds of cubic millimeters per milliliter of culture per hour frequently is noted before a maximum population develops. Increased availability of oxygen is often the factor responsible for the secondary growth noted in media from which the primary crop of bacteria has been removed.

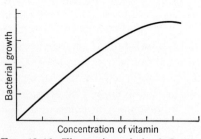

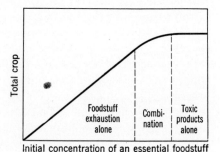

FIG. 13-16. Illustration of the influence of concentration of a particular vitamin or other limiting nutrient on extent of bacterial growth.

FIG. 13-17. General effect of the initial concentration of an essential foodstuff on the yield of bacteria.

It should be stressed that no one factor limits growth in all instances. The concentration of an essential substance (Fig. 13-16), whether it be oxygen, the energy source, or a specific organic or inorganic nutrient, is known to limit growth in many instances. Growth may be limited either by depletion of this essential material or by growth continuing to such an extent that waste products accumulate in inhibitory amounts. In some instances the accumulation of specific autoinhibitory agents can be demonstrated. The general relationship between the initial concentration of a particular essential substance and the total population is depicted in Fig. 13-17. This graph well illustrates the fact that either the exhaustion of a particular nutrient or the accumulation of an inhibitory (specific or nonspecific) product may be the controlling factor for crop yield with the same organism in the same medium, the only variable being the concentration of some one essential constituent of the medium.

In the first part of Fig. 13-17 it is readily apparent that the total population is proportional to the initial concentration of the essential substance. We have seen (Chap. 12) that this relationship is employed in microbiological assays for various amino acids or vitamins. Monod (1942) presented considerable data indicating that the total crop produced is proportional to the initial concentration of a sugar when the sugar is the only energy source. Other studies have indicated that a similar proportionality exists when the concentration of phosphate, of ammonia, of an essential amino acid, or of a growth factor is the growth-limiting factor. Within the limits imposed by other factors the concentration-population relationship can be expressed by the equation

$$G = KC \qquad (13\text{-}14)$$

where G = amount of bacterial substance formed
C = initial concentration of limiting nutrient
K = growth-yield constant

Some slight variation may be noted owing to change in size or mass of the cells with increasing age of the culture, but this is generally of minor importance.

The relationship described above implies that the amount of limiting nutrient utilized in the formation of a unit quantity of cell substance is independent of the initial concentration of the nutrient, or $G/C = K$ = amount of bacterial substance formed/amount of limiting nutrient utilized. Monod (1942) reported a K value of 0.233 for *E. coli* with glucose as the carbon-energy source in a synthetic medium, the dry weight of the cells produced being employed as the measure of growth. If we assume that the carbon content of the cells is approximately 50 per cent of the dry weight, the data of Monod indicate that approximately 8 mg. of glucose is utilized per milligram of cellular carbon formed. Calculations employing the data of Siegel and Clifton (1950) indicate a yield of approximately 1 mg. of cellular carbon per 5 mg. of glucose utilized during the first 5 hr. of growth of another strain of *E. coli*. Similar considerations indicate like yields in other studies of bacterial growth and metabolic activity. In the study of Siegel and Clifton (Table 13-1), approximately 80×10^7 cells per milliliter were formed during the first 5 hr. of incubation. On the assumption that 50 per cent of the glucose was assimilated and 50 per cent oxidized to completion, it can be shown that approximately 1 mg. of glucose was required for the formation of these cells. If growth and glucose utilization per cell continued at the same rates, the following relationships would be noted:

1 mg. glucose would yield $\quad$ 80 $\times$ 10^7 cells per ml.
2 mg. glucose would yield $\quad$ 160 $\times$ 10^7 cells per ml.
4 mg. glucose would yield $\quad$ 320 $\times$ 10^7 cells per ml.
8 mg. glucose would yield $\quad$ 640 $\times$ 10^7 cells per ml.
16 mg. glucose would yield 1,280 $\times$ 10^7 cells per ml.

Sixteen milligrams of glucose per milliliter corresponds to a 1.6 per cent solution, and at such concentrations glucose often tends to be inhibitory because of osmotic-pressure effects.   It is readily apparent why the maximum population cannot be increased above a rather definite value by further increases in initial concentration of a bulk foodstuff.   Oxygen demand is also enormous at these high population levels.   The maximum crop can, however, be increased in vigorously aerated cultures by the intermittent addition of concentrated glucose solutions.   This procedure is employed in the production of baker's yeast and of bacteria.   Such a procedure has been adapted to the production of bacteria in a continuous flow of medium.   Conditions can be so adjusted (see review by Novick, 1955) that the rate of flow of medium into the culture flask and of the culture from the flask is such that enough foodstuff is supplied to keep the cells dividing at a constant rate.   A higher maximum population than noted in regular cultures develops and can be maintained indefinitely. The removal of waste products may play some part in the maintenance of a high, stable population.   It has long been known that cells produced in a continuous flow of medium tend to exhibit quite constant physiological characteristics.

A certain minimum amount of energy appears to be required for the maintenance of bacteria.   They continue to respire in the absence of utilizable substrates in their environment, respiration being at the expense of endogenous reserves.   Ultimately these reserves are depleted, and death of the cell must follow.   This may be the major cause of death observed in cultures in which otherwise optimal conditions exist.   This is far from true in most cultures, and death may result from a variety of causes.   Substances released from dead cells may permit multiplication of a few of the more hardy cells in the mixture.   We have seen in the earlier part of this chapter that rather distinct phases of growth often are observed as a culture ages, and these phases can be due to a variety of factors.   Death will be considered in the following chapter.

Growth, multiplication, and death of bacteria must be considered as highly dynamic processes involving numerous reactions within the cell and between it and its environment.   The first two phenomena represent the establishment of dynamic equilibria which, when fully established, culminate in the steady state noted during the logarithmic phase of multiplication.   Any appreciable change in the cell or the medium results in an alteration of the steady-state conditions and, if the cell is unable to adjust to the change, will result in an inhibition of cellular activity. Inability to adapt to changing conditions will result ultimately in death of the cell.

We have considered growth primarily of a culture, treating the population as a statistical one, rather than considering the behavior of a single cell and of its descendants. Some of the offspring, presumably by chance, will undergo change during the duplication process and, generally by loss variation, will differ in some respect from the statistically average cell. These altered cells may or may not be able to survive under the conditions prevailing at the time. This could introduce a departure from the normal behavior that would become evident with time, e.g., the production of a mutant capable of utilizing a substance not serving as a substrate for the other cells could result in growth of the mutant and the establishment of a secondary culture. The end result would be the formation of a population different from the one normally observed.

Our considerations have dealt with growth in pure cultures, and these are the exception rather than the rule under natural conditions. Relatively little is known concerning the behavior of any one species in a mixed population, growth equilibria then being a resultant not only of the behavior of a cell in its quest for nutrients but also of the competitive effects between the cells of one species and those of others present in the environment. Population equilibria are established in which certain species predominate, others survive in reduced numbers, and others are eliminated. Likewise, growth in living tissues or cells presents more complicated problems than growth in a test tube. As more is learned concerning growth in complex situations, we will be in a better position to understand the nature of parasitism and the unfavorable balance which is exhibited with the development of pathogenicity.

REFERENCES

Britten, R.: Extracellular metabolic products of *Escherichia coli* during rapid growth, *Science*, **119**, 578 (1954).

Buchanan, R. E., and E. I. Fulmer: "Physiology and Biochemistry of Bacteria," 3 vols., The Williams & Wilkins Company, Baltimore, 1928.

Dagley, S., E. A. Dawes, and G. A. Morrison: Factors influencing the early growth of *Aerobacter aerogenes*, *J. Gen. Microbiol.*, **4**, 437–447 (1950).

Davies, R., and E. F. Gale (eds.): "Adaptation in Micro-organisms," Cambridge University Press, London, 1953.

Henrici, A. T.: "Morphological Variation and the Rate of Growth of Bacteria," Charles C Thomas, Publisher, Springfield, Ill., 1928.

Hershey, A. D., and J. Bronfenbrenner: Factors limiting bacterial growth. III. Cell size and "physiological youth" in *Bacterium coli* cultures, *J. Gen. Physiol.*, **21**, 721–728 (1938).

Hinshelwood, C. N.: "The Chemical Kinetics of the Bacterial Cell," Oxford University Press, London, 1946.

Malmgren, B., and C.-G. Hedén: Studies of the nucleotide metabolism of bacteria, I–V, *Acta Path. et Microbiol. Scand.*, **24**, 417–504 (1947).

Mazia, D.: The life history of the cell, *Am. Scientist*, **44**, 1–32 (1956).

Mitchell, P., and J. Moyle: Relationships between cell growth, surface properties *and* nucleic acid production in normal and penicillin-treated *Micrococcus pyogenes*, *J. Gen. Microbiol.*, **5**, 421–438 (1951).

Monod, J.: "Recherches sur la croissance des cultures bactériennes," Hermann & Cie. Paris, 1942.

———: The growth of bacterial cultures, *Ann. Rev. Microbiol.*, **3**, 371–394 (1949).

Novick, A.: Growth of bacteria, *Ann. Rev. Microbiol.*, **9**, 99–110 (1955).

Porter, J. R.: "Bacterial Chemistry and Physiology," John Wiley & Sons, Inc., New York, 1946.

Rahn, O., "Physiology of Bacteria," The Blakiston Division, McGraw-Hill Book Company, Inc., New York, 1932.

——— and G. L. Richardson: Oxygen demand and oxygen supply, *J. Bacteriol.*, **44**, 321–332 (1942).

Siegel, B., and C. E. Clifton: Oxidative assimilation of glucose by *Escherichia coli*, *J. Bacteriol.*, **60**, 113–118 (1950).

White, J., and D. J. Munns: The effect of aeration and other factors on yeast growth and fermentation, *Wallerstein Labs. Communs.*, **14**, 199–221 (1951).

Winslow, C.-E. A., and H. A. Walker: The earlier phases of the bacterial culture cycle, *Bacteriol. Rev.*, **3**, 147–186 (1939).

CHAPTER 14

DEATH OF BACTERIA

During the course of time the population in a culture will decrease, often slowly at first, but the rate of death gradually increases and reaches a maximum. This maximum rate ordinarily is maintained for a time, and a plot of the logarithms of numbers of survivors against time yields a straight-line relationship. Ultimately, the rate of death may decrease and even become insignificant, a few cells surviving for days or months if evaporation of water is prevented. The mechanisms of survival are unknown, some workers postulating that the bacteria pass into a resting state. Survival time is increased on storing the cells at low temperatures. When bacteria are dried from the quick-frozen state (lyophilized) they can be preserved over long periods of time. Under such conditions they are truly in a state of suspended animation. It is possible under normal conditions of incubation that occasional multiplication occurs in old cultures, probably at the expense of nutrients derived from dead cells. The phases of positive and negative acceleration of death and of exponential death were indicated in Fig. 13-1. The duration of these phases will vary with the nature of the organism and medium and with conditions prevailing in the external environment.

A species is maintained in the laboratory by storing the cells under conditions most suitable for their survival and by transfer to fresh media when necessary. Under natural conditions a species maintains itself by continuous multiplication, a balance being established between the rates of death and of multiplication. This balance can be upset by changes in moisture content, availability of oxygen and of nutrients, the presence of inhibitory agents, competition with other species, and other factors encountered in the environment. The population balance is a highly dynamic one, shifting with changing conditions, but the species survives owing to the existence of the various cycles of the elements maintained in mixed populations of micro and macro forms of life. Constituents of any one cell in time serve as nutrients for other members of the same or of different species.

Man is vitally interested in the control of bacteria and other microorganisms since their activities so directly influence his welfare, whether it be for good or bad.   He attempts to provide favorable conditions for their activity and survival when they are of benefit in agriculture or in industry; to control or destroy them when they threaten his food supplies, other possessions, or himself.   Man learned by experience and without knowledge of microorganisms that food could be preserved, or desirable changes induced in it, by suitable procedures.   It was not until the studies of Pasteur on the "diseases" of wine that it became truly evident that microorganisms are a common cause of spoilage, which can be inhibited by heating the material at a relatively low temperature.   Many reports dealing with the ability of heat and of various chemicals to prevent fermentation, putrefaction, movement of microorganisms, and so on, soon appeared in the literature.   The absence of growth in cultures or subcultures was employed as the criterion of bactericidal action following Koch's development of pure-culture techniques in 1881.   Various methods for testing the bactericidal action of different agents were proposed during the next couple of decades, and quantitative methods were evolved.   Results of these studies led to two general theories concerning the death of bacteria.   These can be summarized as follows:

1. The reaction between the poison and the cell is a chemical one, obeys the ordinary laws relating to chemical reactions, and results in a relationship between survivors and time that generally can be expressed by the equation for a unimolecular chemical reaction.
2. The resistance of different cells in the same culture to an inimical agent varies, and this variation in resistance is responsible for the time-survivor relationships noted in studies on disinfection.

The death of bacteria can be induced by a wide variety of chemical or physical agents.   No single group of agents can be spoken of as disinfectants.   Most chemicals in appropriate concentration can induce death of bacteria; relatively few do so in a short period of time and in a concentration that would be practical for ordinary use.   Agents that exert a bactericidal effect in certain concentrations are generally inhibitory in lower concentrations and may stimulate growth as the concentration of the agent is further reduced.   All degrees of intergradation may be observed, depending on the nature and concentration of both the organism and the chemical agent as well as on environmental factors.   Hueppe clearly recognized the influence of the concentration of an agent upon biological activity in 1896 when he concluded that every substance which in a definite concentration will kill protoplasm inhibits development in lower concentrations, and in still lower concentrations may act as a stimulant.   This behavior can be visualized in the form of a disinfectant spectrum (Fig. 14-1), the disconnected lines indicating that no sharp line of demarcation can always be established.   Furthermore, the width of the different bands for any agent varies with the nature of the organism and with conditions of application.

The disinfectant spectrum indicates that any substance can, in certain concentrations, exert a killing effect on bacteria.   In popular usage, however, a disinfectant is considered to be a substance which exerts a marked bactericidal effect in relatively low concentration.   In a more strict sense, as used by the U.S. Food and Drug Administration, the various terms commonly employed for agents intended for the control of destructive microbic action, and hence of the microorganisms themselves, can be defined as follows:

The term *sterilization* implies the *killing or the removal of all forms of life.* The term *disinfectant* implies *an agent employed for the destruction of microorganisms capable of producing an infection.   Germicide, fungicide, bactericide,* and *viricide* are terms employed for agents which in appropriate

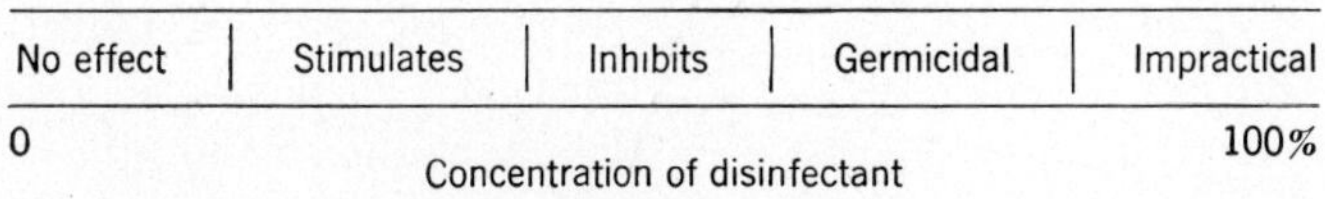

No effect	Stimulates	Inhibits	Germicidal	Impractical

0   100%
                        Concentration of disinfectant

FIG. 14-1. Disinfectant spectrum.   (*From Marshall and Hrenoff, 1937, courtesy of the Journal of Infectious Diseases.*)

concentration can be employed for the purpose indicated by the name. The term disinfectant is intended to apply to agents used for the killing of infectious agents away from the host animal and on inanimate objects. In common usage the term is not limited to the destruction of pathogenic species.

An *antiseptic* is defined as *an agent intended for the control of infectious organisms on epithelial surfaces, on mucous membranes, or in superficial wounds.*   In other words, it is a substance which in appropriate concentration can be used to retard growth or activity of infectious organisms but does not necessarily elicit complete inhibition or death under the conditions of use.   Hence it may exert either a bacteriostatic or a bactericidal effect, the former activity usually being associated with the term antiseptic.

The terms *disinfection* and *disinfectant* will be employed here, primarily from habit on the part of bacteriologists, to represent the killing process (bactericidal action) induced by any agent (disinfectant) in vitro when employed in suitable concentration or intensity against bacteria or their spores, whether the organism is infectious or noninfectious in character. The definitions can never be absolute in character since it is theoretically possible that one agent might be employed in a definite concentration as a disinfectant, in lower concentration as an antiseptic, and in still lower concentration as a chemotherapeutic agent.   The actual killing of bacteria will be considered in this chapter, while the action of chemo-therapeutic agents and related compounds will be discussed in Chap. 17.

The Course of Disinfection. Disinfection is considered as that action whereby bacteria are killed in a reasonable period of time. This period is arbitrarily set in many tests but can be varied to suit a particular study or task. A consideration of time numbers of viable bacteria relationships (after Marshall and Hrenoff, 1937) in replicate cultures containing increasing amounts of a particular agent illustrates the effect both of time and of concentration. In Fig. 14-2 increases or decreases in numbers of bacteria with time are plotted for cultures in the logarithmic phase of growth to which different amounts of a chemical agent were added at zero time. In the presence of sufficiently small amounts of the agent the growth curve follows the normal pattern. As the concentration of the test material is increased, a point is reached at which slight stimulation of growth might be noted. At still higher concentrations the rate of growth decreases below that noted in the control and, with increasing concentration, approaches zero, i.e., complete inhibition but no death of the organisms in relatively short periods of time. Further increases in concentration of the chemical results in the death of some cells per unit of time, eventually a concentration being reached at which all the organisms are killed in a short period of time, a condition commonly regarded as true bactericidal action, i.e., disinfection.

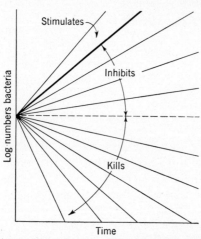

FIG. 14-2. Influence of the concentration of a chemical agent on the growth and death of bacteria. (*From Marshall and Hrenoff*, 1937, *courtesy of the Journal of Infectious Diseases.*)

Actually, it is possible to think that any rate of growth less than zero represents bactericidal action exerted by the test substance, while any positive rate less than normal represents bacteriostatic activity. This bacteriostatic action was considered too infrequently in the past, particularly when dealing with infections, since a slight degree of bacteriostasis (inhibition) could be sufficient in many instances to enable the normal defense mechanisms of the host to control proliferation and spread of the invading parasite. Higher concentrations of the agent might retard the defense mechanisms of the host without bringing about death of the invader.

The time course of disinfection is ordinarily determined by removing at regular intervals of time measured portions of a bacterial suspension containing the toxic agent, test conditions being maintained as uniform as possible. The numbers of viable cells in the samples are determined by dilution and plating methods. The toxic agent must be diluted in the subcultures to such an extent that it is no longer inhibitory to multiplication of viable cells, or it must be neutralized in an appropriate manner. In more routine tests counts of survivors are not made, and instead only the time required for a given concentration of the agent to render all of the cells nonviable under the test conditions is determined.

The customary concept of dead bacteria is that they cannot multiply when transferred to nutrient agar or broth. This concept can be fallacious in some instances since "death" to some degree is influenced by the nature of the medium employed for the subcultures. This is illustrated by results of an early study on the killing of anthrax spores by steam. Ten to twelve minutes of heating resulted in apparent death of the spores when they were tested for viability in nutrient broth. Some spores germinated in broth enriched with 3 per cent glucose and 5 per cent horse serum, even after the spores had been heated for as long as 25 min. With another medium even longer exposures of the same test suspension to steam might be required to destroy completely any possibility of the spores reviving and germinating. Length of the incubation period, temperature, and other conditions of incubation may also influence the results of studies on disinfection. Death is, therefore, partially a function of the conditions under which viability is determined.

Mathematical Relationships. When a suspension of organisms is exposed to a disinfectant under uniform conditions, not all the cells die at once. Death of bacteria in most cases is a gradual process of measurable velocity. The process leading to death may be reversible by the cell, after removal of the cause, during the first stage of the process. Gradually the process becomes irreversible by the cell, but it may still be subject to outside antidotes. After a time it reaches an irreversible stage, i.e., the cell is unable to multiply under favorable conditions although it may still possess other characteristics associated with living matter. The bacteriologist, by necessity, must employ a rather unique criterion of death.

The decrease in numbers of viable organisms with time under relatively mild conditions occurs gradually and generally uniformly, i.e., the number dying during any period of time being a certain fraction of the number living at the beginning of the test period. This behavior, as we have considered for unimolecular chemical reactions and for the growth of bacteria during the logarithmic period, can be represented by the simple equation

$$-\frac{dN}{dt} = kN \tag{14-1}$$

where N = number of survivors at any time t, commonly expressed in
minutes

k = a constant for each disinfectant and organism under a given
set of conditions

$-dN/dt$ = a small decrease in numbers dN in a short interval of time dt

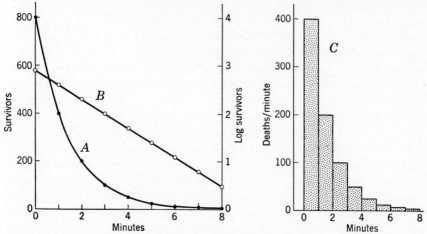

Fig. 14-3. Plots of (A) numbers of survivors, (B) logarithms of survivors, and (C) numbers of cells killed per unit of time against time.

This equation, as considered in the other applications, can be converted
to the form

$$K = \frac{2.303}{t} \log N_0 - \log N_t \tag{14-2}$$

where N_0 = number of viable cells at start of time interval t

N_t = number at end of period

On plotting the results of disinfection studies on an arithmetic scale, a
logarithmic scale of survivors, and a distribution of mortality scale against
time (Fig. 14-3), it can be noted in the first plot that disinfection is an
orderly but gradual process, approaching completion as time progresses.
The distribution curve indicates that a constant percentage of the survivors is killed per unit time, which behavior, as we have seen, means
that a straight-line relationship exists when logarithms of numbers of survivors are plotted against time. The ideal relationship is indicated in
Fig. 14-3; actually, deviations from the logarithmic order of death are
frequently noted. Typical deviations observed include increase or

decrease of the death rate with time, the former often resulting in a marked lag period in death followed by an exponential phase.

Considering the general behavior only, let us assume that we have a suspension containing 1 million viable cells per milliliter and that 90 per cent of the surviving cells are killed per minute. This means that there are 100,000 survivors at the end of 1 min., 10,000 at the end of 2 min., and so on, and that the velocity constant of death $K = 2.303$. In the first minute 900,000 cells are killed, 90,000 in the second minute, and so on; i.e., the numbers dying per unit of time are proportional to the numbers present at the beginning of the time intervals.

One must determine whether or not a logarithmic order of death prevails under a given set of conditions. When death does follow a logarithmic pattern we cannot conclude that it is the result of a true or even a pseudo unimolecular chemical reaction. It is true that in most instances the disinfectant is employed in excess and undergoes relatively little change in concentration during the course of disinfection. The only factor changing to a marked extent is the number of living cells. Because of this the data frequently fit the equation for a unimolecular reaction, as those do for the hydrolysis of sucrose in acidic solutions when only the relative concentration of the sugar undergoes appreciable change. Studies of the kinetics of disinfection deal with changes in numbers of viable cells and not the kinetics of individual reactions that might be involved. It is theoretically possible that an alteration in some one "sensitive" molecule could lead to death of a bacterium, but it is more probable that such is not the case when death is induced by most physical or chemical agents.

Nature of Bactericidal Action. The hypothesis that death of a bacterium is the result of a unimolecular reaction is based on the assumption that death of a cell is due to a lethal alteration in a single molecule and, in many instances, that the cells are of equal susceptibility to the poison. We have seen (Chap. 2) that molecules must be at a certain energy level before they react. A unimolecular reaction rate is explained on the basis that under fixed conditions some molecules possess more, others less, than the average energy of all the molecules. A relatively definite percentage of the molecules possess at any one moment energy equal to or greater than the critical value. These molecules can undergo change. The reaction rate, therefore, is controlled by the distribution of energy among the individual molecules. It would be necessary to assume a similar distribution of energy among the "sensitive" molecules in the bacterial population if death is truly the result of a unimolecular reaction.

We know that bacteria of different ages, or cells from cultures of different ages, differ in their susceptibility to a given agent. It is possible that individual cells of the same age differ in their susceptibility, and the distribution of susceptibility could be such that a unimolecular rate of death would result on exposure to the disinfectant. One argument in favor of a unimolecular reaction as the cause of death of bacteria, and against the sensitivity-variation hypothesis, resulted from the observation that a certain region (target) in a cell had to be hit and absorb ultraviolet light if death were to result. Kelner (in Kelner, Bellamy, Stapleton, and Zelle, 1955) has pointed out that the target theory has proved unsatisfactory, and it does appear that there is no one light-sensitive molecule whose inactivation is responsible for death of the cell.

Disinfection studies generally are carried out under relatively drastic conditions as regards concentration or intensity of the lethal agent, and death follows in relatively short periods of exposure. Minor differences in resistance of individual cells are not detected. As the concentration of a lethal agent is decreased under carefully controlled conditions, and hence the time required for disinfection to proceed to a definite end point is increased, departures from the logarithmic relationship become more pronounced. This behavior is well illustrated in studies by Jordan and Jacobs (1944) in which the viable population in cultures of *E. coli* was maintained at a constant level in control flasks by the frequent addition of nutrients. Changes in the viable population were determined in other cultures receiving the same treatment but to which different amounts of phenol had been added. Typical results of their work are summarized in Fig. 14-4. It is evident that under carefully controlled conditions marked deviations from the logarithmic order of death can be noted as the concentration of the toxic agent is decreased. It is possible that under the conditions of their tests some of the cells do multiply in the presence of phenol and the tests do differ from the customary disinfection ones. The results do, however, reflect the balance between life and death of bacteria in the presence of a toxic agent in an environment otherwise conducive to multiplication.

Price (1950), from the results of a number of elementary tests, concluded that sensitivity varies markedly among the cells in any population and that this is responsible for bacteriostatic and bactericidal effects. He exposed a large number of agar plates lightly and uniformly seeded with *E. coli* to a temperature of 46°C. for various times before incubating them at 37°. Similar tests were carried out with cells exposed to a low temperature, 4°C. In either test, results of which are depicted in Fig. 14-5, reduction in numbers of viable cells is a gradual process. Typical results illustrating the effect of exposure of *E. coli* to $M/80$ HCl or 1:50,000 merthiolate are included in Fig. 14-5. In these tests the acid was neutralized, or sodium thiosulfate employed as an antidote for the merthiolate, before plate counts were started. The effect of simple dilution of the merthiolate-containing suspension on the viable count is also indicated in Fig. 14-5. Price concluded that the results of the various tests can be explained most readily on the basis of differences in sensitivity between individual cells.

Price suggested that the vital activity of a single cell might be reduced with time (Fig. 14-6) of exposure to an inhibitory agent to a level so low that the cell could not recover from the effect, inhibition or bacteriostasis reaching an irreversible level. At any intermediate time of exposure

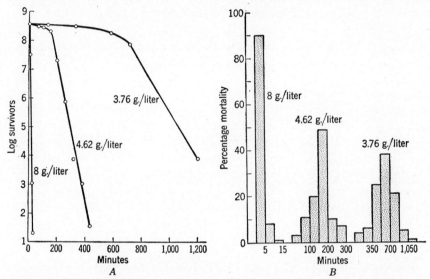

FIG. 14-4. Plots of logarithms of survivors and percentage mortality of *Escherichia coli* against time in the presence of different concentrations of phenol. (*Redrawn from Jordan and Jacobs, 1944, courtesy of Journal of Hygiene.*)

inhibition of vital activity would not be enough to damage the cell irreversibly, and it could recover its normal activity and multiply following removal or neutralization of the lethal agent. When the effect of the agent is reduced by dilution the cell can recover normal activity if dilution is carried out to a sufficient extent; otherwise the time required for inhibition to reach the irreversible state is increased. When cells differ in sensitivity (Fig. 14-7) the same type of behavior is noted with the exception that the period of time during which inhibitory effects are reversible increases with increasing resistance of the cells. It should be borne in mind that a cell sensitive to one substance could be highly resistant to a second, while another cell could exhibit the reverse response. The length of the inhibitory period for a given degree of sensitivity would be controlled by the concentration of the inhibitory agent.

The various observations on the disinfection process point to the conclusion that three factors—sensitivity of the cells, concentration (or intensity) of the inhibitory agent, and time—must be considered in any logical application of the process. The two latter factors can be determined; we have no accurate measure of the former. It is controlled by the rate

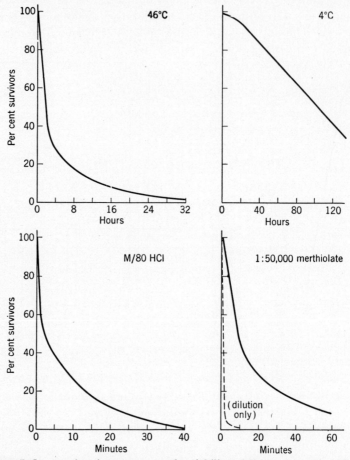

Fig. 14-5. Influence of various agents on the viability of *Escherichia coli*. (*Data from Price*, 1950.)

at which the agent comes into contact with some vital component(s) of the cell and the resultant rate(s) at which dependent activities essential to multiplication are decreased. There are three major reactive systems—membrane, enzymes, and nucleus—in the cell whose normal functioning is essential to life and multiplication.

The cell membrane can be attacked by some agents (e.g., phenol, detergents) with resultant increase in permeability of the cell. This could result in a diffusion of essential metabolites out of the cell with resultant injury and eventual death. Or a change might be induced which could result in decreased permeability, particularly to an essential ingredient of the medium, and death. When the toxic agent reacts only with intra-cellular components, particularly enzymes, the rate of death of the cells

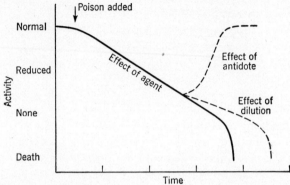

FIG. 14-6. Schematic representation of the effect of a mercurial on a bacterium. (*From Price*, 1950, *courtesy of the New York Academy of Sciences.*)

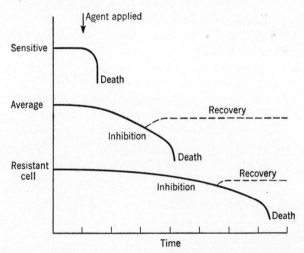

FIG. 14-7. Schematic representation of the effects of a toxic agent on bacterial cells which vary in susceptibility. (*From Price*, 1950, *courtesy of the New York Academy of Sciences.*)

will depend to some extent upon the rate at which the substance can penetrate the cell membrane and diffuse through the cytoplasm. Entry into the cell often depends upon the state of ionization of the agent and/or membrane constituents; hence pH can exert marked influence on the rate of death. Furthermore, pH can influence the strength of the bond between the agent and cellular constituents in many instances, the firmness of union between a positively charged toxic molecule and a protein increasing with increase in pH, and vice versa. Reaction of the agent with cytoplasmic constituents, generally proteinaceous and enzymatic in character, can be relatively specific or nonspecific. Disruption of the forces that maintain proteins in an organized state can be induced by appropriate concentrations of many agents of widely different nature, and this denaturation may or may not be reversible. The inhibitory agent may be more specific in its action, mercurials, for example, uniting with sulfhydryl groups, anionic detergents with basic groups, cationic compounds with acidic groups, and carbon monoxide or cyanide with iron-containing compounds.

When the primary reaction induced by the agent results in the inhibition, neutralization, or destruction of a system involved in a reaction, or reaction chain, essential to life of the cell and one which cannot be bypassed, death will follow as cellular activities diverge further and further from their normal dynamic balance or steady-state conditions. In some instances the toxic agent may react with nuclear components and any physical or chemical change resulting in failure of genetic material to be duplicated will lead to eventual bactericidal action, i.e., inability of the cell to multiply under test conditions.

Concentration Effects. We have been considering concentration effects in a general way and have seen that the rate of death, all other factors being maintained constant, is dependent upon the concentration of the bactericide. This fact can be expressed mathematically on the assumption that K, the velocity constant for a disinfection process, is composed of two factors, one of which we can represent as k and the other by C^n, C representing the concentration of the disinfectant and n a constant called the concentration coefficient. Then we can write that

$$K = kC^n \tag{14-3}$$

Two different concentrations of disinfectant C and C_1 and the times t and t_1 required to reduce a viable population by an equal amount are related by the equation

$$C^n t = C_1^n t_1 \tag{14-4}$$

The value of n can be calculated from experimentally determined K values by means of the equation

$$n = \frac{\log (K_1/K)}{\log (C_1/C)} \tag{14-5}$$

where K_1 = velocity constant at higher concentration C_1.

The value of n can also be determined graphically and is the slope of the line obtained when the log of the time required for killing is plotted against the log of the concentration of disinfectant. The equation representing this line can be written as

$$\log t = -n \log C + \log A \qquad (14\text{-}6)$$

where $\log A$ = intercept on concentration axis.

It can be seen from this equation that if the value of n is large, then small changes in concentration will alter markedly the time required for disinfection. A substance such as phenol, for which the value of n is relatively large, rapidly loses its efficacy as a disinfectant on dilution. A low value of n indicates that the agent can be diluted to an appreciable extent without marked decrease in bactericidal activity. A low value for n also indicates a wide range of concentration in the disinfectant spectrum over which the agent can exert a bacteriostatic effect, while a high value indicates a narrow bacteriostatic range. The time required for disinfection with a substance such as phenol exhibiting concentration effects expressed by a coefficient of 4 is increased 16 times when the solution is diluted to one-half strength and 256 times when the original solution is diluted to one-fourth its original concentration. The time required for disinfection by a substance such as mercuric chloride with a concentration coefficient of 1 is increased only two and four times, respectively, when the solution is diluted 1:2 and 1:4. This variation in the relative activities of different disinfectants on dilution is considered too infrequently in many tests and applications. It should be pointed out that the value of n varies not only with the nature of the disinfectant but can vary with the nature of the test medium, the temperature at which the tests are conducted, and with the test species.

We have considered that the numbers of bacteria in the test suspension, within reasonable limits, have relatively little effect on the time required for disinfection. This can be illustrated by an example in which the velocity of disinfection constant has a value of 0.5. An initial population of 1 million cells per milliliter would be reduced to 10 viable cells in 23 min., while only 27.6 and 32.2 min. would be required to reduce initial populations 10 and 100 times as large to the same level, respectively.

The concentration and nature of foreign matter in the test suspension will influence the course of disinfection. In many instances organic compounds markedly reduce the efficacy of a disinfectant, generally by reaction with it, thereby also reducing the actual concentration of the agent available for reaction with cellular material. Disinfectants frequently are tested in the absence of extraneous matter and also in the presence of organic matter, serum often being employed in the latter test. Salts, in concentrations not bactericidal by themselves, can influence disinfection. Sodium chloride tends to reduce the activity of mercuric chloride, in part at least by a common ion effect which reduces the concentration of mercuric ions.   On the other hand, it enhances the bactericidal activity of phenol, apparently by altering the distribution of phenol between water and cells in such a manner as to increase the uptake of phenol.   The influence of hydrogen-ion concentration is well known and is mentioned above.   Even the concentration of water can alter the course of disinfection, the extreme case being the more rapid rate of killing exerted by steam than by dry air at the same temperature.

Temperature.   The rate of death normally increases with increasing temperature in the presence of a constant amount of the test agent.   Two factors may be involved here: the increased temperature catalyzing the disinfection process as would be predicted from the Arrhenius equation (Chap. 2) and thermal effects by themselves inducing death of the bacteria.   Van Eseltine and Rahn (1949) reported that although the bactericidal effect of various agents increases with increasing temperature, the bacteriostatic effect may decrease.   Fifty parts per million of $HgCl_2$ were required to prevent growth of a staphylococcus at 20°C., while 150 p.p.m. were needed at 30°C.   With most organisms and agents tested, maximal tolerance to an agent was observed at 7 to 10°C. below the optimal temperature for growth.   They explained this on the basis of two opposing processes.   Temperature increases the growth rate and at the same time increases the rate of reaction between the chemical and cellular constituents.   The difference between these two effects determines the growth rate in the presence of inhibitory concentrations of the test agent.

As the temperature is increased above the optimum for growth there is a tendency for the enzymes to break down at an increasing rate.   As soon as the rate of denaturation exceeds that of synthesis, the cell begins to lose the struggle for existence.   Hydrogen bonding appears to be a major factor in maintaining proteins in their natural, active state, and it is highly sensitive to thermal effects.   But the cell is also susceptible to effects of low temperatures, the effects apparently being induced in a different manner.   At the minimal temperature for growth of a species, cell division is almost completely arrested, but the rate of loss of viability is generally very low.   At the upper temperature limit for growth, the cell-division rate remains high, but the rate of death approaches the multiplication rate and passes it as the temperature is increased to only a slight extent.   Mitchell (in Werkman and Wilson, 1951) describes the low-temperature type of stasis as cell bacteriostasis and the upper one as culture bacteriostasis, the latter indicating that the behavior of a culture is more complex than that of its component cells.

Bacteria can remain alive for a long time at low temperatures, the most rapid mortality being observed at the freezing point of cytoplasmic constituents.   If freezing is conducted in such a manner as to reduce the size of ice crystals to minimal values, then the rate of death at the transition point is reduced. Repeated freezing and thawing is more lethal than are marked temperature changes in the low-temperature range. The bactericidal effect of rapid and marked temperature changes at ordinary temperatures is often overlooked in temperature-effect studies. This effect, at times, appears to be associated to a considerable extent with the stage of division of the cells.

Relatively little is known concerning the mechanism of thermal damage, death often being ascribed to irreversible denaturation of enzymes, to alteration of cellular permeability, and to disorganizations induced by alterations in the various balances of reaction rates that must be properly coordinated to maintain steady-state conditions. The influence of temperature on protein denaturation, i.e., a high value for Q_{10}, is very similar to that observed in the thermal inactivation of bacteria. The value for Q_{10} can be determined from the relationship $K_1/K_2 = Q_{10}$, where K_1 is the velocity of death constant at one temperature and K_2 that at a temperature 10°C. lower. In studies on the thermal death rate of *Salmonella typhosa* the value of Q_{10} between 49 and 59°C. was found to be quite high, near 100. This corresponds to approximately 1.6 per degree $(100 = 1.6^{10})$. A velocity constant of death value of 0.1 and a Q_{10} of 100 at 49°C. would indicate that a population of 1 million cells could be reduced to 10 per milliliter in 115 min., while only 45, 18, 7, 2.7, and 1.1 min., approximately, are required for the same reduction at 51, 53, 55, 57, and 59°C., respectively.

Two indices of killing bacteria by heat are in use, one, the *thermal death point*, being defined as the temperature at which all cells in a suspension are killed during 10 min. exposure, and the other, the *thermal death rate*, as the time required to kill all the cells at a given temperature. Either value for any one species is subject to variation with the history of the culture or with test conditions. The latter index is of considerable value in any process involving sterilization of material. Higuchi and Busse (1950) derived a modified form of the Arrhenius equation which indicates the relation between time required for sterilization and the temperature at which heat sterilization is conducted. This relationship can be expressed as

$$\log S_t = \frac{0.219E}{T} + K \qquad (14\text{-}7)$$

where S_t = time required for sterilization

E = apparent heat of activation of killing most heat-resistant species (or spores)

T = absolute temperature

K = a constant depending on number and kind of the most heat-resistant organisms present

E has a value of 50 to 100 kcal. for the more resistant organisms.

A plot of logarithms of sterilization times against reciprocals of the absolute temperatures of sterilization gives a straight line. Such information can be of considerable importance in industrial applications. The thermal resistance of spores is a well-known characteristic and creates major problems in sterilization by either heat or chemicals. Some of the problems in this field have been discussed recently by Schmidt (1955).

Testing of Disinfectants. Disinfectants are commonly evaluated by comparison of their bactericidal activity with that of phenol as a standard in the phenol-coefficient test. Evaluation tests are carried out under carefully controlled conditions.[1] A specific strain of *Salmonella typhosa* is generally employed as the test bacterium. A more satisfactory evaluation is obtained when the test is repeated with a gram-positive organism such as a staphylococcus. An arbitrarily chosen time for killing of all the test organisms is used in the determination of the phenol coefficient. The phenol coefficient can be defined as the ratio of the highest dilution of the test agent in which all the test cells are killed in a 10-min., but not in a 5-min., exposure period to the highest dilution of phenol required to produce an equivalent bactericidal action. If chemical agent X in a 1:300 dilution kills all the test bacteria during a 10- but not a 5-min. period while the highest dilution of phenol exercising the same effect is 1:100, then the phenol coefficient of X is 300/100, or 3.

In the phenol-coefficient test the value of the disinfection velocity constant K is fixed within the limits imposed by the initial number of viable bacteria and the killing time. We have considered that disinfection ordinarily follows a semilogarithmic course, but it is rather difficult to determine accurately that time in which sterility of the test suspension is actually induced, particularly since an asymptotic tendency is often noted as the survival curve approaches the zero end point. For this reason a 5-min. period of latitude in killing time in a total of 10 min. is allowed. A change of the time factor can lead to entirely different results for a phenol coefficient, e.g., mercuric chloride being characterized by a coefficient of 2 in a 2.5-min. killing time, around 150 for a 10-min. period, and 550 in a sterility-inducing time of 30 min. This is due to the influence of concentration of an agent on its killing time, as indicated by the value of the concentration coefficient n previously discussed. Phenol has a concentration coefficient around 4, and doubling its concentration reduces killing time by about one-sixteenth. Mercuric chloride, with a coefficient of approximately 1, kills only twice as rapidly when its concentration is doubled. Hence, increasing the concentrations of these agents, and thereby reducing killing time, leads to increased effectiveness on the part

[1] In the United States according to those specified by the Food and Drug Administration in *U.S. Dept. Agr. Circ.* 198 (1931).

of phenol as a disinfectant. Dilution, as we have seen, leads to opposite results.

Furthermore, the phenol coefficient does not take into account the temperature coefficient of the test or the standard disinfectant (phenol). An increase in temperature increases the activity of phenol much more rapidly than that of salts of the heavy metals, for example. Likewise, the effect of extraneous matter, particularly organic compounds but at times common ions, is not taken into account. Attempts are made to allow for nonspecific effects by repeating phenol-coefficient tests in the presence of either 3 per cent dried fecal matter or yeast or in 50 per cent serum. Also, the tests are conducted around neutrality, and hence do not indicate the effect of acid or alkaline conditions on the efficacy of the bactericide.

A phenol coefficient of 3 quite frequently is interpreted as indicating that the agent is three times more effective than phenol as a disinfectant. Such a statement can be quite misleading since all that such a phenol coefficient indicates is that, under the test conditions, gram for gram it is three times as active as phenol. Change any of the conditions, and the relative value of the agent may be altered markedly. Phenol coefficients should be interpreted as suggestive rather than as absolute values, and the only real criterion of a disinfectant is the effectiveness of the agent under actual conditions of use.

Errors can be introduced into phenol-coefficient determinations if no check is made on the bacteriostatic properties of the agent. To prevent any bacteriostatic effect in the subcultures, which could be induced by carry-over of the test agent or of phenol, subculturing should be conducted in such a manner that a representative sample is transferred and at the same time dilution is sufficient to eliminate any bacteriostatic effect. Otherwise it is necessary to employ an antidote for the poison to eliminate false values for phenol coefficients.

Various modifications of the phenol-coefficient test have been proposed, the majority of which apply primarily to testing agents intended for use as an antiseptic. In these tests comparisons are made of the relative toxicity of the substance for bacteria and for tissues.

Factors influencing the activity of physical and chemical agents as disinfectants are discussed in some detail in the books by Buchanan and Fulmer, Porter, and Rahn listed in the bibliography for Chap. 13. A rather complete review of the activities and practical methods for use of most commonly employed bactericidal agents is presented by Redish (1954).

Methods of Action. Relatively little can be said concerning the nature of the reactions by means of which most disinfectants induce death of bacteria. Some compounds promote oxidation of cellular material, others bring about hydrolyses or other relatively nonspecific chemical changes. In some instances the effect may be more physical than chemical in character, e.g., mechanical disruption by plasmolytic effects. More actual information is available concerning the mode of action of the more specific agents, particularly the chemotherapeutic and related ones, and this will be discussed in Chap. 17. Considerable interest in the effect of various radiations has developed in recent years, and more is known concerning their bactericidal action than about the action of other general groups of bactericidal agents.

Bactericidal Effects of Radiations. The lethal effect of radiations (for general review of the earlier literature see Lea, 1947) can be studied quite readily since conditions of the tests can be rigidly controlled and likewise the intensity and duration of the exposure. The effect, in experiments of relatively short duration, is dependent upon the product of time and intensity of radiation. In other words, doubling the intensity of the radiation decreases by one-half the time required to produce an equivalent lethal effect, and so on, over a relatively wide time-intensity range. In the majority of tests an exponential order of death is observed. The intensity of the radiant energy, both before and after passage through the test suspension, can be measured accurately. Appropriate corrections can be applied to the data and calculations made of the amount of radiation striking the cell and of the amount absorbed per cell. It has been found that not every hit of a bacterium leads to its death, and this has been interpreted as indicating that there is a "sensitive zone" within which a hit must occur if death is to ensue. Roughly about one hit in twenty results in death of a bacterium, hence the sensitive zone has a volume about one-twentieth that of the cell. Other considerations suggest that there are specific targets within the sensitive zone and that these "targets" approximate in size the larger protein or protein-complex macromolecules. The sensitive zone appears to have the approximate dimensions of a bacterial nucleus, a target those of a gene (nucleoprotein molecule). It has been estimated that there are about 250 targets (genes?) in an *E. coli* cell.

It is assumed in the target theory that the bactericidal effect of radiations is due to a single effective hit and, therefore, to a change induced in a single molecule. This would lead to a first-order lethal effect. No molecule other than one associated with, or actually being, a gene appears to be of such a vital nature that its alteration would lead to death of the cell. Since radiations are effective in inducing mutations in bacteria, as well as in other forms of life, and lethal effects follow closely upon the mutagenic ones, it is generally considered that the two phenomena are similar or identical. Death can be considered as a lethal mutation. The ultraviolet-action spectrum for mutation induction in bacteria exhibits a maximal mutagenic efficiency around 2,650 angstrom units, corresponding to the absorption maximum of deoxyribonucleic acid. A similar maximum for the bactericidal activity of ultraviolet light is also noted. Present concepts (Kelner, Bellamy, Stapleton, and Zelle, 1955) indicate that the target theory is somewhat inadequate; in particular the changes induced by radiations are more complex than indicated above, but they do appear to be initiated by a single hit in a uninucleate cell.

Visible and infrared radiations have little effect on most bacteria, particularly when precautions are employed to prevent thermal effects. As the wavelength of radiations decreases, much more energy is associated with the radiations, the energy E available for absorption being related to characteristics of the radiation by the equation

$$E = \frac{hv}{\lambda} \tag{14-8}$$

where h = Planck constant
  v = velocity
  λ = wavelength of radiation

The absorption of a quantum of energy greater than 1 electron volt raises the energy level of outer (or valence) electrons. This results in the molecule as a whole becoming "excited" or activated. The excited molecule has a short life as such, the energy imparted to it being lost by one of several means. When a quantum having an energy equivalent of more than 5 electron volts is absorbed, orbital electrons may be ejected from an atom with the formation of a positively charged ion. The ejected electron becomes attached to another atom with the formation of a negative ion. Hence ionizing radiations give rise to the formation of ion pairs. It is the chemical action of the ions so produced, particularly the positive ones, that is of major importance in the biological effects of radiations. Ultraviolet light encompasses a quanta range approximately equivalent to 5 to 100 electron volts, X rays from 10,000 to 1,500,000. Energy of ionization averages about 32 electron volts, considerably in excess of the approximate 10 electron volts energy of chemical bonds.

The effect of the absorption of ultraviolet light appears, because of the relatively low quantum yield, to be dependent upon the chemical combination of the atoms involved, while the effect of the shorter radiations is relatively independent of chemical combinations and more dependent upon the atomic number of the atom which is ionized by the radiation. Hence the effects of absorption of ultraviolet light vary somewhat from those induced by X-ray or gamma-ray absorption. Ultraviolet rays have a tendency to elicit mainly gene mutations, while X rays induce aberrations and breaks in chromosomes (if analogies with the behavior of higher forms of life hold true). X-irradiated cells are not so susceptible to reactivation as are ultraviolet-injured ones.   The effect of ultraviolet is not influenced by the absence of oxygen; that of the shorter radiations is markedly reduced.   Other differences are also evident.

Kelner (Kelner et al., 1955) divided the events in an irradiated cell into three periods.   The first embraces the instant of irradiation, the absorption of energy, and resultant excitation or ionization.   The second, or middle, period covers that time after the primary reaction has occurred and before end effects are noted.   In the third, or end, period an alteration or lesion of the cell becomes evident.

Relatively little is known concerning the initial period during ultraviolet irradiation other than the quantitative aspects referred to earlier. It was assumed in the earlier studies that death followed more or less immediately upon hit of a vital target.   It became apparent, however, that irradiated cells subsequently shown to be dead, i.e., incapable of multiplication, continued to respire for some time at or near the normal rate.   Still later it was observed that certain syntheses, particularly those of DNA and of adaptive enzymes, were inhibited.   In 1949 Kelner noted an odd behavior.   During a study of ultraviolet-induced mutations in *Streptomyces griseus* he noted at times an unexpectedly high number of survivors.   This was found to result from exposure of irradiated cells to visible light for some time before they were incubated.   It was observed that the numbers of survivors were up to 10,000 times greater in irradiated suspensions of *E. coli* immediately exposed to visible light after ultraviolet light treatment as compared with survivors in controls not exposed to light.   Some recovery of "killed" cells was noted when the exposure to visible light was made as long as 3 hr. after irradiation.   The phenomenon was termed *photoreactivation*.   It has been observed that the production of mutant strains is also decreased by photoreactivation.   The effective wavelengths for photoreactivation vary to some extent with the species, *S. griseus* exhibiting maximal recovery at 4,350 angstrom units, *E. coli* around 3,750 angstrom units.   Reactivation to a more limited extent can be elicited in the dark by increasing the temperature.

It is evident that irradiation per se does not "kill" the cells during the first period.   A hit does appear to induce an alteration which prevents the cells from multiplying later, although some increase in cell size may occur subsequent to mild irradiation.   Changes are initiated that are reversible to some extent during the middle period.   The formation of DNA appears to be inhibited very rapidly, but it can be reinitiated upon photo- or heat reactivation.   Reactivation exhibits a relatively high Q_{10}, thus suggesting that chemical rather than primarily physical changes are involved during the second period.

X rays and gamma radiations differ from ultraviolet light in some respects in their mode of action.   They are much more active in producing ionizations, their activity is increased in the presence of oxygen, and their lethal effect is not reversed by light. Some recovery is noted, however, when X-irradiated cells of *E. coli* are incubated for 24 hr. at various temperatures between 6 and 30°C., followed by another 24-hr. period of incubation at 37°, comparison being made with numbers of survivors on plates incubated at 37°C. only. A maximal number of survivors was noted when the first incubation period was conducted at 18°C. Stapleton (in Kelner et al., 1955) has interpreted this as indicating that a synthetic process is involved, the rate of which increases with increasing temperature. At the same time a destructive process is occurring, it has a higher temperature coefficient than the synthetic one above 18°C. and overtakes the synthetic process at a higher temperature. The nature of this hypothetical balance is unknown but may involve a radiation-induced increased thermolability of some vital system(s) in the cell. Survival in such experiments is also dependent upon the nature of the media employed in making the plate counts, a much higher recovery being noted on nutrient agar than on a salts-glucose synthetic agar.

It is considered that X rays induce their effects through the mediation of oxidizing radicals, OH and O_2H, formed in intracellular water. The effective yield of these radicals is reduced in the absence of oxygen which can be removed from the cell suspension physically, chemically, or by the respiratory activity of the cells during a preirradiation period. The intracellularly formed radicals can give rise to the production of peroxides which may be the inducers of the lethal or other mutagenic effects. A number of agents—nitrogen or sulfur mustards, epoxides, organic peroxides, and so on—are capable of inducing mutations. Most of these reagents react with sulfhydryl groups, and it is postulated that their mutagenic action is due to such a reaction with these groups in nucleoproteins. Organic peroxides formed as a result of irradiation could react in the same manner. It is of interest to note that strains of *E. coli* relatively resistant to radiations are also more resistant to the mutagenic effect of mustards, and vice versa. Zelle (in Kelner et al., 1955) discussed radiation effects and concluded that a number of mechanisms producing a number of different genetic and lethal effects will be found to be operative during the middle period.

As far as is known the end result, the actual type of mutant produced, is primarily one of chance. It would appear that it depends upon which target in the sensitive zone is hit, and even possibly the area within the target in which the hit is scored. The basic information for the most part supports the concept that the effective absorption of a quantum of ultraviolet energy or an X-ray-induced ionization brings about an immediate and specific inhibition of DNA synthesis and that the other reactions noted are secondary consequences of the primary reaction. The picture is complicated by the fact that apparently a single mutation may suffice to alter markedly the response of the mutant strain to irradiation as contrasted with the behavior of the parent strain.

The various studies on disinfection and bacteriostasis point to the adaptability of the bacterial cell, its powers of repair and recovery being much greater than conceived of by the earlier workers. This indicates once again the dynamic balance characteristic of living cells.

REFERENCES

Higuchi, T., and L. W. Busse: Heat sterilization of thermally labile solutions, *J. Am Pharm. Assoc.*, **39**, 411–412 (1950).

Jordan, R. C., and S. E. Jacobs: Studies in the dynamics of disinfection, *J. Hyg.*, **43**, 275–289 (1944).

Kelner, A.: Photoreactivation of ultraviolet-irradiated *Escherichia coli*, with special reference to the dose-reduction principle and to ultraviolet-induced mutation, *J. Bacteriol.*, **58**, 511–522 (1949).

———, W. D. Bellamy, G. E. Stapleton, and M. R. Zelle: Symposium on radiation effects on cells and bacteria, *Bacteriol. Rev.*, **19**, 22–44 (1955).

Lea, D. E.: "Actions of Radiations on Living Cells," The Macmillan Company, New York, 1947.

Marshall, M. S., and A. K. Hrenoff: Bacteriostasis, *J. Infectious Diseases*, **61**, 42–54 (1937).

Price, P. B.: The meaning of bacteriostasis, bactericidal effect, and rate of disinfection, *Ann. N.Y. Acad. Sci.*, **53**, 76–90 (1950).

Redish, G. F. (ed.): "Antiseptics, Disinfectants, Fungicides, and Chemical and Physical Sterilization," Lea & Febiger, Philadelphia, 1954.

Schmidt, C. F.: The resistance of bacterial spores with reference to spore germination and its inhibition, *Ann. Rev. Microbiol.*, **9**, 387–400 (1955).

Van Eseltine, W. P., and O. Rahn: The effect of temperature upon bacteriostasis, *J. Bacteriol.*, **57**, 547–554 (1949).

Werkman, C. H., and P. W. Wilson (eds.): "Bacterial Physiology," Academic Press, Inc., New York, 1951.

CHAPTER 15

ADAPTATION AND VARIATION

In the introductory remarks it was indicated that the power of adaptation is one of the major characteristics of living cells. Bacteria, like other forms of life, do exhibit this ability to adapt themselves to the prevailing environment. This adaptation is a temporary one which prevails only while the inducing factor is present and only within the limits imposed by the genetic composition of the strain. It can be recognized most readily by changes in colony form, in morphology of the cells, or in their metabolism. Bacteria can also undergo changes of a permanent character which involve a change in, or the loss of, a particular gene. In this latter type of change the environment is not the inducing factor, but it does exert a decisive, selective role in determining whether the mutant can survive and make itself evident. Chemical or physical agents in the environment may, however, influence the rate at which mutation occurs.

It is well known that the descendants of a single bacterium may give rise to the development of several types of colonies during the course of repeated transfers on a nutrient medium. Transplants from a variant colony generally give rise to colonies like the one from which they were derived, thus indicating that the change in character is an inherited trait. It is equally well established that cultures of an organism such as *Proteus vulgaris* tend to spread or swarm over a moist, nutrient agar surface. The addition of phenol to the agar greatly reduces or prevents this spreading type of growth and results in the production of discrete colonies. On transfer back to phenol-free agar, typical spreading growth is observed once again. Here we have an illustration of a change in colony formation induced by a chemical agent added to the medium. It is a temporary change, does not involve alteration of the genetic structure of the bacterium, and is no longer evident after cultivation in the absence of the inducing agent. Changes in morphology and metabolic activity can be noted at the same time. Microscopic examination would reveal that spreading is associated with the presence of flagella, a morphological characteristic, and that the production of flagella is inhibited by phenol. Antigenic analysis would reveal a decrease in or loss of the flagellar antigen, a loss which indicates a change in metabolic activity, suppression of the synthesis of flagellar protein.

Induced change in colonial appearance is probably rather limited in extent, but morphological changes are quite common. One need only observe the changes that occur in size and shape of cells during the different phases of growth of a culture. The increase in cell size observed early in the development of a culture or the involution forms noted as the culture ages are indications of a response to environmental conditions. Change from the typical short rod to long, filamentous forms of *Escherichia coli* can be induced simply by cultivation on an acidic sugar medium, the typical rod being formed again after transfer back to a neutral medium.

Adaptation. Of more interest to the physiologist are those induced, temporary changes in metabolic activity which are engendered during the exposure of the cells to a particular factor or agent. Temperature is a factor which may influence a particular metabolic activity. The synthesis of its characteristic red pigment by *Serratia marcescens* is quite pronounced during growth at room temperature, while little or no pigment is produced at body temperature although growth still occurs quite readily. Hydrogen-ion concentration is another factor that must always be considered in any response of the cell to its environment, as well as the factor that any response to pH may be influenced by other agents in the medium.

Shaughnessy and Winslow (1927) observed that *E. coli* suspended in water adjusted to acidic or alkaline conditions was able to change the pH toward an optimum zone for survival of pH 6.2 to 6.4 by liberation of ammonia in acidic solutions, of carbon dioxide in alkaline ones. This was interpreted as an adaptive reaction, favorable to life of the cell. Here we have an example of alteration in endogenous respiration with the production of substances which tend to neutralize the effect of unfavorable hydrogen or hydroxyl-ion concentrations. Optimum concentrations of sodium or calcium chloride in water promoted the liberation of ammonia or of carbon dioxide by the cells, while higher concentrations decreased ammonia production and increased carbon dioxide liberation. Ions also influence growth response to changes in pH, Sherman and Holm (1922) finding that sodium chloride in 0.2 M concentration broadened the pH range over which *E. coli* multiplied in a peptone medium while sodium citrate in the same concentration narrowed the pH range for rapid growth. These behaviors can hardly be considered as purposeful, knowingly directed attempts on the part of the cell to adapt itself to the environment or to alter the medium to better suit its requirements. Salts do influence the pH response of proteins outside the cell, e.g., the imbibition of water and consequent change in volume of the protein at different hydrogen-ion concentrations. Such factors could play a role in the living cell. The cell must be pictured as being in a state of dynamic equilibrium, and any factor which influences this equilibrium is countered, as in chemical reactions in general, with an attempt to restore the equilibrium or to minimize the effect of the applied force. This behavior was well illustrated in the studies of Larson, summarized in Chap. 4, on the inorganic composition of bacteria. These studies indicated that a portion of the salt content of bacteria was in a free state and that the composition and concentration of the free salts could vary in such a manner with change in ionic composition of the medium that a new equilibrium was readily established.

Gale and Epps (1942) have shown that *E. coli* can multiply in a casein digest broth over a pH range of 4.2 to 9.5 and that during growth the pH of the medium shifts toward neutrality. Adaptation was accomplished, in part at least, by the enhanced production of amino acid decarboxylases in the acidic media, of deaminases in the alkaline ones. Decarboxylations result in the production of alkaline amines which tend to neutralize excess acid; deaminations give rise to acids which neutralize excess alkali. This behavior can be explained on the basis that the undissociated form of the amino acid elicits formation of the enzyme. The decarboxylases, therefore, are formed most readily and are most active in acidic solutions in which dissociation of the carboxyl group is least pronounced. The reverse response is observed with the deaminases, the amino group dissociating less readily in alkaline solution. Changes with pH of the environment in the type of enzyme produced must reflect changes in the internal pH of the cell; otherwise the production of these enzymes should show little change with pH unless permeability alterations are the controlling factor. Other examples apparently of neutralization mechanisms encountered in studies on metabolism are the reduction of butyric acid to butyl alcohol and the conversion of pyruvic acid to acetylmethylcarbinol, these reactions occurring most readily as acidic conditions develop in the test cultures.

In the above examples of enzymes utilizing amino acids the amounts of the enzymes produced appear to be greatest in an environmental pH range near that of optimum activity of the enzyme concerned. With other enzymes, such as the formic acid and ethanol dehydrogenases, catalase, and urease, formation of the enzyme is enhanced within limits as the growth pH is displaced from the optimum pH for activity of the particular enzyme. The result is that the total activity of each remains fairly constant over a wide pH range, i.e., the product of the amount of enzyme times the activity per enzyme molecule is constant over that range. Many of the enzymes in this general group are involved in the removal of substances which tend to be inhibitory to the cell as their concentration increases in the medium.

Adaptive Enzymes.   The conclusions regarding changes in metabolism with pH considered above are for the most part simplifications of the behavior of complex regulatory mechanisms by means of which the cell attempts to counteract unfavorable environmental conditions.   A somewhat more accurate and simpler picture of specifically induced adaptation can be developed regarding the production of specific enzymes by bacteria and other microorganisms (see review by Stanier, 1951).   Karstrom, in 1930, clearly demonstrated that a lactic acid bacterium, *Leuconostoc mesenteroides*, was capable of fermenting glucose immediately upon its addition to washed suspensions regardless of the presence or absence of glucose in the original culture medium.   Washed suspensions of this organism did not ferment lactose immediately unless the organisms had been cultivated in the presence of lactose.   When the lactose-fermenting cells were passed in lactose-free media, they lost the ability to ferment lactose without delay.   Karstrom concluded that the enzymes involved in the fermentation of glucose are always present in the bacteria he studied; hence he termed them *constitutive enzymes*.   Enzymes such as the lactose-utilizing ones which appear only as a response to the presence of the substrate in the culture medium or cell suspension were termed *adaptive enzymes*.   His results indicated that the enzymes involved in the utilization of glucose, fructose, mannose, and sucrose by *L. mesenteroides* are constitutive enzymes, while those activating lactose, galactose, maltose, and arabinose are adaptive ones.   The galactose enzyme appeared when the cells were cultivated in the presence of either galactose or lactose, the latter being hydrolyzed with the formation of galactose and glucose.   This type of behavior will be considered later as the phenomenon of simultaneous adaptation.

Karstrom's work was soon confirmed and extended to other organisms. Four general possibilities have been considered regarding the specific formation of an enzyme or enzymes induced by the presence of a particular substrate in the medium.   These are (1) mutation and selective growth of organisms capable of forming the particular enzyme, (2) the liberation of a suppressed character, (3) alterations of permeability, or (4) impression of a new but transient character on the cells as an adaptive response to the presence of a given substrate in the growth medium.   It was demonstrated that adaptive-enzyme formation can occur in the absence of detectable cell multiplication, e.g., the addition of lactose to nonproliferating, washed cells of *L. mesenteroides* grown in the absence of lactose results in the delayed fermentation of lactose.   This indicates that mutation and selection are not the controlling factors in adaptive enzyme formation.   There is little or no evidence for the second or third possibility, and most results support the fourth hypothesis that enzymatic adaptation is a substrate-induced variation in biochemical activity that does not involve change of genotype.

In many studies on enzymatic adaptation the change may be only a quantitative one, the enzyme involved having been present in the cell but in such small amounts or of such limited activity that its presence was not detectable by ordinary methods of measurement. This can at times lead to difficulty in ascertaining whether an enzyme is a constitutive or an adaptive one since the amount or activity of the former may be influenced to some extent by the presence or absence of its substrate. Actually, the terms should be considered as relative rather than absolute ones. The essential characteristics of enzymatic adaptation are: (1) the amount or activity of the enzyme greatly increases as a result of exposure to the substrate; (2) it occurs in the absence of multiplication sufficient to allow mutation and selection to occur; (3) the adaptive enzymes that can be formed are controlled by the genetic constitution of the species; (4) it appears to require nitrogen and energy sources that may be supplied by the substrate or by endogenous cellular reserves in many instances; (5) it involves synthesis of the enzyme, the term synthesis being employed in its broadest sense, which includes alteration of an existing enzyme; and (6) it can be inhibited by agents such as sodium azide or 2,4-dinitrophenol which inhibit oxidative assimilation or by bacteriophages which inhibit the normal synthesis of cellular constituents.

The three latter characteristics are well illustrated in a study by Pinsky and Stokes (1952a) on the adaptive formation of formic hydrogenlyase by washed suspensions of *E. coli*. They found that sources of energy and amino acids are required for the production of this enzyme. Arginine, aspartic acid, and glutamic acid were essential for its formation; cystine, glycine, serine, and threonine were stimulatory but not essential; while cysteine, histidine, isoleucine, leucine, methionine, and phenylalanine were inhibitory. Metal-binding agents (8-hydroxyquinoline), assimilatory poisons (2,4-dinitrophenol), oxygen, nitrate, and nitrite inhibited the formation of hydrogenlyase. They suggested that formic hydrogenlyase adaptation involves extensive synthesis of the enzyme. In another study (1952b) they demonstrated that adaptability was dependent to a considerable extent on the age of the cells. Formation of either nitrate reductase or formic hydrogenlyase occurred most readily in cells from cultures in the stationary-growth phase. Their production by cells obtained from cultures in the logarithmic phase was markedly less. In other instances the reverse behavior has been noted (Hegarty, 1939).

Monod (Monod and Cohn, 1952) has demonstrated the marked influence of substrate on the production of an adaptive enzyme, β-galactosidase, in cultures of *E. coli*. It is plainly evident in Fig. 15-1 that the enzyme was formed shortly after the addition of the inducing agent, β-galactoside. The amount or activity of the enzyme increased as long as growth occurred in the presence of the specific substrate. When this sugar was completely utilized, no trace being present in the medium, formation of its enzyme ceased, but residual enzyme activity could be noted for some time.   Penicillinase formation in cells in which penicillinase is an adaptive enzyme can be induced by the presence of minute amounts of penicillin in the culture.   Formation of this enzyme will continue, however, in the absence of detectable amounts of penicillin.   It is assumed (Pollock, in Davies and Gale, 1953) that traces of penicillin are in combination with some "organizer" in the cell and penicillinase production occurs as long as this complex is active.   Production of this enzyme is linear with time during exponential growth of the cells, a behavior which supports the concept of an inducer-organizer effect.

The phenomenon of diauxie was mentioned in Chap. 13 as an example of adaptive-enzyme formation.   More recent studies have been reviewed by Cohn and Monod (Davies and Gale, 1953), and they advanced the hypothesis that formation of all enzymes is adaptive in character.   The constitutive enzymes according to their hypothesis are formed because the inducer is a normal constituent of one or more reaction chains in cellular metabolism and, therefore, is always present in the cell.   An adaptive enzyme appears only when the inducer is present in the medium and gains entrance into a cell which is genetically capable of utilizing it.

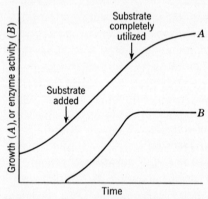

FIG. 15-1. Schematic illustration of the change in activity with time of an enzyme adaptively produced in response to the utilization of a specific substrate during growth of a bacterial culture.

It is not an essential metabolite, but it can, following appropriate conversions, supply molecules that are encountered normally in the metabolism of the cell. They also pointed out that substances related to a substrate such as β-galactoside can serve as an inducer for β-galactosidase formation, although not utilized by the enzyme the formation of which they induce. Furthermore, an enzyme adaptively produced by a species appears to be identical immunologically, chemically, and in its enzymatic activity with the "constitutive" enzyme produced by a mutant of the test organism which appears to utilize the inducer substrate in its normal metabolism.

One earlier concept of adaptive enzyme formation considered that a precursor of the enzyme existed in the cell and that the inducer brought about a conversion of the precursor to the form of the active enzyme. We have considered above that certain amino acids may be essential for adaptive-enzyme formation.   This weakens the concept of an enzyme-precursor molecule. Other studies, particularly one by Rotman and Spiegelman (1954), lend support to the *de novo* concept of adaptive-enzyme formation. Using *E. coli* as the test agent (one reason being that gram-negative cells do not contain a pool of free amino acids) and β-galactosidase as an example of an adaptive enzyme, they found that in cells uniformly labeled with C^{14} less than 1 per cent of the β-galactosidase carbon could have been derived from cellular components existing prior to the addition of the inducer. They also reported that protein synthesis in actively multiplying cultures of *E. coli* is virtually irreversible. They concluded that these findings virtually eliminate any hypothesis which embraces the preexistence of either simple or complex precursor material which could be converted into active β-galactosidase.

Simultaneous Adaptation. We have been considering enzymatic adaptation primarily as a process involving the production of a single enzyme such as formic hydrogenlyase. The adaptive response is frequently a more complex one, adaptive formation of two or more enzymes often being involved before the original substrate is converted into a product capable of being utilized by preexistent enzymes in the metabolic machinery of the cell. A simple example is the enzymatic adaptation of yeast to ferment galactose, an adaptation involving two enzymes, galactokinase and galactowaldenase. The former enzyme catalyzes the phosphorylation of galactose by adenosine triphosphate to galactose-1-phosphate, and this is converted by the second adaptive enzyme to glucose-1-phosphate. The latter compound is on the constitutive glycolytic pathway of the cell. A similar behavior was mentioned earlier, adaptive fermentation of galactose by *L. mesenteroides* being induced by exposure to either lactose or galactose. Detailed studies of simultaneous enzymatic adaptation frequently are of considerable value in tracing the steps involved in the utilization of a substrate.

If we consider a hypothetical pathway for the utilization of a substrate A and the fact that each step is catalyzed by a specific adaptive enzyme we can write

$$A \underset{E_A}{\rightarrow} B \underset{E_B}{\rightarrow} C \underset{E_C}{\rightarrow} D \underset{E_D}{\rightarrow}$$

Cells grown in the absence of A and then placed in contact with it will not utilize A unless adaptive-enzyme formation of the enzyme E_A occurs. Formation of the product B of this reaction provides the substrate for the formation of enzyme E_B, and so on. Cells adapted to the utilization of A will, therefore, be adapted to the utilization of other members of the metabolic chain. On the other hand, cells adapted to D will not be adapted to utilization of the preceding compounds, with the possible exception of C if reaction $C \rightarrow D$ is a reversible one. Let us suppose that C has been postulated to be an intermediate in the dissimilation of A.

Cells adapted to either A or B should be able to utilize C without lag. The enzyme E_C should not be present in cells grown in the absence of A, B, or C, and possibly D. If these criteria hold true, we then have evidence that C is an intermediate in the utilization of A. More complete proof could be obtained with the use of tracers, enzyme preparations, and isolation of the postulated intermediate as discussed by Stanier (1950).

In a typical study of simultaneous adaptation (Stanier and Tsuchida, 1949) evidence was presented that the oxidation of tryptophan by a species of *Pseudomonas* proceeds through kynurenine and kynurenic acid, or

Tryptophan → Kynurenine →

Kynurenic acid

Kynurenic acid is then further oxidized by the cells, ultimately to carbon dioxide and water. Exposure to tryptophan resulted in simultaneous adaptation to oxidation of kynurenine and kynurenic acid, while exposure to kynurenine led to oxidation of kynurenic acid as well as of the former compound. This suggests the two compounds are on the pathway of oxidation of tryptophan by this bacterium. The pathways of oxidation of certain other aromatic compounds have been established in a similar manner, and further utilization of the technique of simultaneous adaptation should increase our knowledge of the metabolic chains involved in the utilization of various substrates.

Mutation. The division of a bacterium gives rise to two cells, each alike in potentialities and like the parent cell from which they were derived. Reasoning by analogy with higher forms we could assume that the cell contains genes which reproduce themselves, one unit ultimately being found in each of the daughter cells. These genes in turn reproduce, and transmission of hereditary characters continues in the same pattern. The gene still remains as a concept rather than as an absolutely proved unit of heredity. In higher forms of life the genes appear to be arranged in a definite order in the chromosomes, and recent observations suggest a similar organization in the bacterial cell. In the introductory remarks to this chapter we considered that a bacterium can undergo sudden, unpredictable change of a permanent character that is transmitted indefinitely in its descendants. This difference between the parent and the mutant is maintained in cultures of variant and parent transferred and maintained under identical conditions and, therefore, is not a temporary variation such as those we have just considered. These relatively permanent, transmissible changes can best be explained as qualitative changes in the genes. Generally a change in only one gene appears to be involved for a particular mutation, and most frequently the change represents loss of some characteristic possessed by the parent cell. At times, however, reverse or gain mutation occurs with regeneration of the transmissible characteristics of the cells in the original culture. These changes in the genes are spontaneous ones which can best be pictured as errors in reduplication during growth, but at the same time not of sufficient magnitude to be lethal in effect, provided that the deficiency can be made good from the environment (or possibly in some cases by use of an alternate metabolic pathway). The genes, which appear to control their own duplication, also appear to control the formation of enzymes and ultimately of other cellular matter. It is further postulated that the formation of some cytoplasmic matter may be under the direct control of gene-like, cytoplasmic particles, the plasmagenes. In these days of rapid progress in microbial genetics the concepts presented herein will not be accepted by all workers, and the student should remember that they are tentative and subject to revision as new facts are obtained or older observations are reinterpreted on the basis of new discoveries. All that can be presented here, without going into details of genetics, is of a rather general nature and is intended primarily as illustrative. For details reference should be made to reviews by Catcheside (1951), Lederberg (1948), Braun (1953), and others as they appear.

It has been evident since the studies of de Kruif around 1921 that many bacteria normally give rise to colonies that are smooth, glistening, and regular in appearance but that occasionally a colony develops that is rough in its general appearance. Transfers from the rough variant give rise to rough colonies. This change from smooth (S) to rough (R) colonies was termed bacterial dissociation and is now considered to be a true mutation. The change in the outward appearance of the colonies is reflected in morphological and biochemical properties. When grown in nutrient broth, the S forms tend to grow diffusely throughout the medium, while the R ones generally settle readily to the bottom, or with some species pellicle formation is noted. This tendency for the cells to aggregate is associated with a change from a hydrophilic to a hydrophobic type of cell surface, the latter giving rise to less stable suspensions, as discussed in Chap. 3. In the S form marked slime layers or capsules of polysaccharide nature are present. This material gives rise to the smooth, glistening appearance of the colonies, is hydrophilic in character, and hence confers suspension stability on the cells. In many pathogenic species it is associated with virulence of the cells, apparently acting as a protective device against the normal defenses of the host. Alteration in the gene controlling this character results in the formation of cells with a predominatingly hydrophobic surface, proteinaceous in character. This dissociation or mutation is most evident when the S cells are cultivated in the presence of an antiserum prepared against the S cells. The antibodies are inhibitory to growth of the S cells, while R mutants, if present, will produce colonies and are, therefore, more readily recognized than when present in small numbers as compared with the S cells. The antiserum does not induce the mutation; it simply enhances the possibility of observing the mutant. In other words, it exerts a selective influence rather than an inducing one such as observed in adaptive-enzyme formation. With *Bacillus anthracis* and certain streptococci the rough-appearing colony is composed of virulent cells. In these organisms the capsular material is polypeptide rather than polysaccharide in character. This confers the appearance of roughness to the colonies, while other characteristics of the cells more closely resemble those of S bacteria. Morphological changes frequently observed in the $S \rightarrow R$ mutations are discussed in Chap. 4 along with other colony forms.

Escherichia coli-mutabile. Another classical variation, consisting of a change from nonlactose to lactose fermentation in a species designated as *Escherichia coli-mutabile* was first reported independently by Neisser in 1906 and by Massini in 1907. In outward appearance the variation closely resembles the phenomenon of adaptive-enzyme formation. Lewis (1934) has shown quite conclusively that the variation is a true mutation which occurs independently of the presence of lactose and the mutant does multiply true to its type in the absence of lactose. The presence of lactose in the culture medium exerts a selective rather than an inducing action (for opposite viewpoint see Stewart, 1943).

When *E. coli-mutabile* is cultured on lactose agar containing a fermentation indicator such as fuchsin-sulfite (Endo agar) the colonies which develop in 24 hr. are colorless, indicating that lactose is not fermented. On longer incubation small red knobs (papillae) develop on some of the white colonies. When subcultures on lactose agar are made from the white colonies, the same behavior is noted, while subcultures from the red papillae give rise to red colonies. Lewis made suspensions of young white colonies and, on dilution and plating in nutrient agar or glucose-synthetic agar, found that the number of cells on the basis of these plate counts per original colony ranged from 71 to 354×10^7. When replicate samples were plated out in a synthetic agar with lactose as the only carbon source, the colony counts indicated an initial population of only from 2,080 to 6,300 bacteria per original colony. These cells were capable of utilizing lactose; the majority of the cells in the colonies were not. From the results of experiments of this type he concluded that only approximately 1 cell in every 100,000 cells of his strain was a lactose-fermenting mutant, actually or potentially. This is near the range 1 mutation in every 10^6 to 10^8 cell divisions commonly encountered with other mutations. The observed behavior is explicable on a genetic basis and represents the production of mutants so few in number that they do not appreciably influence the behavior of the culture on lactose agar until the majority of the cells have ceased growing, owing to the depletion of readily available nutrients. The one lactose fermenter statistically present in every 100,000 cells should give rise to an initially red colony. This

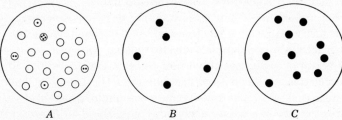

A $\qquad$ B $\qquad$ C

FIG. 15-2. Evidence for the spontaneous origin of bacterial mutants. (*After Newcombe*, 1949. See text for details.)

colony would not be observed readily on lactose agar plates because of its low frequency of occurrence. Mutations in fermentative power, pigment production, capsule formation, drug resistance, and other physiological properties are frequently observed if one looks for them. Their recognition is greatly enhanced by the use of selective media or methods (Lederberg, 1950; Bryson and Szybalski, 1952).

Evidence of Spontaneous Mutation. Additional evidence for spontaneous mutation, rather than specific induction of mutation, is provided in experiments by Newcombe (1949). Plates were lightly incubated with a species of bacteria and incubated for 3 to 6 hr. At the end of the preliminary incubation period some of the plates were sprayed immediately with a bacteriophage suspension active against the test bacterium. The growth on a replicate plate was spread over the surface of the agar before addition of the phage. The majority of the cells were sensitive to the phage and were lysed by it, only a few colonies of resistant mutants developing on incubation. If adaptation is responsible for the mutation to phage resistance, there should be no marked difference in the numbers of phage-resistant colonies developing on the plates, spread or unspread. Actually, larger numbers of resistant colonies were noted on the spread plates, thus suggesting that mutation had occurred prior to exposure to the phage and that the latter exerted a selective action. This is schematically illustrated in Fig. 15-2 in which the actual behavior is greatly exaggerated.   Petri dish A represents 20 colonies developing on the agar before exposure to the phage, and a resistant mutant cell is pictured as a black dot in the colony.   In some colonies only one mutant is depicted, in others two or four resistant cells have developed from the mutant one. The blank colonies are composed entirely of susceptible cells, and as depicted in B, these disappear as a result of the lytic action of the added phage, only five colonies developing from those five pictured in A as containing mutants.   When cells from replicates of A are spread over the agar as in C, the resistant cells present at the time are distributed over the surface along with the phage-susceptible cells.   These mutant cells will, therefore, give rise to ten resistant colonies as shown in C, a greater number than in B since they arise from individual resistant cells rather than from individual colonies containing resistant mutants.   Experiments of this type in which selective agents other than phage are employed give essentially similar results.   This further supports the conclusion that mutations can occur in the absence of the test agent and that the latter exerts a selective action on growth, suppressing the growth of cells susceptible to its action.   A higher rate of mutation might, however, be observed in the presence of some agents since they could conceivably confer survival protection upon the newly formed mutant.

Lederberg and Lederberg (1952) carried out similar experiments on drug resistance.   A culture was plated out on drug-free agar, and after colonies had developed they were lightly pressed onto a piece of sterile velvet.   The plate was then removed from the velvet, and the agar in a second plate containing the test drug, e.g., penicillin, was lightly pressed against the velvet.   Some of the cells clinging to the nap were transferred to the agar and, on incubation, gave rise to an occasional colony.   From the position of a colony on the second plate, the location of the parent colony on the first plate could be determined and cells from this parent colony could be shown to possess resistance to penicillin although grown in the absence of the drug.

Mutagenic Action of Radiations.   When bacteria, yeasts, or molds are exposed to X rays, ultraviolet light, mustard gas, hydrogen peroxide, or certain other radiations or chemical agents, it is frequently observed that the rate of mutation is increased.   The mutants that appear, however, apparently are chance ones since these agents do not tend to favor the development of particular mutants.   The mechanism of action of these mutagenic agents remains obscure.   It was generally assumed that the radiations acted by provoking a change in a gene as a result of the absorption of a quantum of energy.   More recent observations with ultraviolet light indicate that the action is induced by organic peroxides formed in a photoreaction and that the effect can be duplicated by irradiation of the medium rather than the cells or by the addition of hydrogen peroxide to the medium. The latter could react with organic compounds to give organic peroxides which may be the mutagenic agent in either the light- or the peroxide-induced mutations. One curious behavior noted with irradiated cells is that the apparent rate of death during irradiation, and also the rate of mutation, are lowered upon subsequent exposure to visible light, a phenomenon we considered as photorecovery.

Phenotypic Lag. In some studies a delay, termed phenotypic lag, in the appearance of the mutant becomes evident. Several cell divisions may be needed before the genotypic change becomes phenotypically evident. This might possibly be explained on the basis of multicellularity or of multinucleated cells, several divisions being required before the off-spring have a complete complement of the mutated gene. It is also possible that at times a metabolite required by the mutant for growth is present in the cell in amounts sufficient to permit limited division. The phenomenon of phenotypic lag is imperfectly understood, and the true explanation is probably more complex. Phenomena such as photorecovery and phenotypic lag do complicate, in our present state of knowledge, complete understanding of bacterial mutation.

Mutation during the Course of an Infectious Disease. Mutations of considerable interest are observed during the course of relapsing fever in man. This disease, caused by a number of species of *Borrelia*, is characterized by a number of relapses, as the name suggests. After the febrile period in man, the organisms disappear from the blood stream and antibodies exhibiting spirocheticidal, lytic, and agglutinating properties appear. A few spirochetes apparently survive, mutants arise from them during the afebrile period, these mutants do not react with the originally formed antibodies, and upon their establishment in numbers a relapse occurs. Antibodies are produced against this new antigenic type, and the spirochetes again disappear from the blood. Several antigenic mutations, each followed by relapse and recovery, may be noted during the course of the disease. A particular antigenic type which has appeared and against which antibodies have been formed does not reappear during the course of the infection. *B. duttonii*, in particular, appears to be a highly plastic species antigenically, and as many as nine distinct serological types have been reported. This is an excellent example of mutations occurring in the body during an infection and the selection of mutants under the influence of specific antibodies. Mutations in virulence of other bacteria also occur under both natural and laboratory conditions.

Transformation. We have been stressing spontaneous mutations of bacteria, but in certain organisms specifically induced ones have been reported. This is most strikingly illustrated in type transformation with pneumococci. *Diplococcus pneumoniae* is a species composed of possibly over one hundred types, each type being characterized by a specific capsular polysaccharide while the underlying cell appears to be common to all types.   When a cell loses the ability to form the type-specific polysaccharide, it reverts to a non-type-specific pneumococcus, a rough mutant.   Griffith in 1928 observed that cells from an *R* mutant culture derived from a type II (*S*-II) culture were unable to produce an infection in mice.   When the *R* cells were injected together with heat-killed *S*-III cells, the mice came down with a pneumococcal infection caused by *S*-III cells.   The living noncapsulated pneumococci derived from the original *S*-II culture acquired the capsular structure and serological specificity of *S*-III pneumococci.

Subsequent observations confirmed this finding, and it was later demonstrated that this transmutation could be induced, under rather complex conditions in vitro, with extracts of *S*-III pneumococci added to cultures of the *R* form from *S*-II.   Later Avery and his coworkers (see review by McCarty, 1946) were able to show that this type transformation was induced by a deoxyribonucleic acid apparently free of protein and of the type III polysaccharide.   This inducing agent can be obtained from the induced *S*-III cells even after they have been repeatedly transferred in media suitable for capsule formation.   The amounts recovered far exceed those employed in eliciting the transformation.   It is susceptible to destruction by deoxyribonuclease, but not by ribonuclease or by proteolytic enzymes.   Transformations of other types and also in other species have been reported.   No completely acceptable explanation of the nature of the transforming principles and of the transformation itself has been advanced.   One suggestion that has been offered is that the agent is a genetic substance (or a naked gene) that enters, or alters, the genetic constitution of the cell, either in the nucleus or as a plasmagene.

Transduction.   A phenomenon resembling transformation of types has been reported by Zinder and Lederberg (1952) with *Salmonella* species. They observed that hereditary properties can be transferred (transduced) from one *Salmonella* strain to another by filtrates from the first *Salmonella* strain lysed by a suitable phage.   As a rule only one cell in roughly one million recipient cells acquired a new character, the transfer of more than one character to a cell never being observed.   Cells which had acquired a new character, e.g., the *i* flagellar antigen from *S. typhimurium* transduced to *S. typhosa* to give a new serotype containing the *i* antigen, transmitted it to their progeny in series.   They believed that the genetic factor transferred was associated with a filtrable agent or phage.   It was not destroyed by deoxyribonuclease, possibly because of its inaccessibility to this enzyme.   The pneumococcal transformation principle, on the other hand, is inactivated by deoxyribonuclease.   Transduction differs from recombination in that the transfer of only one character has been noted in the former and there is no need for direct contact to be established between the donor and the recipient cells. The transduction of single nutritional, fermentative, drug resistance or antigenic characters has been observed in appropriate experiments.

Biochemical Genetics. Bacterial genetics is a field of considerable interest to the physiologist, and one aspect, biochemical genetics, is of particular importance in the elucidation of pathways of synthesis. A basic concept in this field is that genes are the ultimate controlling factor of all biochemical reactions which the organism is able to carry out. If a mutant is formed that possesses a biochemical synthetic deficiency, this mutant will be unable to grow in the absence of the substance X synthesized by the enzyme whose formation was controlled by the particular unmutated gene. Other mutant cells might also be selected, lacking ability to synthesize precursors of X, and ultimately blocks might be found at different stages of synthesis. A study of the nutritional requirements and biochemical activities of these mutants would lead to an understanding of the mode of synthesis of X. Studies of this nature were initiated by Beadle and Tatum with the red bread mold *Neurospora crassa* and have led to a better understanding of synthetic mechanisms (see reviews by Beadle, 1945, and in *Cold Spring Harbor Symposia on Quantitative Biology* and *Annual Review of Microbiology*).

N. crassa is a much more ideal test organism than are bacteria in that a distinct sexual reproduction can be observed which makes it more suitable for a combination of genetic and biochemical studies. Asexual spores are irradiated or treated with chemical mutagens, and after germination a cross is made with the opposite sex type. Mycelia of the two types fuse, and fruiting bodies containing sexual spores in asci develop. Eight spores arise in an ascus as a result of three nuclear divisions, the first two being meiotic and the last one mitotic. All products of the reduction divisions are recovered as sexual spores and in the order in which they are formed. The nuclei in the vegetative growth (the hyphae) are haploid and carry only one set of genes in seven chromosomes. Genetic characteristics are expressed without complication by dominant or recessive traits being evident. Growth of the wild type occurs in the presence of a suitable carbon source, nitrates, essential salts, and biotin.

The eight spores in an ascus are transferred separately to a complete medium, i.e., one containing amino acids, growth factors, and other substances, the syntheses of which might be blocked by mutation. In this manner eight strains derived from single ascospores are produced, and each strain multiplies asexually in a genetically homogenous manner. Asexual spores, conidia, are produced and can be employed as inocula for biochemical tests. These spores are transferred to the basic medium, and growth will not occur from four of the strains, the mutant ones, if a deficient mutant had been formed and selected. Growth of the other four strains will occur since they have the genetic composition of the wild type. This behavior indicates that a synthetic ability possessed by the original strain has been lost, that it was genetically controlled, and that its nature can be determined by systematic tests.

Transfers of conidia from strains which do not grow on the minimal medium are made to this basic medium supplemented with growth factors, with amino acids, or with other substances in which the investigator might be interested. The procedure to this point is illustrated in Fig. 15-3.

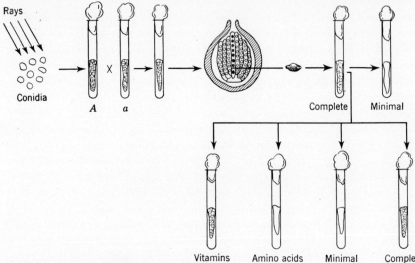

FIG. 15-3. Experimental procedure by which biochemical mutants are obtained and detected. (*After G. Beadle, Genes and chemistry of the organism, Am. Scientist,* **34,** 37, 1946, *courtesy of the Yale University Press.*)

In this example, growth in the presence and not in the absence of vitamins implies that the mutant strain has lost the ability to synthesize one of the known vitamins. Conidia are then transferred to the minimal medium supplemented with individual vitamins. Growth in the basal medium supplemented with pantothenic acid would indicate that the mutant had lost the ability to synthesize pantothenate. Possible precursors of pantothenic acid could be supplied in the medium to determine if they would support growth, and eventually the point (enzyme) at which the mutant is blocked can be determined.

Srb and Horowitz (1944) were the first to demonstrate the occurrence of a number of genetic blocks in the synthesis of a substance, arginine, by mutants of *N. crassa* which required arginine for growth. They isolated mutants with genetic blocks of biochemical activity at seven different points. A similar pathway of synthesis in *Penicillium notatum* was observed by Bonner (1946).   The combined data indicate a pathway of synthesis as presented in Fig. 15-4.   This scheme indicates that a mutant requiring any one substance in the chain can grow if that substance, or any of the ones to its right, is provided in the medium.   A citrulline-requiring mutant, for example, would grow if either citrulline or arginine were supplied.   Proline is not on the direct pathway of synthesis of arginine but appears to be formed from, or to give rise to, an intermediate compound between glutamic acid and ornithine.   Arginine can be broken down into ornithine and urea by *N. crassa*, and this completes a metabolic cycle similar to that which occurs in mammalian liver.

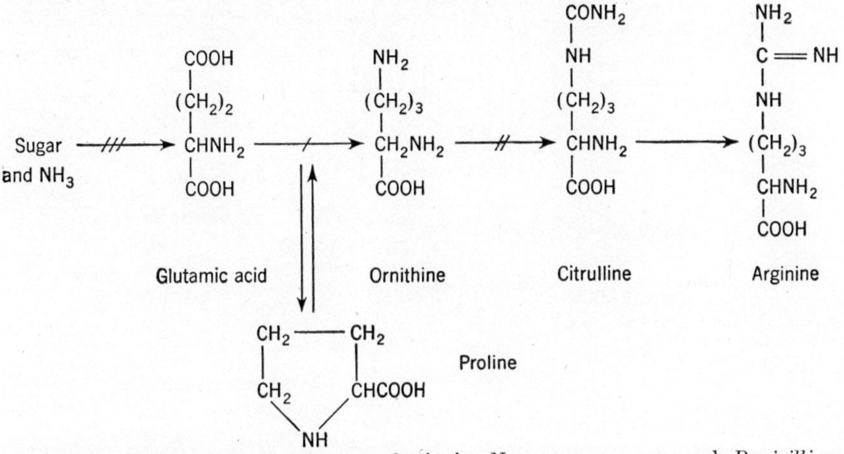

FIG. 15–4. Pathway of arginine synthesis in *Neurospora crassa* and *Penicillium notatum*. The diagonal lines through the arrows indicate probable intermediate steps for which suitable intermediates or mutants have not as yet been obtained.

Various workers have established other metabolic chains on the basis of studies with mutant organisms, simultaneous-adaptation studies, and reactions noted with isolated enzyme systems.   One such chain, not all details of which have been firmly established, depicting the biosynthesis of tryptophan and nicotinic acid, is presented in Fig. 15-5.   Certain of the reactions are the same as postulated earlier in this chapter for the oxidation of tryptophan as determined with studies on simultaneous enzyme adaptation in a species of *Pseudomonas*.   It should be pointed out that indole formation from tryptophan, or the reverse reaction, in bacteria such as *E. coli* does not appear to involve the formation or utilization of serine.   Other differences may be noted between different organisms, but considerations of such chains serve as excellent starting points for studies on pathways in a specific organism.

Biochemical mutants of nutritionally simple bacteria such as *E. coli* have been obtained in relatively large numbers in recent years.   Each biochemical mutant has a growth requirement for an amino acid, a growth factor, or for some other substance not required by the parent cell. The rate of formation of these mutants is increased by agents mutagenic for other microorganisms. The presence of a substrate is not required for the mutations, they commonly involve the loss of a specific synthetic ability although mutation may occur in the opposite direction, and in other respects they resemble mutations in the higher fungi. All indications point to an alteration of genetic characteristics. A mutation is generally evidenced by a change in one character only, but secondary

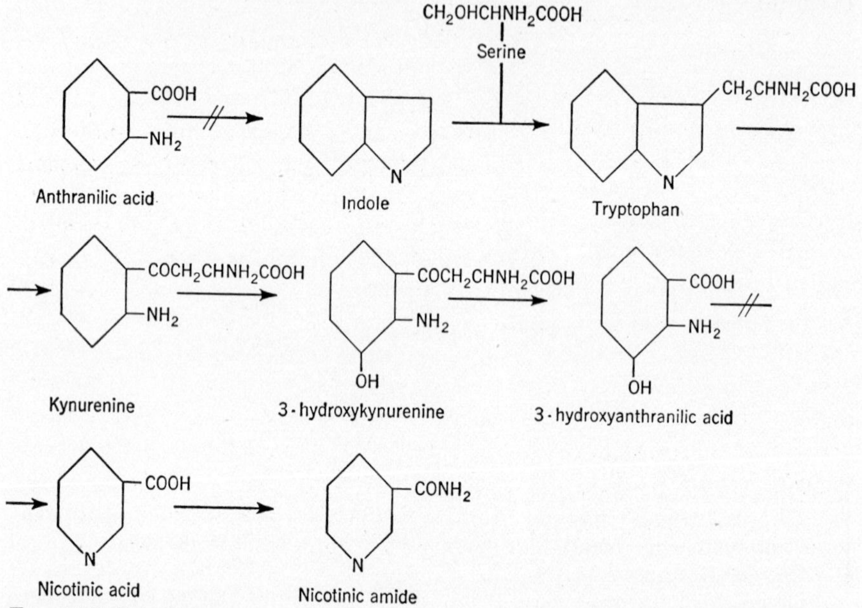

Fig. 15-5. Possible pathway for the synthesis of tryptophan and its conversion to nicotinic acid and amide.

effects may become evident. Reversion of a mutant may occur with formation of the prototroph, i.e., one like the wild type in its characteristics. Mutant strains can undergo further mutation, and eventually a strain may be obtained differing in several respects from the original wild-type parent. Insufficient numbers of mutants of any one species have been obtained to permit the establishment of complete metabolic chains, but with time this should be accomplished.

The mutants must be selected from the nonmutated population, and their selection can be facilitated by use of appropriate methods (Lederberg, 1950). One method consists in plating a suspension of cells treated with a mutagenic agent onto a minimal agar medium. The inoculated medium is then covered with a thin layer of the agar to hold the cells in position, and the preparation is incubated until nonmutant colonies are well developed. A layer of complete medium is then poured over the minimal agar. Substances essential for growth of the mutants diffuse from the biochemically rich agar, and colonies develop from mutant cells that are still viable at this time. These colonies can be selected and cultures established for determinations of their nutritional requirements or differences in their metabolic activities.

Sexual Recombination. The Eubacteriales appear to multiply exclusively by the asexual method of binary fission. Some morphological observations do suggest fusion of cells or of nuclear material which could result in redistribution of characters according to the laws of genetics. Incomplete evidence that sexual recombination of genetic characters can occur was obtained by Sherman and Wing (1937) and by Gowen and Lincoln (1942) with different mutants, but spontaneous mutations could not be entirely ruled out as being responsible for the observed changes. Tatum and Lederberg (1947; see also Lederberg and Tatum, 1953) were the first to demonstrate conclusively that recombination of genetic characters can occur. They produced mutants of the K-12 strain of *E. coli* (which was found to be exceptionally active as regards genetic recombination), lacking in different abilities, mixed these mutant strains, and then plated out in minimal media on which only a cross could develop. This can be illustrated in the following manner. Suppose we have a mutant able to grow in the absence of substance A and that substance B is required for growth. This is represented by the symbols $A+B-$. A second mutant, $A-B+$, requires A but not B for growth. Neither mutant will grow on a medium lacking compounds A and B unless back mutation occurs. When strains $A+B-$ and $A-B+$ are placed in a medium containing A and B, sexual crosses may occur with formation of the prototroph $A+B+$. When these $A+B+$ cells, washed to prevent a carry-over of A and B, are streaked on minimal medium, they will develop colonies while $A-B+$ or $A+B-$ cells will not. This suggests that sexual recombination had taken place, but it must be demonstrated that the number of crosses greatly exceeds those that might be produced by back mutation, reversion. It also must be shown that cells $A+B+$ are formed and will multiply by themselves on repeated transfer in media free of A and B.

In order to circumvent the problem of reversion, which plagued the earlier workers, Lederberg and Tatum used the multiple mutants $B-M-P+T+$ and $B+M+P-T-$, the letters referring to biotin, methionine, proline, and threonine, respectively. When washed samples of mixed cultures of $B-M-P+T+$ and $B+M+P-T-$ were plated out in minimal agar, about 100 colonies developed per 10^9 cells inoculated. No colonies appeared after inoculation of either mutant strain alone.

The recombinants grew on repeated transfers on agar media lacking biotin, methionine, proline, and threonine.   Their other observations were of a similar character.   After various considerations they concluded that the development of the prototroph, $B+M+P+T+$, was due to a segregation of $B+$, $M+$, $P+$, and $T+$ genes into the same cell, the frequency of this segregation being too large to be accounted for on the basis of multiple reversions.   These experiments have been confirmed by others, extended to include other markers than growth factor or amino acid deficiencies, and to other strains of *E. coli* and to other species as well. Recombination, however, has not been demonstrated in all species or strains of a species.

These studies, along with cytological and other ones (including observed pairing between different fertile strains), lead to the conclusion that *E. coli* K-12 in the vegetative state contains one or more haploid nuclei usually alike, each containing one set of genes in a single chromosome. DeLamater (1953), on the basis of mitotic figures, suggests three chromosomes per nucleus in *K*-12.   Haploid cells fuse occasionally, and this is followed by fusion of one pair of nuclei with formation of a diploid nucleus. The diploid nucleus seldom multiplies as such and generally appears to segregate, giving rise to four haploid nuclei.   This picture may need revision with further observations but appears to represent the general behavior as known at the present time.

It is readily apparent that great strides have been made during the past few years in our understanding of the genetics of bacteria.   The numerous studies in this field hold promise for a better understanding of both the mechanics and the physiology of genetic changes in bacteria and other microorganisms.   Certain of the filtrable viruses, particularly the bacterial viruses, also appear to undergo genetic changes, and these will be discussed in Chap. 17.   Changes involved in adaptation to drug resistance will be considered in Chap. 18.

REFERENCES

Beadle, G. W.: Biochemical genetics, *Chem. Rev.*, **37,** 15–96 (1945).

Bonner, D.: Production of biochemical mutations in *Penicillium, Am. J. Bot.*, **33,** 788–791 (1946).

Braun, W.: "Bacterial Genetics," W. B. Saunders Company, Philadelphia, 1953.

Bryson, V., and W. Szybalski: Microbial selection, *Science*, **116,** 45–51 (1952).

Catcheside, D. G.: "The Genetics of Micro-organisms," Sir Isaac Pitman & Sons, Ltd., London, 1951.

Davies, R., and E. F. Gale (eds.): "Adaptation in Micro-organisms," Cambridge University Press, London, 1953.

DeLamater, E. D.: The mitotic mechanism in bacteria, *Cold Spring Harbor Symp. Quant. Biol.*, **18,** 99–100 (1953).

Gale, E. F., and H. M. R. Epps: The effect of the pH of the medium during growth on the enzymatic activity of bacteria and the biological significance of the changes produced, *Biochem. J.*, **36**, 600–618 (1942).

Gowen, J. W., and R. E. Lincoln: A test for sexual fusion in bacteria, *J. Bacteriol.*, **44**, 551–554 (1942).

Hegarty, C. P.: Physiological youth as an important factor in adaptive enzyme formation, *J. Bacteriol.*, **37**, 145–152 (1939).

Lederberg, J.: Problems in microbial genetics, *Heredity*, **2**, 145–198 (1948).

———: Isolation and characterization of biochemical mutants of bacteria, in R. W. Gerard (ed.), "Methods of Medical Research," Year Book Publishers, Inc., Chicago, 1950.

——— and E. M. Lederberg: Replica plating and indirect selection of bacterial mutants, *J. Bacteriol.*, **63**, 399–406 (1952).

——— and E. L. Tatum: Sex in bacteria: genetic studies, 1945–1952, *Science*, **118**, 169–175 (1953).

Lewis, I. M.: Bacterial variation with special reference to behavior of some mutabile strains of colon bacteria in synthetic media, *J. Bacteriol.*, **28**, 619–638 (1934).

McCarty, M.: Chemical nature and biological specificity of the substance inducing transformations of pneumococcal types, *Bacteriol. Rev.*, **10**, 63–71 (1946).

Monod, J., and M. Cohn: La biosynthèse induite des enzymes (adaptation enzymatique), *Advances in Enzymol.*, **13**, 67–119 (1952).

Newcombe, H. B.: Origin of bacterial variants, *Nature*, **164**, 150–151 (1949).

Pinsky, M. J., and J. L. Stokes: Requirements for formic hydrogenlyase adaptation in nonproliferating suspensions of *Escherichia coli*, *J. Bacteriol.*, **64**, 151–161 (1952a).

——— and ———: The influence of age on enzymatic adaptation in microorganisms, *J. Bacteriol.*, **64**, 337–345 (1952b).

Rotman, B., and S. Spiegelman: On the origin of the carbon in the induced synthesis of β-galactosidase in *Escherichia coli*, *J. Bacteriol.*, **68**, 419–429 (1954).

Shaughnessy, H. J., and C.-E. A. Winslow: The diffusion products of bacterial cells as influenced by the presence of various electrolytes, *J. Bacteriol.*, **14**, 69–99 (1927).

Sherman, J. M., and G. E. Holm: Salt effects in bacterial growth. II. The growth of *Bact. coli* in relation to H-ion concentration, *J. Bacteriol.*, **7**, 465–470 (1922).

——— and H. U. Wing: Attempts to reveal sex in bacteria; with some light on fermentative ability in the coli-aerogenes group, *J. Bacteriol.*, **33**, 315–321 (1937).

Srb, A. M., and N. H. Horowitz: The ornithine cycle in *Neurospora* and its genetic control, *J. Biol. Chem.*, **154**, 129–139 (1944).

Stanier, R. Y.: Problems of bacterial oxidative metabolism, *Bacteriol. Rev.*, **41**, 179–191 (1950).

———: Enzymatic adaptation in bacteria, *Ann. Rev. Microbiol.*, **5**, 35–56 (1951).

——— and M. Tsuchida: Adaptative enzymatic patterns in the bacterial oxidation of tryptophan, *J. Bacteriol.*, **58**, 45–60 (1949).

Stewart, F. H.: A review of some recent work on papillary variation in bacteria and bacterial cytology, *J. Hyg.*, **43**, 136–141 (1943).

Tatum, E. L., and J. Lederberg: Gene recombination in the bacterium *Escherichia coli*, *J. Bacteriol.*, **53**, 673–684 (1947).

Zinder, N. D., and J. Lederberg: Genetic exchange in *Salmonella*, *J. Bacteriol.*, **64**, 679–699 (1952).

CHAPTER 16

PHYSIOLOGICAL ASPECTS OF INFECTION

In its broadest aspects parasitic life is similar to predatory life, an attempt to secure a supply of food under environmental conditions suitable for the maintenance of the species. In one hypothesis it is postulated that parasites originated from saprophytic ancestors which became adapted to growth with or upon other species and finally to growth within living tissues. In the course of adaptation many parasitic species could have lost certain synthetic powers possessed by related saprophytic forms. The saprophyte is relatively independent of other forms of life; the parasite is directly dependent upon a host, frequently a specific one, for its maintenance. This dependence in some instances is a skillful one; in other instances the parasite is a bungler and may produce such an amount of destruction in its host as to lead to the death of the latter in a short period of time. Parasites eliciting disturbing reactions in a host are spoken of as pathogens, or pathogenic microorganisms.

A number of bacteria are capable of establishing themselves in the tissues of a host, multiplying therein, and producing an infectious disease of a severity dependent upon the nature of the relationship between host and parasite. The term *virulence* is employed as a measure of the degree of pathogenicity of a bacterium, a pathogenic species or strain being classified as one of high, low, or intermediate virulence. The term virulence (Watson and Brandly, 1949) frequently is considered as a relative measure of the ability of an organism to produce disease, either due to its invasiveness, to toxic agents it produces, or to combinations of these factors, in a specified host when inoculated by a specified route. Hence virulence is not a property of the bacterium alone but is associated also with the nature of the host and with the route of introduction into the host. Since both host and parasite are subject to variation, and different strains of the parasite may differ in their ability to produce disease, it is readily apparent that any determination of the "virulence" of an organism is limited, unless otherwise specified, to the average response of a supposedly normal group of animals to the introduction of a particular culture of the pathogenic species, or of the toxins it produces. It may be expressed in terms of the median lethal dose, LD_{50}, which is the amount of the agent required to elicit death of 50 per cent of the animals inoculated by a specified route.

Burnet (1940) illustrated infectious disease in its simplest form by analogy to relationships between an amoeba and a bacterium. Amoebae frequently flow around bacteria and then proceed to digest the ingested organism in a vacuole into which the amoeba secretes digestive enzymes. When the amoeba succeeds in converting the ingested bacterium into assimilable foodstuff, we consider it as a simple act of digestion. Let us imagine, however, that the ingested bacterium resists digestion and instead multiplies within the amoeba and brings about death of the latter. This would represent a disease as far as the amoeba is concerned, a source of nutrients from the viewpoint of a bacterium. The nature of infectious diseases is not this simple, but the analogy has its merits since we are prone to consider infections of man from the viewpoint of man alone rather than from the broader base of the struggle for existence between an animal (or plant) and a parasite, often poorly adapted to existence in its host.

Commonly an infectious disease is described as a conflict between two species, the parasite being considered as possessing certain aggressive mechanisms conferring upon it a degree of virulence, while the host, once external barriers are breached, can mobilize general and later specific defense forces. Such a concept should be considered as descriptive only; actually, it indicates that there is relatively little information that would enable us to describe in physiological terms the factors involved in infection and resistance.

The invasive power of microorganisms involves their ability to penetrate surface barriers and to multiply within and spread through the tissues once invasion has been accomplished. A few potentially pathogenic species (e.g., staphylococci on the skin) are able to live indefinitely on surface barriers and only penetrate under relatively unknown conditions, generally after a break occurs in the barrier. Others are more dependent upon a chain of infections, or upon carriers, for their maintenance since they do not appear to be able to exist upon the barriers. In either case a rather definite portal of entry into the deeper tissues is involved, invasion frequently being dependent upon injury of the barrier induced by either mechanical or chemical factors or upon subtle changes in the host.

After bacteria, either pathogenic or saprophytic species, have gained entrance to the tissues, they may encounter substances present in body fluids which have bacteriostatic or bactericidal properties. When the invading organism is a saprophytic form, it is quickly removed and destroyed by amoeba-like cells known as phagocytes. Pathogenic forms, on the other hand, often are more resistant to engulfment or to destruction by phagocytes and other forces, e.g., the inflammatory responses become involved in the struggle for existence. When the parasite succeeds in developing within the host, growth of the former generally continues until more specific forces exert their influence.

The most specific defense mechanism is the formation of antibodies against the parasite, or its toxic products. Specific union between antibodies and antigens of the parasite occurs, and in more or less unknown manner, further multiplication of and invasion by the pathogen may be halted. Consideration of the immunological reactions is far afield from bacterial physiology and gives little information bearing directly on the major problems concerning the physiological aspects of the phenomena associated with the establishment of a virulent organism within a host.

One major problem is why saprophytic bacteria, frequently more resistant to many inimical conditions and often able to grow under more diverse situations than the parasitic species, are unable to initiate a disease process. A number of the saprophytes, however, are able to multiply in the tissues as secondary invaders. An answer to the above problem, one more specific than just their relative susceptibility to phagocytosis, would be of considerable value in elucidating the general nature of virulence, particularly when the latter is associated primarily with invasiveness. Other major problems are the tissue specificity frequently associated with a particular species and the specificity of tissue responses to a pathogen as evidenced by specificity of clinical symptoms in many diseases. The establishment of distinct disease states indicates that the underlying physiological disturbance is not the same for each host-parasite relationship. Possibly a clue to the tissue specificity exhibited by many pathogens lies in similarities between properties of the host and the parasite rather than in differences which have been searched for in the past (for a recent review of mechanisms of microbial pathogenicity, see Howie and O'Hea, 1955).

For purposes of discussion (Pappenheimer, in Racker, 1954) we can consider three main types of disease-producing organisms according to their tendency to localize in the body. These may be summarized as follows:

1. Bacteria multiplying in necrotic tissue or on mucous membranes and producing toxic agents which are primarily responsible for the major symptoms of the disease
2. Organisms relatively resistant to phagocytosis and multiplying primarily in tissue fluids
3. Highly parasitic species which tend to multiply within rather than outside of tissue cells

Exotoxin-producing Bacteria. Botulinus poisoning or intoxication is induced by the ingestion of botulinus toxin present in spoiled foodstuffs within which *Clostridium botulinum* has multiplied and liberated its toxin. Rare instances have been reported in which fatal intoxication in man has resulted from contamination of deep wounds with the bacillus (or its spores) and subsequent multiplication of and toxin production by *C. botulinum*. The bacterium is essentially a saprophytic species and possesses no invasive ability. There are several types of this species, and each type gives rise to the formation of slightly different toxins. These toxins differ from most others in being effective when taken by mouth, thus indicating that they are relatively resistant to the action of proteolytic enzymes.

Type *A* botulinus toxin has been crystallized and characterized as a globulin-like protein containing 19 different amino acids (for general reviews of the nature of toxins, see Pillemer and Robbins, 1949, and Van Heyningen, 1950). Type *B* toxin appears to differ slightly from the *A* type in its general characteristics. Little is known regarding the nature of the toxins produced by types *C*, *D*, and *E* of the botulinus organism. One milligram of the botulinus toxin is sufficient to kill about 20 million mice. This exotoxin, like the other highly toxic exotoxins, is a good antigen as compared with the endotoxins. Likewise, it can be detoxified with formaldehyde without losing its antigenic characteristics. It has been suggested that toxicity is associated with free amino groups in these toxin molecules and that these groups are masked upon reaction with formaldehyde in the formol reaction. There is no concrete evidence that this is actually the case.

Botulinus toxin appears to be preferentially adsorbed in the body by certain portions of the nervous system. Its action is supposedly limited to myoneural junctions, the adsorbed toxin in some manner interfering with conduction of impulses only at the terminal twigs of motor nerves and proximal to the site of acetylcholine release. There is evidence that it does interfere in some manner with the release of acetylcholine.

Staphylococci, and possibly streptococci and other bacteria, produce an exotoxin which gives rise to symptoms of food poisoning in man. The staphylococcus enterotoxin is formed most readily when foods containing starch as a thickening agent are allowed to stand for a number of hours in a warm room. It is highly irritating but not lethal to man, the period of incubation after partaking of the enterotoxin in foodstuffs being much shorter than that for most other toxins. Nothing is known concerning the mechanism of action of the enterotoxin.

The Shiga neurotoxin, elaborated by *Shigella dysenteriae*, is not a true exotoxin since it is released primarily upon disruption of the cells. In its marked toxicity, good antigenicity, and heat lability, it more nearly resembles the exotoxins than the endotoxins. Like the diphtheria toxin, production of Shiga neurotoxin is dependent upon the iron content of the medium. There is some evidence suggesting that the neurotoxin is associated with, or related to, the cytochromes. Relatively little is known concerning the nature of this toxin.

Tetanus toxin (tetanospasmin) is a toxic protein formed and released during multiplication of *Clostridium tetani* in the body. The tetanus bacillus primarily is a saprophyte, growing only in dead tissues in deep wounds and showing no particular tendency to spread in the body. The toxin is adsorbed, supposedly by end organs of the motor nerves, and then travels along axis cylinders of the peripheral nerves to the central nervous system. A slow rate of adsorption and a low rate of travel in the nervous system are believed to be factors responsible for the delay in the induction of symptoms, even following injection of relatively large doses of the toxin. Its mode of action is unknown.

The gas gangrene group, *Clostridium perfringens* (*welchii*) and related species, particularly *C. septicum* and *C. novyi*, produces a number of toxins. Most or all of these toxins appear to be enzymatic in character. The gas gangrene organisms are more invasive in character than is *C. tetani*, spread of *C. perfringens* apparently being facilitated by its κ-toxin (the Duran-Reynals spreading factor). The κ-toxin, a collagenase, can hydrolyze the muscle protein, collagen, causing its dissolution and subsequent disruption of the reticular structure. This breakdown of tissue structure enables the bacillus to spread into the surrounding tissues. At the same time carbohydrate materials are liberated, and these are fermented with the production of considerable quantities of gas, hence the name gas gangrene. Spread of certain clostridia (and of staphylococci and streptococci) is facilitated also by their secretion of hyaluronidase, an enzymatic toxin that elicits the hydrolysis of the polysaccharide hyaluronic acid, the "ground substance" or "cement" of connective tissues. Many strains form a fibrinolysin (see streptokinase) which may aid in the spread of the organism. Various hemolysins are also produced.

While the κ-toxin is relatively toxic, most of the lethal effect of *C. perfringens* is due to its α-toxin. The α-toxin is a lecithinase, an enzyme which hydrolyzes lecithin with the formation of a diglyceride and phosphocholine. It is both hemolytic and necrotic in its action, hemolysis in vitro, however, requiring incubation at 37°C. followed by a period of incubation at 2 to 4°C. (hot-cold lysis). Most or all of the protective value of antitoxins is directed against the α-toxin.

The general nature of the gas gangrene infection can be described as follows. Bacillary spores, along with other bacteria in the soil, gain entrance into a wound. Aerobic saprophytes may respire or multiply to a limited extent in the devitalized tissue and thereby aid in the establishment of reducing conditions favorable for germination of clostridial spores and subsequent multiplication of these anaerobes. Extracellular enzymes diffuse into adjacent tissues and injure or destroy cells, thus creating conditions favorable for the spread of the clostridia. Hyaluronidase and fibrinolysin undoubtedly play an important role in the spread of the bacilli, while collagenase is also quite active, as judged by the pulped appearance of muscle in the infected area. Acid and gas production also contributes to the damage produced in the infected area. At the same time general intoxication occurs as well, one evidence of toxin activity being an apparent destruction of red blood cells with consequent bronzing of the skin. Relatively little is known concerning the mechanism of the general intoxication induced during the infection. Most or all of the characteristic systemic symptoms can be induced following the injection of culture filtrates.

Corynebacterium diphtheriae is virulent primarily because of its ability to produce a highly active exotoxin during growth of the organism, usually on mucous membranes of the throat or nasopharynx. The organism, can, however, multiply in other parts of the body, thus suggesting that it does have slight invasive power. The major local response in cases of typical diphtheria is a degeneration of epithelial cells, extending to the underlying tissues. This is accompanied by a profuse fibrinous exudation, and the formation of the characteristic diphtheric membrane which is composed of fibrin, dead tissue cells, leucocytes, and bacteria. The membrane may interfere mechanically with breathing although the major systemic effects are produced by the toxin formed by the bacillus. The kidneys, heart, and nerves are most severely affected by the toxin, marked fatty degeneration being observed both in heart muscle and in the nervous system. The toxin has been crystallized and is a protein, apparently related to the protein moiety of diphtherial cytochrome b_1.

Toxin is produced most abundantly during the aerobic growth of *C. diphtheriae* in media of relatively fixed iron content. At minimal concentrations of iron both growth and toxin production are quite limited. Growth and toxin production increase with increasing iron content of the medium, maximum toxin production being noted around 100 μg. of iron per liter of medium. Growth is enhanced at higher iron concentrations, but toxin production falls off to practically zero around 600 μg. of iron per liter. In a medium of relatively low iron content growth continues in a normal manner until most of the iron in the medium is used up. The bacteria continue to multiply to some extent, but their total iron and cytochrome contents fall to levels dependent upon the strain of bacteria tested. At the same time that iron deficiency develops, diphtheria toxin and free coproporphyrin are released into the medium. Above the optimal iron concentration for toxin production, production of both the toxin and the free porphyrin decreases. It has been shown that, in general, for each additional four molecules of iron in the medium, four molecules less of porphyrin and one less of diphtheria toxin are liberated. The various results have been interpreted as indicating that in media of low iron content, the cells form the toxin and the porphyrin but are unable to link many of the molecules together owing to the iron deficiency. The unlinked molecules are excreted into the medium. The molecules are linked together in the cells in the presence of higher amounts of iron, and the complex appears to function as a respiratory enzyme.

There is little evidence that diphtheria toxin interferes with the activity of the cytochrome system directly. Some studies indicate that the toxin acts by blocking the synthesis of one or more components of the cytochrome system. The most concrete evidence for the nature of diphtheria toxin comes from studies with the *Cecropia* silkworm. This silkworm is highly sensitive to the toxin during the larval and the developing adult stages but is relatively resistant during the stage of dormancy (pupal state). Cytochromes b_5 (e?) and $a + a_3$ predominate in most of the tissues in the pupal state, b_5 being particularly important in pupal heart muscle and in the fat body. It is insensitive to cyanide, carbon monoxide, antimycin A, and toxin. It appears to be autooxidizable at a slow rate. Diphtheria toxin does elicit necrosis in and disappearance of striated muscle during the pupal stage of the silkworm. Cytochromes $a + a_3$, b, and c predominate in striated muscle, and this system is sensitive to the poisons to which b_5 is resistant. This suggests that diphtheria toxin interferes with the formation of a cytochrome (possibly cytochrome b) in susceptible tissues, since preformed cytochromes are insensitive and also because there is a considerable lag period following inoculation of the adult insects before symptoms become evident. Other possibilities exist regarding the mode of action of diphtheria toxin, but much of the present evidence points to an involvement of the cytochrome system in the action of the toxin.

It is of interest that nontoxigenic (avirulent) strains of *C. diphtheriae* give rise to toxigenic ones when exposed to a bacteriophage isolated from virulent cultures. This apparent mutation to toxigenicity appears to be similar to the transduction of a genetic characteristic in the *Salmonella* species discussed in Chap. 15.

In certain diseases of plants (Wooley, also Pappenheimer, in Racker, 1954) the invading parasite produces a toxin which by itself can produce typical lesions of the disease. The fungus *Fusarium lycopersici* is the causative agent of a wilting disease of tomato plants. It produces a toxic agent known as lycomarasmin, a low-molecular-weight peptide composed of asparagine, glycine, and α-hydroxyalanine and reported to have the following structure:

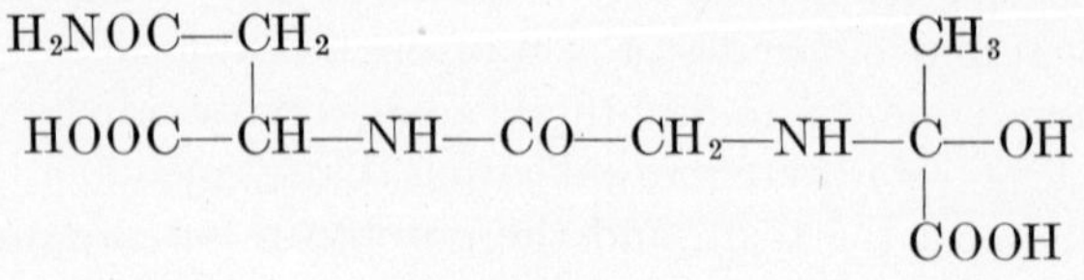

$$\begin{array}{ccc} H_2NOC\!-\!CH_2 & & CH_3 \\ \Big| & & \Big| \\ HOOC\!-\!CH\!-\!NH\!-\!CO\!-\!CH_2\!-\!NH\!-\!C\!-\!OH \\ & & \Big| \\ & & COOH \end{array}$$

Lycomarasmin antagonizes the growth-promoting activity of streptogenin for bacteria, and streptogenin can decrease, noncompetitively, the toxic effects of small amounts of lycomarasmin.

Pseudomonas tabaci, the causative agent of wildfire disease of tobacco and certain other crops, forms a toxic agent responsible for the formation of the clorotic spots characteristic of this infection. This agent, also, is an amino acid derivative of low molecular weight and appears to act like lycomarasmin as an antimetabolite. Wooley and his coworkers found that it is an unstable substance which breaks down to form formic acid and a new amino acid, α,ϵ-diamino-β-hydroxypimelic acid, called tabtoxinine. The toxic activity of this agent can be reversed, competitively, in some plants by methionine, and its activity can be simulated by a synthetic antimetabolite of methionine, methionine sulfoximine. A comparison of the structural formulas of these compounds indicates similarities between them.

$$HOOC-\overset{\overset{\displaystyle H}{|}}{\underset{\underset{\displaystyle NH_3}{|}}{C}}-CH_2-CH_2-S-CH_3$$

Methionine

$$HOOC-\overset{\overset{\displaystyle H}{|}}{\underset{\underset{\displaystyle NH_2}{|}}{C}}-CH_2-CH_2-\overset{\overset{\displaystyle O}{\|}}{\underset{\underset{\displaystyle NH}{\|}}{S}}-CH_3$$

Methionine sulfoximine

$$HOOC-\overset{\overset{\displaystyle H}{|}}{\underset{\underset{\displaystyle NH_2}{|}}{C}}-CH_2-CH_2-\overset{\overset{\displaystyle HO}{|}}{\underset{\underset{\displaystyle H}{|}}{C}}-\overset{\overset{\displaystyle H}{|}}{\underset{\underset{\displaystyle NHCHO}{|}}{C}}-COOR$$

P. tabaci toxin

Here we have two examples of relatively simple antimetabolites produced by microorganisms, and there may well be others. Crown gall of tomato plants is caused by *Agrobacterium tumafaciens*, but lesions free of this organism are produced at sites away from that of the inoculation and first lesion or gall. An associated virus has been suggested as the inciting agent, but it might be a toxin. The proteinaceous exotoxins we have been considering may be antimetabolites of proteins rather than of simpler molecules.

Extracellular Multiplication. In a number of infectious diseases the causative species multiply primarily in extracellular fluids. Pneumococcal pneumonia and anthrax are typical examples, and the infectious agents are characterized by their general lack of ability to form toxic agents. Staphylococci and streptococci, because of their invasive properties, are included for discussion in the group, but their formation of a number of toxic agents would enable them to be considered in group 1 as well. Likewise *Salmonella typhosa* and other enteric pathogens are included with the extracellular group, but these organisms multiply both extra- and intracellularly in the host. They are not, however, absolute intracellular parasites and, to complicate matters, they produce an endotoxin. Hence any classification of the nature considered here must be considered as relative and suggestive rather than as highly specific in character.

The lesions in pneumococcal pneumonia and in anthrax, as well as in many other disease processes, are most likely due in great part to the host's response rather than to any specific action of the bacteria or of their products. Large numbers of killed or even of avirulent pneumococci (*Diplococcus pneumoniae*) have relatively little effect when injected into an animal susceptible to virulent strains. The symptoms of pneumonia are evident only when actively multiplying pneumococci are present in relatively large numbers in the tissues. Large numbers of bacteria, in the blood stream for example, do not necessarily elicit any marked symptoms in the host. Hence we must conclude that as yet we know almost nothing concerning the nature of many infectious processes.

Virulence of the pneumococci is ascribed to their possession of capsules which render these organisms quite resistant to ingestion by phagocytes. Pneumococci, therefore, are able to evade the second line of defense. Their establishment in the tissues may be aided by a spreading factor (Raffel, 1953). This is evidenced by the fact that injection of autolysates of pneumococci along with sublethal doses of the bacteria render the doses lethal for rabbits. Avirulent strains injected together with the autolysate elicit no response in the host. This is another indication of the association of capsular material with virulence of pneumococci. It has been reported that the unknown factor in pneumococcal autolysates exerts an action similar to that of hyaluronidase. When natural recovery from pneumococcal pneumonia occurs, it follows the appearance of antibodies in the blood stream. The effective antibodies are directed primarily against capsular material and sensitize pneumococci to phagocytosis. Capsular material in these organisms is protective in character but does not account alone for the ability of the pneumococcus to multiply in the body and to elicit characteristic symptoms of the disease.

Bacillus anthracis likewise appears to have no particular toxic characteristics, symptoms resulting from or after the development of large numbers of the bacilli in body fluids. Here again peculiar characteristics of the capsular material, a peptide of L-glutamic acid, appear to inhibit phagocytosis, but immunity does not depend upon antibodies sensitizing the bacteria to phagocytosis. The capsular material neutralizes the bactericidal activity of a basic polypeptide of high lysine content, the so-called anthracidal factor normally present in many animals. An "immunizing factor" is formed and excreted by anthrax bacilli in vivo and also in laboratory media containing tissue fluids and exposed to an atmosphere enriched with carbon dioxide. It is not formed in ordinary media. This factor does not elicit the formation of demonstrable antibodies, but there is some indication that it elicits the formation of a substance which may induce disruption of the bacilli in vivo.

In these two examples of infections caused by pathogenic bacteria multiplying extracellularly in the host, it is possible that symptoms could result from interference with normal metabolism and behavior of cells of the latter's tissues. This interference could be due to competition for essential nutrients or nutrilites or to the production of antimetabolites. The latter mechanism was evident in the plant diseases considered above, but has not been demonstrated with anthrax bacilli or pneumococci. Actually, there is no concrete evidence that any of the factors suggested above are involved in the infectious processes induced by these organisms. The nature of the reactions, and of many of the effects, remains obscure.

In the case of the enteric pathogens such as *Salmonella typhosa* large numbers can be found in local areas and are also widely distributed at times. They are not strictly extracellular in their growth, many being found within cells in which they can multiply. Here again we know nothing concerning the characteristics which enable them to multiply quite readily in vivo. The enteric bacteria produce certain structural components, rather superficially located, consisting of complexes of polysaccharide, lipid, and protein. This type of complex, often extremely irritating to a host, is referred to as an endotoxin; it is liberated following death of the bacteria and is toxic, although not so potent as the exotoxins considered earlier. Many of the symptoms of the enteric disorders are due to the release and activity of the endotoxin in the mammalian body. A few typhoid bacteria injected into splanchnic ganglions in rabbits can elicit typical typhoid syndromes (Lwoff, in Racker, 1954). A similar response is observed either when a small amount of the endotoxin or when an electrical stimulus is applied to the splanchnic nerve. The location of the typhoid infection in the body, which enables the toxin to come into contact with these nerves, rather than the nature of the toxin alone, is responsible for the symptoms. Other manifestations may be due to similar, relatively nonspecific physiological stimuli. This activity of the endotoxin explains why, in contrast to pneumococci and anthrax bacilli, the injection of large numbers of dead enteric bacteria can give rise to symptoms of the disease. The presence of the complex antigen in the cell, however, does not confer upon it properties of virulence. *E. coli*, for example, does contain such a toxic component, but *E. coli* is a relatively avirulent parasite of the intestinal tract.

The staphylococci and streptococci multiply to a great extent extracellularly. Their ability to multiply and to spread in the body frequently is abetted by their formation of toxic agents which generally possess enzymatic characteristics. The character of the infectious processes can be attributed to a considerable extent to the activities of these products.

The most frequent route of infection by staphylococci (*Micrococcus pyogenes* var. *aureus*) is through hair follicles. The infection is characterized commonly by the formation of a localized, purulent area more or less completely walled off from surrounding tissues. The staphylococci multiply within this region and may spread to other parts of the body, giving rise to secondary foci of infection and at times to a bacteremia. The close association between virulence and the formation of coagulase and α- and δ-lysins tends to incriminate these agents in the infectious process.

Coagulase activity is associated to a marked degree with virulence and can be demonstrated following the addition of a coagulase-positive strain of staphylococci to plasma. Strictly speaking, the staphylococcal factor is a procoagulase which reacts with a cofactor or activator present in plasma to form the clotting agent, coagulase. It has been suggested that the deposition of fibrin induced around an infected area would provide a mechanical barrier against phagocytes. Some strains of staphylococci produce a fibrinolysin (staphylokinase), but this agent more commonly is associated with streptococci. Likewise staphylococci may produce the spreading factor, hyaluronidase. These latter two agents do not appear to be as closely associated with the ability of staphylococci to multiply in the tissues as is coagulase.

The pyogenic strains of staphylococci are characterized in part by their β-hemolytic activity on blood agar. Hemolytic activity can be demonstrated in cell-free culture fluids and is due to the activity of several hemolysins or staphylolysins. The α- and δ-lysins are the most active. They are proteinaceous in character, but little is known concerning the nature of their action on red blood cells and of their activity in the infectious process. They do not exhibit the lecithinase activity of the α-toxin of *C. perfringens*. The α-staphylolysin also exerts leucocidal activity, while the δ-lysin is both dermonecrotic and lethal as well as hemolytic. The enterotoxin of staphylococci has been mentioned earlier and does not appear to be involved in virulence of the species.

The β-hemolytic streptococci in group A of *Streptococcus pyogenes* can produce a variety of pathological responses which are dependent upon the nature of the host, the strain of streptococci, and the portal of entry into the host. The organisms may remain localized, or they may spread throughout the body, frequently producing secondary lesions in specific organs or tissues. Again little is known concerning the development of the pathological process and the role played by various agents and enzymes characteristic of the virulent forms. The erythrogenic or scarlatinal toxin does not appear to be involved in the ability of strains producing this substance to establish themselves in the tissues. It is, however, responsible for the characteristic rash of scarlet fever. Hypersensitive responses of the host often play an important role in the production of symptoms in diseases of streptococcal etiology.

One agent, originally termed fibrinolysin but more commonly known today as streptokinase, has the ability to lyse or dissolve fibrin clots and to inhibit the clotting of plasma. It is not a lytic agent by itself but is a kinase that activates plasminogen, the precursor of plasmin. Plasmin is a plasma protease occurring in the euglobulin fraction of blood and is the actual lytic agent. Virulent strains of streptococci commonly produce streptokinase. Streptodornase, or streptococcal deoxyribonuclease, depolymerizes deoxyribonucleic acid and appears to be involved with the invasive characteristics of streptococci. These two agents are employed in the therapeutic, enzymatic *débridement* of damaged tissues, streptokinase breaking down freshly formed adhesions and fibrin barriers and being aided in the liquefaction of exudates by streptodornase. As a result of this enzymatic treatment, removal of pus and necrotic tissues is facilitated, chemotherapeutic agents gain access more readily to the bacteria in the infected area, and the host more rapidly repairs damage done in the area.

The β-hemolytic group *A* streptococci elaborate two hemolysins known as streptolysins O and S. Streptolysin O is a sulfhydryl-containing protein which is hemolytic only in the reduced state, while the S-lysin is an oxygen-stable protein. The leucocidin of streptococci appears to be identical with streptolysin O. Many strains of streptococci produce hyaluronidase, but some form capsules rich in hyaluronic acid. It is apparent that virulent strains of streptococci possess a number of potentially disturbing agents active against mammalian cells or their constituents, but here again we are unable to assess their contributions to the establishment and spread of the infectious agent in the body of the host.

Intracellular Parasites. A number of pathogenic species, particularly of the Rickettsiales and Virales but also the malaria parasites and the leprosy bacillus, are limited to intracellular multiplication. *Pasteurella tularensis, Mycobacterium tuberculosis*, and other bacteria may multiply to a considerable extent intracellularly, but intracellular growth is not an absolute requirement. Little is known regarding the relationships between these pathogens and the cells they parasitize within a host. One suggestion is that the strict intracellular parasites are dependent upon transient intermediates of metabolism as well as upon various essential nutrilites for growth.   The viruses appear to utilize such substances as well as diverting enzymatic mechanisms of the parasitized cell for their own purposes.   Probably more studies have been carried out regarding the virulence mechanisms of the tubercle bacillus (Dubos, 1954; both Dubos and Bloch, in Racker, 1954) than of any other bacteria in this group with the possible exception of the host-parasite relationships between certain bacteriophages and bacteria of the *E. coli* group.

A host often responds to the presence of a foreign body by a complex series of reactions known collectively as the inflammatory process.   Glycolysis is quite pronounced; lactic acid accumulates and the pH decreases; there is a decrease in oxygen available and an increase in carbon dioxide tension; and changes occur in cellular permeability and blood flow to the affected area together with a local increase in temperature.   Certain of these changes may be inhibitory to bacteria, avirulent strains of the tubercle bacillus, e.g., tending to be inhibited by them to a greater extent than are virulent strains.   More pronounced changes may be induced in leucocytes than are noted in the extracellular milieu.   Dubos suggested that accumulation of lactic acid is one of the major factors involved in limiting the growth of avirulent tubercle bacilli.   Substances that influence general metabolic behavior of the host, e.g., thyroid or dinitrophenol, may exert an effect at the cellular level that renders the cells more favorable for the growth of tubercle bacilli.   The hypersensitive state that develops can also alter growth response.

Tubercle bacilli, either from virulent, attenuated, or avirulent strains, are readily engulfed by phagocytes.   Avirulent ones may multiply to a limited extent within the phagocytes but soon die off, attenuated ones do multiply and persist for some time, while virulent strains do so to a greater extent.   In time some degree of immunity may be established owing to a tissue response to the presence of tubercle bacilli that are living but not necessarily multiplying.   The reasons for these behaviors are not known, nor are the actual factors responsible for determining whether or not a virulent strain will multiply to a considerable extent and even spread throughout the body.

An apparent, but not absolute, difference between virulent and avirulent strains of tubercle bacilli lies in the formation of the "cord factor" by virulent strains.   Cells of virulent strains tend to be arranged in bundles or cords.   This arrangement is ascribed to their formation of the cord factor, a somewhat toxic lipid-carbohydrate-nitrogenous complex. It has been suggested that release of the cord factor in vivo causes an injury to cells of the host which provides conditions more favorable for the growth of tubercle bacilli.   In this manner, it may act as an "aggresin."

It might be well to consider in the intracellular group a plant infection of considerable economic advantage rather than liability, i.e., the infection of root systems of leguminous plants by species of *Rhizobium*. These symbiotic, nitrogen-fixing bacteria, like other infectious bacteria, show considerable host specificity (in fact are classified primarily on this basis) and a characteristic infection pattern.

As a leguminous plant develops, lateral roots branch out from the tap-root, and these are covered with roothairs, thin-walled, hair-like extensions of epidermal cells. If cells of a suitable species of *Rhizobium* are present in the soil, they can infect the roothairs which they enter, causing curling and other local deformities to develop. They do not attack cellulose but enter the roothair where cellulose is lacking or where the roothair has been damaged. Soon after invasion has been accomplished an infectious thread becomes apparent. This thread is composed of a mass of bacteria surrounded by a tube or membrane composed primarily of cellulose and pectic materials. This membrane, apparently composed entirely of plant materials, might be considered to be the result of a walling-off process. The infection thread passes through cell walls, and bacteria enter some of the cells, generally those that are tetraploid, i.e., ones possessing double the ordinary number of chromosomes. Hundreds or even thousands of rhizobia may develop within an infected cell.

The nodule, a tumor-like process, develops from division and enlargement of the infected plant cells and also from rapid division and enlargement of uninfected cells of the cortex or pericycle. Stimulation of growth of the uninfected cells appears to be caused by an auxin, apparently indoleacetic acid, formed by the bacterium and diffusing from it into the surrounding area. As the nodule enlarges, vascular bundles are formed in the cortex and connect with the vascular system of the root. Two-way passage of dissolved materials occurs through these bundles. As the plant matures the bacteria within the nodules die off and tend to disappear, the nitrogen fixed by the bacteria in this symbiotic and parasitic relationship being adsorbed by the plant.

Here we have an example of contamination, invasion, and the development of a pathological response that has been studied in considerable detail. As yet little is known concerning the factors involved in the specificity exhibited and in the mechanisms involved in invasion by and development of the parasite. In this case the relationship is one of mutual benefit, the parasite obtaining nutrients from the host and the host in the long run obtaining nitrogen fixed by the parasite. Although local damage is done to the host, the balance sheet appears to favor the host rather than the bacterium. In this respect it is an unusual pathological process. As a general rule, crops from infected plants, in which the symbiotic relationship is well developed, are richer in protein content than are those from uninfected plants.

In general, we have considered some of the simpler aspects of various infectious processes, knowing that variations and complications frequently are encountered. It is necessary, however, to gain some idea of the basic nature of the relationships between cells of host and parasite in the infectious processes before it is possible to consider the variations that develop. It is realized that there are many similarities between the metabolism and other activities of bacteria and of tissue cells, but there are differences also. Once these physiological differences have been fully recognized, it may be possible to outline the events that transpire between contamination of the host and the development of the infection and the accompanying symptoms. The tendency for many parasites to attack specific hosts and to localize in particular tissues in a host should warn us to look for similarities as well as dissimilarities.

REFERENCES

Burnet, F. M.: "Biological Aspects of Infectious Disease," Cambridge University Press, London, 1940.

Dubos, R. J.: The gold-headed cane in the laboratory, *Pub. Health Rep.*, **69,** 365–371 (1954).

Howie, J. W., and A. J. O'Hea (eds.): "Mechanisms of Microbial Pathogenicity," Cambridge University Press, London, 1955.

Pillemer, L., and K. C. Robbins: Chemistry of toxins, *Ann. Rev. Microbiol.*, **3,** 265–288 (1949).

Racker, E. (ed.): "Cellular Metabolism and Infections," Academic Press, Inc., New York, 1954.

Raffel, S.: "Immunity—Hypersensitivity—Serology," Appleton-Century-Crofts, Inc., New York, 1953.

Van Heyningen, W. E.: "Bacterial Toxins," Blackwell Scientific Publications, Oxford, 1950.

Watson, D. W., and C. A. Brandly: Virulence and pathogenicity, *Ann. Rev. Microbiol.*, **3,** 195–220 (1949).

CHAPTER 17

THE BACTERIOPHAGE

Bacteria, as well as higher forms of life, are subject to infectious disease. In 1915 Twort observed that degenerative changes occurred in a culture of staphylococci and that the agent inducing the change could be transmitted in series from one culture to another. Two years later d'Herelle observed a similar phenomenon, i.e., lysis of a multiplying culture of dysentery bacilli following the addition to it of a filtrate prepared from feces of patients ill with bacillary dysentery. Bacterial-free filtrates of the lysed culture induced lysis in new cultures, and so on in series. D'Herelle postulated that lysis was induced by an invisible living agent to which he gave the name bacteriophage (bacteria eater). The term frequently is shortened to phage. It was soon recognized that many bacteriophages exist, that they exhibit a high degree of host specificity, and that they have many of the general characteristics of the filtrable viruses. Hence they are often spoken of as bacterial viruses. The lytic phenomenon is spoken of as bacteriophagy. Here we have an example of what appears to be a simple infectious process of the intracellular type and one that has been studied in considerable detail. Bacteriophagy is of particular interest as a physiological problem since a phage induces marked changes in the physiological activities of a susceptible host bacterium, so altering them as to induce formation primarily or entirely of phage rather than of bacterial substance in the diseased host.

Bacteriophages active against a wide variety of bacteria have been isolated from a number of sources, sewage being one of the most common sources. They are recognized primarily on the basis of their lytic activity on a suitable host under conditions otherwise favorable to multiplication of the latter. Chemically, they are composed primarily or entirely of protein and deoxyribonucleic acid (DNA), the latter being enclosed in a protein coat or membrane. They are small particles, generally of the order of 50 to 100 mμ in diameter and round or tadpole-like in shape (Figs. 17-1 and 17-2). Phages are commonly named after the host upon which they are parasitic, although attempts have been made to assign to them specific generic and species designations. After infection of a sensitive host they very rapidly alter the host's synthetic mechanisms,

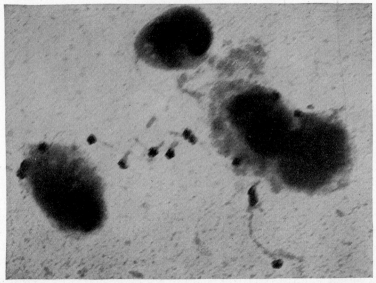

FIG. 17-1. Electron micrograph of *Pseudomonas aeruginosa* and of a bacteriophage active against it.   (*Courtesy of E. W. Schultz.*)

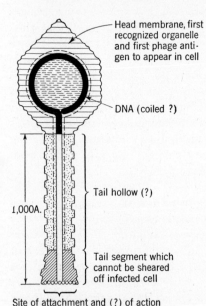

FIG. 17-2. Schematic representation of the structure of a phage particle. (*Modified from Anderson, 1953, and Pollard, 1954.*)

directing them toward the formation of phage rather than of bacterial substances. In a relatively short period of time, often 30 to 60 min., more than 100 phage particles may be formed in a bacterium infected originally with one phage particle. These phages are then set free by lysis of the cell.

An estimate of the concentration of phage particles in a suspension can be obtained by determining the highest dilution of the preparation eliciting lysis in broth cultures of the susceptible bacterium. A more accurate count can be obtained by a dilution and plating technique, the number of bacteriophage colonies or plaques (clear glassy areas in an otherwise opaque film of bacterial growth) developing in a thin layer of diluted nutrient agar inoculated with phage-sensitive bacteria and with a known amount of the diluted phage suspension. The diluted agar-phage-bacterium mixture is spread over a layer of regular nutrient agar, the bacterial inoculum being so adjusted as to yield, during the incubation period, a relatively dense growth of bacteria in those areas where phage particles were not present originally. Methods for determining phage activity and concentration are described by Delbrück (1950). Much of the recent work on bacteriophage is presented or reviewed in a series of

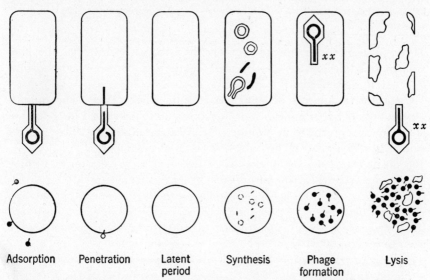

| Adsorption | Penetration | Latent period | Synthesis | Phage formation | Lysis |

FIG. 17-3. Schematic representation of the various phases of bacteriophagy.

papers in volume 18 of the *Cold Spring Harbor Symposia on Quantitative Biology* (1953) and in "Dynamics of Virus and Rickettsial Infections" (Hartman, Horsfall, and Kidd, 1954) and by Luria (1953) and Evans (1954).

In addition to the lytic type of bacterium-phage relationship, many strains of bacteria carry phage from generation to generation without noticeable lysis. Generally a few of the cells undergo lysis, the presence of this phage being recognizable by ordinary lytic tests if another strain of bacteria susceptible to the phage is available. Phage-bearing cultures of this nature are known as *lysogenic cultures*. Phages that can or have established a lysogenic relationship with a bacterial host are called *temperate phages*, while those that do induce lysis of the host are spoken of as *virulent phages*. Mutations of bacteria to phage resistance may occur in a sensitive strain and give rise to the development of secondary cultures consisting of resistant mutants. Phages may also undergo mutation.

The phases of bacteriophagy (Fig. 17-3) that can be noted in electron micrographs and in general physiological studies can be classified as follows:

1. Adsorption of a phage particle or particles to a sensitive bacterium
2. Penetration of the bacterium by phage material, primarily DNA
3. A latent period (vegetative) in which no phage or phage material is evident within the infected cell
4. A phase during which synthesis of phage components first becomes evident but complete phage particles are absent
5. Appearance of fully formed phage particles in the cell
6. Dissolution or lysis of the cell with the release of a large number of active phage particles

These phases tend to merge together, and in many instances the phenomena of bacteriophagy are grouped together into three periods, adsorption, latent period, and lytic phase.

Quantitative Aspects of Phage-Bacterium Interaction. The quantitative study of bacteriophage developed rapidly following the introduction of the one-step growth technique of Ellis and Delbrück (1939). Most studies have been carried out with a series of seven phages (T1, T2, . . . , T7) active against a common host, *Escherichia coli*, strain *B*. These phages can be distinguished from each other by the nature of the plaques they produce, their host range, serological behavior, and other factors. The main features of bacteriophagy to be considered here will deal with the T group of phages. Differences are noted in particular behaviors in this series, and with other phage-bacterium systems. Conclusions regarding any one system, therefore, are not necessarily applicable to all.

To determine either the time between infection of the cell and its lysis or the yield of phage per bacterium, various modifications of the one-step technique can be employed. In tests of a general nature a heavy suspension of the sensitive host is mixed with phage, and adsorption of the latter is allowed to proceed for a short period of time. The mixture is then diluted to such an extent that adsorption is practically halted, or the phage free in the medium can be neutralized following the addition of a specific antiphage serum. The neutralizing antibodies do not interfere with subsequent action of phage that has been adsorbed before its addition. Quantitative platings for plaque counts are made at frequent intervals. During the latent period each infected bacterium theoretically gives rise to a single plaque if experimental conditions are satisfactory, regardless of its intracellular content of phage particles. The concentration of infective particles within a cell at any time can be determined following premature lysis of the cell induced by cyanide or other chemical agents or by physical methods such as decompression. Each liberated particle, or those liberated by normal lysis, gives rise to individual plaques if uniformly distributed in the phage-agar layer.

Under normal cultural conditions a rise in plaque count can be observed as lysis of some of the cells is initiated. The count rises to a maximum and a plateau is established if there are no more susceptible bacteria in the mixture. This behavior is illustrated in Fig. 17-4. It is apparent from this figure that the plaque count remains constant during the latent period, increases markedly during the so-called rise period, and reaches a maximal value when all the cells have been lysed. One can determine the time required for lysis by inspection of the phage-production curve. The ratio of the plaque count at the end to that at the beginning is known as the *step size*. Having determined this value and knowing the approximate number of infected bacteria, it is possible to calculate the average *burst size*, i.e., the number of active phage particles produced per cell.

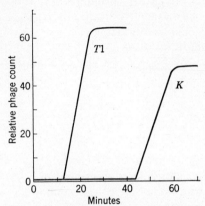

FIG. 17-4. Increase in free phage with time following infection in two systems, T1 against *Escherichia coli* and K against *Micrococcus pyogenes* var. *aureus*.

Individual burst sizes can be determined by a simple modification of the one-step procedure. After adsorption of phage by bacteria, the suspension is so diluted that a single drop (or small measured volume) contains on the average less than one bacterium. Individual drops are distributed into a series of tubes of broth, and samples from each tube are plated out for plaque counts after a sufficient period of time has elapsed for lysis to occur. Some plates will show no plaques, i.e., there were no infected bacteria in the sample plated. Others will contain for the most part a number of plaques representing the yields from single bursts. A few may show much larger counts, generally multiples of the average count. Application of the Poisson distribution equation enables one to calculate from the data obtained as above the average yield of phage particles per lysed cell. Some variation is noted in the amount of phage produced per bacterium. In a typical experiment the plaque count ranged from around 30 to more than 400 per plate, many of the plates showing roughly 100, 200, or 400 plaques. Application of the Poisson equation to the data indicated an average individual burst size near 100.

Adsorption. The adsorption of phage particles by susceptible bacteria can be demonstrated in electron micrographs (Fig. 17-1). It can be followed quantitatively by determining the number of unadsorbed phage particles in a phage-bacterium mixture at different times, the bacteria being separated from the free phage by centrifugation. The concentra-

tion of phage in the supernatant fluid can then be determined by the usual
dilution and plating method.   Numbers of bacteria and of phage in the
original suspensions before mixing can also be determined by dilution and
plating techniques.

Phage adsorption, i.e., the rate of attachment of phage to bacteria, was
shown in early studies by Krueger and by Delbrück to follow a first-order
course with respect to concentrations of free phage $[P_f]$ and of bacteria $[B]$,
or

$$\frac{d[P_f]}{dt} = -K[P_f][B] \tag{17-1}$$

or

$$\frac{[Pf]}{[P]} = e^{-K[B]t} \tag{17-2}$$

In a typical experiment 70 per cent attachment of phage to susceptible
cells of $E.\ coli$ was noted in 3 min. and 90 per cent in 10 min.   From a
knowledge of K, the amount of phage adsorbed by a given number of
bacteria in any time period can be calculated over a fairly wide range of
concentration of phage or of bacteria.

The number of phage particles adsorbed per bacterium can vary with
experimental conditions, the ratio P_{ads}/B giving an index of the *multiplicity
of infection*.   Since this ratio may be less than 1 at times, the term is
slightly misleading.   The number of phage particles adsorbed per cell
follows a typical Poisson distribution pattern, the rate of adsorption being
diffusion-limited with nonmotile cells.   The adsorption of more than one
particle per cell does not appear to influence the course of bacteriophagy,
with the exception that a high multiplicity of infection may lead to lysis
of the cell without phage production, i.e., the phenomenon of lysis from
without.   Lysis appears to be induced by the protein fraction of a phage,
possibly even a protein found only in the tail portion.

The adsorption of phage by sensitive cells is influenced to some extent
by the age of the cells and most markedly by the composition of the
medium.   Adsorption requires the existence of complementary electrostatic and geometric relationships between host and phage (Puck, 1955)
and occurs as a result of contact established by diffusion, violent shaking
preventing effective contact.   In highly dilute salt solutions, adsorption
of the T system of phages does not occur.   Increasing the concentration
of cations renders adsorption possible, the effective concentration range
for a particular cation being dependent upon characteristics of the phage
rather than of the bacterium.   Adsorption of a phage by a cationic-
exchange resin exhibits the same specific salt dependence as does attachment to the host cell.   Host bacteria are not adsorbed by the resin.   In
some instances adsorption requires the presence of an organic cofactor

such as tryptophan in addition to the salt requirement. Adsorption in relatively dilute salt solutions is reversible by dilution. At higher salt concentrations it may be reversible for a short period of time but rapidly becomes irreversible. In the T2 system, positively charged amino groups on the phage particle appear to be involved in a union with negatively charged carboxyl ones on the bacterium, while both groups are involved on both reactants in the T1 system.

In many instances a good correlation exists between the possession of certain antigens by the cell and its ability to adsorb a specific phage. Some phages active against *Salmonella typhosa* are adsorbed only by strains possessing the *Vi* antigen. These phages, and substrains of them, are employed in the phage typing of this organism. Phage typing can be used with other organisms as well. There are, however, exceptions to the general similarity between antigenic structure and phage suscepti- bility. It is possible that the active portions of phage receptors and antigens overlap but are not necessarily identical. Multiple infection can occur with upward of one-third of the cell surface theoretically being covered by adsorbed particles of phage. Phage can be adsorbed specifi- cally by cell-wall preparations from sensitive cells. Cell-wall material is slowly destroyed upon incubation with phage, thus suggesting some enzymatic activity.

Reversible adsorption of phage is followed by an irreversible binding. Two phases can be distinguished in some systems. The first, in the T7 system, involves irreversible binding, is independent of the temperature, and occurs with either living or heat-killed cells. The second phase is temperature-dependent, does not occur with heat-killed cells, and involves splitting of the virus particle. With T2, however, splitting of phage adsorbed by heat-killed cells does occur with release of DNA into the medium. Under normal physiological conditions the splitting of a coli- phage involves the transfer of the bulk of the phage DNA into the bac- terial cell. The protein membrane remains attached to the cell and can be removed by vigorous agitation without interfering with subsequent multiplication of the phage and lysis of the cell.

The use of the term splitting (or fragmentation) may be a little mis- leading in that the phage particle does not break into two or more discrete parts. Instead a separation, more or less complete, of protein and DNA components is implied by the term. A portion of the DNA may enter the suspending fluid rather than the cell, there being some doubt as to whether the extracellular phage DNA is excreted directly into the medium or whether it represents material that leaks out of the cell. The processes have been studied in detail with the aid of the electron microscope and with isotopes as tracers.

Puck and Lee (1955), in a continuation of their studies on increased cellular permeability which becomes noticeable within seconds after the irreversible attachment of T1 or T2 phages to *E. coli*, concluded that a true increase in permeability occurs rather than an unpeeling of surface components. Leakage of cellular constituents does not occur in dilute salt solutions which permit only reversible adsorption. They presented evidence that an intracellular enzyme participates in the leakage; that a permeability disturbance is created which spreads over the bacterial surface; and that this is followed by a sealing reaction. The latter prevents further leakage and at the same time renders the cell refractory to initiation of a second lytic action by freshly adsorbed phage. They proposed that the early phase of bacteriophage invasion involves the following steps:

1. Reversible electrostatic attachment
2. Splitting (separation) of viral DNA from its protein coat
3. Initiation of a lytic reaction at the site of attachment
4. Injection (passage) of viral DNA through the hole produced as a result of reaction 3
5. A spreading disturbance over the cell surface making it more permeable and more susceptible to lysis from without
6. Sealing of the hole and initiation of a reaction making the cell refractory to the initiation of a second lytic reaction

Pollard (1954), from a consideration of physical as well as chemical studies, reached conclusions similar in a general way to those of Puck and Lee. He suggested (Fig. 17-2) that phage DNA is a long unit, coiled up into the head and pointed into the tail of a phage particle. The tail is plugged by an enzyme, probably having the function of opening a hole in the cell wall of the host. He advanced the concept that once a hole is opened, cellular enzymes liquefy material in the tail, thus enabling material to flow from the bacterium into the phage. This could induce an increase in pressure within the head, which, exerted upon the DNA, could force the latter into the bacterium. Other factors could aid in the passage of phage DNA from the phage head into the bacterial cell. The evidence for this concept is incomplete, but the hypothesis does enable one to develop a mental picture of DNA transfer. Since adsorption and splitting of the phage particle can occur in some systems with heat-killed cells, it is unlikely that cellular enzymes would participate in the reaction in the detail outlined by Pollard (see also Pardee and Williams, 1953).

The Latent Period. It is not known if all of the phage DNA is transferred into the cell and all of the protein is excluded. Studies with isotopes of S, N, and P as tracers indicate that there is little or no transfer of protein, while most of the viral DNA is taken up by, and remains in, the infected cell (Evans, 1954; Hershey and Chase, 1952). There are suggestive observations that the injected DNA may fragment and that it does come into contact with nuclear material of the host. It may become integrated with host DNA as prophage, or, as is usually the result in sensitive systems, it so alters the metabolism of the host that activities of the cell are shunted from the formation of bacterial substance to the synthesis of phage components. Phages induce, and are products of, altered metabolism of the phage-infected cell.

Cytological studies (Luria and Human, 1950) indicate that disruption of chromatinic bodies follows after phage infection of *E. coli*, the changes being somewhat different with different phages. Disruption of the nuclear apparatus of the T-even group is followed by swelling of the cells which become filled with granular chromatinic matter (phage nucleoprotein?). Murray, Gillen, and Heagy (1950) reported that T2 induces the formation of a "marginated appearance," the chromatin from each nuclear body being distributed along the adjacent cytoplasmic membrane. Later the chromatinic material appeared as irregularly distributed granules which increased in size and density until the cells lysed. With T5, Murray and Whitfield (1953) noted cessation of cell division; partial loss of cytoplasmic basophilic staining matter (mainly pentosenucleic acid); complete loss of stainable nuclear chromatin; and progressive disruption of nuclear sites. Synthesis of new chromatinic matter was noted later, and this progressed with the formation of a fairly granular core. Observations of this nature indicate that infection with phage does alter markedly the nuclear apparatus, physiological studies supporting this conclusion as evidenced by change in the syntheses carried out by the cell.

The studies of Cohen and others (Cohen, in Hartman, Horsfall, and Kidd, 1954) established that cells of *E. coli* infected with the T group continue to respire and to use the enzymatic machinery of the cell but shift synthesis toward the production of phage rather than of bacterial DNA and protein. Bacterial growth is suppressed and also the formation of adaptive enzymes. Formation of phospholipid and of ribonucleic acid is inhibited. Cohen interpreted the inhibition of synthesis of RNA and increased synthesis of deoxypentose to be a result of an alteration in the normal carbohydrate metabolism of the cell, the oxidative hexose monophosphate pathway being blocked to such an extent that most of the sugar was utilized over the Embden-Meyerhof route. Hartman, Mudd, Hillier, and Beutner (1953) reported that bacterial nuclei were disrupted early in the latent period, while 2,3,5-triphenyltetrazolium reductase activity remained at a constant level in the T2 system. There is some evidence that this activity persists in the lysate, it being postulated that bacterial mitochondria are not destroyed during lysis.

As the latent period progresses it is possible to demonstrate with the aid of the electron microscope the accumulation of a number of biologically inactive, tailless particles ("doughnuts") in numbers approximately equal to the average burst yield of active phage particles. These doughnuts

are proteinaceous in character.   Tailed particles devoid of nucleic acid
also may be observed.   Counts of the doughnuts in prematurely lysed
cells increase with time.   This increase is followed by an increase in tailed
forms, suggesting that a transformation of doughnuts into tailed particles
does occur.   Viral DNA appears in the cells separately, and in some
unknown manner maturation
occurs with the formation of complete particles.   The number of
intracellular phage particles increases with time, as judged by
plaque counts on artificially lysed
preparations, until phage production ceases and the cells undergo
lysis (Fig. 17-5).

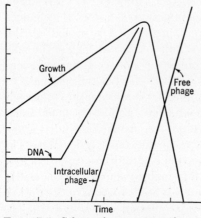

Wyckoff (1953) summarized his
studies and concluded that the
cytoplasm of healthy or of newly
infected E. coli cells consists
largely of spherical macromolecules.

Fig. 17-5. Schematic representation of
growth occurring in a bacterial culture
infected with phage and the changes with
time in number of bacteria and concentrations of phage DNA, of intracellular
phage, and of free phage.

After infection with phage these
bodies were replaced by fibrous
material, much of which has approximately the diameter of phage
tails.   Heads became attached to
the tails and later were filled with nucleic acids characteristic of the infective particle.

Chemical Aspects of Bacteriophagy.   The source of material from
which bacteriophage progeny are produced has been the subject of many
interesting studies, isotopes of S and N being employed as tracers of protein synthesis, of P for nucleic acid synthesis, and of C for bulk C and
energy sources.   These labels can be present in the test cells, the phage,
or the medium.   The use of P^{32} has one limitation, decomposition of this
element leading to the formation of S and loss of activity of the nucleic
acid labeled with it.   In addition to the use of tracers, Wyatt and Cohen
(Cohen, 1953) observed that the T-even phages contain a pyrimidine,
5-hydroxymethylcytosine, which is not present in the bacterial host.
This phage-specific component can be determined and provides, therefore,
an additional "tracer" of phage synthesis.

It has been found (Evans, 1954) that phage progeny contain materials
derived from the particles infecting the cell, from the cell itself, and from
the medium.   The older idea that phage catalyzed the conversion of a
precursor into active phage is not supported by the results of tracer
studies.   Various considerations suggest that phage introduces new

enzymes into the host, not as preformed enzymes, however, but as genetic patterns for enzyme synthesis. One bit of evidence in support of this concept is that *E. coli* cells, after treatment with nitrogen mustard (Herriott, 1951), no longer synthesize DNA, but do continue to synthesize and accumulate RNA. Infection with T2 halts RNA synthesis in these cells and initiates synthesis of phage DNA. T2 contributes the pattern for phage DNA synthesis and phage production in the above example in which the cells had lost the power to synthesize their own DNA.

Using labeled phage it has been observed that phage label is confined for the most part to phage formed early in the course of bacteriophagy. By the time that roughly 25 per cent of the total burst yield is produced, as judged by labeling in phage released by artificially induced lysis, most of the phage label has been transferred. The phosphorus that is contributed by the infecting particle(s) is uniformly distributed in the phage progeny DNA, thus suggesting that no specific portion of phage DNA is transferred to the newly formed particles. Distribution of N^{15} from N^{15}-labeled phage supports the same conclusion. The various data, including those from studies in which the cells were subjected to mixed infection, indicate that phage DNA is broken down into fragments which are used for phage synthesis in a nonspecific manner. Experiments with labeled thymine indicate that thymine is not the source of 5-hydroxy-methylcytosine. Since a portion of the latter compound is derived from host pyrimidines, it appears that host cytosine is the source of 5-hydroxy-methylcytosine. Deoxyribonuclease activity increases in the *E. coli*–T2 system. Whether this is an actual increase in amount of enzyme or increased activity due to destruction of an inhibitor is not known. This increased activity would suggest that the enzyme aids in the provision of appropriate building blocks for phage DNA synthesis from bacterial DNA. These various observations show that phage production is not by division (fission) and subdivision of phage as such.

Evans (1954) and Kozloff (1953) summarized the recent studies regarding contributions of the infecting phage, the host, and the medium to phage synthesis (Figs. 17-6 and 17-7). It is apparent that with the T-even series most of the phage protein and nucleic acid is derived from components of the medium as judged by labeled-isotope studies. In the T7 system, however, a considerable portion of host-cell protein, as well as of host DNA, serves as a source of phage material. It is further apparent from the diagrams that the infecting particle contributes little to the chemical constituents of the phage particles resulting from the infectious process.

A few cases have been reported in which the nutritive requirements for growth of the host differ from those for phage production. This would suggest that a synthesis is involved that does not occur in the host under certain conditions, or, if so, at a rate too low for virus synthesis.   Not only phage production but also the burst size can vary to some extent with the nature of medium.   Likewise, a synthetic medium supporting growth and phage production may not suffice to enable visible lysis to occur.   This might suggest that specific host-cell enzymes are involved in the lytic process and that they are not formed under all conditions in which growth can occur.

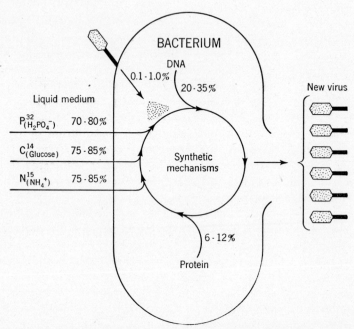

Fig. 17-6. Diagrammatic representation of the origin of the phosphorus, nitrogen, and carbon of phages T2, T4, and T6.   (*From Evans, 1954, courtesy of Annual Reviews, Inc.*)

Modification of the host as well as of the medium can induce a change, either to phage resistance or in the nature of the phage produced by it. Luria (1955) summarized his studies on one aspect of the latter behavior in which T2 phage induced lysis of a single mutant of *E. coli*.   No phage active against the mutant strain could be detected in the lysate.   On testing the lysate against *Shigella dysenteriae*, which is susceptible to T2, rather than against *E. coli*, it was noted that the dysentery culture was lysed.   It was also found that a considerable concentration of phage was present in the original lysate.   One passage on *S. dysenteriae* resulted in the phage reverting to the type active against both coli and dysentery bacteria.   Passage on the mutant strain of *E. coli* gave the dysentery-active, mutant *E. coli*–inactive phage again.   Normal phage was pro-

duced on the original strain of *E. coli*.   The change in the phage induced
in the *E. coli* mutant is a nonhereditary modification of the phage imposed
upon it by the host.   It is nonadaptive in character since the altered
phage cannot multiply in the host inducing the change.   A single change
in the genetic make-up of *E. coli* so altered the bacterium's characteristics

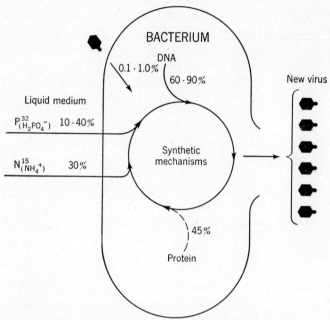

Fig. 17-7. Diagrammatic representation of the origin of the phosphorus and nitrogen
of phage T7.   (*From Evans, 1954, courtesy of Annual Reviews, Inc.*)

that it influenced the nature of the phage produced in it.   The change
in the phage must have been relatively simple since the phage reverted
to its original type on one passage in a normal host.   Perhaps some slight
chemical change is involved, but whether this is in adsorbability or some
other characteristic was not determined.

   The Release Phase.   Relatively little is known concerning the nature
of reactions occurring during the release phase.   Phage particles are
organized in their final, active form shortly before they are released by
lysis of the host cell.   The maturation process is irreversible, and no
transfer of characteristics occurs between fully formed particles.   These
particles do not multiply in the cell in which they are formed.   Lysis
involves a more or less complete dissolution of the cell in some systems,
while in others there is a tendency for breaks to occur in the cell through
which phage passes into the medium.   The cellular ghosts break down
on standing.

Temperate Phage. We have seen that cell-free filtrates of some cultures in which visible lysis was not evident may induce lysis of other strains of the same species.   This phenomenon of lysogenicity has been reviewed by Lwoff (1953, 1954) and by Evans (1954).   When a bacterium is exposed to a temperate phage the latter may be adsorbed but is unable to complete the infection process, i.e., infection is aborted, the cell can grow and multiply, and the phage disappears.   In other cases either the host is killed without multiplication of the phage or normal lytic behavior can be noted, the phage acting as a virulent one.   The final type of phage-bacteria relationship that can be observed is that the phage is adsorbed and the infected bacterium continues to multiply, giving rise to a lysogenic clone in which the temperate phage can be detected.   The carrying of a temperate phage by its host represents true lysogenesis.

Each cell of a lysogenic strain is a phage carrier, but phage particles as such cannot be demonstrated in the cell, with the possible exception of an occasional mutant cell.   It is believed that in the infectious process the phage DNA is "reduced" to prophage, a bit of phage matter attached to a bacterial chromosome and acting as if it were a normal constituent of the bacterium's genetic apparatus.   It either behaves as a bacterial gene or so alters one that prophage is replicated during each bacterial division and transmitted to the daughter cells.   At least the ability to perpetuate formation of prophage is carried from one generation to the next.   An occasional mutation occurs with the formation and liberation of active phage.   The presence of prophage in the cell may modify the cell in other ways than the new character alone.   For example, nontoxic strains of *Corynebacterium diphtheriae* may revert to toxin producers upon establishment of the lysogenic state.

With certain lysogenic systems, but not all, it is possible to demonstrate that each cell apparently contains prophage.   Treatment of the cells with inducing agents such as X rays, ultraviolet light, nitrogen mustard, or peroxides results in lysis of the culture and release of active phage identical with the infecting particle that established the lysogenic relationship originally.   When induction occurs, bacterial growth proceeds without cell division for a time corresponding to one or two generations.   During the latter part of this growth period mature, active virus particles can be demonstrated in cells subjected to premature lysis by artificial methods. The concentration of these particles increases with time until a full yield is produced and the cell undergoes typical phage lysis.   Phage production appears to be practically identical with that noted with a virulent phage, a major difference being in the longer duration of the vegetative phase in the induced system.   Induction, however, has less effect on activities of the host cell during the early part of the latent period than does infection with virulent phage.   The cell continues to grow and to form RNA, has ability to form adaptive enzymes, and so on, until the shift from prophage to the virulent form of phage has been accomplished. Lwoff visualizes the prophage as a nucleic acid molecule without accompanying protein since serological tests indicate the absence of phage protein in lysogenic strains. He believes that the prophage is associated with a definite genetic character of the host and that it is located at a specific site in a bacterial chromosome. Prophage is regarded as the bacterial virus's genetic material bound to a specific site in the bacterium and responsible for definite characteristics of the lysogenic bacterium. The presence of prophage renders the bacterium immune to infection by the original phage and by genetically related ones. The inducing agent is assumed to displace the phage-genetic material from its specific site, and prophage matter then reacts with other cellular components in a manner similar to infectious material from a virulent phage. Displacement of prophage, in other words, destroys the immune state and makes the cell susceptible to lysis by progeny resulting from this activation of prophage.

The relationship between bacterium and phage is more than a simple host-parasite one, as is noted in many infectious diseases. In the latter case the parasite generally elicits only a disturbance of the physiological activities and possibly cellular structure of the host, although these changes may be so profound as to lead to death of the host. A similar relationship is noted in the bacterium-phage relationship, but it goes a step further in that a virulent phage takes over nuclear control of the events to follow. This may also be the case in a number of mammalian diseases of viral origin. Phage is not only lethal, it is also directive in its activities and directs synthesis of more of itself.

REFERENCES

Anderson, T. F.: The morphology and osmotic properties of bacteriophage systems, *Cold Spring Harbor Symp. Quant. Biol.*, **18**, 197–203 (1953).

Cohen, S. S.: Growth requirements of bacterial viruses, *Bacteriol. Rev.*, **13**, 1–24 (1949).

———: Studies on controlling mechanisms in the metabolism of virus-infected bacteria, *Cold Spring Harbor Symp. Quant. Biol.*, **18**, 221–235 (1953).

Delbrück, M. (ed.): "Viruses 1950," California Institute of Technology, Pasadena, 1950.

Ellis, E. I., and M. Delbrück: The growth of bacteriophage, *J. Gen. Physiol.*, **22**, 365–384 (1939).

Evans, E. A.: Bacterial viruses, *Ann. Rev. Microbiol.*, **8**, 237–256 (1954).

Hartman, F. W., F. L. Horsfall, Jr., and J. G. Kidd (eds.): "Dynamics of Virus and Rickettsial Infections," The Blakiston Division, McGraw-Hill Book Company, Inc., New York, 1954.

Hartman, P. E., S. Mudd, J. Hillier, and E. H. Beutner: Persistence of mitochondria and reductase activity during infection of *Escherichia coli* B with T2 phage, *J. Bacteriol.*, **65**, 706–714 (1953).

Herriott, R. M.: Nucleic acid synthesis in mustard gas-treated *E. coli* B, *J. Gen. Physiol.*, **34**, 761–764 (1951).

Hershey, A. D., and M. Chase: Independent functions of viral protein and nucleic acid in growth of bacteriophage, *J. Gen. Physiol.*, **36**, 39–56 (1952).

Kozloff, L. M.: Origin and fate of bacteriophage material, *Cold Spring Harbor Symp. Quant. Biol.*, **18**, 209–220 (1953).

Luria, S. E.: "General Virology," John Wiley & Sons, Inc., New York, 1953.

———: The T2 mystery, *Sci. American*, **192**, 92–98 (1955).

——— and M. L. Human: Chromatin staining of bacteria during bacteriophage infection, *J. Bacteriol.*, **59**, 551–560 (1950).

Lwoff, A.: Lysogeny, *Bacteriol. Rev.*, **17**, 269–337 (1953).

———: The life cycle of a virus, *Sci. American*, **190**, 34–37 (1954).

Murray, R. G. E., D. H. Gillen, and F. C. Heagy: Cytological changes in *Escherichia coli* produced by infection with phage T2, *J. Bacteriol.*, **59**, 603–615 (1950).

——— and J. F. Whitfield: Cytological effects of infection with T5 and some related phages, *J. Bacteriol.*, **65**, 715–726 (1953).

Pardee, A. B., and I. Williams: Enzymatic activity and bacteriophage infection, *Ann. inst. Pasteur*, **84**, 147–156 (1953).

Pollard, E. C.: The physics of viruses, *Sci. American*, **191**, 62–70 (1954).

Puck, T. T., and H. H. Lee: Mechanism of cell wall penetration by viruses, *J. Exptl. Med.*, **101**, 151–175 (1955).

Wyckoff, R. W. G.: Electron microscopic evidence on virus proliferation, in "Symposium: Interaction of Viruses and Cells," pp. 54–57, supplement to *Rend. ist. super. sanità*, distributed by Charles C Thomas, Publisher, Springfield, Ill., 1953.

CHAPTER 18

CHEMOTHERAPEUTIC AGENTS

The killing of bacteria by physical or chemical agents was considered in Chap. 14, particular emphasis being placed on the general protoplasmic poisons. A limited number of chemical agents are quite specific in their action, often inhibiting specific groups of microorganisms and having relatively little or no activity against mammalian cells in the concentrations normally employed in therapy. Some, the antibiotics, are products of microbial activity; others are products of the chemical laboratory. The line of demarcation is not absolute since some of the antibiotics can be synthesized on an industrial scale.

Various chemicals have been employed in attempts to treat diseases for many centuries, quinine for malaria being the classical example of a relatively successful chemotherapeutic agent against what is now recognized as an infectious disease. With the establishment of the germ theory of infectious disease, interest began to develop in the possibility of the destruction, with the aid of specific chemicals, of the causative agents of disease in the body. Ehrlich, around the beginning of this century, advanced the concept that the objective of chemical attack upon pathogenic agents in vivo should be to interfere with a specific process of the parasite, the host being unaffected by the drug. He reasoned that, while there are many metabolic similarities between host and parasite, there must be points of difference. Ehrlich suggested that there are specific groups or "receptors" on the cell, and if one of the groups essential to activity of the parasite could be blocked or inhibited, the resultant damage would lead to death of the cell. He concluded that "only those substances can be anchored at any particular part of the organism which fit into the molecule of the recipient combination as a piece of mosaic fits into a certain pattern."

The use of mercuric salts was shown to have little or no therapeutic value by Ehrlich, while arsenicals appeared to be effective in some instances. An arsenic-containing compound, atoxyl, was shown by Thomas in 1905 to be of value in the treatment of trypanosome infections of mice.   This led Ehrlich to test the possibilities of organic arsenicals as therapeutic agents against syphilis.   He synthesized and tested many new compounds.   The 606th compound to be tested was salvarsan; it was found to exert an antispirochetal action, and it was used for many years in the treatment of syphilis.   Several other organic arsenicals were found to be useful in the treatment of trypanosome infections, but the search for "magic bullets" was not very successful for many years.   The search consisted primarily in testing wide varieties of compounds for possible chemotherapeutic activity, physiological studies not having reached a stage where any idea of the nature of the reaction between drug and parasite could be established and employed as a guide in further studies.

It was realized later that many of the mercurials, arsenicals (at the arsenoxide level), and similar compounds reacted readily with sulfhydryl groups which are so important in cellular systems.   Since these groups are present in the host as well as in the parasite, sulfhydryl inhibitors are quite limited in their application in man.   In recent years marked advances have been made in our understanding of the vital processes of the cell, making it possible in some instances to define specific targets in terms of cellular physiology, to understand in part the mode of action of some of the antimicrobial agents, and to search more rationally for other agents.   Nevertheless, the search is still primarily one of trial and error, but it is guided by principles that have been established on the basis of a fuller understanding of the behavior of host and of parasite and of mutual relations between them.

Sulfonamides.   The problem of finding suitable antimicrobial chemotherapeutic agents appeared to be hopeless until the discovery of the chemotherapeutic properties of the dye prontosil synthesized by Domagk in 1932.   Dyes such as crystal violet and the acriflavines were known to possess bacteriostatic and bactericidal properties, to some extent rather specific in character, but their use was limited primarily to topical applications.   It was soon ascertained that prontosil broke down in the animal body with the formation of p-aminobenzene sulfonamide (sulfanilamide) and that this compound was the effective agent in the treatment of streptococcal and other infections.   Attempts were made to alter the structure of sulfanilamide in the hope of obtaining more effective chemotherapeutic agents.   These led to the development of sulfapyridine, sulfadiazine, sulfathiazole, and other derivatives of sulfanilamide which differ to some extent from the parent compound in their solubility, degree of dissociation, range of antimicrobial activity, pharmacological effects upon the host, and so on.   Basically, the mode of action of these various sulfa drugs appears to be the same.   The structures of the parent compound and of some of its effective derivatives are indicated as follows:

SO_2NH_2 ... Sulfanilamide SO_2NH- ... Sulfapyridine SO_2NH- ... Sulfadiazine SO_2NH- ... Sulfathiazole

Sulfanilamide Sulfapyridine Sulfadiazine Sulfathiazole

Substitution of a succinyl group for one hydrogen on the *p*-amino nitrogen of sulfathiazole gives sulfasuxidine (succinyl sulfathiazole). Other substitutions in this amino group or in the sulfonic acid one have led to both active and inactive compounds.

The sulfonamides are bacteriostatic for both gram-positive and gram-negative bacteria with the exception primarily of those bacteria requiring folic acid for growth. It is this factor which renders the sulfa drugs effective for clinical use, the mammalian host requiring folic acid and being resistant to these agents. They are used alone, or in combination with each other, or with antibiotics in the treatment of various infections, being particularly effective against the meningococcus and dysentery bacilli. Sulfa-resistant mutants are quite common, many of them produce an excess of *p*-aminobenzoic acid which neutralizes sulfa activity, and some strains have developed which require sulfonamides for growth. This latter behavior is explained on the basis that these strains produce an excess of *p*-aminobenzoic acid (PAB) which by itself is inhibitory, and its inhibitory action is neutralized by the sulfa compound.

It was observed that extracts of certain bacteria or of yeast were inhibitory to the antibacterial activity of sulfanilamide. Woods, in 1940, identified the active agent as *p*-aminobenzoic acid (PAB) and, together with Fildes, advanced the concept that PAB is an essential metabolite for the growth of susceptible species. They proposed that the sulfonamides inhibit growth by interference with the utilization of PAB, the sulfa drug competing with PAB for an enzyme site owing to their structural similarity, which is evident in the following formulas:

SO_2NH_2 ... NH_2 — Sulfanilamide

$COOH$ ... NH_2 — *p*-Aminobenzoic acid

Sulfanilamide *p*-Aminobenzoic acid

Proof soon followed that PAB is an essential nutrilite or growth factor for certain organisms.   Hence it is very apt to be an essential metabolite for those species not requiring it or a product derived from it.   PAB was found to be present in many species of bacteria and enters into the structure of folic acid and related pteroyl compounds that are utilized as growth factors by various bacteria.

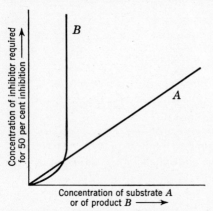

FIG. 18-1. Schematic illustration of competitive (A) and noncompetitive (B) inhibition of bacterial growth.

Exhaustive studies have been carried out regarding the mode of action of the sulfa drugs, and the results are in fundamental agreement with the Woods-Fildes hypothesis.   The competition between PAB and a sulfa drug is a competitive one (Fig. 18-1), much like that considered earlier for the competition between malonic and succinic acids for the succinic acid enzyme site.   Products of reactions catalyzed by PAB-containing systems can also neutralize the activity of sulfa drugs but in a noncompetitive manner.   These competitions can be illustrated (after Woods, 1952; Fig. 18-2) in the following manner.   Let us consider a series of reactions $A \rightarrow B \rightarrow C$ involved in the synthesis of the essential cellular component C.   Also suppose that a growth factor F is the precursor of coenzyme F, the prosthetic group of the enzyme involved in the transformation of B into C.   Growth of the bacterium would not occur in the

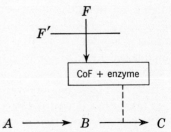

FIG. 18-2. Schematic representation of the inhibition of a reaction chain by an analogue F' of the growth factor F, the latter substance being a precursor of coenzyme F required in the conversion of B to C. (After Woods, 1952.)

absence of factor F unless C as such is supplied in the medium and the organism is permeable to C.   Evidence of this sort suggests that C is a product of a reaction, or reaction chain, in which the coenzyme form of F plays an essential part.

Growth frequently can be inhibited or prevented by the addition to the culture medium of an analogue F' of the growth factor.   There is considerable evidence that this inhibition is due to a competition between F and F' for the enzyme concerned in the transformation of F into the coenzyme form.   This inhibition usually can be reduced or overcome completely in a competitive manner by the addition of F, while it may be overcome noncompetitively by the addition of the coenzyme or the product C of the reaction in which coenzyme F participates. The same coenzyme may also be involved in the formation of other compounds, and the reactions leading to their formation would likewise be inhibited by F'. Some of the reactions might be inhibited more readily than others, and quantitative differences, therefore, would exist between the extents to which the different reactions would be inhibited and the concentration of the analogue F'. Likewise, the addition of various products would alter the inhibitory activity of F'.

The bacteriostatic activity of sulfanilamide, for example, can be competitively neutralized by the addition of PAB to the medium, noncompetitively by folic acid (or suitable derivatives) or by products of folic

TABLE 18-1. EFFECT OF SULFANILAMIDE ON THE GROWTH OF *Escherichia coli* IN SYNTHETIC MEDIA*

Supplement (10 mg./liter each)	Ratio of sulfanilamide to PAB required for growth inhibition	
	Supplement	Supplement + B_{12}†
None..	3,000	10,000
Methionine.................................	10,000	30,000
Methionine + xanthine.....................	30,000	100,000
Methionine + xanthine + serine.............	About 75,000	About 250,000
Methionine + xanthine + serine + folic acid†	About 150,000	About 400,000

* From Shive (1950), courtesy of the New York Academy of Sciences.
† B_{12} at 0.05 and folic acid at 3 μg./liter.

acid–dependent reactions. This is well illustrated in studies summarized by Shive (1950, 1952). One molecule of PAB per 3,000 molecules of sulfanilamide neutralizes the inhibitory activity of the latter compound on the growth of *E. coli* in a simple synthetic medium; hence PAB has an inhibition index of 3,000. Vitamin B_{12} in the medium reduces the inhibitory activity of sulfanilamide; in its presence around 10,000 molecules of the sulfa drug are required for inhibition per molecule of PAB. The activity of B_{12} may be due to its participation in an essential synthesis or, less likely, conversion of part of the molecule to a purine.

As indicated in Table 18-1 and Fig. 18-3, the inhibition of growth of *E. coli* by sulfanilamide is influenced by several different agents. The first limiting transformation is the biosynthesis of methionine, presumably from homocysteine, since addition of methionine to the synthetic medium removes the inhibitory effect. When the concentration of sulfanilamide is increased beyond the point where methionine no longer neutralizes the sulfa inhibition, growth of *E. coli* can occur if one of several purines, in addition to methionine, is added to the medium. Purine synthesis appears to occur from 4-amino-5-imidazole carboxamide since this substance accumulates in the medium under conditions limiting purine synthesis. Glycine or threonine (less effectively) also induces an increase in carboxamide accumulation. When the concentration of sulfanilamide is further increased, its inhibitory action in the presence of methionine and a purine such as xanthine can be neutralized by the addition of serine. Inhibition induced in the presence of methionine, a purine, and serine can be neutralized by thymine, thymidine, or folic acid with an inhibition index around 100,000.

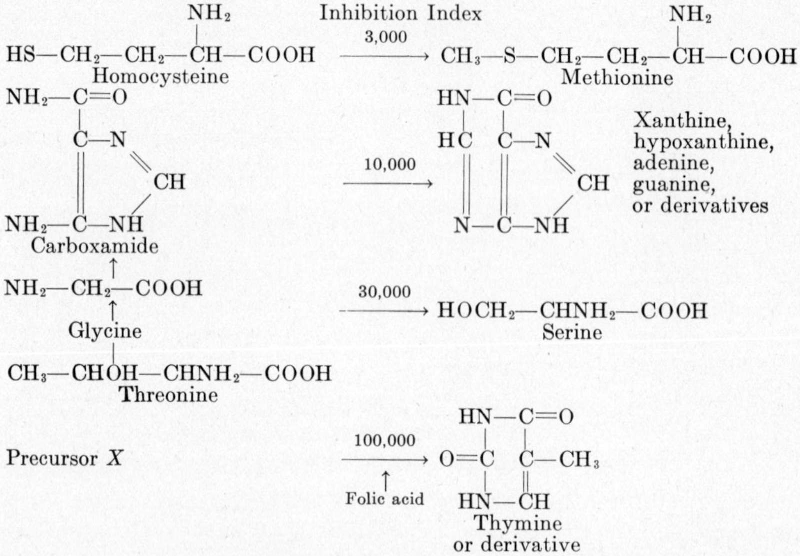

$$\text{HS—CH}_2\text{—CH}_2\text{—}\overset{\overset{\displaystyle NH_2}{|}}{\text{CH}}\text{—COOH} \quad \xrightarrow{\text{3,000}} \quad \text{CH}_3\text{—S—CH}_2\text{—CH}_2\text{—}\overset{\overset{\displaystyle NH_2}{|}}{\text{CH}}\text{—COOH}$$

Inhibition Index

Homocysteine — Methionine

Carboxamide $\xrightarrow{10,000}$ Xanthine, hypoxanthine, adenine, guanine, or derivatives

$$\text{NH}_2\text{—CH}_2\text{—COOH}$$
Glycine

$$\text{CH}_3\text{—CHOH—CHNH}_2\text{—COOH}$$
Threonine

$\xrightarrow{\text{30,000}}$ HOCH$_2$—CHNH$_2$—COOH
Serine

Precursor X $\xrightarrow[\text{Folic acid}]{\text{100,000}}$ Thymine or derivative

FIG. 18-3. The influence of various chemical agents on the inhibitory action of sulfanilamide on the growth of *Escherichia coli*. (*After Shive*, 1950.)

One explanation of the effects summarized above is that compounds such as methionine, purines, and so on might serve in the synthesis of folic acid or its derivatives. The evidence, however, indicates that the reverse is true and that folic acid is involved in the synthesis of these compounds. It would appear that PAB is utilized in the synthesis of folic acid and that folic acid is involved in the formation of methionine, purine bases, and serine, probably acting as a coenzyme in the transfer of formyl groups as suggested by the reactions depicted in Fig. 18-3. The evidence so far available is for the most part in accord with Shive's hypothesis of a coenzyme function for folic acid. Some variations, however, are observed between different bacteria. Only a few organisms which require PAB for growth are able to utilize folic acid. In those which do not utilize folic acid, sulfonamides may inhibit the biosynthesis of compounds related to folic acid and it would be expected that the derivative would be utilized, providing the cell is permeable to it.

In the chemotherapeutic use of the sulfa drugs the host does not appear to be able to furnish the parasite with all of the end products of PAB activity or with sufficient PAB or folic acid in utilizable form to overcome the inhibitory effect of the drug. Some antimetabolites (analogues of essential metabolites) are, however, inhibited in their activity by the high level of the metabolite in certain species of animals.

Other effects of the sulfa drugs have been reported, e.g., inhibition of respiration. These, however, appear to be secondary effects, presumably elicited as a result of deficiencies developing in the treated cells and usually evident only in the presence of high concentrations of the drug. Secondary effects may also be evident in the treated host, but these do not appear to involve the folic acid system. One effect, for example, arises from the low solubility of these agents and from their tendency to crystallize in the kidneys. Allergic reactions and other manifestations can also be observed.

Other Metabolite Antagonists. Woods's discovery of the competitive relationship between PAB and the sulfa drugs when bacteria are exposed to the latter led to a large number of studies concerning the biological effects of compounds structurally related to known essential metabolites or nutrilites. Modifications of the structure of such a compound do not necessarily lead to an analogue inhibiting the utilization of the metabolite. Usually an inert compound is formed, in a few instances an inhibitory agent results, while in others a compound possessing the biological activity, qualitatively, of the metabolite is formed. The problem has been reviewed by Shive (1952), who described typical analogues of the B vitamins, the pyrimidines and purines, and the amino acids. Only a few of these antimetabolites are effective in preventing or curing infections in man and other animals. Two agents, isonicotinic acid hydrazide (isoniazid) and p-aminosalicylic acid, have been found to be of value in the treatment of tuberculosis. Isoniazid has been shown competitively to antagonize B_6-catalyzed reactions in $E.\ coli$ and can be considered as a structural analogue of pyridoxine. p-Aminosalicylic acid is much weaker as an antimycobacterial agent. Its mode of action may be a competition with PAB. The structures of these agents, and of pyridoxine for comparison with isoniazid, are indicated as follows.

Isoniazid   Pyridoxine   p-Aminosalicylic acid

Isoniazid-resistant tubercle bacilli develop rather rapidly, and for this reason the drug is used quite frequently in combination with p-amino-salicylic acid or streptomycin.

Although antimetabolites have not made much progress as chemo-therapeutic agents, the use of these compounds has been of some value in studying pathways of metabolism and of the coenzymes involved in various reactions.   In many instances the failure of an inhibitory ana-logue as a chemotherapeutic agent arises from the requirement of both host and parasite for the essential metabolite.

Antibiotics.   Pasteur observed in 1877 that the infectivity of the anthrax bacillus was reduced by the presence of a second bacterium at times.   This suggested to his inquiring mind the possibility that antago-nistic action of this sort might be employed in the treatment of infectious diseases.   Around the beginning of this century it was observed that *Pseudomonas aeruginosa* produced a substance, pyocyanase, which was inhibitory to the growth of a number of bacteria.   Clinical application of the crude material was found to be limited by its toxicity for animals as well as for bacteria.

Various observations were made of an antagonistic action between dif-ferent species of microorganisms, the most important being Fleming's observation in 1929 that an accidental mold contaminant on an agar-plate culture of staphylococci inhibited and destroyed the bacteria in its vicinity.   The antagonistic activity of the fungus, *Penicillium notatum*, was traced to the elaboration by the mold of a substance which Fleming called penicillin.   The addition of this material in crude form to culture media suppressed the growth of gram-positive bacteria but had little effect on most gram-negative species.

In 1936 Weindling and Emerson isolated the antibiotic gliotoxin pro-duced by *Gliocladium fimbriatum* that inhibits the damping-off fungus *Rhizoctonia solani*, which kills many seedling plants.   In 1939 Dubos re-ported the formation of tyrothricin by *Bacillus brevis* and the activity of this material against a wide variety of bacteria. Tyrothricin was found to be composed of two agents, gramicidin and tyrocidin, the latter possessing local chemotherapeutic properties, but too toxic for general internal use. In 1939 Chain, Florey, and coworkers found evidence that penicillin could be employed in the treatment of various infectious diseases, and in the following years their preliminary observations have been confirmed and extended. Numerous other antibiotic agents have been described during the ensuing years, and the search is still in progress. Most are toxic for man as well as for bacteria, and as yet, of the twenty or so exhibiting microbial specificity and relatively low toxicity to man, only four groups have been found to possess good therapeutic properties. These are the penicillins, the streptomycins, the tetracyclines, and chloramphenicol. Others are more limited in their applications or have not been tested on a large enough scale as yet. The four major groups differ markedly from each other in chemical structure, in range of activity, in mode of action, and in pharmacological properties. Among the more recent reviews are those by Wyss, Smith, Hobby, Oginsky, and Pratt (1953), Umbreit (1953, 1955), and Eagle and Saz (1955). It is of particular interest that there is little evidence indicating that the antibiotics are of much importance for the survival under natural conditions of those organisms producing them or that they produce them to any marked extent. In recent years it has been observed that addition of various antibiotics to animal diets stimulates growth of the animals. No satisfactory explanation for this behavior has been advanced.

The various antibiotics have different ranges of activity as regards the species against which they exert inhibitory effects. Penicillin is active primarily against the gram-positive bacteria, treponemas, and the gram-negative gonococci and meningococci. Streptomycin covers a somewhat broader range, being active against many gram-negative rods and the tubercle bacillus as well as against gram-positive bacteria. Chloramphenicol and the tetracyclines are active against many gram-positive and -negative species and also against certain amoebae, rickettsiae, and the larger viruses. Some of the newer antibiotics exert an antifungal action. The sensitivity of a culture to a particular antibiotic is determined most readily by placing a series of filter-paper disks containing graded amounts of the antibiotic onto the surface of agar inoculated with the test bacterium and noting the degree of inhibition surrounding the disk. Sensitivity-test disks are available commercially.

Quantitative assays for antibiotics can be carried out in some instances by chemical methods, but for the most part physiological ones are employed. The latter are based on inhibition of growth in broth cultures in the presence of different amounts of the test fluid or on the width of the zone of inhibition of growth around the material placed on an agar-plate culture of the test organism, the results being compared with those elicited by different amounts of a standard preparation of the antibiotic.

Penicillin. Penicillins are produced by *Penicillium notatum, P. chrysogenum,* several species of *Aspergillus,* the trichophyton *Malbranchea pulchella,* and a *Cephalosporium.* Mutants of *P. chrysogenum* are commonly employed for the production of penicillin, cultural conditions being adjusted to promote maximum yields. The details of many of the processes are industrial secrets, but it was observed early in the course of cooperative studies that the substitution of lactose for glucose and the addition of corn steep liquor to the basal medium markedly stimulated penicillin production. It was observed later that the addition of phenylacetic acid promoted the formation of penicillin G. Tracer studies indicate that C^{14}-carboxyl-labeled phenylacetic acid is converted to penicillin with the same activity as the acid, 82 per cent of the activity being associated with the phenylacetic residue of penicillin G.

After isolation of various penicillins in pure states, it was found that they possess the basic structure (Regna, 1955) and substituent groups R* listed below.

$$
\begin{array}{c}
\text{S} \\
\diagup\diagdown \\
\text{O}{=}\text{C—HN—CH—CH} \quad \text{C(CH}_3)_2 \\
\ \mid \qquad\quad\ \mid \qquad\qquad\ \ \mid \\
\text{R*} \quad \text{O}{=}\text{C——N———CHCOOH}
\end{array}
$$

Penicillin	*Side chain R
G. Benzyl	⟨⟩CH₂—
X. *p*-Hydroxylbenzyl	HO—⟨⟩CH₂—
F. 2-Pentenyl	$CH_3CH_2CH{=}CHCH_2$—
3-Pentenyl	$CH_3CH{=}CHCH_2CH_2$—
F. (Dihydro)	
n-Amyl	$CH_3CH_2CH_2CH_2CH_2$—
K. *n*-Heptyl	$CH_3CH_2CH_2CH_2CH_2CH_2CH_2$—

Still other penicillins have been reported. Penicillin G is the one most commonly employed therapeutically and is at times used as the procaine salt, or in other combinations, since this lowers the solubility and tendency to be eliminated rapidly from the body, decreases allergenic reactions, and reduces pain at the site of injection.

We are most interested here in the mode of action of the major antibiotics, and that of penicillin has been studied in most detail. Unfortunately, considerable confusion and controversy exist since it is extremely

difficult to determine the primary lesion induced by the drug.   Furthermore, relatively little or no activity is noted with resting cells or cellular
extracts, and most studies, therefore, are complicated by growth effects.
It was noted early that penicillin inhibited division of susceptible bacteria
under conditions otherwise conducive to growth and that filamentous
cells developed in the presence of low concentrations of the agent.   It
was also noted that many species of penicillin-resistant bacteria produced
an enzyme, penicillinase, which destroyed the activity of the penicillin
molecule.   Not all resistant strains, or mutants of susceptible ones, however, produce penicillinase.   Relative impermeability, as in yeast, is often
the resistance factor of importance.

Gale (1948) reported that glutamic acid assimilation is impaired in the
presence of penicillin and that the development of penicillin-resistant
mutants is associated with a decreased requirement for this amino acid.
Mutants of a staphylococcus were finally isolated with an extremely high
degree of resistance (greater than 1,500 units per milliliter), very marked
decrease in growth requirements, and loss of gram positivity.   Penicillin
sensitivity, however, is not always associated with a requirement for
glutamic acid or the ability to accumulate glutamic acid to a marked
extent within the cell.   Hotchkiss's (1950) finding that penicillin-treated
staphylococci released polypeptides into the medium suggested a derangement of protein synthesis, while Mitchell and Moyle (1951) noted an
increase in free nucleotide and nucleoside in the cells, less free purine,
and decreased synthesis of RNA and DNA.   Other studies (see Eagle
and Saz, 1955) point to a derangement of RNA metabolism as the primary
point of attack of penicillin.

In intact staphylococci (Gale, 1955) antibiotics such as chloramphenicol, Aureomycin, or Terramycin at limiting bactericidal concentrations completely inhibit protein synthesis by washed cells in the presence
of essential amino acids and an energy source.   Penicillin has no influence
on protein synthesis except in extremely high concentration.   Incorporation of glutamic acid, however, from a glutamic acid solution is not
inhibited by chloramphenicol or the tetracyclines but is inhibited by
penicillin.

Gale and Folkes reported that cell particulates prepared from *Micrococcus pyogenes* var. *aureus* following ultrasonic disintegration can, in the
presence of amino acids, synthesize RNA from a mixture of purines and
pyrimidines, as judged by uptake of labeled uracil.   No uptake of thymine could be detected.   The adaptive formation of β-galactosidase by
staphylococci is inhibited by penicillin in low concentrations, while a concentration of 30 units per milliliter inhibits by 80 per cent the formation
by cell particulates of this enzyme and the incorporation of uracil by
65 per cent.   Much of the evidence obtained so far points to penicillin

inhibiting or altering some stage of nucleic acid synthesis, but the site of the primary lesion has not been so definitely established as in the case of the sulfa drugs.

The resistance of mammalian cells, and of many bacteria, to penicillin appears to be associated with their inability to bind penicillin to a marked extent.   Once bound, penicillin apparently has the same toxicity for all bacteria if bound in sufficient amount (Eagle and Saz, 1955).   Approximately 900 to 1,200 molecules per cell were found to be bound without appreciably influencing the growth of a number of bacterial species, while inhibition was observed in the range of 1,500 to 1,700 molecules per cell and definite bactericidal activity above this range.   A penicillin-binding component appears to be associated with the cell wall and may be lipid in character.   Eagle and Saz conclude that bacteria normally contain an essential penicillin-vulnerable component in excess of their minimum requirement and that death results only when most of this component is inactivated by combination with penicillin.   Inhibition could result at concentrations of bound penicillin below those required to elicit a bactericidal effect.

Streptomycin.   With streptomycin, as with penicillin and the other major antibiotics, numerous observations of the inhibition or alteration of various processes have been reported, but there is no general agreement as to the primary point of attack.   A study of the antibiotics produced by the Streptomycetaceae led to the discovery by Waksman and his coworkers of actinomycin, streptothricin, and streptomycin.   The latter substance, produced by *Streptomyces griseus*, was found to be relatively nontoxic to man and to be effective against both gram-positive and -negative species, being particularly active against the tubercle bacillus. Resistant mutants appear more readily than do penicillin-resistant ones. Streptomycin, like penicillin, is prepared in submerged cultures grown in well-aerated tanks containing a relatively complex medium.   Difficulty is encountered at times owing to the development of an actinophage active against *S. griseus*.

The chemical structure of penicillin bears some relation to that of a nucleoside, while components of streptomycin (Fig. 18-4) are related to components of chitin (streptosamine), antimalarials like paludrine (the two guanidine groups of streptidine), and inositol (streptose).   This might suggest that streptomycin could react with more than one cellular component.

As with penicillin, there have been many reports of the inhibition of various reactions by streptomycin, but these may be secondary effects in a dying cell.   Among the various observations are inhibition of dephosphorylation of mononucleotides and of depolymerization of nucleic acids, inhibition of diamine oxidase, interference with inositol metabolism and pantothenic acid synthesis, stimulation of respiration with some substrates and inhibition with others, and so on. Umbreit (1955) stresses an inhibition of a condensation of pyruvate and oxalacetate to yield a product other than citric acid. A 2-phospho-4-hydroxy-4-carboxy adipic

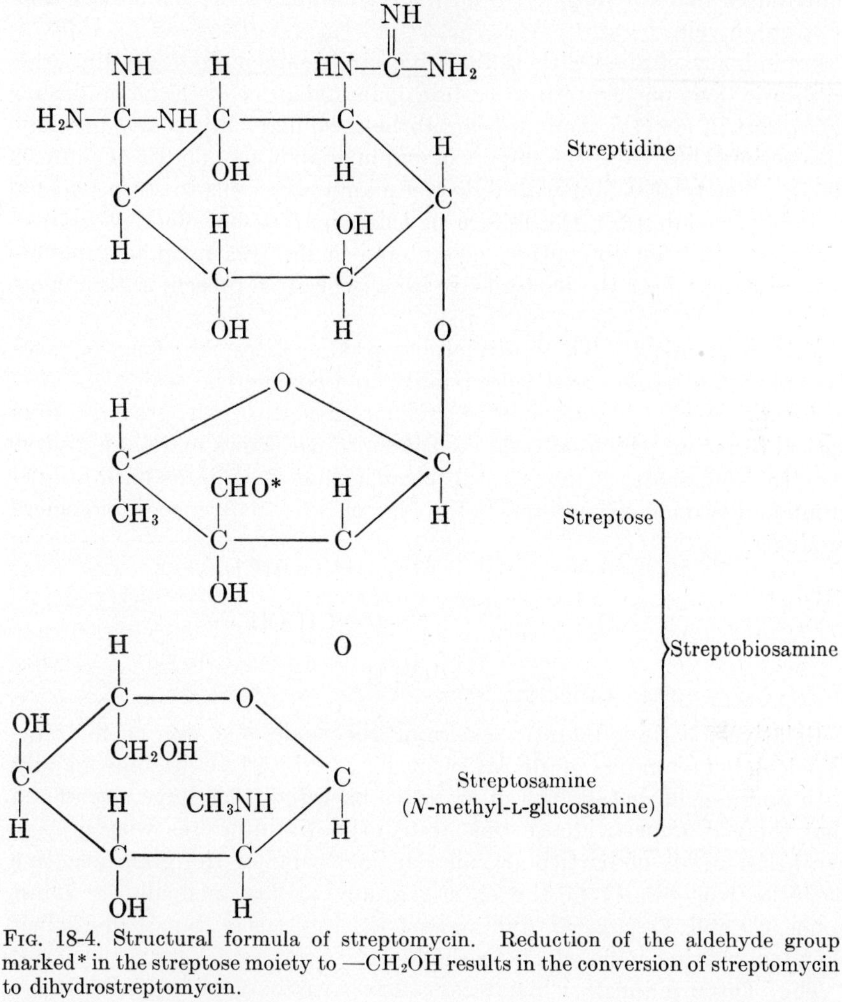

FIG. 18-4. Structural formula of streptomycin. Reduction of the aldehyde group marked* in the streptose moiety to —CH₂OH results in the conversion of streptomycin to dihydrostreptomycin.

acid has been identified as an intermediate, and its formation by E. coli is inhibited by streptomycin. Considerable variation is noted between strains and even in the same strain grown under different cultural conditions. The evidence for interference with the pyruvate-oxalacetate condensation is suggestive, but far from conclusive, as evidence for the major cytotoxic effect. Streptomycin often is effective against resting cells as well as against those in a medium conducive for growth and for this reason can be studied somewhat more readily than is the case with penicillin. Considerable variation is noted between streptomycin-resistant mutants obtained from the same parent culture, but study of these mutants has contributed little or nothing to an understanding of the mode of action of streptomycin.

Preliminary studies with radioactive streptomycin indicate that the antibiotic does penetrate into certain mammalian cells (Eagle and Saz, 1955), but in general there appears to be a cellular barrier and possibly an additional barrier at the surface of mammalian mitochondria (Umbreit, 1955). The relative impermeability of mammalian cells to streptomycin probably accounts for the failure of this agent to be effective against brucellosis and for difficulties encountered in the treatment of tuberculosis, diseases where the bacteria are usually or often present within body cells.

Chloramphenicol. This antibiotic is produced by *Streptomyces venezuelae* but can be prepared more readily on a commercial scale by a synthetic process. Chloramphenicol (Chloromycetin) can exist in four optical forms, of which only the D(-)threo isomer shows marked activity. Its structure, shown below, is of interest in that it contains both a nitro group and two chloride atoms, both being of rare occurrence in biological products.

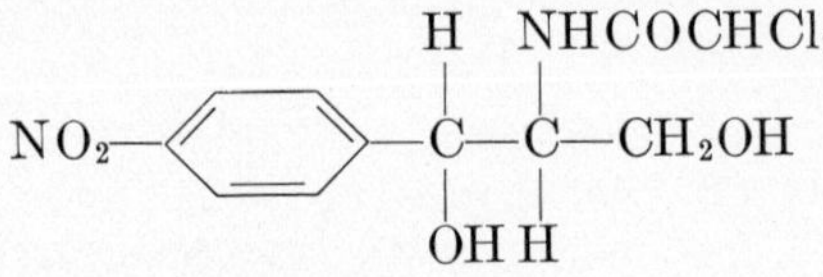

$$NO_2 - \langle \bigcirc \rangle - \overset{\overset{\displaystyle H}{|}}{\underset{\underset{\displaystyle OH}{|}}{C}} - \overset{\overset{\displaystyle NHCOCHCl_2}{|}}{\underset{\underset{\displaystyle H}{|}}{C}} - CH_2OH$$

Relatively little is known concerning the mode of action of chloramphenicol, but a number of reports suggest that it interferes in some manner with amino acid metabolism of sensitive bacteria. We have considered that there is some evidence that this antibiotic interferes with protein synthesis. It is of particular value against some of the gram-negative bacteria, particularly of the enteric group, against penicillin-resistant gonococci and *Treponema*, and against the rickettsiae, but it does elicit slowly appearing toxic effects in the host.

The Tetracyclines. Chlortetracycline (Aureomycin), produced by *Streptomyces aureofaciens*, was the first of the tetracyclines to be discovered. This was followed by the discovery of oxytetracycline (Terramycin) from *S. rimosus*, and tetracycline. The latter is formed by a species of *Streptomyces* but can be prepared most readily by selective catalytic hydrogenolysis of chlortetracycline. The structural formulas of these antibiotics are given in Fig. 18-5. These compounds exhibit similar antibiotic activities as well as chemical structure, but some differences in the former have been reported. Resistance to one, however, leads to resistance to all three agents. Here again, relatively little is known concerning the mode of action of these agents. Inhibition or derangement of protein synthesis appears to be of considerable importance with some alteration in nucleic acid synthesis, particularly at slightly higher concentrations of these antibiotics. Other studies suggest that these agents inhibit various enzymes, and also the growth of susceptible organisms, by virtue of their affinity for essential inorganic cations.

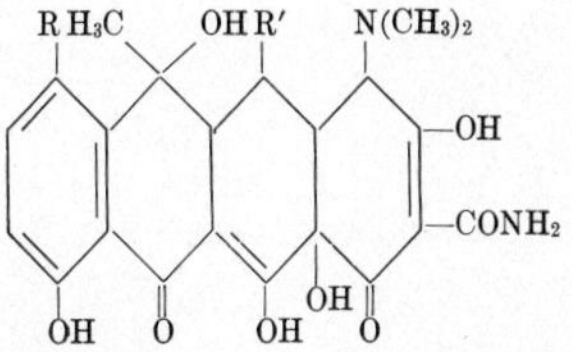

Tetracycline   R = H, R' = H
Chlortetracycline   R = Cl, R' = H
Oxytetracycline   R = H, R' = OH

Fig. 18-5. The tetracyclines.

Miscellaneous Antibiotics. There are numerous scattered observations on the mode of action of other antibiotics, the majority of which have little clinical value. Actually, clinical value is of relatively little importance in bacterial physiology with the exception that it reflects selective toxicity on the part of the chemical agent. A number of the antibiotics are surface-active agents and alter the physical structure and permeability of the cells; others (antimycin A) have been reported to inhibit one step in a respiratory chain, to form a complex with cytochrome c (Ballomycin B), to interfere with the synthesis of biotin (actithiazic acid), or to interfere with pantothenic acid synthesis or activity (Erythromycin).

The sulfa drugs and vitamin analogues do interfere with known systems, while, as we have seen, much remains to be learned concerning the modes of action of the numerous antibiotics. Such studies would be of considerable value in the further development not only of chemotherapy but of our understanding of the bacterial cell as well.

REFERENCES

Eagle, H., and A. K. Saz: Antibiotics, *Ann. Rev. Microbiol.*, **9**, 173–226 (1955).
Gale, E. F.: The nitrogen metabolism of gram-positive bacteria, *Bull. Johns Hopkins Hosp.*, **83**, 119–175 (1948).
———: From amino acids to proteins, in W. D. McElroy and B. Glass (eds.), "Amino Acid Metabolism," Johns Hopkins Press, Baltimore, 1955.
Hotchkiss, R. D.: The effect of penicillin upon protein synthesis by bacteria, *Ann. N.Y. Acad. Sci.*, **53**, 13–17 (1950).

Mitchell, P., and J. Moyle: Relationship between cell growth, surface properties, and nucleic acid production in normal and penicillin-treated *Micrococcus pyogenes*, *J. Gen. Microbiol.*, **5**, 412–438 (1951).

Regna, P. P.: Chemistry of antibiotics of clinical importance, *Am. J. Med.*, **18**, 686–716 (1955).

Shive, W.: The utilization of antimetabolites in the study of biochemical processes in living organisms, *Ann. N.Y. Acad. Sci.*, **52**, 1212–1234 (1950).

———: Biological activities of metabolite analogues, *Ann. Rev. Microbiol.*, **6**, 437–466 (1952).

Umbreit, W.: Mechanisms of antibacterial action, *Pharm. Rev.*, **5**, 275–284 (1953).

———: Mode of action of the antibiotics, *Am. J. Med.*, **18**, 717–722 (1955).

Woods, D. D.: Vitamin-B-group substances, especially folic acid and B_{12}, in the metabolism of micro-organisms, in Microbial growth and its inhibition, *World Health Organization, Monograph Ser.* 10, Geneva (1952).

Wyss, O., G. N. Smith, G. L. Hobby, E. I. Oginsky, and R Pratt: Symposium on the mode of action of antibiotics, *Bacteriol. Rev.*, **17**, 17–49 (1953).

INDEX